Basic
ENGLISH
Grammar and Composition
Level G

Master the Basics One Step at a Time

edited by
Bearl Brooks
and
Marie-Jose Shaw

Teacher's Edition

ESP Publishing, Inc.
Jonesboro, Arkansas

The Authors: Basic English Grammar and Composition is a compilation of language arts materials written by professional classroom teachers.

Book Design: Bearl Brooks

Editors: Bearl Brooks and Marie-Jose Shaw

Cover Design: Nancy Baldridge

Graphic Arts Credits: Nancy Baldridge, Donna Bearden, Tim G. Brasher, Margie Luster, Barry L. Prine, James D. Redding, Jetta Skillern, Janet E. Thiel, Judy Warren

Teacher's Edition

Order number: EGC-GT

ISBN 0-8209-0647-6

Published by
ESP Publishing, Inc.

Copyright © 1986

3

Recognizing a Noun

A noun names a person, a place, or a thing.

EXAMPLES:

person	place	thing
a. president	a. city	a. Pontiac
b. Carolyn	b. Texas	b. luxury

 Underline the nouns.

1. dictionary
2. attorney
3. Phoenix
4. inside
5. driver
6. motto
7. aardvark
8. yellow
9. beast
10. freedom
11. pushed
12. almanac
13. attorney
14. rude
15. Jackson
16. wicked
17. taxes
18. threat
19. proceed
20. United States
21. journey
22. war
23. important
24. verse
25. decision

26. silly
27. deadline
28. gossip
29. question
30. doctor
31. bitter
32. drenched
33. appearance
34. Fairway Drive
35. tennis
36. generally
37. penalty
38. mermaid
39. obedience
40. suggest
41. underneath
42. ambition
43. whistle
44. today
45. different
46. amendment
47. replace
48. Ken Davis
49. again
50. remedy

51. shall
52. chilly
53. fake
54. drowsy
55. parachute
56. carefully
57. tornado
58. first
59. statement
60. pledge
61. Dr. Weston
62. roam
63. imagine
64. Ginger
65. password
66. nurse
67. fluffy
68. clue
69. nightmare
70. expected
71. lower
72. King Kong
73. soldier
74. newspaper
75. ordinary

76. zone
77. skeleton
78. signature
79. more
80. obligation
81. wisdom
82. Oklahoma
83. country
84. tomorrow
85. finally
86. guests
87. Janice
88. secret
89. bleach
90. lately
91. frown
92. missing
93. beach
94. truth
95. explode
96. license
97. forgetful
98. disaster
99. confidence
100. career

COMPOSITION EXERCISE

List 20 nouns.

1. _____
2. _____
3. _____
4. _____
5. _____
6. _____
7. _____
8. _____
9. _____
10. _____
11. _____
12. _____
13. _____
14. _____
15. _____
16. _____
17. _____
18. _____
19. _____
20. _____

Unit 1 cont'd

Common Nouns

A common noun names any person, place, or thing.

EXAMPLES:

person	place	thing
a. daughter	a. home	a. machine
b. man	b. city	b. money
c. lieutenant	c. school	c. sign

 Underline the common nouns.

1. giant
2. interesting
3. opinion
4. protection
5. country
6. difficult
7. lonesome
8. sailor
9. suddenly
10. business
11. laughter
12. own
13. potato
14. driver
15. dangerous
16. music
17. possible
18. house
19. prisoner
20. anxiously
21. glue
22. education
23. favorite
24. quit
25. valley
26. giraffe
27. thief
28. hermit
29. usually
30. dinner

31. rumor
32. helpless
33. carpet
34. better
35. before
36. vocabulary
37. sofa
38. water
39. cowardly
40. snowman
41. dictionary
42. learn
43. syllable
44. program
45. notebook
46. frequently
47. used
48. race
49. spring
50. intelligent
51. chain
52. wordy
53. story
54. glance
55. important
56. over
57. become
58. because
59. treasure
60. definitions

61. At night the ghosts danced on the tables.
62. The airport was closed because of the snow.
63. Breakfast is the most important meal of the day.
64. The captain of the ship gives the orders.
65. The deadline is next week.
66. My teacher has lived in six countries.
67. The elephant is the largest animal on land.
68. The information is interesting but worthless.
69. The officer repeated the question.
70. His family owns the property.
71. The men pulled the piano up the stairs.
72. My sister works at the newspaper office.
73. The voice on the telephone sounded muffled.
74. Don't forget your umbrella today.
75. The money was hidden in the tree.
76. The children watched the clowns perform tricks.
77. The assignment covered four chapters.
78. The boy lacks confidence.
79. The glass fell off the table and shattered.
80. My mother bought three tickets to the game.
81. Grapes grow on a vine.
82. The hostess greeted her guests at the door.
83. In autumn the leaves fall to the ground.
84. The castle was built on a mountain.
85. My favorite story is about a dog.
86. The jewel is very valuable.
87. The basketball rolled under the parked truck.
88. The zoo is closed for the winter.
89. The police are looking for the owner of the car.
90. The city condemned the building.

Recognizing Common Nouns

A common noun names any person, place, or thing.

EXAMPLES: a. The <u>building</u> collapsed. c. A <u>plane</u> flew over the <u>sea</u>.
b. My <u>brother</u> bought a <u>car</u>. d. That <u>fish</u> is a <u>shark</u>.

✱ Underline the common nouns. Each sentence contains at least one.

1. My <u>book</u> fell on the <u>floor</u>.
2. That <u>girl</u> is in my <u>class</u>.
3. The <u>trip</u> was tiring.
4. A <u>skeleton</u> fell out of the <u>closet</u>.
5. An <u>almanac</u> is an interesting <u>book</u>.
6. The <u>deadline</u> has passed.
7. The <u>call</u> came too late.
8. <u>Ignorance</u> is forbidden.
9. The <u>battle</u> is over.
10. <u>Jewels</u> are a <u>luxury</u>.
11. The <u>school</u> was rebuilt.
12. The <u>baby</u> ate his <u>food</u>.
13. The <u>doctor</u> stood by the <u>door</u>.
14. A <u>decision</u> was made.
15. The <u>men</u> found a <u>raft</u>.
16. The <u>swallows</u> built a <u>nest</u>.
17. The <u>amendment</u> passed.
18. My <u>dad</u> talked to the <u>owner</u>.
19. The <u>crown</u> broke.
20. The <u>teacher</u> gave her <u>opinion</u>.
21. The <u>obstacle</u> was removed.
22. The <u>flowers</u> bloomed.
23. Her <u>class</u> sang the <u>song</u>.
24. The <u>circus</u> is in <u>town</u>.
25. The <u>password</u> is ''<u>contest</u>.''

26. Your <u>goal</u> is to be a <u>pilot</u>.
27. That <u>man</u> is our <u>guest</u>.
28. The <u>wind</u> is strong.
29. The <u>parachute</u> did not open.
30. Your <u>suggestions</u> are good.
31. The <u>team</u> painted the <u>fences</u>.
32. My <u>mother</u> made our <u>lunch</u>.
33. The <u>rooms</u> were empty.
34. The <u>man</u> shot the <u>lion</u>.
35. This <u>clue</u> solved the <u>puzzle</u>.
36. The <u>prisoner</u> is in the <u>dungeon</u>.
37. The <u>farmer</u> sold his <u>land</u>.
38. The <u>boy</u> answered my <u>questions</u>.
39. The <u>damages</u> were great.
40. The <u>man</u> lacked <u>wisdom</u>.
41. <u>Bleach</u> will ruin this <u>shirt</u>.
42. The <u>plants</u> died.
43. That <u>woman</u> is his <u>attorney</u>.
44. <u>Cowboys</u> ride <u>horses</u>.
45. The <u>people</u> voted.
46. The <u>bees</u> stung the <u>children</u>.
47. The <u>kite</u> blew away.
48. The <u>family</u> moved.
49. <u>Elephants</u> love <u>peanuts</u>.
50. The <u>thief</u> stole my <u>license</u>.

COMPOSITION EXERCISE

Write a sentence for each of these common nouns.

(airplane) 1. _____
(patrol) 2. _____
(choice) 3. _____
(village) 4. _____
(birthday) 5. _____

(ribbon) 6. _____
(canoe) 7. _____
(swimmer) 8. _____
(coins) 9. _____
(barn) 10. _____

Unit 2 cont'd →

Common Nouns Puzzle

Other Common Nouns

girl	uncle
day	aunt
country	theater
holiday	lake
nation	building
autumn	south
fall	boy
summer	railroad
document	sea

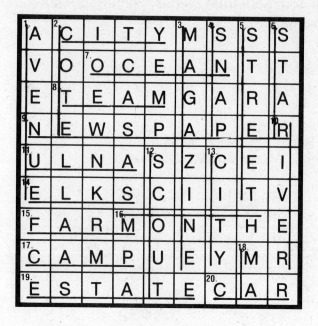

 Fill in the blanks. Then complete the puzzle.

Down

1. **A V E N U E** city thoroughfare

2. **C O T E** shed for small animals

3. **M A G A Z I N E** periodical

4. **S N A P** quick, sharp sound

5. **S T R E E T** public road in a city

6. **S T A R** heavenly body appearing at night

10. **R I V E R** large, natural stream of water

12. **S C O U T** sent to find the enemy

13. **C I T Y** important town

18. **M A** mother (informal)

Across

2. **C I T Y** same as "13" down

7. **O C E A N** great body of salt water

8. **T E A M** people working together, especially in a game

9. **N E W S P A P E R** sheets of printed paper telling the news

11. **U L N A** thin, long bone of the forearm

14. **E L K S** large, red deer

15. **F A R M** land used to raise crops

16. **M O N T H** one-twelfth of a year

17. **C A M P** permanent military station

19. **E S T A T E** property; possessions

20. **C A R** automobile

What Is a Common Noun?

A common noun names any person, place, or thing.

EXAMPLES:

person	place	thing
a. doctor	a. meadow	a. fish
b. pilot	b. home	b. list
c. widow	c. country	c. table

 Underline the common nouns.

1. mermaid	26. on	51. question	76. clue
2. smile	27. lawyer	52. not	77. laugh
3. until	28. grape	53. rule	78. please
4. home	29. is	54. classroom	79. a
5. the	30. echo	55. coward	80. word
6. lake	31. hobby	56. surround	81. bus
7. tornado	32. cowboy	57. point	82. pitcher
8. fence	33. now	58. sign	83. student
9. cartoon	34. sun	59. ability	84. under
10. forest	35. animal	60. huge	85. carrot
11. there	36. repay	61. rude	86. roam
12. statement	37. city	62. lower	87. pirate
13. was	38. wink	63. sky	88. office
14. hockey	39. breeze	64. subway	89. game
15. roast	40. artist	65. cheek	90. thumb
16. didn't	41. always	66. teeth	91. pretty
17. cube	42. up	67. school	92. license
18. hike	43. build	68. principal	93. jail
19. solve	44. friend	69. cozy	94. star
20. ocean	45. meter	70. answer	95. stupid
21. finally	46. never	71. sound	96. crayon
22. camel	47. match	72. an	97. radio
23. and	48. note	73. seen	98. carton
24. mountain	49. thief	74. square	99. over
25. frown	50. plan	75. camp	100. habit

COMPOSITION EXERCISE

List 20 common nouns not used in this lesson.

1. _____	6. _____	11. _____	16. _____
2. _____	7. _____	12. _____	17. _____
3. _____	8. _____	13. _____	18. _____
4. _____	9. _____	14. _____	19. _____
5. _____	10. _____	15. _____	20. _____

Unit 3 cont'd →

What Is a Proper Noun?

A proper noun names a particular person,
place, or thing. It is always capitalized.

EXAMPLES:

person	place	thing
a. Dad	a. Salt Lake City	a. November
b. Jason	b. Delaware	b. Pepsi Free
c. Mr. Collins	c. Pacific Ocean	c. Cracker Jacks

A Underline the proper nouns.

1. Monday
2. Connie
3. day
4. ocean
5. Lubbock
6. subway
7. Spike
8. food
9. Ford
10. Fritos
11. Skippy
12. holiday
13. English
14. Eric
15. George
16. driver
17. Lana
18. Aim
19. month
20. June
21. Rocky Mountains
22. Chevrolet
23. Mr. Allen
24. school bus
25. West School
26. Metro Beach
27. comedian
28. Christmas
29. Atlantic Ocean
30. avenue
31. Saturday
32. Mississippi River
33. America
34. United States
35. Bill Cosby
36. neighborhood
37. Lakeside Drive
38. Jamis Street
39. Miss Lane
40. Texas

B Write a proper noun in each blank to complete the sentence.
Choose it from part "A."

1. My name is _____Eric_____.
2. _____LANA_____ is my sister.
3. _____MR. ALLEN_____ is our neighbor.
4. My dog's name is _____SPIKE_____.
5. We live on _____JAMIS STREET_____.
6. Our town is called _____LUBBOCK_____.
7. It is in the state of _____TEXAS_____.
8. I go to _____WEST SCHOOL_____.
9. My teacher is _____MISS LANE_____.
10. I like to eat _____FRITOS_____.
11. My mom drives a _____FORD_____.
12. Tomorrow is _____MONDAY_____.
13. Our country is the _____UNITED STATES_____.
14. Have you ever seen the _____ATLANTIC OCEAN_____?
15. The _____ROCKY MOUNTAINS_____ are very large.
16. _____CHEVROLET_____ is a good car.
17. The driver is _____GEORGE_____.
18. _____CHRISTMAS_____ is a holiday.
19. I like sandwiches with _____SKIPPY_____.
20. _____CONNIE_____ is in my class.
21. I speak _____ENGLISH_____.
22. Mom bought _____AIM_____.
23. I have seen _____BILL COSBY_____.
24. We crossed the _____MISSISSIPPI RIVER_____.

COMPOSITION EXERCISE

List 20 proper nouns not used in this lesson.

1. _____
2. _____
3. _____
4. _____
5. _____
6. _____
7. _____
8. _____
9. _____
10. _____
11. _____
12. _____
13. _____
14. _____
15. _____
16. _____
17. _____
18. _____
19. _____
20. _____

Proper Nouns

A proper noun names a particular person, place, or thing. It is capitalized.

EXAMPLES:
a. This is <u>Eric Davison</u>.
b. <u>Paul</u> drives a <u>Pontiac</u>.
c. <u>France</u> is my home.
d. We visited <u>Ohio</u> and <u>Utah</u>.

* Underline the proper nouns. Each sentence contains at least one.

1. My house is on <u>Pennsylvania Avenue</u>.
2. The man ordered a <u>Pepsi</u>.
3. <u>Dr. Wesley</u> is my neighbor.
4. <u>Napoleon</u> lived in <u>France</u>.
5. Our club watched <u>Superman</u>.
6. <u>John</u> bought a new book.
7. <u>Kathy</u> will bring the <u>Fritos</u>.
8. Where is <u>Charlie Brown</u>?
9. The girl bought <u>Cracker Jacks</u>.
10. <u>Chicago</u> is a big city.
11. The <u>Dr. Pepper</u> is too sweet.
12. The cartoon is about <u>Donald Duck</u>.
13. This bus goes to <u>Jackson Street</u>.
14. We shopped at <u>Macy's</u>.
15. <u>Dan</u> lives in <u>Senath</u>, <u>Missouri</u>.
16. Tomorrow will be <u>Saturday</u>.
17. Today we'll read about <u>England</u>.
18. <u>Linda</u> is <u>Bob's</u> sister.
19. The house on <u>Kate Street</u> burned.
20. <u>Karen</u> is in <u>St. Joseph's Hospital</u>.
21. Tomorrow we are going to <u>Central Park</u>.
22. <u>Mrs. Denson</u> moved to <u>New York</u>.
23. We ate lunch at <u>Wendy's</u>.
24. My mom was born in <u>Australia</u>.
25. <u>Snoopy</u> is everyone's favorite.
26. <u>Jill</u> is a good friend.
27. That pen is a <u>Bic</u>.
28. <u>Capt. King</u> is our pilot.
29. The lady lives in <u>Denver</u>.
30. Look in <u>Webster's</u> store.
31. Our school is on <u>Woodward Avenue</u>.
32. Let's read <u>Robinson's</u> novel.
33. The monkey likes <u>Dennis</u>.
34. <u>Texas</u> is a big state.
35. <u>Mrs. Johnson</u> was angry with us.
36. <u>Daniel</u> and <u>Kay</u> were chosen.
37. The next street is <u>Camden Avenue</u>.
38. The train left <u>Boston</u> on time.
39. He robbed <u>Second National Bank</u>.
40. The store is on <u>Horace Street</u>.
41. <u>Aunt Dee</u> is from <u>Hawaii</u>.
42. We studied <u>World War II</u>.
43. <u>Jerry</u> is <u>Don's</u> brother.
44. My grandmother lives in <u>Alabama</u>.
45. Let's go to <u>Winslow Park Zoo</u>.
46. He attends <u>West High School</u>.
47. <u>Mattel</u> makes good toys.
48. Our class will visit <u>Reeve's Donut Shop</u>.
49. May I introduce <u>Capt. Jay Turney</u>?
50. <u>Tuesday</u> is the last day in <u>April</u>.

COMPOSITION EXERCISE

Write a sentence for each of these proper nouns.

(Dr. Houston)   1. _____
(Main Street)   2. _____
(Germany)   3. _____
(United Airlines)   4. _____
(Erica)   5. _____
(New York)   6. _____

(Overton Zoo)   7. _____
(Garfield)   8. _____
(Wednesday)   9. _____
(Red River)   10. _____
(Big Ben)   11. _____
(July)   12. _____

Unit 4 cont'd

Using Proper Nouns

A proper noun names a particular person, place, or thing. A proper noun is always capitalized.

EXAMPLES:

person	place	thing
a. Franklin	a. Reno	a. Chevrolet
b. Arnold	b. Indiana	b. Saturday
c. Margie	c. Atlantic Ocean	c. Jello

A Complete each sentence with a proper noun which names a person.

1. __Mr. Griffin__ owns the building.
2. __Richard__ and I are studying math.
3. The dog belongs to __Jenny__.
4. __Columbus__ discovered America.
5. __Dr. Overton__ is my uncle.
6. Ask __Timothy__ to wait for me.
7. __Matthew__ is my partner.
8. Have you met __Ms. Stephens__?
9. __Washington__ was our first President.
10. This letter is for __Bob__.

11. Our new teacher is __Mr. Smith__.
12. We saw __Brad__ at the market.
13. Did you tell __Dale__ what to do?
14. __Martin__ was elected treasurer.
15. __Walter__ bought a used car.
16. My middle name is __Theodore__.
17. The pilot's name is __Capt. Lewis__.
18. __Mrs. Turner__ wants to see you now.
19. Let's visit __Katie__.
20. I'll write __Paul__ a note.

B Complete each sentence with a proper noun which names a place.

1. Have you ever been to __New York__?
2. __Los Angeles__ is a very big city.
3. We vacationed in __Florida__.
4. We ate lunch in __Memphis__.
5. __Richmond__ will always be my home.
6. The family moved to __Kansas__.
7. In the summer we live in __Denver__.

8. The next town will be __Omaha__.
9. __Spain__ is a foreign country.
10. My address is 411 __Bravado__.
11. George was born in __Montana__.
12. We visited __Italy__ in June.
13. The language of __France__ is French.
14. I have never been to __Mexico__.

C Complete each sentence with a proper noun which names a thing.

1. __December__ is the last month of the year.
2. Yesterday was __Tuesday__.
3. Would you like some __Fritos__?
4. All of us enjoyed "__King Kong__"
5. Does he own a __Honda__?
6. We moved here in __August__.

7. Who ordered a __Pepsi__?
8. We are studying the __Revolutionary War__.
9. My hero is __Superman__.
10. The car was a blue and white __Ford__.
11. Ann's birthday is in __January__.
12. I'll buy the __Cracker Jacks__.

Singular Nouns

A singular noun refers to one person, place, or thing.

EXAMPLES: a. The <u>door</u> slammed.   c. The <u>bus</u> is late.
          b. <u>Dave</u> loves <u>dessert</u>.   d. <u>Mississippi</u> is my <u>home</u>.

A Underline the singular nouns.

1. sky	36. chicken
2. ghosts	37. prize
3. numbers	38. deadline
4. holiday	39. pennies
5. eye	40. echo
6. eagles	41. sun
7. orange	42. dimes
8. blankets	43. breeze
9. mouth	44. nurses
10. airport	45. branches
11. children	46. streets
12. zoo	47. clown
13. markets	48. flowers
14. person	49. comedian
15. vacation	50. gifts
16. piano	51. journey
17. owners	52. exercise
18. tunnels	53. captains
19. wolves	54. calves
20. promise	55. rule
21. leaf	56. jewels
22. offices	57. ideas
23. minute	58. men
24. nights	59. habit
25. mistake	60. snack
26. classes	61. cartoons
27. sign	62. balloons
28. secrets	63. garden
29. list	64. feet
30. doctor	65. fruit
31. crowns	66. bricks
32. knives	67. half
33. pencil	68. lady
34. animal	69. sentence
35. smiles	70. banana

B In each blank write the singular form of the noun in the parentheses.

(umbrellas) 1. Don't forget your __umbrella__.
(loaves) 2. I need a __LOAF__ of bread.
(opinions) 3. What's your __OPINION__?
(packages) 4. Will you mail this __PACKAGE__?
(bees) 5. Greg was stung by a __BEE__.
(guests) 6. Mrs. Phillips is our __GUEST__.
(days) 7. It is a beautiful __DAY__!
(apples) 8. The __APPLE__ tasted sour.
(sisters) 9. My __SISTER__ is at school.
(friends) 10. David is my best __FRIEND__.
(lights) 11. Turn on the __LIGHT__.
(melons) 12. The __MELON__ was not ripe.
(mice) 13. The __MOUSE__ ran under the sofa.
(squares) 14. Draw a small __SQUARE__.
(contests) 15. James won the __CONTEST__.
(jokes) 16. I know a funny __JOKE__.
(decisions) 17. Have you made a __DECISION__?
(rooms) 18. Your __ROOM__ is a mess!
(teeth) 19. The dentist pulled my __TOOTH__.
(tables) 20. The __TABLE__ was cluttered.
(windows) 21. Open the __WINDOW__.
(cities) 22. Los Angeles is a big __CITY__.
(islands) 23. I want to live on an __ISLAND__.
(horses) 24. The __HORSE__ jumped the fence.
(women) 25. The __WOMAN__ was an actress.
(licenses) 26. Show me your __LICENSE__.
(reasons) 27. Your __REASON__ sounds logical.
(families) 28. The __FAMILY__ moved to Utah.
(bicycles) 29. Louis has a new __BICYCLE__.
(spoons) 30. The __SPOON__ fell on the floor.
(buttons) 31. Push the red __BUTTON__.
(stores) 32. The __STORE__ is closed today.
(results) 33. The __RESULT__ was surprising.
(endings) 34. The __ENDING__ was sad.
(stories) 35. I like the __STORY__.

Unit 5 cont'd ➡

Plural Nouns

A plural noun refers to more than one person, place, or thing.

EXAMPLES: a. The <u>men</u> are on strike.   c. <u>Plants</u> need sunshine.
b. Bradley picked the <u>flowers</u>.   d. The <u>roads</u> were closed.

A Underline the plural nouns.

1. <u>stars</u>
2. picture
3. amendment
4. <u>birds</u>
5. <u>mornings</u>
6. <u>skeletons</u>
7. school
8. knife
9. <u>baskets</u>
10. fact
11. habit
12. <u>excuses</u>
13. <u>ideas</u>
14. <u>children</u>
15. letter
16. adjective
17. dictionary
18. <u>steps</u>
19. kitchen
20. baby
21. address
22. <u>problems</u>
23. goose
24. sun
25. storm
26. <u>women</u>
27. <u>heroes</u>
28. aunt
29. <u>straws</u>
30. valley
31. <u>baths</u>
32. minute
33. <u>lights</u>
34. <u>wings</u>
35. board

36. fence
37. <u>numbers</u>
38. <u>newspapers</u>
39. <u>penalties</u>
40. war
41. <u>clocks</u>
42. zebra
43. <u>dollars</u>
44. room
45. <u>businesses</u>
46. accident
47. chance
48. <u>vines</u>
49. nickel
50. <u>hands</u>
51. box
52. <u>words</u>
53. <u>watermelons</u>
54. clue
55. floor
56. <u>uncles</u>
57. curtain
58. <u>stones</u>
59. island
60. <u>reports</u>
61. moon
62. year
63. <u>notebooks</u>
64. sky
65. <u>bodies</u>
66. <u>owls</u>
67. louse
68. <u>trees</u>
69. title
70. <u>heads</u>

B In each blank write the plural form of the noun in the parentheses.

(eye) 1. Close your _eyes_.
(bench) 2. We painted the **BENCHES** green.
(tooth) 3. The dentist checked my **TEETH**.
(game) 4. What **GAMES** can we play?
(country) 5. I have lived in two **COUNTRIES**.
(jewel) 6. The thief stole the **JEWELS**.
(plate) 7. Put the **PLATES** on the table.
(foot) 8. Gerald has big **FEET**.
(house) 9. Both **HOUSES** look alike.
(ghost) 10. Do you believe in **GHOSTS**?
(castle) 11. **CASTLES** are haunted.
(error) 12. Recheck for **ERRORS**.
(exercise) 13. Let's do **EXERCISES**.
(penny) 14. I have sixty-five **PENNIES**.
(banana) 15. Monkeys eat **BANANAS**.
(book) 16. Kelly dropped her **BOOKS**.
(fox) 17. The **FOXES** chased the rabbit.
(lunch) 18. Mom fixed our **LUNCHES**.
(frown) 19. **FROWNS** get you nowhere.
(sentence) 20. Write four **SENTENCES**.
(month) 21. Twelve **MONTHS** make one year.
(snake) 22. Betsy is afraid of **SNAKES**.
(mouse) 23. I have two pet **MICE**.
(story) 24. He wrote many great **STORIES**.
(day) 25. We stayed there for six **DAYS**.
(jacket) 26. Don't forget your **JACKETS**.
(city) 27. Name five big **CITIES**.
(flower) 28. Don't pick the **FLOWERS**.
(bee) 29. **BEES** make honey.
(glass) 30. Fill the **GLASSES** with ice.
(cat) 31. Mr. Pearson has thirty **CATS**.
(monkey) 32. I like to watch the **MONKEYS**.
(car) 33. The two **CARS** collided.
(cave) 34. Let's explore the **CAVES**.
(teacher) 35. The **TEACHERS** are absent.

14

Comprehension Check

(A) Why is each of these words considered a noun?

1. country	names a place/thing		16. Disneyland	names a place
2. Dr. Jamison	names a person		17. pirates	names persons
3. police	names persons		18. Mr. Steiner	names a person
4. theatre	names a place/thing		19. junkyard	names a place
5. Kentucky	names a place		20. movie	names a thing
6. chocolate	names a thing		21. Montana	names a place
7. Milky Way	names a thing		22. Vincent	names a person
8. yacht	names a thing		23. patient	names a person
9. puzzles	names things		24. ribbon	names a thing
10. Lucille	names a person		25. college	names a place
11. computer	names a thing		26. farms	names places
12. lawyer	names a person		27. Delta	names a thing
13. Canada	names a place		28. mirrors	names things
14. pattern	names a thing		29. place mat	names a thing
15. Barton	names a person		30. American	names a person

(B) Underline the nouns.

1. clouds	11. cave	21. exercise
2. Anthony	12. ground	22. lesser
3. inside	13. suddenly	23. and
4. husband	14. helicopter	24. mailbox
5. television	15. newspaper	25. alarm
6. give	16. ouch	26. Mexico
7. bump	17. feather	27. onto
8. behind	18. football	28. spaceship
9. comic	19. neighbor	29. Hollywood
10. Sunday	20. brain	30. beautiful

(C) Identify the nouns. Write "c" for common noun and "p" for proper noun.

c 1. meter	c 9. magazine	c 17. sunshine	c 25. library
p 2. Theodore	p 10. Oldsmobile	p 18. Murphy	c 26. whale
c 3. doctor	c 11. circus	p 19. Mrs. Worth	c 27. maid
c 4. bathroom	c 12. basket	c 20. teacher	c 28. record
c 5. bicycle	p 13. Mr. Carter	p 21. Memphis	p 29. Ohio
p 6. Dr. Newton	p 14. Indian	p 22. United States	c 30. face
p 7. Mississippi	c 15. telephone	c 23. education	p 31. Lawrence
p 8. Angela	p 16. Casey	c 24. rain	p 32. Texas

15

Test 1 cont'd

Comprehension Check (continued)

D **Identify the number of each noun. Write "s" for singular and "p" for plural.**

_s_	1. bird	_s_	11. elephant	_p_	21. automobiles	_s_	31. ocean
_p_	2. umbrellas	_s_	12. painting	_s_	22. chicken	_s_	32. street
_s_	3. camera	_p_	13. dreams	_p_	23. mountains	_s_	33. dollar
_s_	4. tooth	_p_	14. cookbooks	_s_	24. hamster	_s_	34. corner
_s_	5. porch	_s_	15. attic	_p_	25. offices	_p_	35. pairs
_p_	6. shelves	_p_	16. pictures	_s_	26. board	_p_	36. trucks
_p_	7. dancers	_s_	17. novel	_p_	27. jackets	_p_	37. classes
_s_	8. window	_p_	18. flowers	_s_	28. flashlight	_p_	38. bottles
_p_	9. pillows	_p_	19. boxes	_p_	29. friends	_s_	39. necklace
_s_	10 number	_p_	20. prisoners	_s_	30. dictionary	_p_	40. benches

E **Complete each sentence with a common noun.**

1. The __cowboy__ rode a white horse.
2. Put the box on the __table__ .
3. Randy wore a yellow __hat__ .
4. A __mosquito__ bit me on the arm.
5. I will write Phil a __note__ .
6. Let's visit the __museum__ .
7. The __actor__ signed the autograph.
8. Jackie collected the __money__ .
9. Where is my new __scarf__ ?
10. The __news__ shocked everyone.
11. It looks like a __monkey__ .
12. Tell me the right __answers__ .

F **Complete each sentence with a proper noun.**

1. Did you talk to __Walter__ ?
2. Isaac bought a new __Toyota__ .
3. I want a __Snickers__ and milk.
4. __Lisa__ made the highest score.
5. The family visited __Disney World__ .
6. __Roscoe__ is a coward.
7. We can relax at __Lake Winds__ .
8. She ate __Jello__ for dessert.
9. Dr. Harper travelled to __Africa__ .
10. __December__ is a cold month.
11. You should go to __Europe__ .
12. __Miranda__ slid on the icy pavement.

Write a paragraph about a favorite pastime of you and your friends. Underline the proper nouns.

_____
_____
_____
_____
_____
_____
_____
_____
_____
_____
_____

Singular and Plural Nouns

A singular noun refers to one person, place, or thing. A plural noun refers to more than one person, place, or thing.

EXAMPLES:
a. war
b. sheriff
c. sandwich
d. world
e. color
f. parent
g. doctor
h. universe

Underline the singular nouns. The nouns you do not underline are plural.

1. motto
2. delays
3. almanac
4. accounts
5. skeletons
6. site
7. spoon
8. cartoons
9. breezes
10. budget
11. tragedy
12. threat
13. exercises
14. bomb
15. guests
16. remedy
17. luxury
18. battles
19. escort
20. triumph
21. voyages
22. clearing
23. mermaids
24. signature
25. hike

26. suggestions
27. ambition
28. deadlines
29. effort
30. career
31. amendments
32. obstacle
33. zones
34. penalties
35. parachute
36. tornado
37. statements
38. exclamation
39. questions
40. commands
41. liberties
42. gem
43. junction
44. library
45. mall
46. storms
47. fork
48. family
49. pronouns
50. thumbs

51. magnet
52. habit
53. disaster
54. dungeons
55. clue
56. festivals
57. wink
58. shortage
59. appearances
60. sentences
61. ocean
62. garden
63. sleighs
64. kangaroo
65. hotel
66. chimney
67. corporation
68. calfskin
69. titles
70. alphabet
71. fences
72. depot
73. candles
74. seat
75. pictures

76. income
77. frowns
78. verses
79. license
80. sections
81. ability
82. echo
83. earnings
84. ghost
85. automobile
86. hippopotamus
87. comedies
88. century
89. mirror
90. radios
91. television
92. company
93. decisions
94. interjection
95. moccasin
96. password
97. wrenches
98. branch
99. comedian
100. attorneys

COMPOSITION EXERCISE

List 10 singular nouns and 10 plural nouns.

singular

1. _____
2. _____
3. _____
4. _____
5. _____
6. _____
7. _____
8. _____
9. _____
10. _____

plural

1. _____
2. _____
3. _____
4. _____
5. _____
6. _____
7. _____
8. _____
9. _____
10. _____

Unit 6 cont'd

Nouns and Number

A singular noun refers to one person, place, or thing. A plural noun refers to more than one person, place, or thing.

EXAMPLES: a. *one sound — two sounds*
b. *one card — two cards*
c. *one flag — two flags*
d. *one house — two houses*

 Write "S" if the noun refers to one person, place, or thing. Write "P" if the noun refers to more than one person, place, or thing.

1. rabbit	s	26. gentlemen	P	51. taxi	S
2. cows	P	27. supplies	P	52. magnet	S
3. friend	S	28. signal	S	53. mermaids	P
4. cartoons	P	29. voyage	S	54. doctor	S
5. clues	P	30. belief	S	55. animals	P
6. license	S	31. talents	P	56. questions	P
7. skin	S	32. attitude	S	57. verse	S
8. decisions	P	33. forest	S	58. nightmare	S
9. gift	S	34. oceans	P	59. tornado	S
10. snacks	P	35. newspapers	P	60. nurses	P
11. melons	P	36. warning	S	61. squaw	S
12. tablet	S	37. password	S	62. worry	S
13. acts	P	38. jail	S	63. chills	P
14. breezes	P	39. results	P	64. silence	S
15. frown	S	40. beating	S	65. presents	P
16. smile	S	41. records	P	66. life	S
17. answers	P	42. ground	S	67. problems	P
18. statement	S	43. places	P	68. exercises	P
19. ladies	P	44. noise	S	69. comedian	S
20. signs	P	45. remarks	P	70. puppets	P
21. slice	S	46. shares	P	71. avenue	S
22. men	P	47. look	S	72. games	P
23. poem	S	48. reason	S	73. fears	P
24. dreams	P	49. cause	S	74. woman	S
25. note	S	50. objects	P	75. wink	S

COMPOSITION EXERCISE

Write 5 sentences using singular nouns and 5 sentences using plural nouns.

singular

1. _____
2. _____
3. _____
4. _____
5. _____

plural

1. _____
2. _____
3. _____
4. _____
5. _____

Adding "s" to Form the Plural

Most nouns form the plural by adding "s."

EXAMPLES:
- a. signals
- b. governors
- c. bicycles
- d. comedians
- e. roots
- f. animals

In each blank write the plural form of the word in parentheses.

(page) 1. The **pages** were torn.
(cartoon) 2. The **cartoons** were funny.
(snack) 3. Your **snacks** are ready.
(gift) 4. Bring the **gifts**.
(moccasin) 5. I am wearing **moccasins**.
(decision) 6. The **decisions** are yours.
(tablet) 7. The **tablets** are blue.
(whale) 8. The **whales** swam to shore.
(fence) 9. The **fences** were repaired.
(swallow) 10. The **swallows** returned.
(forest) 11. Take care of our **forests**.
(tree) 12. The **trees** were huge.
(melon) 13. The **melons** tasted sweet.
(trip) 14. We take many class **trips**.
(breeze) 15. The **breezes** felt cool.
(reason) 16. Those are good **reasons**.
(thumb) 17. I have two **thumbs**.
(spear) 18. The **spears** are sharp.
(voice) 19. I hear **voices**.
(owner) 20. The house has three **owners**.
(crown) 21. The **crowns** will be gold.
(turtle) 22. I have six **turtles**.
(balloon) 23. The **balloons** popped.
(bicycle) 24. Our **bicycles** were stolen.
(sentence) 25. I wrote **sentences**.

(habit) 26. You have strange **habits**.
(newspaper) 27. Tom delivers **newspapers**.
(language) 28. I speak two **languages**.
(sister) 29. My **sisters** are twins.
(artist) 30. The **artists** have arrived.
(straw) 31. May I have two **straws**?
(robber) 32. The **robbers** were caught.
(jewel) 33. They took the **jewels**.
(grape) 34. These **grapes** are sour.
(clue) 35. Give me some **clues**.
(jaw) 36. My **jaws** hurt.
(lawyer) 37. Our **lawyers** were arguing.
(question) 38. The test had **questions**.
(orange) 39. I need two **oranges**.
(sea) 40. The **seas** were calm.
(word) 41. No **words** were spoken.
(horse) 42. We rode the **horses**.
(key) 43. I lost my **keys**.
(picture) 44. Mom takes the **pictures**.
(noun) 45. Names are proper **nouns**.
(letter) 46. Mail those **letters**.
(answer) 47. The **answers** are long.
(grade) 48. Liz makes good **grades**.
(movie) 49. Let's go to the **movies**.
(garden) 50. The **gardens** are ready.

COMPOSITION EXERCISE

List 20 plural nouns that form the plural by adding "s."

1. _____
2. _____
3. _____
4. _____
5. _____
6. _____
7. _____
8. _____
9. _____
10. _____
11. _____
12. _____
13. _____
14. _____
15. _____
16. _____
17. _____
18. _____
19. _____
20. _____

Unit 7 cont'd →

Adding "es" to Form the Plural

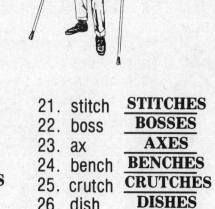

Nouns which end in "ch," "sh," "ss," "s," "x," or "z" form the plural by adding "es."

EXAMPLES: a. dishes   c. branches   e. lasses
            b. arches   d. watches   f. batches

A Write the correct plural forms.

1. one box, two	**BOXES**	11. match	**MATCHES**	21. stitch **STITCHES**
2. one church, two	**CHURCHES**	12. fox	**FOXES**	22. boss **BOSSES**
3. one cross, two	**CROSSES**	13. gas	**GASES**	23. ax **AXES**
4. one watch, two	**WATCHES**	14. brush	**BRUSHES**	24. bench **BENCHES**
5. one inch, two	**INCHES**	15. wrench	**WRENCHES**	25. crutch **CRUTCHES**
6. one bush, two	**BUSHES**	16. patch	**PATCHES**	26. dish **DISHES**
7. one dress, two	**DRESSES**	17. perch	**PERCHES**	27. finch **FINCHES**
8. one bus, two	**BUSES**	18. grass	**GRASSES**	28. branch **BRANCHES**
9. one tax, two	**TAXES**	19. toss	**TOSSES**	29. miss **MISSES**
10. one witch, two	**WITCHES**	20. pass	**PASSES**	30. kiss **KISSES**

B Underline the correct plural forms.

1. These (<u>boxes</u>, boxs) must go.
2. The (buss, <u>buses</u>) are late.
3. My (dresss, <u>dresses</u>) are too long.
4. The paper measured six (<u>inches</u>, inchs).
5. I have two (<u>watches</u>, watchs).
6. Don't play with (matchs, <u>matches</u>).
7. Your football (passs, <u>passes</u>) are great.
8. The (bosss, <u>bosses</u>) were angry.
9. The (<u>stitches</u>, stitchs) broke.
10. The (finchs, <u>finches</u>) flew away.
11. I lost the (<u>wrenches</u>, wrenchs).
12. Those (quizs, <u>quizzes</u>) are easy.
13. The (<u>taxes</u>, taxs) are too high.
14. The (<u>witches</u>, witchs) laughed.
15. The (bushs, <u>bushes</u>) were burned.
16. The (<u>crosses</u>, crosss) are very pretty.
17. The (churchs, <u>churches</u>) are open.
18. The (<u>foxes</u>, foxs) hid under the house.
19. Those are dangerous (<u>gases</u>, gass).
20. The (axs, <u>axes</u>) are sharp.
21. The (<u>benches</u>, benchs) were painted.
22. The (losss, <u>losses</u>) were enormous.
23. The (<u>branches</u>, branchs) hit my window.
24. Dad washed the (dishs, <u>dishes</u>).

COMPOSITION EXERCISE

Write a sentence with the plural form of each noun.

(box)   1. _____   (ranch)   6. _____
(march)   2. _____   (brush)   7. _____
(pass)   3. _____   (sketch)   8. _____
(inch)   4. _____   (fox)   9. _____
(six)   5. _____   (blotch) 10. _____

Changing Singular Nouns to Plural

Most nouns form the plural by adding "s."
However, when a noun ends in "ch," "sh,"
"z," "s," "j," "ss," or "x" the plural is
formed by adding "es."

EXAMPLES:
a. room — rooms
b. beach — beaches
c. gas — gases
d. skeleton — skeletons

 Add "s" or "es" to form the plural of each
singular noun.

1. cracker	s	26. mass	ES	51. parachute	S
2. box	ES	27. bleach	ES	52. boss	ES
3. water	S	28. book	S	53. buzz	ES
4. arch	ES	29. wrench	ES	54. dress	ES
5. bush	ES	30. business	ES	55. gossip	S
6. battle	S	31. breeze	S	56. peach	ES
7. account	S	32. dog	S	57. toss	ES
8. zone	S	33. amendment	S	58. damage	S
9. watch	ES	34. miss	ES	59. sheet	S
10. deadline	S	35. threat	S	60. watermelon	S
11. sorrow	S	36. loss	ES	61. plant	S
12. glass	ES	37. finch	ES	62. catch	ES
13. tax	ES	38. press	ES	63. plumber	S
14. decision	S	39. squaw	S	64. voyage	S
15. window	S	40. batch	ES	65. grass	ES
16. bonus	ES	41. career	S	66. trench	ES
17. bed	S	42. fox	ES	67. magnet	S
18. loss	ES	43. ambition	S	68. pass	ES
19. suggestion	S	44. cross	ES	69. moccasin	S
20. guest	S	45. hat	S	70. frown	S
21. church	ES	46. budget	S	71. beach	ES
22. robin	S	47. ax	ES	72. signature	S
23. password	S	48. sentence	S	73. nightmare	S
24. fence	S	49. pouch	ES	74. soup	S
25. skeleton	S	50. sketch	ES	75. branch	ES

COMPOSITION EXERCISE

Write a sentence with the plural form of each noun.

(lock) 1. _____

(page) 2. _____

(noun) 3. _____

(tax) 4. _____

(fruit) 5. _____

(stitch) 6. _____

(tree) 7. _____

(couch) 8. _____

(sack) 9. _____

(wrench) 10. _____

Unit 8 cont'd ⟶

Plurals of Nouns Ending in "y"

If a noun ends in "y" and a vowel comes before the "y," form the plural by adding "s."
If a noun ends in "y" and a consonant comes before the "y," form the plural by changing the "y" to "i" and adding "es."

EXAMPLES: a. ray — rays   c. pony — ponies
           b. boy — boys   d. puppy — puppies

A Underline the correct spelling of each plural form.

1. family — <u>families</u>, familys
2. monkey — monkeies, <u>monkeys</u>
3. turkey — <u>turkeys</u>, turkeies
4. party — partys, <u>parties</u>
5. candy — candys, <u>candies</u>
6. puppy — <u>puppies</u>, puppys
7. bluejay — bluejaies, <u>bluejays</u>
8. country — <u>countries</u>, countrys
9. highway — highwaies, <u>highways</u>
10. cowboy — <u>cowboys</u>, cowboies
11. daisy — <u>daisies</u>, daisys
12. company — companys, <u>companies</u>

13. day — daies, <u>days</u>
14. city — <u>cities</u>, citys
15. toy — toies, <u>toys</u>
16. body — <u>bodies</u>, bodys
17. baby — <u>babies</u>, babys
18. fly — <u>flies</u>, flys
19. copy — copys, <u>copies</u>
20. sky — <u>skies</u>, skys
21. lady — ladys, <u>ladies</u>
22. key — <u>keys</u>, keies
23. decoy — <u>decoys</u>, decoies
24. berry — <u>berries</u>, berrys

B Write the plural of each word in parentheses.

(baby)   1. The ___*babies*___ cried.
(party)   2. Your ___*parties*___ are fun.
(story)   3. These ___*stories*___ are too long.
(day)   4. We waited for two ___*days*___ .
(copy)   5. The ___*copies*___ are great.
(family)   6. Both ___*families*___ went home.
(berry)   7. The ___*berries*___ were sour.
(lady)   8. The sign said ___*ladies*___ .
(key)   9. The ___*keys*___ didn't work.
(fly)   10. The ___*flies*___ are gone now.

(monkey)   11. We watched the ___*monkeys*___ .
(highway)   12. Two ___*highways*___ met.
(daisy)   13. The ___*daisies*___ were beautiful.
(candy)   14. The ___*candies*___ were eaten.
(toy)   15. The ___*toys*___ were broken.
(puppy)   16. Those ___*puppies*___ are cute.
(cowboy)   17. ___*Cowboys*___ ride horses.
(turkey)   18. The ___*turkeys*___ chased us.
(country)   19. I've visited six ___*countries*___ .
(bluejay)   20. The ___*bluejays*___ flew away.

COMPOSITION EXERCISE

Write a sentence with the plural form of each of the nouns that end in "y."

(strawberry) 1. _____
(puppy)   2. _____
(turkey)   3. _____
(family)   4. _____
(highway)   5. _____

(county)   6. _____
(guppy)   7. _____
(fly)   8. _____
(baby)   9. _____
(birthday)   10. _____

Unusual Plurals

Some nouns that end in "f" or "fe" form the plural by changing "f" or "fe" to "ve" and adding "s." Some nouns change their spellings to form the plural.

EXAMPLES: a. ox — oxen   c. mouse — mice
                     b. life — lives   d. leaf — leaves

 Connect the singular word with its correct plural. In each sentence write the plural of the word in parentheses.

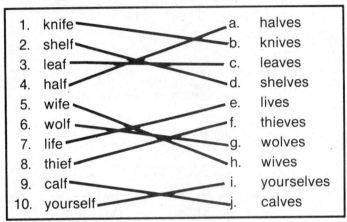

1. knife   a. halves
2. shelf   b. knives
3. leaf   c. leaves
4. half   d. shelves
5. wife   e. lives
6. wolf   f. thieves
7. life   g. wolves
8. thief   h. wives
9. calf   i. yourselves
10. yourself   j. calves

(half)   1. Two __halves__ make a whole.
(knife)   2. The __knives__ are sharp.
(wife)   3. Their __wives__ waited.
(calf)   4. The __calves__ came home.
(yourself) 5. Take care of __yourselves__.
(thief)   6. The __thieves__ were caught.
(shelf)   7. The __shelves__ are too high.
(leaf)   8. The __leaves__ are green.
(wolf)   9. The __wolves__ are hungry.
(life)   10. Our __lives__ are important.

Notice how these nouns stay the same in the singular and plural forms: sheep, fish, moose, corps, swine, deer, people, scissors, news, pants, politics, trousers, athletics, and food.

1. mouse   a. teeth
2. tooth   b. mice
3. foot   c. lice
4. louse   d. women
5. goose   e. feet
6. man   f. men
7. woman   g. children
8. ox   h. geese
9. child   i. cacti
10. cactus   j. oxen

(mouse)   1. The __mice__ ate our cheese.
(man)   2. The __men__ washed the train.
(ox)   3. The __oxen__ pulled the plow.
(foot)   4. My __feet__ hurt.
(tooth)   5. Brush your __teeth__.
(child)   6. The __children__ played.
(louse)   7. My dog has __lice__.
(cactus)   8. __Cacti__ grow in the desert.
(goose)   9. The __geese__ chased us.
(woman)   10. The __women__ were busy.

COMPOSITION EXERCISE

Write a sentence with the plural form of each of these nouns.

(woman)   1. _____
(scissors)   2. _____
(shelf)   3. _____
(child)   4. _____
(news)   5. _____

(mouse)   6. _____
(sheep)   7. _____
(foot)   8. _____
(half)   9. _____
(tooth)   10. _____

Unit 9 cont'd

Practice with Plurals

Most words form the plural by adding "s" or "es." Words that end in "f" or "fe" usually form the plural by changing the "f" or "fe" to "v" plus "es." (There are words that end in "f" that form the plural by adding "s.") Words that end in "y" preceded by a vowel add "s." Words that end in "y" preceded by a consonant change the "y" to "i" and add "s." Some words change the spelling to form the plural.

EXAMPLES:
- a. tree — trees
- b. box — boxes
- c. loaf — loaves
- d. roof — roofs
- e. play — plays
- f. lady — ladies
- g. mouse — mice
- h. news — news

A Write the plural of each word.

(Change <u>f</u> or <u>fe</u> to <u>v</u> + <u>es</u>.)

1. life — *lives*
2. wife — **WIVES**
3. scarf — **SCARVES**
4. self — **SELVES**
5. thief — **THIEVES**
6. loaf — **LOAVES**
7. calf — **CALVES**
8. leaf — **LEAVES**
9. knife — **KNIVES**

B Write the plural of each word.

(word + s)

1. belief — *beliefs*
2. beef — **BEEFS**
3. chief — **CHIEFS**
4. roof — **ROOFS**
5. cuff — **CUFFS**
6. sheriff — **SHERIFFS**
7. reef — **REEFS**
8. tariff — **TARIFFS**
9. puff — **PUFFS**

C Match the singular word with its plural.

g	1. ox	a. children
K	2. bench	b. lice
O	3. suggestion	c. donkeys
C	4. donkey	d. joeys
B	5. louse	e. cacti
F	6. woman	f. women
D	7. joey	g. oxen
Q	8. boss	h. libraries
H	9. library	i. masters
A	10. child	j. attorneys
S	11. sandwich	k. benches
M	12. parrot	l. feet
I	13. master	m. parrots
L	14. foot	n. teeth
R	15. key	o. suggestions
J	16. attorney	p. men
E	17. cactus	q. bosses
T	18. mouse	r. keys
P	19. man	s. sandwiches
N	20. tooth	t. mice

COMPOSITION EXERCISE

List 16 plural nouns.

1. _____ 5. _____ 9. _____ 13. _____
2. _____ 6. _____ 10. _____ 14. _____
3. _____ 7. _____ 11. _____ 15. _____
4. _____ 8. _____ 12. _____ 16. _____

Rules for Forming the Plural

Rule 1 Most nouns form the plural by adding "s."
telephone — telephones

Rule 2 If a noun ends in "ch," "sh," "x," "z," "s," or "ss," form the plural by adding "es."
bush — bushes

Rule 3 If a noun ends with a vowel plus "y," add "s" to form the plural.
highway — highways

Rule 4 If a noun ends with a consonant plus "y," change the "y" to "i" and add "es"
to form the plural.
family — families

Rule 5 If a noun ends in "f" or "fe," change the "f" or "fe" to "ve" and add "s" to form
the plural.
wolf — wolves

Rule 6 If a noun ends in a vowel plus "o," add "s" to form the plural.
radio — radios

Rule 7 If a noun ends in a consonant plus "o," add "es" to form the plural.
echo — echoes

Rule 8 Some nouns change their spellings to form the plural.
child — children

 Write the number of the rule which was used to form the plural of each noun.

8	1. children	6	26. zoos	2	51. sketches	3	76. highways
1	2. kittens	8	27. women	2	52. dresses	3	77. boys
6	3. rodeos	1	28. secrets	1	53. eyes	2	78. branches
3	4. plays	3	29. kidneys	8	54. cacti	4	79. puppies
2	5. bushes	1	30. decisions	7	55. potatoes	5	80. selves
7	6. tomatoes	4	31. memories	1	56. flowers	1	81. accidents
4	7. families	6	32. trios	3	57. toys	8	82. men
5	8. wives	7	33. zeroes	5	58. calves	7	83. volcanoes
1	9. chances	2	34. peaches	2	59. glasses	2	84. businesses
1	10. examples	4	35. libraries	5	60. knives	4	85. centuries
6	11. cameos	5	36. lives	4	61. cities	1	86. voices
3	12. holidays	1	37. daughters	1	62. adventures	2	87. buses
4	13. countries	1	38. opinions	3	63. keys	4	88. copies
8	14. geese	1	39. guests	2	64. inches	1	89. reasons
1	15. mistakes	4	40. skies	4	65. treaties	2	90. finches
3	16. monkeys	3	41. attorneys	7	66. mosquitoes	4	91. flies
5	17. leaves	8	42. lice	4	67. berries	5	92. halves
2	18. watches	7	43. buffaloes	2	68. taxes	3	93. birthdays
2	19. beaches	2	44. axes	2	69. foxes	1	94. careers
1	20. ideas	5	45. scarves	5	70. thieves	6	95. folios
8	21. teeth	1	46. promises	1	71. cabins	1	96. fields
7	22. echoes	2	47. dishes	8	72. oxen	2	97. crosses
5	23. loaves	8	48. feet	2	73. sandwiches	4	98. parties
2	24. churches	8	49. mice	1	74. ghosts	3	99. turkeys
4	25. ladies	3	50. journeys	4	75. babies	2	100. losses

Unit 10 cont'd

Plural Nouns Puzzle

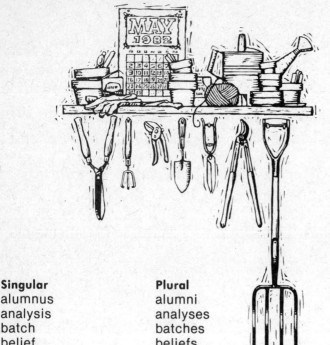

The puzzle grid:

S	J	O	Y	S	C	U	B	S
T	A	X	I	S	H	E	E	P
A	S	E	T	W	I	V	E	S
R	T	N	E	G	L	I	C	E
S	O	F	E	E	D	T	A	A
M	R	E	T	E	R	A	L	$
I	I	E	H	S	E	X	V	O
C	E	T	M	E	N	E	E	N
E	S	A	S	H	E	S	S	$

Singular
alumnus
analysis
batch
belief
brother
bunny
day
dish
echo
elf
half
knife
lady
leaf
navy
pass
radio
scarf
species
turf

Plural
alumni
analyses
batches
beliefs
brethren
bunnies
days
dishes
echoes
elves
halves
knives
ladies
leaves
navies
passes
radios
scarves
species
turfs

 Fill in the blanks. Then complete the words in the puzzle.

Across

2. __J O Y S__ glad feelings; expressions of happiness

4. __C U B S__ young foxes, lions, tigers, bears, or other wild animals

5. __T A X I S__ automobiles for hire

6. __S H E E P__ animals raised for wool, meat, or skins

9. __W I V E S__ women who have husbands; married women

12. __L I C E__ small insects that infest the hair or skin of people

19. __M E N__ adult male persons

20. __S A S H E S__ ornaments or belts worn around the waists of women

Down

1. __S T A R S__ heavenly bodies appearing as bright points in the sky at night

3. __O X E N__ full-grown males of domestic cattle

4. __C H I L D R E N__ young boys or girls; sons and daughters

7. __S T O R I E S__ records, recitals, narratives, fibs, lies, and newspaper articles

8. __T E E T H__ hard, bonelike parts in the mouth used for biting

10. __S E A S O N S__ the four periods of the year

11. __G E E S E__ wild or tame birds like ducks; ganders

13. __C A L V E S__ young cows or bulls; young elephants or whales

14. __F E E T__ end parts of legs that a person or animal stands on

15. __T A X E S__ monies paid by people for support of government

16. __M I C E__ small, gnawing rodents found around the world

17. __A X E S__ tools with sharp blades fastened to handles used for chopping

18. __S O N S__ male children; male descendants

Comprehension Check

(A) Fill in the blanks.

Rule 1   Most nouns form the plural by adding _____*s*_____ .

Rule 2   If a noun ends in "ch," "sh," "x," "z," "s," or "ss," form the plural by adding _____*es*_____ .

Rule 3   If a noun ends with a vowel plus "y," add _____*s*_____ to form the plural.

Rule 4   If a noun ends with a consonant plus "y," change the "y" to _____*i*_____ and add _____*es*_____ to form the plural.

Rule 5   If a noun ends in "f" or "fe," change the "f" or "fe" to _____*ve*_____ and add _____*s*_____ to form the plural.

Rule 6   If a noun ends in a vowel plus "o," add _____*s*_____ to form the plural.

Rule 7   If a noun ends in a consonant plus "o," add _____*es*_____ to form the plural.

Rule 8   Some nouns change their _____*spellings*_____ to form the plural.

(B) Write the plural of each word. Then tell which rule from part A was used.

1. room	*rooms*	*rule 1*	11. mouse	*mice*	*rule 8*
2. body	*bodies*	*rule 4*	12. tomato	*tomatoes*	*rule 7*
3. dish	*dishes*	*rule 2*	13. mattress	*mattresses*	*rule 2*
4. play	*plays*	*rule 3*	14. ocean	*oceans*	*rule 1*
5. radio	*radios*	*rule 6*	15. loaf	*loaves*	*rule 5*
6. wolf	*wolves*	*rule 5*	16. foot	*feet*	*rule 8*
7. puppy	*puppies*	*rule 4*	17. kangaroo	*kangaroos*	*rule 6*
8. woman	*women*	*rule 8*	18. trail	*trails*	*rule 1*
9. echo	*echoes*	*rule 7*	19. city	*cities*	*rule 4*
10. clock	*clocks*	*rule 1*	20. brush	*brushes*	*rule 2*

(C) Underline the plural nouns.

1. workbooks	11. business	21. matches	31. life
2. wives	12. teeth	22. envelope	32. pantries
3. smiles	13. knives	23. skies	33. oxen
4. piano	14. drawer	24. sentence	34. rodeo
5. children	15. buses	25. funnies	35. baskets
6. birthdays	16. rivers	26. notebooks	36. park
7. island	17. cross	27. tax	37. zippers
8. butterflies	18. witches	28. kitchens	38. catalog
9. desk	19. seals	29. posters	39. leaves
10. volcanoes	20. house	30. berries	40. addresses

Test 2 cont'd

Comprehension Check (continued)

D Complete each sentence with a singular noun.

1. The _bridge_ was closed for repairs.
2. I found a _penny_ on the floor.
3. My _sister_ is studying finance.
4. The _mechanic_ fixed my car.
5. No one knew where the _key_ was.
6. Is that a _giraffe_ ?
7. Sally ate a _sandwich_ for lunch.
8. Where is your _house_ ?
9. I bought a _T-shirt_ from Heath.
10. The _car_ sold for $15,000.
11. I am looking for a _pencil_ .
12. The _mouse_ scampered away.
13. Who is the _person_ responsible for this?
14. The _taxi_ honked its horn twice.
15. Do you believe Richard's _story_ ?
16. _Dinner_ will be served at six.
17. Why can't I have a _pie_ ?
18. You should buy a new _book_ .
19. When is the _party_ ?
20. Nathan works as a _cashier_ .
21. The _moon_ is full tonight.
22. Mail this _letter_ for me.
23. Someone took the _stereo_ !
24. The _road_ was blocked off.

E Complete each sentence with a plural noun.

1. _Cars_ were parked everywhere.
2. All the _glasses_ were broken.
3. Bring home a dozen _eggs_ .
4. The _votes_ have been counted.
5. Don't forget the _chips_ .
6. I sent Mom _flowers_ for Christmas.
7. Suzanne tells funny _jokes_ .
8. The _boxes_ were delivered Friday.
9. _Spiders_ scare me.
10. We are out of _pickles_ .
11. Mark wrote ten _pages_ of notes.
12. _Houses_ are expensive.
13. The _rooms_ all looked alike.
14. Six _students_ were sent to the office.
15. I've read all his _books_ .
16. Jean sat through four _movies_ .
17. I don't have any _dimes_ .
18. All the _planes_ were grounded.
19. It costs thirty _dollars_ .
20. _Bees_ make honey.
21. Stephanie made the sugar _cookies_ .
22. Let's have _peaches_ for dessert.
23. Add some _peas_ to the soup.
24. Should we make more _pancakes_ ?

Write a paragraph about a hobby you have or in which you are interested. Underline the plural nouns.

_____
_____
_____
_____
_____
_____
_____
_____
_____

Recognizing Singular and Plural Forms

Singular refers to one person, place, or thing. Plural refers to more than one person, place, or thing.

EXAMPLES:
  a. minute - minutes   d. tomato - tomatoes
  b. reward - rewards   e. beach - beaches
  c. fox - foxes   f. tragedy - tragedies

A Underline each singular form once and each plural form twice.

1. secret	secrets	21. nights	night	41. umbrella	umbrellas
2. men	man	22. tunnel	tunnels	42. leaf	leaves
3. match	matches	23. country	countries	43. holiday	holidays
4. ghosts	ghost	24. change	changes	44. business	businesses
5. fact	facts	25. artists	artist	45. excuse	excuses
6. home	homes	26. journey	journeys	46. life	lives
7. accidents	accident	27. jewel	jewels	47. prices	price
8. penny	pennies	28. cacti	cactus	48. idea	ideas
9. wolves	wolf	29. zoos	zoo	49. echoes	echo
10. reasons	reason	30. potato	potatoes	50. cabin	cabins
11. dessert	desserts	31. goose	geese	51. students	student
12. wife	wives	32. flowers	flower	52. comedy	comedies
13. radios	radio	33. key	keys	53. opinions	opinion
14. army	armies	34. dollars	dollar	54. boxes	box
15. deadlines	deadline	35. puppy	puppies	55. name	names
16. shelf	shelves	36. woman	women	56. sky	skies
17. donkeys	donkey	37. mouse	mice	57. eyes	eye
18. lesson	lessons	38. habit	habits	58. color	colors
19. branches	branch	39. circles	circle	59. peaches	peach
20. line	lines	40. glass	glasses	60. oxen	ox

B Write "S" for singular and "P" for plural.

S	1. telephone	P	9. newspapers	S	17. hour	P	25. cameras
P	2. breakfasts	S	10. dozen	P	18. contests	S	26. license
P	3. teeth	S	11. promise	S	19. zero	S	27. period
P	4. numbers	S	12. automobile	P	20. calves	S	28. roof
S	5. family	S	13. birthday	S	21. fly	S	29. bonus
P	6. foxes	S	14. parachute	P	22. skeletons	P	30. fences
S	7. half	S	15. attorney	S	23. knife	S	31. library
P	8. sidewalks	P	16. grounds	S	24. foot	P	32. boards

Unit 11 cont'd

Articles

"The" is a definite article. "A" is an indefinite article. It is used in front of a noun that begins with a consonant sound. "An" is an indefinite article. It is used in front of a noun that begins with a vowel sound.

EXAMPLES: a. *The room was empty.*   c. *I need an ink pen.*
           b. *Did you hear a scream?*   d. *This is the best one.*

✳ Write either "a," "an," or "the" in the blanks.

1. Alex is __a__ shrewd man.
2. This book is __AN__ almanac.
3. Did you see __THE__ explosion?
4. __THE__ mystery was solved.
5. __THE__ deed has been signed.
6. I saw __A__ mermaid.
7. When is __THE__ deadline?
8. __AN__ aardvark is __AN__ animal.
9. __THE__ statement is not true.
10. Diane is __A__ nurse.
11. Who made __THE__ decision?
12. He is __A__ bitter person.
13. I heard __AN__ echo.
14. Mr. Jackson is __THE__ owner.
15. __THE__ people will rebel.
16. Connie is __A__ guest.
17. I voted for __THE__ amendment.
18. George is __AN__ unhappy boy.
19. It was __A__ long journey.
20. I disapprove of __THE__ plan.
21. We found __AN__ empty box.
22. __THE__ magician is __A__ fake.
23. __THE__ monster was enormous.
24. Mother sang __A__ lullaby.
25. I will explain __THE__ problem.

26. That is __AN__ old automobile.
27. __THE__ river is wide and deep.
28. I need __A__ spoon.
29. Did you take __THE__ money?
30. I love to watch __THE__ monkeys.
31. __THE__ angry bull chased us.
32. Let's have __A__ snack.
33. It was __AN__ important meeting.
34. __THE__ trip was cancelled.
35. He is __A__ famous poet.
36. We need __A__ clue.
37. Where was __THE__ treasure?
38. I forgot __THE__ combination.
39. You must choose __A__ career.
40. __THE__ bottle has __A__ green cap.
41. Do you have __AN__ opinion?
42. It's __AN__ ordinary house.
43. That was __A__ stupid joke.
44. I know __THE__ way.
45. We are __A__ family.
46. Give me __AN__ answer.
47. __THE__ cartoon was nonsense.
48. Bring your father __A__ wrench.
49. I don't know __THE__ password.
50. __THE__ dungeon was cold and dark.

COMPOSITION EXERCISE

Write ten sentences which illustrate the uses of "the," "a," and "an."

1. _____
2. _____
3. _____
4. _____
5. _____

6. _____
7. _____
8. _____
9. _____
10. _____

Using "A" and "An"

"A" is used before nouns which begin with consonant sounds. "An" is used before nouns which begin with vowel sounds.

EXAMPLES:
  a. *a snake*   c. *an empty cup*   e. *an alarm*
  b. *an oak tree*   d. *a dictionary*   f. *a wheel*

 Write either "a" or "an" in the blanks.

1. _a_ nurse	26. AN owner	51. A holiday	76. A game
2. AN alligator	27. A bitter taste	52. A good time	77. AN aardvark
3. AN old friend	28. A liberty	53. AN eye	78. AN arrow
4. A monkey	29. A habit	54. A little boy	79. A treat
5. A walk	30. AN older sister	55. A driver	80. AN act
6. A bird	31. A school bus	56. A cab	81. A shortage
7. AN apple	32. AN arm	57. AN automobile	82. A forest
8. AN ice cube	33. AN abbreviation	58. A singer	83. AN easy test
9. AN extra page	34. AN order	59. A dime	84. A sentence
10. A green car	35. A rule	60. AN icicle	85. A blank
11. A low branch	36. AN adult	61. A desk	86. AN egg
12. AN odd number	37. A bet	62. AN umbrella	87. AN income
13. A comedian	38. AN adverb	63. A valentine	88. AN insect
14. A mean man	39. AN elephant	64. A wagon	89. A fish
15. AN enemy	40. A verb	65. A barn	90. A gate
16. AN appearance	41. AN example	66. A finger	91. AN event
17. A breeze	42. AN adjective	67. AN ugly witch	92. A crayon
18. AN ink pen	43. A nose	68. AN uncle	93. A sound
19. A quiz	44. A movie	69. A ship	94. AN ounce
20. A clue	45. A lake	70. A rose	95. AN aunt
21. A doctor	46. A frown	71. A monster	96. A laugh
22. AN ill person	47. AN even number	72. A niece	97. AN idea
23. A twin	48. A photo	73. AN inch	98. AN evil man
24. AN only child	49. AN ear	74. A jaw	99. AN artist
25. A noun	50. AN ocean	75. AN echo	100. A fire

COMPOSITION EXERCISE

List 10 words which could be used with "a" and 10 which could be used with "an."

a		an	
1. _____	6. _____	1. _____	6. _____
2. _____	7. _____	2. _____	7. _____
3. _____	8. _____	3. _____	8. _____
4. _____	9. _____	4. _____	9. _____
5. _____	10. _____	5. _____	10. _____

Unit 12 cont'd

Indefinite Articles

Both "a" and "an" are indefinite articles.
"A" is used before words which begin with consonant sounds.
"An" is used before words which begin with vowel sounds.

EXAMPLES: a. Have you ever visited an airport?
b. Hemingway is a famous writer.
c. I'm studying for an English test.
d. Bring a dozen eggs.

✳ Write "a" or "an" in each blank.

1. Did you bring __an__ umbrella?
2. I think I saw __A__ ghost!
3. He works in __A__ hospital.
4. That was __AN__ interesting story.
5. Sammy needs __A__ job.
6. Give me __AN__ example.
7. My dad has __A__ new office.
8. That was __AN__ easy test.
9. I need __AN__ adding machine.
10. Look it up in __AN__ almanac.
11. Do you want __A__ bicycle?
12. We made __A__ deal.
13. Would you like __AN__ apple?
14. I caught __A__ fish.
15. That was __A__ terrible thing to do.
16. Mr. Cummings is __A__ nurse.
17. Liz wore __A__ yellow coat.
18. Three is __AN__ odd number.
19. You are __AN__ honest person.
20. Do you have __AN__ excuse?
21. Was there __AN__ accident?
22. There will be __A__ short delay.
23. She deserves __A__ chance.
24. I wrote __A__ story about sailing.
25. __A__ thief stole my bag.

26. Mr. Cameron is __A__ teacher.
27. I brought you __A__ present.
28. Canada is __A__ large country.
29. We saw __AN__ aardvark at the zoo.
30. Paul is reading __A__ book.
31. Wait __A__ minute.
32. Do you have __A__ question?
33. Tell us __A__ joke.
34. __AN__ ostrich crossed the road.
35. That is quite __AN__ accomplishment.
36. Jake ordered __A__ hamburger.
37. I know how to ride __A__ horse.
38. Marian found __A__ dollar.
39. Let's give the dog __A__ bath.
40. The whale is __AN__ enormous animal.
41. May I borrow __A__ pencil?
42. Have you made __A__ decision?
43. I'm watching __A__ cartoon.
44. He was in __A__ hurry.
45. The man became __A__ writer.
46. That animal is __A__ nuisance.
47. The car hit __A__ tree.
48. They hid in __AN__ old building.
49. I don't have __A__ key.
50. Suddenly there was __AN__ explosion.

Identifying Noun Markers

"A," "an," and "the" are noun markers.
They let you know that a noun will
soon follow.

EXAMPLES: a. The grapes were sour.   c. This is an inch too long.
           b. We get milk from a cow.   d. I ate the last piece of pie.

 Write either "a," "an," or "the" in each blank.

1. __The__ show is over.
2. That was __A__ dirty joke.
3. I found __AN__ old shoe.
4. __THE__ woman was angry.
5. I heard __A__ loud noise.
6. Give me __A__ cookie.
7. This is __AN__ arrow.
8. I made __AN__ apple cake.
9. __THE__ man was famous.
10. __A__ farmer visited our class.
11. __THE__ owner caught us.
12. We are __A__ family.
13. Did you hear __A__ voice?
14. I heard __AN__ echo.
15. That is __AN__ ugly dog.
16. __THE__ voyage lasted two months.
17. This is __A__ beautiful day.
18. __THE__ mailman is here.
19. I ride __A__ school bus.
20. My brother owns __AN__ orange car.
21. We will need __A__ long rope.
22. __THE__ yellow one is mine.
23. __AN__ apple is good for you.
24. I want __AN__ ice-cream cone.
25. __THE__ comedian was funny.

26. __THE__ clown is silly.
27. Do you have __AN__ extra pen?
28. I want __THE__ square cake.
29. Ray is __A__ friend.
30. That is __AN__ awful joke.
31. __THE__ money is gone.
32. I knew __THE__ answer.
33. Give us __A__ clue.
34. Joann is __AN__ only child.
35. That is __THE__ question.
36. I won __THE__ bet.
37. James ate __AN__ egg.
38. __THE__ ship sank.
39. __THE__ package arrived early.
40. I opened __THE__ letter.
41. Please sing __A__ song.
42. I have __AN__ idea.
43. Close __THE__ book.
44. __THE__ flowers are beautiful.
45. Let's play __A__ game.
46. It is __AN__ enemy ship.
47. __THE__ door was closed.
48. She gave __AN__ easy test.
49. Our dog found __THE__ newspaper.
50. That was __A__ sad story.

COMPOSITION EXERCISE

Write 10 sentences using noun markers.

1. _____
2. _____
3. _____
4. _____
5. _____

6. _____
7. _____
8. _____
9. _____
10. _____

Unit 13 cont'd

Noun Markers Puzzle

Noun markers help to identify nouns. Almost all sentences contain noun markers. They point out that a noun is to follow. A noun marker is an excellent way of telling whether a word is a noun.

  Fill in the blanks; then complete the puzzle.

The grid reads:

1 A	2 E	3 B	4 S	T	5 H	E	S	E
L	A	O	O	H	6 M	7 O	R	E
L	C	8 T	M	I	9 A	N	10 N	11 M
12 T	H	H	E	S	N	E	O	O
13 W	H	A	T	14 T	H	15 O	S	E
O	16 M	17 T	H	E	T	H	A	T
19 F	20 A	N	Y	21 W	H	I	C	H
E	N	22 S	E	V	E	R	A	L
W	Y	23 E	V	E	R	Y	24 A	N

Down

1. __A L L__ every one of; the whole of; every kind or sort

2. __E A C H__ everyone considered separately or one by one

3. __B O T H__ the two; the one and the other

4. __S O M E__ certain or particular but not known or named

5. __T H I S__ indicating the nearer of two

7. __O N E__ single unit or individual; single kind

8. __T H A T__ pointing out a certain one

9. __A N O T H E R__ one more; not the same; a different one

10. __N O__ word used to say you can't or won't

11. __M O S T__ greatest in amount, quantity, measure, degree, or number

12. __T W O__ one more than one; a set of one and one

15. __O T H E R__ remaining; different; additional or further

16. __M A N Y__ numerous; considering a great number

19. __F E W__ not many; amounting to a small number

24. __A__ indefinite article; one like; another

Across

5. __T H E S E__ indicating the ones nearest

6. __M O R E__ greater in amount, quantity, measure, degree, or number

13. __W H A T__ used in asking questions about people or things

14. __T H O S E__ pointing out or indicating certain ones

17. __T H E__ shows that a certain one is meant

18. __T H A T__ indicating a certain one

20. __A N Y__ one out of many; no matter how great or how small

21. __W H I C H__ referring to the one or ones specified

22. __S E V E R A L__ being more than two or three

23. __E V E R Y__ each one of the entire number

24. __A N__ indefinite article; one; any; each

34

Possessives

Nouns and pronouns can show ownership.

A singular noun shows ownership by adding "'s." A plural noun shows ownership by adding an apostrophe (').

EXAMPLES: a. Ralph + 's = Ralph's   b. families + ' = families'
A pronoun shows ownership by changing its spelling.

EXAMPLES: a. you - your   b. they - their

A Write the possessive of each noun.

1. dog	**DOG'S**
2. frogs	**FROGS'**
3. Adam	**ADAM'S**
4. ship	**SHIP'S**
5. winter	**WINTER'S**
6. Dad	**DAD'S**
7. trees	**TREES'**
8. Rhonda	**RHONDA'S**
9. earth	**EARTH'S**
10. country	**COUNTRY'S**
11. Dyanna	**DYANNA'S**
12. woman	**WOMAN'S**
13. children	**CHILDREN'S**
14. nurses	**NURSES'**
15. captain	**CAPTAIN'S**
16. teachers	**TEACHERS'**
17. Mrs. West	**MRS. WEST'S**
18. hunter	**HUNTER'S**
19. Quincy	**QUINCY'S**
20. bird	**BIRD'S**

B Write the possessive of each pronoun.

1. I	**MY**	**MINE**
2. you	**YOUR**	**YOURS**
3. he	**HIS**	
4. she	**HER**	**HERS**
5. it	**ITS**	
6. we	**OUR**	**OURS**
7. they	**THEIR**	**THEIRS**

C Complete each sentence with the possessive form of the word in the parentheses.

(Mother)   1. I wrapped **Mother's** present in blue.

(you)   2. Is this **your** jacket?

(Mr. Olson)   3. **Mr. Olson's** house is next door.

(reporter)   4. What was the **reporter's** name?

(sergeant)   5. The **sergeant's** orders were to stay here.

(we)   6. Mrs. Parkinson is **our** math teacher.

(ghosts)   7. The **ghosts'** home was a deserted mine.

(man)   8. The dog is **man's** best friend.

(eagle)   9. The **eagle's** nest was at the top of the hill.

(they)   10. **Their** rooms are ready.

(Norman)   11. Sarah is **Norman's** sister.

(visitors)   12. This room is the **visitors'** waiting room.

(Jackie)   13. **Jackie's** cat ate my flowers.

(monkey)   14. The jungle is the **monkey's** home.

(Dr. Parker)   15. Where is **Dr. Parker's** office?

(movie)   16. I didn't enjoy the **movie's** ending.

(I)   17. The first choice is **mine**.

(Capt. Marsdon)   18. **Capt. Marsdon's** car is blocking us.

(guest)   19. Take our **guest's** luggage upstairs.

(Kate)   20. I borrowed **Kate's** bicycle.

(he)   21. What was **his** answer?

(principal)   22. Fred was sent to the **principal's** office.

(students)   23. He listened to the **students'** complaints.

(cat)   24. My **cat's** name is Mortimer.

(Louise)   25. Mr. Filmore read **Louise's** report.

(brother)   26. My **brother's** shoes don't fit me.

(Jill)   27. **Jill's** eyes are brown.

(she)   28. **Her** argument was well stated.

(they)   29. These packages are **theirs**.

(child)   30. The **child's** mother watched.

35

Unit 14 cont'd

How Nouns Show Possession

Singular nouns show possession by adding "'s."
Plural nouns show possession by an apostrophe.

EXAMPLES: a. mountain — mountain's — mountains'
b. American — American's — Americans'

 Add "'s" or "s'" to each word to form the correct possessive.

	Singular	Plural		Singular	Plural
1. book	book's	books'	23. mermaid	mermaid's	mermaids'
2. voice	voice's	voices'	24. comedian	comedian's	comedians'
3. nurse	nurse's	nurses'	25. squaw	squaw's	squaws'
4. lawyer	lawyer's	lawyers'	26. clue	clue's	clues'
5. monkey	monkey's	monkeys'	27. echo	echo's	echoes'
6. storm	storm's	storms'	28. habit	habit's	habits'
7. question	question's	questions'	29. tornado	tornado's	tornados'
8. answer	answer's	answers'	30. moccasin	moccasin's	moccasins'
9. trip	trip's	trips'	31. cartoon	cartoon's	cartoons'
10. breeze	breeze's	breezes'	32. magnet	magnet's	magnets'
11. forest	forest's	forests'	33. voyage	voyage's	voyages'
12. swallow	swallow's	swallows'	34. aardvark	aardvark's	aardvarks'
13. fence	fence's	fences'	35. camel	camel's	camels'
14. ship	ship's	ships'	36. snake	snake's	snakes'
15. license	license's	licenses'	37. alligator	alligator's	alligators'
16. road	road's	roads'	38. elephant	elephant's	elephants'
17. rabbit	rabbit's	rabbits'	39. master	master's	masters'
18. blanket	blanket's	blankets'	40. program	program's	programs'
19. farmer	farmer's	farmers'	41. owner	owner's	owners'
20. clown	clown's	clowns'	42. meadow	meadow's	meadows'
21. fruit	fruit's	fruits'	43. giraffe	giraffe's	giraffes'
22. thumb	thumb's	thumbs'	44. zebra	zebra's	zebras'

COMPOSITION EXERCISE

Write 10 singular nouns that show possession and 10 plural nouns that show possession.

singular

1. _____ 6. _____
2. _____ 7. _____
3. _____ 8. _____
4. _____ 9. _____
5. _____ 10. _____

plural

1. _____ 6. _____
2. _____ 7. _____
3. _____ 8. _____
4. _____ 9. _____
5. _____ 10. _____

Nouns of Ownership

A singular noun shows ownership by adding "'s." A plural noun usually shows ownership by adding an apostrophe (').

EXAMPLES:
  a. George's dad likes to fish.
  b. The toys' colors were bright.
  c. The lawyer's office was large.
  d. Tom's grades are terrible.

 If the underlined noun is singular, add "'s." If the underlined noun is plural, add an apostrophe after the "s."

1. The dog's name is Theo.
2. The tables' legs were metal.
3. Sam's mother is here.
4. The car's lights are on.
5. The owners' names are here.
6. This is my sister's room.
7. The cats' house is gone.
8. These programs' titles are funny.
9. The table's leg is broken.
10. The lawyer's office is there.
11. The story's ending was happy.
12. The kittens' claws are sharp.
13. The coat's pocket was torn.
14. These books' pages are yellow.
15. All of the stores' doors were locked.
16. Danny's bike was stolen.
17. The boat's motor stalled.
18. The chief's hat was stolen.
19. The cat's toy is missing.
20. The knives' edges are sharp.
21. Our mothers' tempers are flaring.
22. The gate's lock is broken.
23. Mr. Taylor's car is ready.
24. He took the baby's chair.
25. The girl's brother is waiting.
26. The farmers' crops are ready.
27. Katy's bus is always late.
28. We saw the lights' glow.
29. Phil is Sally's neighbor.
30. The road's surface is rough.
31. Where is George's house?
32. Peter's answers were correct.
33. Those clowns' faces look real.
34. The book's cover is red.
35. Each room's floor was waxed.
36. The brick hit the store's window.
37. Karen's mom is a doctor.
38. I heard the train's whistle.
39. The teachers' meetings are tomorrow.
40. This is Jay's boat.
41. I pulled the monkey's tail.
42. The bike's tires are flat.
43. The woman's money disappeared.
44. The tests' questions were difficult.
45. Sandy's paper was the best.
46. This is my friend's house.
47. Those curtains' hems are torn.
48. Barry's coat is blue and yellow.
49. The elephant's home is in India.
50. Did you hear the man's warning?

COMPOSITION EXERCISE

Write 12 sentences which contain nouns of ownership.

1. _____
2. _____
3. _____
4. _____
5. _____
6. _____
7. _____
8. _____
9. _____
10. _____
11. _____
12. _____

Unit 15 cont'd

Choosing Correctly Spelled Nouns

A noun names a person, place, or thing.

EXAMPLES: a. officer   c. telephone
               b. photograph   d. neighborhood

 Complete each sentence with the noun which is spelled correctly.

1. Jamie wants a ___career___ in medicine. (a) carear   (b) career   (c) coreer
2. Christmas is my favorite ___HOLIDAY___. (a) holliday   (b) holaday   (c) holiday
3. What's your ___OPINION___? (a) opinion   (b) oppinion   (c) openion
4. Is this his ___SIGNATURE___? (a) signature   (b) signeture   (c) cignature
5. Let's watch ___TELEVISION___. (a) tellevision   (b) television   (c) televishun
6. The ___ACCIDENT___ happened yesterday. (a) acksident   (b) accidunt   (c) accident
7. Do you know the ___PASSWORD___? (a) password   (b) passwurd   (c) pastword
8. ___EDUCATION___ is important. (a) Edukation   (b) Education   (c) Edducation
9. The ___SKELETON___ was found here. (a) skeleton   (b) skeletun   (c) skellton
10. Repeat the ___QUESTION___. (a) kwestion   (b) queshton   (c) question
11. May I have your ___PERMISSION___? (a) permission   (b) purrmision   (c) permishion
12. Ask Samuel for the ___INFORMATION___. (a) infurmation   (b) information   (c) infermation
13. Did you get an ___INVITATION___? (a) invitation   (b) invatation   (c) envitation
14. Dave had another ___NIGHTMARE___. (a) nitmare   (b) nightmare   (c) nightmer
15. The ___DECISION___ is up to you. (a) decision   (b) dicision   (c) desishon
16. You have an ___OBLIGATION___ to fulfill. (a) obligation   (b) oblagation   (c) oblegation
17. We are the new state ___CHAMPIONS___. (a) champeons   (b) champions   (c) champiens
18. Joel speaks a foreign ___LANGUAGE___. (a) langauge   (b) language   (c) languag
19. Help me work this ___PROBLEM___. (a) problim   (b) problum   (c) problem
20. I have never broken a ___PROMISE___. (a) promise   (b) promus   (c) promis
21. Don't forget to give her the ___MESSAGE___. (a) messege   (b) message   (c) mesage
22. Our ___GOVERNMENT___ is a democracy. (a) goverment   (b) government   (c) governmint
23. ___LAUGHTER___ filled the room. (a) Laughter   (b) Laufter   (c) Laffter
24. It's only your ___SHADOW___. (a) shaddow   (b) shadowe   (c) shadow
25. The party will be a ___SURPRISE___. (a) surprise   (b) surprize   (c) serprise
26. Their ___OPPONENT___ forfeited. (a) opponant   (b) opponint   (c) opponent
27. Lewis comes from a big ___FAMILY___. (a) familly   (b) famaly   (c) family
28. I finished my ___REPORT___. (a) reporte   (b) report   (c) repourt
29. The coldest season is ___WINTER___. (a) wintur   (b) winter   (c) wintir
30. Kelly lives in an ___APARTMENT___. (a) apartmint   (b) appartment   (c) apartment
31. My ___POCKET___ has a hole in it. (a) pickit   (b) pocket   (c) pockut
32. Liza is ___PRESIDENT___ of the club. (a) presedent   (b) pressident   (c) president
33. Who broke the ___MIRROR___? (a) mirror   (b) mirrer   (c) miror
34. Which ___DIRECTION___ did he go? (a) direcktion   (b) direction   (c) direcshun
35. Wally's ___BIRTHDAY___ is tomorrow. (a) burthday   (b) berthday   (c) birthday

Comprehension Check

(A) Write "a" or "an" before each noun.

1. _a_ zoo
2. _an_ aardvark
3. _an_ umbrella
4. _a_ gate
5. _a_ camel
6. _an_ exam
7. _a_ highway
8. _an_ ocean
9. _a_ game
10. _an_ iron

11. _an_ officer
12. _an_ ostrich
13. _an_ eagle
14. _a_ sock
15. _a_ temperature
16. _an_ uncle
17. _a_ trip
18. _an_ arrow
19. _an_ island
20. _a_ journal

21. _a_ falcon
22. _a_ pool
23. _a_ shadow
24. _an_ elevator
25. _an_ evening
26. _a_ contest
27. _a_ hair
28. _a_ wind
29. _an_ orange
30. _an_ education

(B) Supply the noun markers.

1. _Both_ men volunteered to go.
2. I prefer _the_ green one.
3. Jim ate _several_ cookies.
4. Have you _any_ money?
5. _Many_ people voted for her.
6. We gave him _some_ food.
7. I checked _each_ part.
8. _These_ books belong to me.
9. _All_ classes were dismissed.
10. _Few_ people ask for a refund.
11. Give Greg _more_ spaghetti.
12. Do you like _that_ shirt better?

13. Have _another_ piece of cake.
14. The boy had _no_ patience.
15. Jerry brought me _a_ sweater.
16. _Those_ clothes are mine.
17. Benjamin examined _every_ room.
18. You can have _both_ copies.
19. Carol has _many_ friends.
20. _All_ grades will be posted.
21. Do you have _other_ hobbies too?
22. _An_ elephant followed me home.
23. When did you get _that_ picture?
24. _Some_ songs are better than others.

(C) Underline the nouns of ownership.

1. Stephen's short story ended sadly.
2. The monsters' homes were caves.
3. Show me Katherine's room.
4. Is that Wallace's mother?
5. Cats' claws are sharp.
6. Who ate Robert's lunch?
7. The man's eyes were dark brown.
8. Where is Mr. Smith's class?
9. Blake's locker is empty.
10. I spoke to Deborah's brother.

11. How did you recognize Alan's cat?
12. When is Doug's birthday?
13. Diane's ring is too small.
14. We used the Johnsons' boat.
15. Larry's uncle owns the station.
16. All the houses' roofs were damaged.
17. Did you find Bert's glasses?
18. Is he Anna's grandfather?
19. Benny's house is next door.
20. The cat ate the dogs' food.

Test 3 cont'd →

Comprehension Check (continued)

D Write the singular and plural possessive forms.

1. teacher	teacher's	teachers'		16. doctor	doctor's	doctors'
2. book	book's	books'		17. family	family's	families'
3. patient	patient's	patients'		18. writer	writer's	writers'
4. machine	machine's	machines'		19. parrot	parrot's	parrots'
5. tourist	tourist's	tourists'		20. owner	owner's	owners'
6. friend	friend's	friends'		21. diver	diver's	divers'
7. agent	agent's	agents'		22. ship	ship's	ships'
8. clerk	clerk's	clerks'		23. song	song's	songs'
9. camel	camel's	camels'		24. river	river's	rivers'
10. desert	desert's	deserts'		25. robber	robber's	robbers'
11. state	state's	states'		26. street	street's	streets'
12. train	train's	trains'		27. town	town's	towns'
13. leader	leader's	leaders'		28. puppy	puppy's	puppies'
14. show	show's	shows'		29. child	child's	children's
15. neighbor	neighbor's	neighbors'		30. forest	forest's	forests'

E Complete each sentence with a possessive noun.

1. The _library's_ doors were unlocked.
2. Take us to _Jill's_ house.
3. _Kevin's_ family went with him.
4. The woman bought _Dad's_ car.
5. Someone sat on _Sue's_ hat.
6. The _team's_ uniforms are gray.
7. Look at the _owl's_ feathers.
8. It hit the _truck's_ fender.
9. _Lucy's_ home is Topeka, Kansas.
10. I read _Gary's_ paper on travel.
11. Do you know where _Jan's_ pen is?
12. What is _Andy's_ last name?
13. _Tony's_ aunt lives in New York.
14. The _animal's_ home is in the jungle.
15. _Brad's_ birthday is tomorrow.
16. The _principal's_ desk was cluttered.
17. _Noel's_ nose was broken.
18. The _trees'_ leaves had turned yellow.
19. I lost _Hank's_ keys!
20. Do you have _Rita's_ homework?

Write a paragraph about a pet you have had. Underline the possessive nouns.

_____
_____
_____
_____
_____
_____
_____
_____
_____

Working with Personal Pronouns

Pronouns that refer to people are called
personal pronouns.

EXAMPLES: *I   you   he   she   we   they   me   him   her   us   them*

A Underline the personal pronouns.

1. I saw <u>her</u> yesterday.
2. <u>He</u> loves to ski.
3. <u>She</u> talks too much.
4. Are <u>we</u> early?
5. Will <u>you</u> give <u>him</u> a message?
6. <u>They</u> are twins.
7. The call is for <u>me</u>.
8. <u>She</u> told <u>us</u> the answer.
9. I saw <u>them</u> leave.
10. <u>She</u> picked the flowers for <u>you</u>.
11. George visited <u>me</u>.
12. <u>You</u> always bring <u>her</u> along.

13. <u>He</u> sits next to <u>me</u>.
14. I want to talk to <u>her</u>.
15. <u>We</u> decided to wait for <u>you</u>.
16. <u>They</u> stopped at the store.
17. Don't <u>you</u> know <u>him</u>?
18. Grandma sent <u>her</u> a card.
19. I answered the letter.
20. When will <u>you</u> tell <u>us</u>?
21. I didn't hear <u>him</u>.
22. <u>You</u> pushed <u>her</u>.
23. <u>He</u> looks like <u>me</u>.
24. I already called <u>them</u>.

B Write a personal pronoun in each blank. Try to use each personal pronoun at least once.

1. __*I*__ put the book away.
2. Is __HE__ your brother?
3. Where are __THEY__ going?
4. __WE__ are finished.
5. The candy is for __HER__.
6. __YOU__ knew it was wrong.
7. __SHE__ is a beautiful girl.
8. The old man warned __THEM__.
9. The package was for __ME__.
10. Are __YOU__ eating again?

11. __I__ see __THEM__.
12. Show __US__ the answer.
13. __I__ want __HIM__ to leave.
14. __THEY__ took our bus.
15. __I__ am tired.
16. Did __YOU__ find __HIM__?
17. Are __YOU__ ready to go?
18. __HE__ is an old man.
19. __WE__ will eat at school.
20. __HE__ stayed in his room.

COMPOSITION EXERCISE

Write 10 sentences using the personal pronouns listed in the examples.

1. _____
2. _____
3. _____
4. _____
5. _____

6. _____
7. _____
8. _____
9. _____
10. _____

Unit 16 cont'd

Noun Substitutes

Pronouns are noun substitutes. They can take the place of nouns.

EXAMPLES:
a. I	e. it	i. him
b. you	f. we	j. her
c. he	g. they	k. us
d. she	h. me	l. them

 Rewrite each sentence using a pronoun to substitute for the underlined noun or nouns.

1. That girl is my sister.
   She is my sister.

2. The machine works perfectly.
   It works perfectly.

3. Joshua is our best player.
   He is our best player.

4. I like John, Thomas, and George.
   I like them.

5. Our class bought the stove.
   Our class bought it.

6. Sarah wants to be a pilot.
   She wants to be a pilot.

7. The night was cold and dark.
   It was cold and dark.

8. The bike belongs to Jim and me.
   The bike belongs to us.

9. Mr. Larson was my first teacher.
   He was my first teacher.

10. A fierce wind destroyed the house.
    It destroyed the house.

11. Janice moved to Boston.
    She moved to Boston.

12. The zone ends here.
    It ends here.

13. Janice and I have decided to go.
    We have decided to go.

14. Eddie, Joe, and Bob surrendered.
    They surrendered.

15. Everyone knows Mr. Johnson.
    Everyone knows him.

16. The war finally ended.
    It finally ended.

17. Karen and I are confused.
    We are confused.

18. Mother forbids gossip.
    Mother forbids it.

19. Did anyone tell Charlotte?
    Did anyone tell her?

20. Your advice is welcomed.
    It is welcomed.

21. Our guests are leaving.
    They are leaving.

22. The almanac is missing.
    It is missing.

23. Sam and Eric are greedy.
    They are greedy.

24. Who wrote the motto?
    Who wrote it?

COMPOSITION EXERCISE

Write a sentence with each of these noun substitutes.

(I)   1. _____

(you) 2. _____

(he)   3. _____

(she) 4. _____

(it)   5. _____

(we)   6. _____

(they) 7. _____

(me)   8. _____

(him)   9. _____

(her) 10. _____

(us)   11. _____

(them) 12. _____

Using Pronouns

Pronouns take the places of nouns. Sometimes they are called noun substitutes.

EXAMPLES: My teacher was so happy that my <u>teacher</u> cried.
My teacher was so happy that <u>she</u> cried.

A Underline the nouns which would sound better as pronouns.

1. Sarah wants to be a nurse. <u>Sarah's</u> mother is a nurse. Sarah pretends <u>Sarah's</u> dolls are sick people. <u>Sarah</u> makes <u>Sarah's</u> dolls better when the <u>dolls</u> are sick. Sarah's mother gave <u>Sarah</u> a nurse's kit for <u>Sarah's</u> birthday. Now Sarah can play like a real nurse.

2. The machine is working again. The machine was broken but John fixed the <u>machine</u>. The machine makes ice cream. John wished <u>John</u> had an ice cream machine at <u>John's</u> house. Then <u>John</u> could eat <u>John's</u> ice cream all day long. John says <u>John</u> would never get tired of ice cream.

3. This hat is my favorite. I wear <u>the hat</u> everywhere I go. The hat even sleeps with me. I named the hat "Nonsense" because <u>the hat</u> looks so funny. The hat likes the <u>hat's</u> name because <u>the hat</u> knows <u>the hat</u> is special.

B Write the noun substitute in each blank.

1. Sarah wants to be a nurse. __*Her*__ mother is a nurse. Sarah pretends __HER__ dolls are sick people. __SHE__ makes __HER__ dolls better when __THEY__ are sick. Sarah's mother gave __HER__ a nurse's kit for __HER__ birthday. Now Sarah can play like a real nurse.

2. The machine is working again. The machine was broken but John fixed __IT__. The machine makes ice cream. John wished __HE__ had an ice cream machine at __HIS__ house. Then __HE__ could eat __HIS__ ice cream all day long. John says __HE__ would never get tired of ice cream.

3. This hat is my favorite. I wear __IT__ everywhere I go. The hat even sleeps with me. I named the hat "Nonsense" because __IT__ looks so funny. The hat likes __ITS__ name because __IT__ knows __IT__ is special.

COMPOSITION EXERCISE

Write 12 sentences which contain pronouns.

1. _____
2. _____
3. _____
4. _____
5. _____
6. _____

7. _____
8. _____
9. _____
10. _____
11. _____
12. _____

Unit 17 cont'd

Pronouns of Possession

Possessive pronouns are pronouns that show ownership.

EXAMPLES: a. I need *your* help. c. This is *my* sister.
b. *Its* home is in Africa. d. I found *her* book.

 In each blank write the possessive form of the pronoun in the parentheses.

(I) 1. This is __*my*__ home.
(you) 2. __YOUR__ mother has called.
(he) 3. __HIS__ team is losing.
(she) 4. What is __HER__ name?
(it) 5. Look at __ITS__ teeth!
(we) 6. __OUR__ class isn't going.
(they) 7. I heard __THEIR__ story.
(I) 8. The ring is __MINE__.
(you) 9. That paper isn't __YOURS__.
(we) 10. Dave told __OUR__ secret.
(she) 11. Susan lost __HERS__.
(I) 12. I want __MINE__ now.
(we) 13. Tomorrow is __OUR__ last day.
(you) 14. Who cut __YOUR__ hair?
(they) 15. __THEIR__ name is Bergen.
(you) 16. Does he know __YOUR__ brother?
(it) 17. __ITS__ eyes were huge.
(you) 18. Where is __YOUR__ home?
(he) 19. __HIS__ nose was broken.
(I) 20. You can't have __MINE__.
(she) 21. __HER__ plane is leaving.
(he) 22. That boat is __HIS__.
(you) 23. The man called __YOUR__ name.
(we) 24. There goes __OUR__ bus.
(I) 25. I left __MINE__ at home.

(It) 26. The house lost __ITS__ charm.
(she) 27. __HER__ father was furious.
(they) 28. It is __THEIR__ decision.
(I) 29. __MY__ throat is sore today.
(you) 30. __YOUR__ ideas are too crazy.
(I) 31. Did you see __MINE__?
(he) 32. Have you tried __HIS__ number?
(It) 33. __ITS__ engine failed.
(I) 34. Someone is at __MY__ door.
(we) 35. Where are __OUR__ lunches?
(It) 36. Do you like __ITS__ colors?
(he) 37. I borrowed __HIS__ skates.
(we) 38. Everything is __OURS__.
(you) 39. Are __YOUR__ parents coming?
(she) 40. Will you buy __HER__ candy?
(he) 41. I've never seen __HIS__ car.
(they) 42. This is __THEIR__ last chance.
(you) 43. Someone took __YOURS__.
(I) 44. I ate all of __MINE__.
(he) 45. The hammer hit __HIS__ hand.
(you) 46. __YOUR__ story is unbelievable.
(It) 47. __ITS__ ending was sad.
(I) 48. __MY__ grades are terrible.
(she) 49. I don't want __HER__ desk.
(I) 50. I'm taking __MY__ time.

COMPOSITION EXERCISE

Write a sentence with each of these possessive pronouns.

(my) 1. _____
(mine) 2. _____
(your) 3. _____
(yours) 4. _____
(her) 5. _____
(hers) 6. _____

(his) 7. _____
(its) 8. _____
(our) 9. _____
(ours) 10. _____
(their) 11. _____
(theirs) 12. _____

44

Pronouns of Ownership

Pronouns which show ownership are called possessive pronouns.

EXAMPLES:
- a. mine or my — belonging to me
- b. your or yours — belonging to you
- c. its — belonging to it
- d. his — belonging to him
- e. her or hers — belonging to her
- f. our or ours — belonging to us
- g. their or theirs — belonging to them

 Write the possessive pronoun of each word in parentheses.

(you) 1. *Your* mother has come for you.
(me) 2. This is *my* favorite hat.
(us) 3. *Our* house is being repainted.
(them) 4. *Their* ideas are good.
(you) 5. What is *your* name?
(me) 6. The monkey took *my* banana.
(him) 7. *His* habits are terrible.
(her) 8. That is *her* signature.
(me) 9. You may have *mine*.
(him) 10. *His* nose looks funny.
(me) 11. *My* mom was furious.
(him) 12. *His* watch is expensive.
(us) 13. Mrs. Winters is *our* mother.
(you) 14. Was that *yours* to give?
(them) 15. *Their* questions were silly.
(her) 16. What is *her* name?
(me) 17. *My* answers are correct.
(her) 18. Why is *hers* the best?
(it) 19. The snowman lost *its* hat.
(him) 20. The thief broke *his* leg.
(them) 21. Isn't that *their* car?
(you) 22. The decision is *yours*.
(me) 23. I misplaced *my* glasses.
(it) 24. The tornado lost *its* power.
(us) 25. *Ours* is missing.

(us) 26. Give us *our* share.
(it) 27. The car lost *its* license.
(me) 28. I can hear *my* echo.
(you) 29. I ate *yours* too.
(them) 30. *Their* song was beautiful.
(him) 31. *His* story is a mystery.
(it) 32. The snake shed *its* skin.
(her) 33. Jane broke *hers*.
(her) 34. *Her* room is upstairs.
(me) 35. Is this *my* old doll.
(them) 36. *Their* decision is important.
(you) 37. *Your* gloves are torn.
(him) 38. The comedian forgot *his* jokes.
(us) 39. *Our* trip was great.
(you) 40. *Your* bike has a flat tire.
(me) 41. Where are *mine*?
(him) 42. *His* glass is empty.
(me) 43. Did you pick *my* flowers?
(him) 44. He lost *his* voice.
(you) 45. I got *your* message.
(me) 46. *My* straw doesn't work.
(them) 47. *Their* time has come.
(it) 48. *Its* eyes are orange.
(her) 49. The nurse dropped *her* cap.
(us) 50. You have *our* permission.

COMPOSITION EXERCISE

Write a sentence with each of these possessive pronouns.

(my) 1. _____
(mine) 2. _____
(your) 3. _____
(yours) 4. _____
(its) 5. _____
(his) 6. _____

(her) 7. _____
(hers) 8. _____
(our) 9. _____
(ours) 10. _____
(their) 11. _____
(theirs) 12. _____

Unit 18 cont'd

Proper Use of "I" and "Me"

"I" is used as a subject. "Me" is used as an object.

EXAMPLES: a. It was easy for me. c. I ignored the insult.
b. I am not greedy. d. She tried to discourage me.

✱ Write "I" or "me" in each blank.

1. __I__ need some advice.
2. The skeleton scares __ME__.
3. __I__ persuaded Jill to go.
4. __I__ can't meet the deadline.
5. Is the letter for __ME__?
6. __I__ borrowed the money.
7. __I__ am not a mermaid.
8. Tell __ME__ the password.
9. __I__ was not invited.
10. Don't talk to __ME__.
11. __I__ misplaced your address.
12. __I__ am very sorry.
13. The dog bit __ME__.
14. The bullet missed __ME__.
15. __I__ heard an echo.
16. Will you come with __ME__?
17. Janice is helping __ME__.
18. The coat fits __ME__ perfectly.
19. __I__ will arrive on time.
20. Do __I__ know you?
21. The call was for __ME__.
22. Read the note to __ME__.
23. __I__ don't remember his number.
24. __I__ found an old coin.
25. She invited __ME__ to stay.

26. Don't spill the bleach on __ME__.
27. They will surrender to __ME__.
28. __I__ am afraid of it.
29. You will assist __ME__.
30. Give __ME__ your promise.
31. May __I__ help someone?
32. __I__ am sure you'll like it.
33. The noise woke __ME__.
34. __I__ am waiting for a bus.
35. __I__ must leave early.
36. The kitten likes __ME__.
37. Did anyone call __ME__?
38. __I__ introduced them.
39. __I__ think it is nonsense.
40. You asked __ME__.
41. It is important to __ME__.
42. __I__ told you the truth.
43. __I__ forbid you to talk.
44. Nothing can hurt __ME__.
45. __I__ choose to stay here.
46. __I__ thought you had moved.
47. It is interesting to __ME__.
48. __I__ was elected secretary.
49. Now __I__ am confused.
50. __I__ understand the assignment.

COMPOSITION EXERCISE

Write five sentences with "I" and five with "me."

I

1. _____
2. _____
3. _____
4. _____
5. _____

me

1. _____
2. _____
3. _____
4. _____
5. _____

46

"Your" — "You're"

"Your" shows possession. "You're" means "you are." It is a contraction.

EXAMPLES:
   a. This is <u>your</u> pencil.
   b. <u>You're</u> making me angry.
   c. <u>You're</u> too early.
   d. I am <u>your</u> teacher.

 Write either "your" or "you're" in each blank.

1. <u>Your</u> bus is leaving.
2. <u>YOU'RE</u> hurting me.
3. <u>YOU'RE</u> a good student.
4. Is this <u>YOUR</u> book?
5. Where is <u>YOUR</u> brother?
6. <u>YOU'RE</u> going with me.
7. <u>YOUR</u> teacher is Ms. Sims.
8. I will tell <u>YOUR</u> mother.
9. May I use <u>YOUR</u> pen?
10. <u>YOU'RE</u> my best friend.
11. Today is <u>YOUR</u> birthday.
12. <u>YOU'RE</u> talking again.
13. <u>YOU'RE</u> going to school.
14. Here is <u>YOUR</u> present.
15. <u>YOUR</u> hands are dirty.
16. <u>YOU'RE</u> riding my bike.
17. <u>YOU'RE</u> spilling the water.
18. I found <u>YOUR</u> hat.
19. <u>YOUR</u> mom was angry.
20. They took <u>YOUR</u> wagon.
21. Did you eat <u>YOUR</u> lunch?
22. <u>YOU'RE</u> sitting in my chair.
23. <u>YOU'RE</u> too busy.
24. I hope <u>YOU'RE</u> ready.
25. <u>YOU'RE</u> eating too much.

26. Go to <u>YOUR</u> room.
27. I heard <u>YOUR</u> story.
28. <u>YOU'RE</u> the best player.
29. <u>YOUR</u> hair is wet.
30. <u>YOU'RE</u> from Montana.
31. Bring <u>YOUR</u> skates.
32. <u>YOU'RE</u> sure it was Jay?
33. <u>YOU'RE</u> standing on my coat.
34. <u>YOUR</u> dog bit me.
35. <u>YOU'RE</u> not a doctor.
36. I broke <u>YOUR</u> bat.
37. <u>YOU'RE</u> staying home.
38. <u>YOUR</u> parents are here.
39. Drink <u>YOUR</u> milk.
40. Where is <u>YOUR</u> home?
41. <u>YOU'RE</u> doing it wrong.
42. Here is <u>YOUR</u> paper.
43. Show me <u>YOUR</u> work.
44. <u>YOU'RE</u> not watching the show.
45. What is <u>YOUR</u> reason?
46. <u>YOU'RE</u> late.
47. <u>YOU'RE</u> not listening.
48. Did you do <u>YOUR</u> homework?
49. What is <u>YOUR</u> answer?
50. Let's go to <u>YOUR</u> house.

COMPOSITION EXERCISE

Write five sentences with "your" and five with "you're."

1. _____
2. _____
3. _____
4. _____
5. _____

1. _____
2. _____
3. _____
4. _____
5. _____

Unit 19 cont'd ➡

The Position of Verbs

A verb tells what happens in the sentence.
Usually the verb follows the subject.

EXAMPLES: a. Eric hesitated.   c. Mrs. Jay explained the lesson.
          b. You ignored everyone.   d. Mom disapproves of John.

✱ Underline the subject once and the verb twice.

1. The ghost vanished.
2. I replaced the bulb.
3. Our club pledged $50.00.
4. It aroused my curiosity.
5. I spoke to Betsy.
6. The problems confused us.
7. We climbed to the top.
8. The troop halted.
9. Dan suggested the plan.
10. The noise sounded nearby.
11. The bridge fell.
12. He transferred to Oakdale.
13. The horse galloped.
14. James paid the bill.
15. The nurse retired.
16. Joshua solved the mystery.
17. They raced to the corner.
18. Everyone laughed.
19. She hid the package.
20. Lana cleared the table.
21. No one confessed.
22. Our team painted the sign.
23. The teacher told my parents.
24. I forgot my coat.
25. The prisoner escaped.

26. I misplaced the keys.
27. Someone lives here.
28. We postponed the game.
29. Dad convinced us.
30. The arrow missed the target.
31. He measured the room.
32. She disobeyed her parents.
33. The police surrounded the house.
34. The air feels cool.
35. He swallowed the penny.
36. The contest ended.
37. Our vacation begins in April.
38. The map fell in the mud.
39. I saw the fight.
40. Karen locked the door.
41. We followed the trail.
42. The mouse scampered away.
43. She wrapped the gift.
44. Lane read all afternoon.
45. I want a new bicycle.
46. Cathi left for work.
47. The leaves burned.
48. We caught the robber.
49. The elevator stopped.
50. The bomb exploded.

COMPOSITION EXERCISE

Write fourteen sentences. Underline the verb in each sentence.

1. _____
2. _____
3. _____
4. _____
5. _____
6. _____
7. _____

8. _____
9. _____
10. _____
11. _____
12. _____
13. _____
14. _____

Practice with Action Verbs

An action verb tells what is happening in the sentence. The verb may be in present, past, or future tense.

EXAMPLES:

	present	past	future
a.	love	loved	will love
b.	place	placed	will place
c.	return	returned	will return
d.	go	went	will go

 Underline the verb in each sentence. In the blank write whether the verb is in present, past, or future tense. Use "PR" for present, "PA" for past, and "FT" for future tense.

__PR__ 1. You ignore me.
__PA__ 2. The monster vanished.
__FT__ 3. The bomb will explode.
__PA__ 4. The limb damaged our car.
__PA__ 5. The monkey opened his cage.
__FT__ 6. I will suggest the idea.
__PR__ 7. This work confuses me.
__PR__ 8. He hesitates too often.
__FT__ 9. She will delay the test.
__PA__ 10. We published a paper.
__FT__ 11. Paul will forget the bread.
__FT__ 12. The child will obey me.
__PA__ 13. The dog barked at us.
__PA__ 14. We measured the windows.
__PR__ 15. Don sells insurance.
__FT__ 16. The contest will end tomorrow.
__PA__ 17. The horse jumped the fence.
__PR__ 18. The soup tastes delicious.
__PA__ 19. We worked all day.
__FT__ 20. I will fix the faucet.
__FT__ 21. She will read us the story.
__PR__ 22. Kate walks to school.
__PR__ 23. Grandma lives in Mexico.
__FT__ 24. Bob will hang the paintings.
__PA__ 25. The ice cream melted.

__PA__ 26. An aardvark followed me home.
__PR__ 27. I want the answer now.
__PR__ 28. This book looks interesting.
__FT__ 29. He will confess to everything.
__PA__ 30. Dad signed the papers.
__PR__ 31. He plays the guitar.
__FT__ 32. No one will understand.
__FT__ 33. Harry will send flowers.
__FT__ 34. We will take the blue car.
__PA__ 35. Sue smiled at the clerk.
__PR__ 36. He builds furniture.
__PR__ 37. I expect him today.
__PA__ 38. Judy estimated our cost.
__FT__ 39. The team will lose the game.
__PR__ 40. Phil needs another nail.
__PR__ 41. I disapprove of the plan.
__PR__ 42. Eva likes camping and fishing.
__PA__ 43. We decided on a motto.
__FT__ 44. Carrie will paint my picture.
__FT__ 45. The movie will end at noon.
__PR__ 46. The people want a change.
__PA__ 47. Sam bought the set.
__PA__ 48. The bull chased us.
__PR__ 49. I hate cold weather.
__FT__ 50. It will destroy our city.

COMPOSITION EXERCISE

List 8 verbs in their present, past, and future forms.

1. _____
2. _____
3. _____
4. _____

5. _____
6. _____
7. _____
8. _____

Unit 20 cont'd →

Using Action Verbs

A verb is a word that tells what is happening in the sentence. Most verbs show action.

EXAMPLES:
   a. I <u>hurt</u> my leg.
   b. Jake <u>caught</u> a frog.
   c. The horse <u>jumped</u> the fence.
   d. The birds <u>flew</u> away.

 Underline the action verb in each sentence.

1. The mermaid <u>swam</u> away.
2. George <u>sneezed</u> twice.
3. My car <u>hit</u> the sign.
4. I <u>waited</u> for an hour.
5. A man <u>opened</u> the door.
6. The baby <u>cried</u>.
7. The music <u>blasted</u>.
8. The paper <u>burned</u> quickly.
9. We <u>painted</u> the fence.
10. Sally <u>sat</u> next to me.
11. The bell finally <u>rang</u>.
12. I <u>turned</u> the radio off.
13. The wagon <u>lost</u> its wheel.
14. The roses <u>bloomed</u>.
15. The children <u>crossed</u> the street.
16. Lynn <u>read</u> her poem.
17. I <u>fell</u> in the mud.
18. The kitten <u>drank</u> her milk.
19. Jerry <u>hit</u> a home run.
20. Mom <u>took</u> a nap.
21. Sara <u>left</u> me a note.
22. The calf <u>followed</u> its mother.
23. Tony <u>stepped</u> on my hand.
24. We <u>went</u> to the park.
25. I <u>passed</u> my test.
26. She <u>pushed</u> the yellow button.
27. The paint <u>costs</u> too much.
28. Jan <u>broke</u> her pencil.
29. The cat <u>ate</u> my flowers.
30. The fire <u>burned</u> slowly.
31. I <u>washed</u> the car.
32. The teacher <u>listened</u> to us.
33. Our class <u>wrote</u> a song.
34. The wind <u>blew</u> the leaves.
35. The child <u>hurt</u> his finger.
36. The crowd <u>shouted</u>.
37. Karen <u>fixed</u> her bike.
38. They <u>found</u> an old hat.
39. Our class <u>sang</u> for the PTA.
40. That man <u>built</u> our house.
41. Dad <u>cut</u> the pie.
42. A tree <u>fell</u> on our car.
43. You <u>dropped</u> my brush.
44. I <u>saw</u> her yesterday.
45. The ship <u>sank</u>.
46. I <u>spilled</u> our Cokes.
47. Kay <u>used</u> my book.
48. Mr. Jones <u>called</u> the police.
49. The dog <u>ran</u> after the car.
50. Our school <u>won</u>.

COMPOSITION EXERCISE

Write 12 sentences which contain action verbs.

1. _____
2. _____
3. _____
4. _____
5. _____
6. _____
7. _____
8. _____
9. _____
10. _____
11. _____
12. _____

Comprehension Check

(A) **Underline the pronouns.**

1. me	6. its	11. them	16. it
2. thing	7. I	12. eye	17. pen
3. her	8. they	13. you	18. him
4. he	9. person	14. mine	19. we
5. ours	10. she	15. us	20. his

(B) **Write a possessive pronoun which could substitute for each noun or noun phrase.**

1. John's	*his*	9. Edna's	*her*	17. Steve's and mine	*our*
2. Dr. Adam's	*his / her*	10. Mr. White's	*his*	18. Julie's and Kay's	*their*
3. monster's	*its*	11. Joe's and Al's	*their*	19. Sarah's	*her*
4. offices'	*their*	12. library's	*its*	20. program's	*its*
5. book's	*its*	13. Karen's	*her*	21. Ms. Watson's	*her*
6. Diane's	*her*	14. trees'	*their*	22. bridges'	*their*
7. Ted's and mine	*our*	15. Mrs. Stuart's	*her*	23. Margie's	*her*
8. Barton's	*his*	16. Seth's and mine	*our*	24. Harry's	*his*

(C) **Rewrite each sentence substituting pronouns for the underlined nouns.**

1. Have you tried the tuna?
   Have you tried it?

2. Nell and I are going to Hawaii.
   We are going to Hawaii.

3. Mrs. Sadler asked the clerk the amount.
   She asked him the amount.

4. I like the green one best.
   I like it best.

5. The houses on this block are new.
   They are new.

6. George ate a candy bar for lunch.
   He ate it for lunch.

7. The woman drove a red convertible.
   She drove a red convertible.

8. Liz and I went to class early.
   We went to class early.

9. Nora made an A on the exam.
   She made an A on it.

10. Can you see the jet?
    Can you see it?

11. Robert took the book home.
    He took it home.

12. Seth and Carter are at the movies.
    They are at the movies.

13. Jill read the paper before dinner.
    She read it before dinner.

14. Don't sit on the couch.
    Don't sit on it.

15. Count the pennies again.
    Count them again.

16. Sue and Ken made the cookies.
    They made them.

17. Mr. Hart plays golf on Saturday.
    He plays golf on Saturday.

18. The members voted for Jeff.
    They voted for Jeff.

19. Vera and I can use the computer.
    We can use it.

20. The boy rode a motorcycle.
    He rode a motorcycle.

Test 4 cont'd

Comprehension Check (continued)

(D) Underline the verbs.

1. We <u>picnic</u> every Saturday.
2. I <u>ordered</u> two hamburgers.
3. Lars <u>wrapped</u> the presents.
4. Mary <u>rushed</u> to school.
5. The snow <u>covered</u> the streets.
6. Ollie <u>left</u> you this note.
7. I <u>heard</u> a loud pop.
8. Madison always <u>chooses</u> blue.
9. He <u>whistles</u> in the shower.
10. We <u>watched</u> the monkeys.
11. You <u>have</u> a neat handwriting.
12. School <u>starts</u> next week.
13. Henry <u>unlocked</u> the gate.
14. Wesley <u>organized</u> the rally.
15. They <u>sold</u> the most tickets.
16. I <u>answered</u> all the questions.
17. They <u>presented</u> the trophy to Roy.
18. Kelly <u>borrowed</u> my umbrella.
19. Terry <u>moved</u> here from Houston.
20. The show <u>begins</u> at three.
21. Fran <u>pushed</u> the red button.
22. Everything <u>fell</u> in the mud.
23. The water <u>ran</u> over the counter.
24. My cat <u>jumped</u> on the table.
25. He <u>stole</u> my lunch!
26. The noise <u>hurts</u> my ears.
27. I <u>took</u> my notes to class.
28. Helen <u>sews</u> beautifully.
29. The apples <u>came</u> from Washington.
30. Pam <u>chased</u> the mouse.

(E) Supply the verbs.

1. I _found_ a penny on the floor.
2. My aunt _keeps_ everything.
3. Frank _stacked_ the books neatly.
4. The story _ends_ sadly.
5. You _used_ my new batteries.
6. I _urged_ him to talk to you.
7. Ben _sleeps_ with the lights on.
8. Uncle Rudy _lives_ in Nebraska.
9. We _learned_ to speak Spanish.
10. She _owes_ me some money.
11. I _drank_ four glasses of water.
12. Alex _reads_ a book a week.
13. This month we _went_ to Boston.
14. Our team _plays_ the Tigers Saturday.
15. Wilson _knows_ everything.
16. Someone _left_ the door open.
17. It _contains_ old letters and cards.
18. I _resisted_ the cheesecake.
19. We _return_ on Wednesday afternoon.
20. Evert _stood_ on the ladder.

Write a paragraph about a family reunion. Underline the pronouns.

_____
_____
_____
_____
_____
_____
_____
_____

Linking Verbs

Linking verbs include "is," "are," "am," "was," and "were." They come between subjects and predicate adjectives or subjects and predicate nouns or noun substitutes.

EXAMPLES:
  a. *I am happy.*
  b. *The price is too high.*
  c. *They are athletes.*
  d. *Jennifer was the leader.*
  e. *We were afraid.*

A Write "am," "is," or "are" in the blanks.

1. My name __is__ George.
2. I __AM__ a student.
3. He __IS__ my brother.
4. She __IS__ our neighbor.
5. We __ARE__ happy here.
6. They __ARE__ fishermen.
7. You __ARE__ my friend.
8. Sharon __IS__ the queen.
9. The house __IS__ too large.
10. The animal __IS__ a fox.
11. They __ARE__ angry.
12. I __AM__ ill.
13. The money __IS__ safe.
14. You __ARE__ greedy.
15. Diamonds __ARE__ a luxury.
16. That woman __IS__ attractive.
17. He __IS__ busy.
18. We __ARE__ hungry.
19. I __AM__ a ghost.
20. The men __ARE__ weak.
21. You __ARE__ a guest.
22. The weather __IS__ cold.
23. The houses __ARE__ modern.
24. The music __IS__ beautiful.

B Write "was" or "were" in the blanks.

1. The test __was__ difficult.
2. Paul and Al __WERE__ a team.
3. The clue __WAS__ significant.
4. The water __WAS__ hot.
5. Cathi __WAS__ shrewd.
6. The men __WERE__ carpenters.
7. The accident __WAS__ tragic.
8. We __WERE__ restless.
9. The dog __WAS__ obedient.
10. The meal __WAS__ delicious.
11. The woman __WAS__ wise.
12. The man __WAS__ famous.
13. They __WERE__ nurses.
14. Josh __WAS__ proud.
15. The cartoons __WERE__ funny.
16. It __WAS__ your signature.
17. Our car __WAS__ a Ford.
18. The moccasins __WERE__ brown.
19. The sentences __WERE__ short.
20. The workers __WERE__ rebels.

COMPOSITION EXERCISE

Write two sentences for each of these verbs.

(am)   1. _____ _____

(is)   2. _____ _____

(are)   3. _____ _____

(was)   4. _____ _____

(were)   5. _____ _____

Unit 21 cont'd

The Position of Linking Verbs

Linking verbs come between subjects and predicate adjectives or between subjects and predicate nouns or noun substitutes.

EXAMPLES: a. My name *is* Poindexter.   c. She *is* my mother.
           b. His hair *was* blonde.   d. The chairs *were* red.

A Underline the linking verb in each sentence.

1. Mike is bashful.
2. It is a monster.
3. The table was dirty.
4. The man is a farmer.
5. The flowers were red.
6. Alex is a comedian.
7. The ideas are foolish.
8. The glass is empty.
9. This poem is nonsense.
10. The rabbits are white.
11. The man is an artist.
12. The candy was sweet.
13. This knife is sharp.
14. The room was warm.
15. You were rude.
16. The lion is wild.
17. The forest was dark.
18. The frog is fat.
19. The wagon is green.
20. They were funny.
21. The grapes are bitter.
22. The milk is sour.
23. John was our doctor.
24. The breeze is chilly.

25. The children were silent.
26. This song is a lullaby.
27. The lemons are sour.
28. That hammer is useless.
29. He was the thief.
30. You were correct.
31. The letter was open.
32. The coat is too small.
33. The floor is wet.
34. His voice is hoarse.
35. The river is deep.
36. An apple is a fruit.
37. I am happy.
38. My eyes are blue.
39. Karen was the maid.
40. The answer is true.
41. The policemen are busy.
42. I am an actor.
43. You are silly.
44. The movie was good.
45. He is my uncle.
46. Perry is handsome.
47. My sister is smart.
48. You were careless.

B In each blank write a linking verb.

1. I __am__ a giraffe.
2. You __ARE__ my enemy.
3. Kim __IS__ the treasurer.
4. My brother __IS__ a baby.
5. The lot __WAS__ vacant.
6. He __IS__ a teacher.
7. The liver __WAS__ delicious.
8. Gene __IS__ an adult.
9. His name __IS__ Peter.
10. The driver __WAS__ my dad.
11. This flower __IS__ a rose.
12. We __ARE__ members.
13. It __WAS__ a tornado.
14. Jack __IS__ the owner.
15. I __AM__ your friend.
16. She __IS__ sad.
17. You __WERE__ a devil.
18. He __WAS__ the principal.
19. Tim and Sue __ARE__ late.
20. The locks __WERE__ secure.
21. Omaha __IS__ a city.
22. The word __IS__ a noun.
23. Fire __IS__ dangerous.
24. The problem __WAS__ easy.

COMPOSITION EXERCISE

Write 12 sentences which contain linking verbs.

1. _____
2. _____
3. _____
4. _____
5. _____
6. _____

7. _____
8. _____
9. _____
10. _____
11. _____
12. _____

Forms of the Verb "Be"

The verb "be" is written in the following ways:

singular	**plural**
I am	*we are*
you are	*you are*
he, she, it is	*they are*

EXAMPLES: a. *He is fishing.*   c. *I am busy.*

           b. *It is snowing.*   d. *They are angry.*

❋   **In each blank write the correct form of the verb "be."**

1. I __am__ a student.
2. You __ARE__ my friend.
3. He __IS__ my brother.
4. She __IS__ pretty.
5. It __IS__ Tuesday.
6. We __ARE__ neighbors.
7. You __ARE__ comedians.
8. They __ARE__ at home.
9. She __IS__ always polite.
10. I __AM__ hungry.
11. It __IS__ raining again.
12. They __ARE__ late for school.
13. The decision __IS__ mine.
14. Alex __IS__ ill.
15. You __ARE__ wrong.
16. Margo __IS__ in the kitchen.
17. Sam and Phil __ARE__ twins.
18. She __IS__ bashful.
19. It __IS__ too hot.
20. This story __IS__ a mystery.
21. You __ARE__ not trying.
22. The nurse __IS__ my aunt.
23. The leaves __ARE__ green.
24. It __IS__ a stupid idea.
25. I __AM__ listening.
26. The river __IS__ too deep.
27. Bob and Tom __ARE__ sleeping.
28. My bike __IS__ gone.
29. I __AM__ writing a poem.
30. The man __IS__ leaving.
31. The noises __ARE__ louder.
32. Jay __IS__ an artist.
33. Dinner __IS__ ready.
34. We __ARE__ planning a vacation.
35. They __ARE__ arriving today.
36. The sentence __IS__ too long.
37. He __IS__ a clown.
38. I __AM__ ready to go.
39. The owner __IS__ angry.
40. She __IS__ calling you.
41. They __ARE__ fighting.
42. The game __IS__ over.
43. It __IS__ true.
44. We __ARE__ going on a hike.
45. The farmers __ARE__ working.
46. The ring __IS__ valuable.
47. I __AM__ drenched.
48. We __ARE__ the best.
49. The question __IS__ simple.
50. It __IS__ important.

COMPOSITION EXERCISE

Write 12 sentences which contain forms of the verb "be."

1. _____
2. _____
3. _____
4. _____
5. _____
6. _____
7. _____
8. _____
9. _____
10. _____
11. _____
12. _____

Unit 22 cont'd

Forms of the Verb "Was"

The verb "was" is written in the following ways:

singular	plural
I was	we were
you were	you were
he, she, it was	they were

EXAMPLES:
a. You <u>were</u> rude.
b. She <u>was</u> smart.
c. It <u>was</u> too easy.
d. They <u>were</u> different.

✳ In each blank write the correct form of the verb "was."

1. I __was__ talking.
2. You __WERE__ chosen to go.
3. He __WAS__ crying.
4. She __WAS__ looking for you.
5. It __WAS__ cold in there.
6. We __WERE__ taking a test.
7. You __WERE__ invited.
8. They __WERE__ eating lunch.
9. The show __WAS__ good.
10. I __WAS__ glad to help.
11. They __WERE__ flying north.
12. The man __WAS__ tired.
13. The candy __WAS__ too sweet.
14. My cats __WERE__ sleeping.
15. Ellen __WAS__ in her room.
16. I __WAS__ afraid to go in.
17. The wind __WAS__ blowing.
18. Mrs. White __WAS__ angry.
19. We __WERE__ going to the circus.
20. The show __WAS__ terrible.
21. The cartoons __WERE__ funny.
22. The letter __WAS__ opened.
23. The grapes __WERE__ sour.
24. The answer __WAS__ false.
25. The clue __WAS__ helpful.
26. The buses __WERE__ gone.
27. We __WERE__ studying.
28. It __WAS__ my birthday.
29. The straw __WAS__ bent.
30. You __WERE__ cheating.
31. My watch __WAS__ missing.
32. He __WAS__ alone.
33. The cowboy __WAS__ resting.
34. The men __WERE__ late.
35. It __WAS__ only last week.
36. They __WERE__ awkward.
37. The breezes __WERE__ cool.
38. The nurse __WAS__ beautiful.
39. We __WERE__ excited.
40. The decision __WAS__ his.
41. The clothes __WERE__ dirty.
42. The snack __WAS__ delicious.
43. The rooms __WERE__ dark.
44. You __WERE__ tricked.
45. She __WAS__ famous.
46. Everyone __WAS__ happy.
47. We __WERE__ trusted.
48. The ink __WAS__ red.
49. The knife __WAS__ sharp.
50. The boxes __WERE__ empty.

COMPOSITION EXERCISE

Write 12 sentences using either "was" or "were."

1. _____
2. _____
3. _____
4. _____
5. _____
6. _____
7. _____
8. _____
9. _____
10. _____
11. _____
12. _____

56

The Position of Auxiliary Verbs

The auxiliary verb usually appears in front of the verb it is helping.

EXAMPLES:
  a. The snake is crawling away.
  b. I am answering your call.
  c. She is watching television.
  d. They were buying the zoo.

 Underline the auxiliary verb and the verb it is helping.

1. I am confused about it.
2. The train is moving slowly.
3. Our team is winning the game.
4. The calves are following us.
5. Jay and I are invited to the party.
6. The check was signed on the back.
7. Susan and Dale were crying again.
8. Larry has forgotten his homework.
9. I have included the answers.
10. The teacher had explained the method.
11. The mail was delivered on time.
12. The child had swallowed a dime.
13. I have accomplished my goals.
14. Sharon is using my pencil.
15. The building was condemned.
16. We are postponing the trip.
17. The men were painting our house.
18. The car was damaged.
19. The truck is pushing the wagon.
20. I am trying to finish early.
21. They were running across the field.
22. The families are eating together.
23. We are pretending to sing.
24. I am hurrying home.
25. We were adding the numbers.
26. The choir is singing.
27. The woman was screaming.
28. The children are playing hopscotch.
29. Your parents have come home.
30. She had seen me.
31. George has broken the vase.
32. Mom and Dad were watching us.
33. The man is stealing our jewels.
34. Dana has cleaned the house.
35. I have heard the story.
36. Johnny is brushing his teeth.
37. We are writing a play.
38. The cat is climbing the tree.
39. They have found the box.
40. She is thinking about me.
41. I am studying for a test.
42. Mark was laughing.
43. The pain has gone.
44. I have watered the garden.
45. Diane had solved the mystery.
46. The class is taking an exam.
47. I am convinced of it.
48. We were losing the contest.
49. Paula is making a cake.
50. You have remembered my birthday.

COMPOSITION EXERCISE

Write 12 sentences which contain auxiliary verbs.

1. _____
2. _____
3. _____
4. _____
5. _____
6. _____
7. _____
8. _____
9. _____
10. _____
11. _____
12. _____

Unit 23 cont'd

Auxiliary Verbs

Auxiliary verbs are helping verbs. They are used to help other verbs.

EXAMPLES:
a. I *am* leaving now.
b. She *is* writing a theme.
c. We *are* moving to Hawaii.
d. The tree *was* growing tall.

e. They *were* waiting for me.
f. John *has* made a new one.
g. You *have* hurt his feelings.
h. It *had* happened twice.

A Write "am," "is," or "are" in the blank.

1. I __am__ going to Toledo tomorrow.
2. The girls __ARE__ leaving for school.
3. Karen and I __ARE__ studying history.
4. The army __IS__ planning an attack.
5. She __IS__ buying your present.
6. The ice __IS__ melting quickly.
7. They __ARE__ taking your car.
8. He __IS__ building a cage.

9. We __ARE__ seeking a solution.
10. George __IS__ holding a tiger cub.
11. The men __ARE__ asking for more money.
12. She __IS__ playing the piano.
13. I __AM__ sending a card.
14. Susan and Dean __ARE__ elected to go.
15. The mission __IS__ accomplished.
16. I __AM__ making a wish.

B Write "was" or "were" in the blank.

1. Jerry __was__ writing his speech.
2. We __WERE__ helping with the decorations.
3. Janet __WAS__ bewildered.
4. You __WERE__ dreaming again.
5. He __WAS__ acting strangely.
6. The two classes __WERE__ combined.

7. The book __WAS__ published in 1881.
8. I __WAS__ listening to the radio.
9. The spies __WERE__ caught.
10. Dale __WAS__ breaking the rules.
11. They __WERE__ calling for help.
12. Al and Joe __WERE__ fishing in the pond.

C Write "has," "have," or "had" in the blank.

1. The ship __had__ sunk.
2. The amendment __HAS__ passed.
3. The guests __HAVE__ arrived.
4. The water __HAS__ evaporated.
5. The flowers __HAVE__ bloomed.
6. He __HAD__ finished the job.

7. We __HAVE__ heard that story.
8. The time __HAS__ come to begin.
9. The alarm __HAD__ rung.
10. The leaves __HAVE__ turned yellow.
11. It __HAS__ begun to rain.
12. No one __HAS__ lived here.

COMPOSITION EXERCISE

Write a sentence using each of these verbs as auxiliary verbs.

(am)   1. _____
(is)   2. _____
(are)   3. _____
(was)   4. _____

(were) 5. _____
(has)   6. _____
(have) 7. _____
(had)   8. _____

Adding Helping Verbs

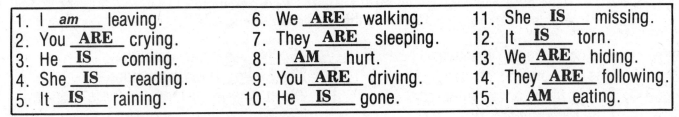

Unit 24

An auxiliary verb is a helping verb. A helping verb is used with an action verb. Helping verbs are "am," "is," "are," "was," "were," "has," "have," and "had."

EXAMPLES:
a. I __am__ working.
b. We __had__ called.
c. She __was__ crying.
d. They __are__ cooking.

A Write either "am," "is," or "are" in each blank.

1. I __am__ leaving.
2. You __ARE__ crying.
3. He __IS__ coming.
4. She __IS__ reading.
5. It __IS__ raining.
6. We __ARE__ walking.
7. They __ARE__ sleeping.
8. I __AM__ hurt.
9. You __ARE__ driving.
10. He __IS__ gone.
11. She __IS__ missing.
12. It __IS__ torn.
13. We __ARE__ hiding.
14. They __ARE__ following.
15. I __AM__ eating.

B Write either "was" or "were" in each blank.

1. I __was__ writing.
2. You __WERE__ talking.
3. He __WAS__ shouting.
4. She __WAS__ running.
5. It __WAS__ freezing.
6. We __WERE__ moving.
7. They __WERE__ playing.
8. She __WAS__ found.
9. They __WERE__ listening.
10. I __WAS__ chased.
11. It __WAS__ fixed.
12. You __WERE__ smiling.
13. He __WAS__ eating.
14. We __WERE__ laughing.
15. It __WAS__ gone.
16. You __WERE__ cheating.
17. He __WAS__ working.
18. They __WERE__ looking.
19. You __WERE__ sleeping.
20. It __WAS__ snowing.
21. He __WAS__ waiting.

C Write either "has," "have," or "had" in each blank.

1. I __have__ tried.
2. You __HAVE__ looked.
3. He __HAS__ gone.
4. She __HAS__ arrived.
5. She __HAS__ swum.
6. We __HAVE__ waited.
7. They __HAVE__ bloomed.
8. I __HAD__ sneezed.
9. You __HAD__ left.
10. It __HAD__ stopped.
11. We __HAD__ won.
12. You __HAVE__ screamed.
13. She __HAS__ moved.
14. It __HAS__ helped.
15. We __HAVE__ come.
16. You __HAD__ gone.
17. It __HAS__ broken.
18. She __HAD__ written.
19. I __HAVE__ finished.
20. We __HAD__ followed.
21. I __HAVE__ called.
22. He __HAD__ paid.
23. We __HAD__ missed.
24. He __HAD__ run.
25. It __HAD__ disappeared.
26. He __HAS__ spoken.
27. You __HAVE__ slept.
28. It __HAS__ worked.
29. We __HAVE__ read.
30. You __HAD__ moved.

COMPOSITION EXERCISE

Write 12 sentences which contain helping verbs.

1. _____
2. _____
3. _____
4. _____
5. _____
6. _____
7. _____
8. _____
9. _____
10. _____
11. _____
12. _____

Unit 24 cont'd

Distinguishing Between Auxiliary and Linking Verbs

Auxiliary verbs are helping verbs. They are used with other verbs. Linking verbs are used alone. They are followed by adjectives or nouns or noun substitutes.

EXAMPLES: auxiliary verbs
a. I <u>am</u> trying to help you.
b. The paper <u>is</u> burning.

linking verbs
a. The metal <u>was</u> hot.
b. That dog <u>is</u> a poodle.

 Write "A" if the sentence contains an auxiliary verb. Write "L" if the sentence contains a linking verb. Underline the verb in each sentence.

A	1.	The sun <u>is shining</u> today.
L	2.	She <u>is</u> a pretty girl.
A	3.	Don <u>is singing</u> our song.
L	4.	I <u>am</u> eleven years old.
A	5.	We <u>are leaving</u> now.
L	6.	That man <u>is</u> my father.
L	7.	You <u>are</u> ruthless.
A	8.	The lights <u>were burning</u>.
A	9.	I <u>have gained</u> ten pounds.
A	10.	I <u>am ignoring</u> you.
L	11.	Eric <u>is</u> a pilot.
A	12.	The dog <u>is sleeping</u> on our sofa.
L	13.	They <u>were</u> cruel to her.
L	14.	Jill and I <u>are</u> friends.
A	15.	I <u>am going</u> to go.
A	16.	The water <u>is freezing</u>.
L	17.	It <u>was</u> an owl.
A	18.	The child <u>is waving</u> good-bye.
L	19.	Your suggestion <u>was</u> great.
A	20.	The amendment <u>was passed</u>.
A	21.	They <u>were helping</u> us.
A	22.	The club <u>is meeting</u> today.
L	23.	The rumor <u>is</u> true.
A	24.	Our team <u>is winning</u>.
L	25.	The stairs <u>are</u> not safe.

L	26.	We <u>are</u> anxious to go.
L	27.	George <u>is</u> always polite.
L	28.	It <u>was</u> important.
A	29.	We <u>are losing</u> money.
L	30.	The jewels <u>are</u> valuable.
A	31.	The family <u>is eating</u> dinner.
A	32.	The damages <u>were estimated</u> today.
A	33.	Mr. Kent <u>is teaching</u> me to swim.
A	34.	Paul and Jack <u>are running</u> the race.
L	35.	We <u>were</u> brave and daring.
L	36.	That dream <u>was</u> a nightmare.
A	37.	A kitten <u>was sitting</u> on our porch.
L	38.	The woman <u>is</u> too fat.
L	39.	I <u>am</u> uncertain.
A	40.	The people <u>were rejoicing</u>.
A	41.	The water <u>has evaporated</u>.
L	42.	Mr. Simon <u>is</u> a famous writer.
A	43.	Gossip <u>is discouraged</u>.
L	44.	You <u>are</u> carefree.
L	45.	This signature <u>is</u> yours.
L	46.	The dungeon <u>was</u> dark.
A	47.	Sandy and I <u>have planned</u> the party.
A	48.	I <u>am wearing</u> a jumpsuit.
L	49.	The password <u>is</u> "carrot."
A	50.	Mother <u>was talking</u> to you.

COMPOSITION EXERCISE

Write 5 sentences which contain auxiliary verbs and 5 which contain linking verbs.

auxiliary verbs
1. _____
2. _____
3. _____
4. _____
5. _____

linking verbs
1. _____
2. _____
3. _____
4. _____
5. _____

Action Verbs — Present Tense

Present tense refers to what is happening now.

EXAMPLES: a. Paul drives a '77 Chevy.   c. My brother goes to college.
           b. Deidre hears everything.   d. I like chocolate.

 Underline the sentences which are written in present tense.

1. Janice reads mysteries.
2. The dog hurt his foot.
3. I will choose the winner.
4. Dane always helps her mother.
5. The puppy follows him everywhere.
6. You will enjoy the show.
7. The coach postponed the game.
8. I advise you to stay.
9. George plans our menus.
10. Monkeys climb trees.
11. The warm weather melted the snow.
12. Mom bakes our bread.
13. I will choose Carl and Barry.
14. My uncle bought the land.
15. Birds fly south in the winter.
16. The fish swam away.
17. The turtle moves slowly but surely.
18. I want a new pair of skates.
19. My dog chases cars.
20. James rode his horse to school.
21. Tim promises to help us.
22. Karen wore my jeans.
23. War threatens our safety.
24. This china breaks easily.
25. We revised our budget.
26. Mr. Kent lives in Houston.
27. The girl looked for you.
28. Dad owns the airplane.
29. The comedian tells jokes.
30. Everyone needs a friend.
31. The river reached flood stage.
32. Bears hibernate.
33. I mailed the letter yesterday.
34. Ghosts frighten me.
35. Alex plays basketball.
36. The teacher will read the schedule.
37. Mona used your books.
38. We ride the bus.
39. The ball rolled under the car.
40. Bonnie works everyday.
41. That bird sleeps all day.
42. Our dog steals shoes.
43. Brenda will pay the clerk.
44. I suggest plan ''B.''
45. My cat likes liver and cheese.
46. She will fall on the ice.
47. The poison kills bugs.
48. I bought my own bicycle.
49. Mr. Sims gives tennis lessons.
50. Seth always wears that hat.

COMPOSITION EXERCISE

List 28 present-tense verbs.

1. _____   8. _____   15. _____   22. _____
2. _____   9. _____   16. _____   23. _____
3. _____   10. _____   17. _____   24. _____
4. _____   11. _____   18. _____   25. _____
5. _____   12. _____   19. _____   26. _____
6. _____   13. _____   20. _____   27. _____
7. _____   14. _____   21. _____   28. _____

Unit 25 cont'd

Working in Present Tense

Present tense refers to what is happening now.

EXAMPLES a. *I am here.*   c. *My leg hurts.*
            b. *I drive a car.*   d. *She wants to see you.*

 Underline the verbs which are in present tense.

1. <u>drink</u>	26. showed	51. <u>go</u>	76. will be
2. <u>walk</u>	27. <u>let</u>	52. ate	77. drank
3. will arrive	28. <u>see</u>	53. <u>build</u>	78. <u>clean</u>
4. <u>love</u>	29. <u>find</u>	54. <u>push</u>	79. <u>tell</u>
5. <u>fall</u>	30. <u>look</u>	55. <u>come</u>	80. <u>hear</u>
6. drove	31. washed	56. <u>smile</u>	81. tore
7. cried	32. <u>roll</u>	57. <u>give</u>	82. will see
8. <u>hope</u>	33. bought	58. <u>sell</u>	83. will find
9. <u>stop</u>	34. <u>move</u>	59. <u>help</u>	84. <u>climb</u>
10. <u>drive</u>	35. <u>watch</u>	60. crushed	85. <u>taste</u>
11. will know	36. <u>eat</u>	61. rolled	86. listened
12. knew	37. <u>take</u>	62. <u>cry</u>	87. <u>plan</u>
13. <u>know</u>	38. will read	63. <u>pay</u>	88. talked
14. <u>run</u>	39. flew	64. will walk	89. <u>sleep</u>
15. <u>scratch</u>	40. <u>need</u>	65. arrived	90. fixed
16. <u>chase</u>	41. <u>listen</u>	66. told	91. <u>bake</u>
17. <u>fix</u>	42. will wash	67. <u>wear</u>	92. followed
18. <u>want</u>	43. broke	68. <u>hang</u>	93. hurry
19. will need	44. <u>buy</u>	69. found	94. <u>scream</u>
20. <u>follow</u>	45. lived	70. <u>break</u>	95. rode
21. <u>hate</u>	46. stole	71. killed	96. <u>live</u>
22. <u>carry</u>	47. <u>ride</u>	72. <u>crush</u>	97. stopped
23. <u>kill</u>	48. ran	73. <u>hurt</u>	98. <u>steal</u>
24. <u>hit</u>	49. <u>cook</u>	74. will run	99. <u>tear</u>
25. smashed	50. <u>wash</u>	75. carried	100. <u>paint</u>

COMPOSITION EXERCISE

Choose 12 of the present-tense verbs from today's exercise. Write a sentence with each.

1. _____
2. _____
3. _____
4. _____
5. _____
6. _____
7. _____
8. _____
9. _____
10. _____
11. _____
12. _____

Comprehension Check

(A) Supply the action verbs.

1. Martin __washed__ the car today.
2. The lions __roared__ .
3. Adam and I __explored__ the cave.
4. We __picked__ the vegetables this morning.
5. Polly __put__ the towels in the closet.
6. The man __asked__ for directions.
7. Someone __knocked__ on the back door.
8. James __carried__ the trash to the dumpster.
9. Carolyn __showed__ us the way out!
10. They __celebrated__ his birthday Friday.

11. Sarah __sits__ in the fourth row.
12. Ed always __eats__ his lunch alone.
13. The news __shocked__ all of us.
14. We __paid__ for our tickets at the door.
15. Darrell __parked__ his car in the garage.
16. Everyone __plans__ to help.
17. They __took__ a plane to Atlanta.
18. I __want__ a new watch for Christmas.
19. Joey __forgot__ to feed the fish.
20. You __know__ what to do.

(B) Supply the linking verbs.

1. We __were__ too tired to eat.
2. The people __are__ ready for change.
3. Your offer __is__ very generous.
4. I __am__ the president of the club.
5. You __look__ happy about it.
6. The room __was__ neat and orderly.
7. Felicia __is__ my cousin.
8. He __seems__ very nice.
9. Brenda __is__ very enthusiastic.
10. Shawn __is__ always considerate.

11. Jenny __became__ a nurse.
12. The surface __feels__ rough.
13. The fresh bread __smells__ delicious.
14. You __are__ my only hope.
15. The bananas __are__ still green.
16. His parents __were__ proud of him.
17. The cake __tastes__ bitter.
18. I __am__ smarter than Jason.
19. Deborah __is__ a good actress.
20. Alexander __is__ energetic.

(C) Supply the auxiliary verbs.

1. It __is__ filled with candy.
2. I __am__ taking the bus to Oregon.
3. Marge __does__ not like to ski.
4. Walter __was__ taken to the hospital.
5. __Have__ you seen my wallet?
6. No one __must__ know our secret!
7. The prize __will__ be $1000.
8. Pamela __has__ made the fewest errors.
9. It __was__ bought in Italy.
10. The medicine __will__ will make you well.
11. Something __has__ bitten me on my arm.
12. The house __was__ sold for $200,000.
13. __Has__ Cameron called yet?
14. What __have__ you done now?

15. The stew __is__ simmering on the stove.
16. __Did__ you see the look on Bob's face?
17. It __will__ take four hours to get there.
18. We __have__ decided not to go.
19. The teacher __has__ graded our tests.
20. You __can__ ride my horse.

Test 5 cont'd

Comprehension Check (continued)

D Identify each underlined verb.

(1) action **(2) linking** **(3) auxiliary**

_1_ 1. The snowman melted.

_2_ 2. The food looks wonderful.

_3_ 3. The train is departing at noon.

_1_ 4. Larry whistled the song.

_2_ 5. I am your new partner.

_1_ 6. David wrote a long poem.

_1_ 7. The mirror broke.

_3_ 8. The shop is opening soon.

_2_ 9. We are anxious to begin work.

_2_ 10. The speech was boring.

_3_ 11. I am getting a haircut.

_1_ 12. Jesse fixed my car.

_3_ 13. The men were repairing the road.

_3_ 14. It is raining again.

_1_ 15. A reporter called for Alex.

_2_ 16. It is Thursday.

_3_ 17. Someone has told on you.

_1_ 18. The thunder scared me.

_2_ 19. My brother is an attorney.

_2_ 20. The bread was stale.

_1_ 21. Lucy sewed the jacket.

_3_ 22. No one will know that.

_1_ 23. He finished second place.

_2_ 24. The music was soothing.

E Write "am," "is," or "are" in each blank.

1. Steven _is_ Sandra's brother.
2. I _am_ reading a novel by Twain.
3. The bus _is_ usually on time.
4. You _are_ sure to win the election.
5. Bert _is_ a hard worker.
6. The teachers _are_ here early.
7. It _is_ too late to go today.
8. Jules _is_ a very good actor.
9. The children _are_ sleeping.
10. I _am_ the driver of the bus.

F Write "was" or "were" in each blank.

1. We _were_ surprised to see you.
2. It _was_ too cold to swim.
3. The lights _were_ left on by mistake.
4. The store _was_ closed for inventory.
5. Andrew _was_ my first choice.
6. I _was_ thinking about a vacation.
7. The frogs _were_ croaking loudly.
8. The book _was_ from the library.
9. You _were_ absent yesterday.
10. The radio _was_ tuned to KPRY.

Write a paragraph about traveling by jet. Underline the verbs.

_____

_____

_____

_____

_____

_____

_____

_____

_____

Working in Past Tense

Past tense refers to what has already happened.

EXAMPLES: a. Theo dug a hole.
b. Tim drank his milk.

c. I closed the window.
d. They moved to California.

A Underline the verbs which are past tense.

1. eat, <u>ate</u>
2. <u>fell</u>, fall
3. <u>ran</u>, run
4. <u>rolled</u>, roll
5. <u>gave</u>, give
6. cry, <u>cried</u>
7. buy, <u>bought</u>
8. wear, <u>wore</u>
9. <u>lived</u>, live
10. come, <u>came</u>
11. love, <u>loved</u>
12. kill, <u>killed</u>
13. <u>left</u>, leave
14. <u>saw</u>, see
15. go, <u>went</u>

16. <u>rode</u>, ride
17. <u>hated</u>, hate
18. hear, <u>heard</u>
19. pay, <u>paid</u>
20. <u>said</u>, say
21. <u>hoped</u>, hope
22. <u>was</u>, is
23. sell, <u>sold</u>
24. take, <u>took</u>
25. fly, <u>flew</u>
26. use, <u>used</u>
27. hide, <u>hid</u>
28. <u>knew</u>, know
29. <u>stole</u>, steal
30. <u>slept</u>, sleep

31. drive, <u>drove</u>
32. pick, <u>picked</u>
33. <u>wanted</u>, want
34. draw, <u>drew</u>
35. <u>built</u>, build
36. show, <u>showed</u>
37. talk, <u>talked</u>
38. <u>cleaned</u>, clean
39. <u>tasted</u>, taste
40. plan, <u>planned</u>
41. <u>washed</u>, wash
42. play, <u>played</u>
43. burn, <u>burned</u>
44. <u>found</u>, find
45. stop, <u>stopped</u>

46. move, <u>moved</u>
47. write, <u>wrote</u>
48. <u>broke</u>, break
49. drink, <u>drank</u>
50. <u>laughed</u>, laugh
51. <u>looked</u>, look
52. melt, <u>melted</u>
53. <u>spilled</u>, spill
54. close, <u>closed</u>
55. hurry, <u>hurried</u>
56. cook, <u>cooked</u>
57. <u>carried</u>, carry
58. <u>phoned</u>, phone
59. scream, <u>screamed</u>
60. watch, <u>watched</u>

B Fill in the blanks with past tense verbs.

1. We __moved__ here from Alaska.
2. Martha __DROVE__ the car.
3. The baby __CRIED__.
4. She __PICKED__ the flowers.
5. We __RAN__ to the window.
6. Jill __SAW__ the ghost.
7. The books __FELL__ on the floor.
8. We __HEARD__ sirens.

9. They __WENT__ to town.
10. I __WROTE__ the letter.
11. Jan __RODE__ her bike.
12. He __GAVE__ us a ride.
13. The boy __SPILLED__ his milk.
14. Everyone __LEFT__ early.
15. The ice __MELTED__.
16. Karen __WASHED__ the car.

COMPOSITION EXERCISE

Choose 14 past-tense verbs from exercise A. Write a sentence with each.

1. _____
2. _____
3. _____
4. _____
5. _____
6. _____
7. _____

8. _____
9. _____
10. _____
11. _____
12. _____
13. _____
14. _____

Unit 26 cont'd

Adding "ed" to Form Past Tense

Many verbs add "ed" to form the past tense.

EXAMPLES: a. Rex killed the spider.
b. The puppy played with my shoe.
c. We planned the party.
d. You wasted the paper.

A Combine each verb with "ed," and write the answer in the blank.

1. climb + ed = _climbed_
2. push + ed = PUSHED
3. laugh + ed = LAUGHED
4. walk + ed = WALKED
5. talk + ed = TALKED
6. play + ed = PLAYED
7. call + ed = CALLED
8. fix + ed = FIXED
9. wish + ed = WISHED
10. live + ed = LIVED
11. hope + ed = HOPED

12. love + ed = LOVED
13. smile + ed = SMILED
14. hate + ed = HATED
15. like + ed = LIKED
16. taste + ed = TASTED
17. use + ed = USED
18. name + ed = NAMED
19. drop + ed = DROPPED
20. slam + ed = SLAMMED
21. stop + ed = STOPPED
22. plan + ed = PLANNED

B Rewrite each sentence in past tense.

1. I help my mother. _____ *I helped my mother.*
2. I walk to school. _____ **I walked to school.**
3. My dog chases cars. _____ **My dog chased cars.**
4. I want to stay. _____ **I wanted to stay.**
5. My sister is baking a cake. _____ **My sister baked a cake.**
6. You talk too much. _____ **You talked too much.**
7. Andy drops everything. _____ **Andy dropped everything.**
8. Lisa plays the piano. _____ **Lisa played the piano.**
9. They look angry. _____ **They looked angry.**
10. I live in town. _____ **I lived in town.**
11. Dave is fixing his bike. _____ **Dave fixed his bike.**
12. The man calls every day. _____ **The man called every day.**

COMPOSITION EXERCISE

List 20 verbs that add "ed" to form the past tense. Do not use those from today's lesson.

1. _____
2. _____
3. _____
4. _____
5. _____
6. _____
7. _____
8. _____
9. _____
10. _____
11. _____
12. _____
13. _____
14. _____
15. _____
16. _____
17. _____
18. _____
19. _____
20. _____

Action Verbs — Past Tense

Past tense refers to what has already happened.

EXAMPLES:
a. Abe ate my candy bar.
b. The boy ran away.
c. I called Brenda.
d. You missed the target.

* In each blank write the past tense of the verb in parentheses.

(burn) 1. Eric __burned__ his finger.
(move) 2. They __MOVED__ here last year.
(like) 3. I __LIKED__ the red one best.
(want) 4. She __WANTED__ to see you.
(play) 5. We __PLAYED__ basketball.
(walk) 6. The man __WALKED__ to town.
(sing) 7. Our class __SANG__ yesterday.
(talk) 8. Jan __TALKED__ to your mom.
(build) 9. We __BUILT__ a sand castle.
(fight) 10. They __FOUGHT__ for freedom.
(drink) 11. No one __DRANK__ the milk.
(fix) 12. Dad __FIXED__ the engine.
(surrender) 13. The army __SURRENDERED__ .
(run) 14. The children __RAN__ home.
(brush) 15. She __BRUSHED__ her hair.
(arrive) 16. The men __ARRIVED__ safely.
(include) 17. The price __INCLUDED__ tax.
(miss) 18. I __MISSED__ you yesterday.
(smear) 19. The paint __SMEARED__ easily.
(replace) 20. Joe __REPLACED__ the bulbs.
(list) 21. She __LISTED__ the items.
(trust) 22. I __TRUSTED__ you.
(match) 23. It __MATCHED__ perfectly.
(choose) 24. The teacher __CHOSE__ Mark.
(expect) 25. We __EXPECTED__ you sooner.

(cook) 26. She __COOKED__ the meal.
(sign) 27. I __SIGNED__ my name.
(eat) 28. The lion __ATE__ quickly.
(grow) 29. The plants __GREW__ .
(shout) 30. Mom __SHOUTED__ at the dog.
(break) 31. The cookie __BROKE__ in half.
(write) 32. Phil __WROTE__ you a letter.
(take) 33. Someone __TOOK__ our money.
(notice) 34. No one __NOTICED__ him.
(press) 35. He __PRESSED__ the buttons.
(gain) 36. I __GAINED__ ten pounds.
(drive) 37. Jay __DROVE__ our bus today.
(comb) 38. She __COMBED__ her hair back.
(crash) 39. The plane __CRASHED__ last year.
(earn) 40. Our club __EARNED__ $40.00.
(convince) 41. We __CONVINCED__ them to stay.
(confess) 42. The thief __CONFESSED__ .
(solve) 43. He __SOLVED__ the mystery.
(pretend) 44. Bill __PRETENDED__ to sleep.
(forget) 45. I __FORGOT__ your birthday.
(bake) 46. Who __BAKED__ this cake?
(freeze) 47. The water __FROZE__ .
(reach) 48. Finally we __REACHED__ the top.
(carry) 49. Paul __CARRIED__ the boxes.
(ring) 50. The bell __RANG__ again.

COMPOSITION EXERCISE

List 20 past-tense verbs.

1. _____
2. _____
3. _____
4. _____
5. _____
6. _____
7. _____
8. _____
9. _____
10. _____
11. _____
12. _____
13. _____
14. _____
15. _____
16. _____
17. _____
18. _____
19. _____
20. _____

Unit 27 cont'd

Writing in Future Tense

Future tense refers to what is going to happen. The word "will" is usually used with the verb.

EXAMPLES: a. I <u>will use</u> this one.   c. He <u>will put</u> it in here.
             b. She <u>will leave</u> us a note.   d. We <u>will live</u> in Texas.

In each blank write the future tense of the verb in parentheses.

(go)	1. Alice **will go** to the store.	(move) 26. Our family **WILL MOVE** in May.
(see)	2. You **WILL SEE** the answer.	(leave) 27. They **WILL LEAVE** Monday.
(work)	3. I **WILL WORK** tomorrow.	(play) 28. Judy **WILL PLAY** us a song.
(eat)	4. The family **WILL EAT** at home.	(pass) 29. Of course, you **WILL PASS**.
(show)	5. Sue **WILL SHOW** you the way.	(drink) 30. We **WILL DRINK** water.
(fix)	6. Dad **WILL FIX** the car.	(plan) 31. We **WILL PLAN** to come.
(call)	7. I **WILL CALL** you.	(find) 32. I **WILL FIND** the money.
(wait)	8. We **WILL WAIT** for you.	(open) 33. John **WILL OPEN** the door.
(paint)	9. Bob and I **WILL PAINT** them.	(tell) 34. Jen **WILL TELL** you the story.
(write)	10. I **WILL WRITE** him a letter.	(cut) 35. You **WILL CUT** your finger.
(look)	11. Don **WILL LOOK** in the den.	(win) 36. Our team **WILL WIN**.
(arrive)	12. The bus **WILL ARRIVE** late.	(follow) 37. The puppy **WILL FOLLOW** you.
(break)	13. The baby **WILL BREAK** it.	(ring) 38. The bell **WILL RING** soon.
(take)	14. She **WILL TAKE** you home.	(read) 39. Now I **WILL READ** the story.
(listen)	15. You **WILL LISTEN** to me.	(give) 40. I **WILL GIVE** you mine.
(pick)	16. He **WILL PICK** the winner.	(climb) 41. She and I **WILL CLIMB** the hill.
(sleep)	17. I **WILL SLEEP** until noon.	(bake) 42. I **WILL BAKE** a cake.
(buy)	18. We **WILL BUY** the present.	(drive) 43. Mrs. Jay **WILL DRIVE** the bus.
(come)	19. The cab **WILL COME** soon.	(carry) 44. I **WILL CARRY** them for you.
(hear)	20. No one **WILL HEAR** you.	(talk) 45. She **WILL** not **TALK**.
(stop)	21. He **WILL STOP** the car.	(walk) 46. George **WILL WALK** you home.
(pay)	22. You **WILL PAY** my price.	(cook) 47. Mom **WILL COOK** our dinner.
(wash)	23. Dad **WILL WASH** the dishes.	(spill) 48. He **WILL SPILL** the soup.
(stay)	24. Fran **WILL STAY** here.	(swim) 49. The mermaid **WILL SWIM**.
(burn)	25. Eric **WILL BURN** the trash.	(help) 50. All of us **WILL HELP** you.

COMPOSITION EXERCISE

Write 12 sentences which contain future-tense verbs.

1. _____
2. _____
3. _____
4. _____
5. _____
6. _____

7. _____
8. _____
9. _____
10. _____
11. _____
12. _____

Action Verbs — Future Tense

Future tense refers to what will happen.
The event has not happened yet.

EXAMPLES: a. Kay will sell her car.
b. The snow will melt soon.
c. Mom will drive the truck.
d. Will you pour the tea?

In each blank write the future tense of the verb in parentheses.

(see) 1. I __will see__ you tomorrow.
(eat) 2. Bruce __WILL EAT__ anything.
(ride) 3. Jason __WILL RIDE__ the bus.
(feed) 4. Donna __WILL FEED__ the dog.
(help) 5. I __WILL HELP__ you.
(keep) 6. Eva __WILL KEEP__ the puppy.
(go) 7. __WILL__ you __GO__ with me?
(make) 8. You __WILL MAKE__ the team.
(pay) 9. Mom __WILL PAY__ us.
(sink) 10. She __WILL SINK__ in the storm.
(walk) 11. Dave __WILL WALK__ to the corner.
(speak) 12. No one __WILL SPEAK__ to you.
(sell) 13. I __WILL SELL__ the bike to Tim.
(know) 14. They __WILL KNOW__ you did it.
(sing) 15. Sara __WILL SING__ the song.
(hide) 16. We __WILL HIDE__ in the closet.
(spend) 17. Katie __WILL SPEND__ our money.
(leave) 18. The train __WILL LEAVE__ soon.
(freeze) 19. The milk __WILL FREEZE__ in there.
(hit) 20. That car __WILL HIT__ the sign.
(kill) 21. The poison __WILL KILL__ it.
(stop) 22. The noise __WILL STOP__ soon.
(study) 23. We __WILL STUDY__ together.
(try) 24. Abe __WILL TRY__ to escape.
(write) 25. I __WILL WRITE__ to you.

(deny) 26. She __WILL DENY__ everything.
(hear) 27. Mom __WILL HEAR__ us leave.
(run) 28. He __WILL RUN__ up the hill.
(sit) 29. The cat __WILL SIT__ in my lap.
(drop) 30. You __WILL DROP__ the box.
(show) 31. I __WILL SHOW__ you the rooms.
(light) 32. He __WILL LIGHT__ the candle.
(lock) 33. Ted __WILL LOCK__ the doors.
(shut) 34. __WILL__ you __SHUT__ the door?
(cut) 35. You __WILL CUT__ your hand.
(have) 36. I __WILL HAVE__ the smaller one.
(expect) 37. We __WILL EXPECT__ you today.
(sleep) 38. He __WILL SLEEP__ until noon.
(invite) 39. I __WILL INVITE__ the guests.
(burn) 40. Fire __WILL BURN__ you.
(escape) 41. We __WILL ESCAPE__ tomorrow.
(question) 42. She __WILL QUESTION__ Phil.
(surround) 43. They __WILL SURROUND__ us.
(repay) 44. Kent __WILL REPAY__ the favor.
(appear) 45. Then a ghost __WILL APPEAR__.
(turn) 46. __WILL__ you __TURN__ around?
(laugh) 47. No one __WILL LAUGH__ at you.
(find) 48. Josh __WILL FIND__ your dog.
(smear) 49. You __WILL SMEAR__ the paint.
(forgive) 50. I __WILL FORGIVE__ you.

COMPOSITION EXERCISE

List 20 future-tense verbs.

1. _____
2. _____
3. _____
4. _____
5. _____
6. _____
7. _____
8. _____
9. _____
10. _____
11. _____
12. _____
13. _____
14. _____
15. _____
16. _____
17. _____
18. _____
19. _____
20. _____

Unit 28 cont'd

Practice with Tense

*Verbs show action. They may be written in
present, past, and future tenses.*

EXAMPLES: present: **The grass is green.**
  past: **The grass was green.**
  future: **The grass will be green.**

  Identify the tense of the verb
  in each sentence.

PR	1. I like spinach.
PA	2. Dan went home.
F	3. He will come tomorrow.
F	4. We will eat soon.
PA	5. The dog needed a bath.
PA	6. The birds flew away.
PR	7. The bus is here.
F	8. The store will open soon.
PA	9. We laughed at the joke.
PA	10. The fire killed the grass.
PR	11. John likes Susan.
PR	12. I know the answers.
PR	13. Dogs bark at night.
PR	14. I don't feel well.
F	15. We will go to the zoo.
PA	16. Mr. Bates sold his truck.
F	17. The cat will scratch you.
PR	18. That man is my neighbor.
PA	19. I lived in Arizona.
F	20. Don will take two.
F	21. We will fish in the river.
F	22. The rain will stop soon.
PA	23. Joan slept all day.
PR	24. I hear someone.
PA	25. I waited for Greg.

F	26. We will begin tomorrow.
PR	27. That cat chases dogs.
PA	28. The lamp broke.
PA	29. The mermaid swam to shore.
PA	30. Dana winked at him.
F	31. Our class will sing.
PR	32. I hear an echo.
PA	33. Together we solved it.
PA	34. I decided to stay.
F	35. The party will be Friday.
PR	36. You are very rude.
F	37. I will study tonight.
PA	38. I rode the bus.
PR	39. The plane is leaving.
F	40. Sam will bring the cake.
PA	41. I opened the box.
PA	42. The rose died.
F	43. Dennis will wash the car.
PR	44. Today is Thursday.
PR	45. I play football.
PR	46. Jane feels dizzy.
PA	47. He knew the answer.
PR	48. I love to travel.
PA	49. Joe asked a question.
F	50. He will leave now.

COMPOSITION EXERCISE

List 6 present-tense verbs, 6 past-tense verbs, and 6 future-tense verbs.

present	past	future
1. _____	1. _____	1. _____
2. _____	2. _____	2. _____
3. _____	3. _____	3. _____
4. _____	4. _____	4. _____
5. _____	5. _____	5. _____
6. _____	6. _____	6. _____

Verb Endings

jump — **A verb shows action.**

jumps — **Most verbs add "s" to form the third person, singular, present tense form.**

jumping — **Most verbs add "ing" to form the progressive form. Progressive forms show continuous action.**

jumped — **Most verbs add "ed" to form the past tense.**

A Add "s," "ing," and "ed" to each verb.

1. turn	*turns*	*turning*	*turned*	11. walk	WALKS	WALKING	WALKED
2. laugh	LAUGHS	LAUGHING	LAUGHED	12. pick	PICKS	PICKING	PICKED
3. climb	CLIMBS	CLIMBING	CLIMBED	13. look	LOOKS	LOOKING	LOOKED
4. kick	KICKS	KICKING	KICKED	14. show	SHOWS	SHOWING	SHOWED
5. want	WANTS	WANTING	WANTED	15. crawl	CRAWLS	CRAWLING	CRAWLED
6. follow	FOLLOWS	FOLLOWING	FOLLOWED	16. pull	PULLS	PULLING	PULLED
7. own	OWNS	OWNING	OWNED	17. ask	ASKS	ASKING	ASKED
8. cook	COOKS	COOKING	COOKED	18. help	HELPS	HELPING	HELPED
9. list	LISTING	IS LISTING	LISTED	19. melt	MELTS	MELTING	MELTED
10. sign	SIGNS	SIGNING	SIGNED	20. weigh	WEIGHS	WEIGHING	WEIGHED

B Complete each sentence with the correct form of the verb in the parentheses.

(milk) 1. The farmer _milked_ the cows.

(call) 2. Dennis is _CALLING_ you.

(protect) 3. The dog _PROTECTED_ his master.

(work) 4. My aunt _WORKS_ in an office.

(fill) 5. Lynn _FILLED_ the glasses.

(clean) 6. George is _CLEANING_ his room.

(sound) 7. It _SOUNDS_ like a dream.

(wash) 8. Jerry _WASHED_ the car.

(start) 9. It has _STARTED_ to rain.

(wait) 10. I am _WAITING_ for Mr. Goth.

(trust) 11. Arnold _TRUSTS_ me.

(collect) 12. He is _COLLECTING_ coins.

(vanish) 13. The ghost _VANISHED_ suddenly.

(play) 14. They are _PLAYING_ football.

(plant) 15. We _PLANTED_ peas and beans.

(gain) 16. Harry has _GAINED_ ten pounds.

(rest) 17. After our hike we _RESTED_ .

(need) 18. Roger _NEEDS_ your help.

(count) 19. The old man _COUNTED_ the money.

(surrender) 20. The army _SURRENDERED_ .

(lift) 21. The fog is _LIFTING_ .

(travel) 22. I have _TRAVELED_ many miles.

(allow) 23. We were not _ALLOWED_ to leave.

(borrow) 24. She is always _BORROWING_ things.

COMPOSITION EXERCISE

List 16 verbs not used in today's lesson. Add "s," "ing," and "ed" to each verb.

1. _____
2. _____
3. _____
4. _____
5. _____
6. _____
7. _____
8. _____
9. _____
10. _____
11. _____
12. _____
13. _____
14. _____
15. _____
16. _____

Unit 29 cont'd

Compound Verbs

*Sentences may have more than one verb.
These verbs are joined together with "and,"
"or," or "but."*

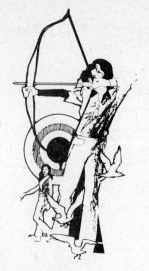

EXAMPLES: a. He *huffed* and *puffed*.
b. Tommy *ran* and *fell*.
c. Jan *aimed* but *missed*.
d. You *listen* and *learn*.

 Underline the compound verbs.

1. We <u>waited</u> and <u>watched</u>.
2. Carl <u>began</u> but <u>stopped</u>.
3. Mother <u>listened</u> and <u>frowned</u>.
4. The army <u>fought</u> but <u>lost</u>.
5. The ghost <u>spoke</u> and <u>vanished</u>.
6. We <u>pushed</u> and <u>pulled</u>.
7. My dad <u>builds</u> and <u>repairs</u>.
8. The horse <u>bucked</u> and <u>kicked</u>.
9. I <u>can print</u> or <u>write</u>.
10. The man <u>slipped</u> and <u>fell</u>.
11. Lennie <u>ran</u> and <u>hid</u>.
12. You <u>will go</u> now or <u>stay</u>.
13. I <u>can sing</u> and <u>dance</u>.
14. He <u>draws</u> and <u>paints</u>.
15. Laura <u>confessed</u> and <u>cried</u>.
16. The puppy <u>sat</u> and <u>waited</u>.
17. He <u>eats</u> and <u>sleeps</u>.
18. I <u>hurried</u> and <u>forgot</u>.
19. Debbie <u>smiled</u> and <u>winked</u>.
20. Mom <u>cooked</u> and <u>baked</u> all day.
21. He <u>lies</u> and <u>steals</u>.
22. You <u>can sit</u> or <u>stand</u>.
23. We <u>walked</u> and <u>talked</u>.
24. I <u>knocked</u> and <u>listened</u>.
25. He <u>hesitated</u> and <u>answered</u>.
26. He <u>repeated</u> the story and <u>left</u>.
27. She <u>wrote</u> and <u>mailed</u> a letter.
28. I <u>went</u> home and <u>ate</u> lunch.
29. Mom <u>cleaned</u> the house and <u>relaxed</u>.
30. The puppy <u>turned</u> and <u>followed</u> me.
31. I <u>rang</u> the bell and <u>waited</u>.
32. She <u>saw</u> the ghost and <u>screamed</u>.
33. We <u>told</u> jokes and <u>laughed</u>.
34. The mouse <u>looked</u> up and <u>ran</u>.
35. The bird <u>saw</u> me and <u>flew</u> away.
36. Ken <u>read</u> the letter and <u>burned</u> it.
37. I <u>worked</u> hard and <u>made</u> the team.
38. Liz <u>took</u> the money and <u>spent</u> it.
39. He <u>dropped</u> the book and <u>ran</u>.
40. Cindy <u>played</u> the piano and <u>sang</u>.
41. I <u>read</u> the paper and <u>signed</u> my name.
42. She <u>brushed</u> and <u>combed</u> her hair.
43. The car <u>swerved</u> and <u>hit</u> the sign.
44. Our dog <u>chases</u> cars and <u>catches</u> birds.
45. We <u>cut</u> the melon and <u>ate</u> it.
46. Mom <u>washed</u> and <u>ironed</u> the clothes.
47. I <u>opened</u> the gate and <u>walked</u> in.
48. Dad <u>chopped</u> and <u>stacked</u> the wood.
49. We <u>planted</u> the garden and <u>watered</u> it.
50. I <u>stayed</u> home and <u>studied</u>.

COMPOSITION EXERCISE

Write a sentence using each set of words as a compound verb.

(ran and hid)   1. _____

(fall and skin)   2. _____

(cooks and cleans)   3. _____

(hit and exploded)   4. _____

(yawned and stretched) 5. _____

Using Compound Verbs

Sentences which have more than one verb have compound verbs. These verbs are connected with conjunctions.

EXAMPLES:
  a. I opened the box and screamed.
  b. She hit her hand and cried.
  c. He started the car and drove away.
  d. Jill bought the candy and ate it.

 In each blank write a verb.

1. I __cut__ the rope and __tied__ a knot.
2. Steve **JUMPED** and **BROKE** his leg.
3. We **CAMPED** and **FISHED**.
4. Joe **TRIPPED** and **FELL**.
5. The baby **SMILED** and **GIGGLED**.
6. I **CLOSED** the book and **THOUGHT**.
7. Our class **LISTENED** and **VOTED**.
8. He **KICKED** and **YELLED**.
9. The children **PLAYED** and **LAUGHED**.
10. Keith **WASHED** and **DRIED** the dishes.
11. He **KICKED** the ball and **RAN**.
12. We **ATE** our lunch and **READ**.
13. The frog **CROAKED** and **HOPPED** away.
14. I **HURRIED** home and **COOKED** dinner.
15. He **PAID** the bill and **LEFT**.
16. **MOVE** over and **WATCH**.
17. Dad **MOWED** and **WATERED** the lawn.
18. We **UNFOLDED** the flag and **RAISED** it.
19. Aaron **CAME** and **SPOKE** to us.
20. The boat **ROCKED** and finally **SANK**.
21. We will **STOP** and **EAT** dinner.
22. I **SWIM** and **SKI**.
23. Sue **LISTENED** and **REPEATED** the story.
24. She **CALLED** and **ORDERED** a pizza.
25. He **TURNED** and **WALKED** away.

26. Lee **PUSHED** the button and **WAITED**.
27. He **CAUGHT** the ball and **THREW** it.
28. I **TOOK** the bike and **RODE** away.
29. We **WATCHED** the game and **CHEERED**.
30. It **RAINED** and **SNOWED**.
31. My dog **EATS** and **SLEEPS**.
32. She **SLAMMED** the door and **CRIED**.
33. The dog **BARKED** and **WHINED**.
34. **MOW** the lawn, and **RAKE** the leaves.
35. Sherry **DRAWS** and **PAINTS**.
36. I **OPENED** the book and **READ** aloud.
37. He **TOOK** the car and **SOLD** it.
38. The window **CRACKED** and **SHATTERED**.
39. I **CLOSED** my eyes and **MADE** a wish.
40. He **SADDLED** the horse and **RODE**.
41. Everyone **SHOUTED** and **CLAPPED**.
42. We **FILLED** the basket and **WENT** home.
43. It was **SOLD** and **DELIVERED**.
44. I **SAT** and **RESTED**.
45. He **TIED** his shoes and **ZIPPED** his coat.
46. I **WORK** and **PLAY**.
47. Doc **HESITATED** and **CAME** forward.
48. The housekeeper **MOPPED** and **DUSTED**.
49. Alice **TRIED** but **FAILED**.
50. The bird **CAUGHT** the worm and **FLEW** away.

COMPOSITION EXERCISE

Write 8 sentences which contain compound verbs.

1. _____
2. _____
3. _____
4. _____
5. _____
6. _____
7. _____
8. _____

Unit 30 cont'd ⟶

Choosing Correctly Spelled Verbs

A verb shows action or state of being.

EXAMPLES: a. I *advise* you to tell her.
b. Someone *knocked* on the door.

 Complete each sentence with the verb which is spelled correctly.

1. ___**Outline**___ the next chapter.
   (a) Owtline   (b) Outline   (c) Outlin
2. Did you **REMEMBER** to call Chuck?
   (a) remimber   (b) remember   (c) remembur
3. Anna is ___**VISITING**___ her grandmother.
   (a) viseting   (b) viziting   (c) visiting
4. Joey **DELIVERS** newspapers.
   (a) delivurs   (b) delivors   (c) delivers
5. I've ___**CHANGED**___ my mind.
   (a) changed   (b) chanjed   (c) changd
6. ___**SEPARATE**___ parts ''A'' and ''B.''
   (a) Seperate   (b) Sepurate   (c) Separate
7. Bears **HIBERNATE** in the winter.
   (a) hiburnate   (b) hibernate   (c) hibernat
8. Don't ___**HESITATE**___ to call.
   (a) hesitate   (b) hessitate   (c) hesatate
9. The city should ___**CONDEMN**___ the building.
   (a) condemn   (b) condem   (c) condimn
10. Donna ___**HURRIED**___ home.
    (a) hurryed   (b) hurryied   (c) hurried
11. My brother **WRECKED** the car.
    (a) wrecked   (b) recked   (c) wreckt
12. Millie ___**ARGUED**___ with the officer.
    (a) argueed   (b) argued   (c) aregued
13. It was ___**RAINING**___.
    (a) rainning   (b) raining   (c) rayning
14. Let's ___**PAINT**___ the barn green.
    (a) paynt   (b) paint   (c) paent
15. Terry ___**DECIDED**___ to wait for us.
    (a) decided   (b) desided   (c) decidded
16. Dad **ASSEMBLED** the bicycle.
    (a) asembled   (b) assembled   (c) asembuld
17. The ghost **VANISHED**.
    (a) vanushed   (b) vanished   (c) vannished

18. This shield will ___**PROTECT**___ your eyes.
    (a) protect   (b) pertect   (c) protek
19. I **UNDERSTAND** the assignment.
    (a) undirstand   (b) understan   (c) understand
20. Columbus **DISCOVERED** America.
    (a) disscovered   (b) discovired   (c) discovered
21. The dog **FOLLOWED** me home.
    (a) folowed   (b) followed   (c) folloed
22. George **KNOCKED** on the door.
    (a) nocked   (b) knocked   (c) knoked
23. Zeke **PROMISED** to come early.
    (a) promised   (b) promized   (c) promused
24. I ___**SUGGEST**___ we reconsider.
    (a) seggest   (b) suggest   (c) suggist
25. Would you ___**EXPLAIN**___ it again?
    (a) eksplain   (b) explane   (c) explain
26. ___**WRITE**___ your name at the top.
    (a) Rite   (b) Write   (c) Wright
27. Mr. Thompson ___**WORKS**___ at the bakery.
    (a) wurks   (b) werks   (c) works
28. Betty ___**APPLIED**___ for the job.
    (a) applyed   (b) applyied   (c) applied
29. We are **STUDYING** our history.
    (a) studying   (b) studdying   (c) studiing
30. No one **BELIEVES** my story.
    (a) beleives   (b) beleves   (c) believes
31. Roy and I will ___**SCRUB**___ the floor.
    (a) skrub   (b) scrubb   (c) scrub
32. Mr. Weston **BOUGHT** the truck.
    (a) bot   (b) boutgh   (c) bought
33. The man **BEGGED** us for a dime.
    (a) begged   (b) beged   (c) beggd
34. Clark **WHISTLED** at the dog.
    (a) wistled   (b) whistled   (c) whisled

Comprehension Check

A Fill in the missing tense forms.

present	past	future
1. take	took	will take
2. forgive	forgave	will forgive
3. mail	mailed	will mail
4. shake	shook	will shake
5. find	found	will find
6. prepare	prepared	will prepare
7. close	closed	will close
8. waste	wasted	will waste
9. go	went	will go
10. practice	practiced	will practice

present	past	future
11. see	saw	will see
12. play	played	will play
13. wish	wished	will wish
14. read	read	will read
15. care	cared	will care
16. fly	flew	will fly
17. decide	decided	will decide
18. believe	believed	will believe
19. harm	harmed	will harm
20. manage	managed	will manage

B Supply the present-tense verbs.

1. John **serves** as a volunteer.
2. My dog **steals** the mail.
3. The house **needs** painting again.
4. I **like** the blue one more.
5. He always **supports** what I do.
6. Joan **writes** ads for the newspaper.
7. The bus **stops** at the corner at noon.
8. Sam **knows** I hate pizza.
9. Mom **makes** the best apple pies.
10. She **works** in a furniture store.
11. The teller **counts** the money carefully.
12. It **looks** like a giant fish.

C Supply the past-tense verbs.

1. Lisa **cut** the flowers for you.
2. The wind **blew** the leaves.
3. Brad **wore** a yellow windbreaker.
4. No one **heard** anything.
5. The weather **was** beautiful.
6. Nancy and I **studied** together.
7. Paul **waited** a long time.
8. I **knew** all the answers on the test.
9. Susan **sent** Aunt Carrie a card.
10. Someone **took** the coat home.
11. Who **made** the peanut candy?
12. The officer **wrote** Tim a ticket.

D Supply the future-tense verbs.

1. Uncle Willis **will visit** us in March.
2. I **will know** their answer next week.
3. The money **will go** for research.
4. Dr. Benton **will be** your teacher.
5. This device **will measure** the temperature.
6. Barbara **will bring** the supplies.
7. We **will plant** the daisies here.
8. **Will** you **donate** the money?
9. It **will snow** on Tuesday.
10. The cat **will scratch** you.
11. Katie **will cook** our supper Monday.
12. Mr. Delson **will assign** the topics.

Test 6 cont'd →

Comprehension Check (continued)

E Identify the tense of each verb.

(1) present **(2) past** **(3) future**

_1_ 1. like	_3_ 11. will plan	_2_ 21. used	_1_ 31. smell
_2_ 2. hurried	_2_ 12. did	_2_ 22. stopped	_3_ 32. will realize
_3_ 3. will answer	_1_ 13. organize	_1_ 23. push	_1_ 33. declare
_1_ 4. is	_1_ 14. open	_3_ 24. will watch	_2_ 34. shopped
_3_ 5. will be	_3_ 15. will spell	_2_ 25. wrote	_1_ 35. enclose
_1_ 6. dance	_2_ 16. listed	_1_ 26. explode	_2_ 36. tried
_2_ 7. went	_1_ 17. buy	_2_ 27. travelled	_2_ 37. studied
_2_ 8. carried	_1_ 18. criticize	_2_ 28. rode	_2_ 38. flew
_3_ 9. shall call	_2_ 19. walked	_3_ 29. will send	_3_ 39. will trust
_1_ 10. listen	_3_ 20. will sign	_3_ 30. shall reply	_1_ 40. unlock

F Identify the verb endings.

ing 1. speaking	_ed_ 6. worried	_s_ 11. reads
_es_ 2. reaches	_ing_ 7. sitting	_ed_ 12. flipped
_s_ 3. talks	_ed_ 8. explored	_es_ 13. teaches
_ed_ 4. locked	_en_ 9. chosen	_en_ 14. written
ing 5. eating	_ed_ 10. measured	_ed_ 15. counted

G Supply the verbs.

1. Did you _drop_ or _shake_ the box?
2. Harry _relaxed_ and _napped_ all day.
3. The girl _looked_ around and _entered_ .
4. Someone _saw_ the note and _took_ it.
5. Will he _come_ home and _help_ us?

6. She _folded_ the clothes and _packed_ them.
7. It _wiggled_ and _squirmed_ .
8. Ike _opened_ the door and _ran_ .
9. Tom _aimed_ carefully but _missed_ .
10. Casey _waited_ until noon and _left_ .

Write a paragraph about your favorite movie. Why is it your favorite? Underline the past-tense verbs.

_____

_____

_____

_____

_____

_____

_____

_____

_____

_____

Nouns Can Become Verbs

A noun can become a verb by its use in the sentence. (Its meaning may change.)

EXAMPLES: a. *Make a wish.*
　　　　　Joey wished for a new bike.

　　　　b. *Help is on the way.*
　　　　　Sherry helped the pack.

 In the blank write the verb form of the underlined noun.

1. The <u>play</u> was interesting.
   She _____*played*_____ the piano.
2. <u>Camping</u> is a bore.
   We **CAMPED** by the river.
3. The <u>bleach</u> ruined my shirt.
   Mom **BLEACHED** the sheets.
4. We repeated the <u>pledge</u>.
   I **PLEDGED** my support.
5. A <u>notice</u> was posted on the board.
   Did you **NOTICE** anything strange?
6. The <u>estimate</u> is too high.
   He **ESTIMATED** our damages.
7. Don needs a <u>match</u>.
   We **MATCHED** the colors.
8. The <u>water</u> was warm.
   Aunt Bea **WATERED** the flowers.
9. I heard a shrill <u>laugh</u>.
   No one **LAUGHED** at the joke.
10. Mom hung the <u>wash</u> outside.
    Dave **WASHED** the cars.
11. Her <u>voice</u> was soft and sweet.
    Teri **VOICED** her opinion.
12. The <u>question</u> was for John.
    The captain **QUESTIONED** his men.

13. <u>Exercise</u> is good for you.
    We **EXERCISED** our leg muscles.
14. The <u>whip</u> is in the barn.
    The man **WHIPPED** the lions.
15. The <u>trip</u> sounds exciting.
    I **TRIPPED** on the rug.
16. The last <u>act</u> is beginning.
    Janet **ACTS** silly.
17. The <u>snack</u> was delicious.
    We **SNACKED** on cheese and crackers.
18. Texas is a big <u>state</u>.
    The attorney **STATED** his case.
19. Each child wore a <u>number</u>.
    She **NUMBERED** the sentences.
20. <u>Time</u> is our only worry.
    The coach **TIMED** the races.
21. The <u>drink</u> was too sweet.
    You must **DRINK** your milk.
22. Your <u>mind</u> is remarkable.
    The dog **MINDS** me.
23. Mr. Simpson is a <u>cook</u>.
    Our class **COOKED** spaghetti.
24. I need a <u>ride</u> home.
    He **RIDES** our bus.

COMPOSITION EXERCISE

Use each of these words as both a noun and a verb.

1. sign

   _____

   _____

2. use

   _____

   _____

3. cover

   _____

   _____

4. meet

   _____

   _____

Unit 31 cont'd →

Verbs Can Become Nouns

A verb can become a noun by its use in the sentence. (Its meaning may change.)

EXAMPLES: a. I *passed* the history test.
We will need a student's *pass*.

b. Linda *cried* for her puppy.
Crying will get you nowhere.

✱ In the blank write the noun form of the underlined verb.

1. The man <u>jumped</u> the fence.
   I can't make the _____**jump**_____.
2. The police <u>spotted</u> the stolen car.
   She couldn't remove the __**SPOT**__.
3. The thief <u>cut</u> the wires.
   The __**CUT**__ is too deep.
4. It <u>rained</u> last night.
   The __**RAIN**__ soaked my clothes.
5. He <u>stopped</u> us from leaving.
   The bus came to a fast __**STOP**__.
6. Dad <u>handed</u> me the money.
   My __**HAND**__ is broken.
7. The noise <u>echoed</u> in the distance.
   Cathi listened to the __**ECHO**__.
8. I can <u>see</u> your house.
   __**SEEING**__ is believing.
9. Connie <u>noted</u> the changes.
   I will leave her a __**NOTE**__.
10. We <u>roasted</u> our hot dogs.
    The __**ROAST**__ is delicious.
11. The thief <u>escaped</u> from jail.
    The prisoners planned their __**ESCAPE**__.
12. Mom <u>frowned</u> at my story.
    A __**FROWN**__ ruins your day.

13. We <u>mapped</u> our course.
    The __**MAP**__ was lost in the storm.
14. May I <u>suggest</u> my ideas?
    Your __**SUGGESTION**__ was accepted.
15. He <u>transferred</u> to another school.
    My dad wants a __**TRANSFER**__.
16. I will <u>care</u> for the dog.
    This animal requires special __**CARE**__.
17. We <u>delayed</u> our plans.
    The __**DELAY**__ lasted an hour.
18. They <u>arrived</u> this afternoon.
    I look forward to your __**ARRIVAL**__.
19. I <u>swallowed</u> a dime.
    The __**SWALLOW**__ flew away.
20. Your joke <u>resulted</u> in an accident.
    The __**RESULT**__ will be announced.
21. Did you <u>locate</u> the owner?
    The __**LOCATION**__ is excellent.
22. The farmer <u>planted</u> cotton.
    This __**PLANT**__ is called ivy.
23. Did you <u>accomplish</u> your goal?
    Her __**ACCOMPLISHMENTS**__ are many.
24. Josh <u>earns</u> $2.00 an hour.
    His __**EARNINGS**__ paid for his bike.

COMPOSITION EXERCISE

Use each of these words as both a noun and a verb.

1. hand

   _____

   _____

2. drive

   _____

   _____

3. seat

   _____

   _____

4. watch

   _____

   _____

Adjectives That Describe Nouns

Adjectives are words that describe nouns.

EXAMPLES: a. <u>white</u> rabbit   c. <u>fourth</u> grade   e. <u>friendly</u> smile
           b. <u>baby</u> brother   d. <u>sharp</u> knife   f. <u>proud</u> man

 Write an adjective before each noun.

1. *red* car	26. *large* hat	51. *oak* tree
2. *chocolate* pie	27. *pretty* girl	52. *beautiful* mermaid
3. *six* students	28. *thick* slice	53. *rude* man
4. *cozy* room	29. *ten* pages	54. *true* statement
5. *long* voyage	30. *bright* color	55. *new* bicycle
6. *tall* lady	31. *small* family	56. *warm* blanket
7. *sweet* tooth	32. *green* meadow	57. *math* teacher
8. *cool* breeze	33. *freight* train	58. *yellow* flower
9. *wrong* answer	34. *huge* mountain	59. *sly* fox
10. *brave* woman	35. *alarm* clock	60. *poor* grades
11. *soft* voice	36. *sore* thumb	61. *calm* seas
12. *green* coat	37. *broken* nose	62. *white* fence
13. *crazy* idea	38. *funny* joke	63. *two* owners
14. *long* hike	39. *helpful* clue	64. *simple* sentence
15. *silly* cartoon	40. *sad* frown	65. *few* questions
16. *bad* storm	41. *car* license	66. *easy* test
17. *fat* cowboy	42. *warm* water	67. *straw* broom
18. *pink* elephant	43. *sour* grape	68. *short* time
19. *narrow* bridge	44. *flower* garden	69. *full* bottle
20. *big* city	45. *happy* people	70. *tall* building
21. *tiny* baby	46. *old* jail	71. *silver* spoon
22. *brown* moccasins	47. *many* abilities	72. *loud* music
23. *eye* doctor	48. *sad* story	73. *burned* cookie
24. *loud* noise	49. *seven* poems	74. *round* table
25. *sound* reason	50. *older* sister	75. *short* quiz

COMPOSITION EXERCISE

List 21 adjective-noun phrases. Do not use words from today's exercise.

1. _____	8. _____	15. _____
2. _____	9. _____	16. _____
3. _____	10. _____	17. _____
4. _____	11. _____	18. _____
5. _____	12. _____	19. _____
6. _____	13. _____	20. _____
7. _____	14. _____	21. _____

Unit 32 cont'd →

The Position of Adjectives

Adjectives usually come in front of the nouns they are describing.

EXAMPLES: a. The <u>first</u> person wins.   c. She wore <u>yellow</u> shoes.
               b. Karen made a <u>banana</u> pie.   d. I want the <u>softest</u> pillow.

 Underline the adjectives.

1. He always wears <u>purple</u> socks.
2. <u>Two</u> students are absent.
3. I made a <u>lemon</u> cake.
4. She bought a <u>straw</u> hat.
5. Dave is a <u>marvelous</u> cook.
6. He is a <u>friendly</u> ghost.
7. The <u>last</u> boy is Bruce.
8. My brother is in the <u>tenth</u> grade.
9. Ms. Jenks is a <u>retired</u> nurse.
10. I love <u>strawberry</u> ice cream.
11. We need a <u>long</u> rope.
12. Here is the <u>missing</u> piece.
13. He ate a <u>hot</u> pepper.
14. The <u>lost</u> puppy cried.
15. This is an <u>excellent</u> report.
16. Mom made <u>vegetable</u> soup.
17. I enjoy <u>ice</u> skating.
18. Jack is a <u>great</u> artist.
19. The <u>yellow</u> roses have bloomed.
20. He turned on a <u>gravel</u> road.
21. It has been a <u>cold</u> winter.
22. Mr. Norton is a <u>busy</u> man.
23. Do you have a <u>flower</u> garden?
24. <u>Sad</u> movies make me cry.
25. I saw a <u>pink</u> elephant.
26. The teacher read us a <u>silly</u> poem.
27. He comes from a <u>large</u> family.
28. They own <u>valuable</u> property.
29. The <u>football</u> game is tonight.
30. We own a <u>green</u> truck.
31. I saw an <u>enormous</u> monster.
32. The <u>strong</u> wind bent our flowers.
33. Let's take a <u>short</u> walk.
34. Darren is my <u>oldest</u> friend.
35. She gave us an <u>easy</u> test.
36. Mom bought a <u>square</u> table.
37. The <u>lonely</u> man walked away.
38. We watched a <u>spooky</u> movie.
39. Look at that <u>green</u> bike.
40. She needs <u>new</u> shoes.
41. It made a <u>loud</u> noise.
42. A <u>new</u> budget is needed.
43. The <u>family</u> portrait is finished.
44. He leads a <u>carefree</u> life.
45. Phil is a <u>terrible</u> player.
46. The <u>orange</u> balloon popped.
47. May I have a <u>cold</u> drink?
48. That is a <u>useless</u> clue.
49. I dialed the <u>wrong</u> number.
50. You have a <u>big</u> mouth.

COMPOSITION EXERCISE

Write 12 sentences which contain adjectives.

1. _____
2. _____
3. _____
4. _____
5. _____
6. _____
7. _____
8. _____
9. _____
10. _____
11. _____
12. _____

Adjectives That Add "er"

To show comparison, adjectives of one or two syllables add "er." (Note: When a one-syllable adjective ends in a single consonant preceded by a single vowel [big], double the consonant before adding "er" [bigger]. An adjective which ends in "y" changes the "y" to "i" before adding "er.")

EXAMPLES:
- a. full — fuller
- b. cloudy — cloudier
- c. new — newer
- d. hungry — hungrier

  Write the correct forms of comparison. Check the rule often to make sure you spell the words correctly.

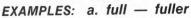

word	+ -er	word	+ -er	word	+ -er
1. small	*smaller*	23. slow	SLOWER	45. kind	KINDER
2. big	BIGGER	24. dark	DARKER	46. quick	QUICKER
3. short	SHORTER	25. late	LATER	47. green	GREENER
4. tall	TALLER	26. early	EARLIER	48. safe	SAFER
5. nice	NICER	27. young	YOUNGER	49. strong	STRONGER
6. sweet	SWEETER	28. old	OLDER	50. white	WHITER
7. easy	EASIER	29. poor	POORER	51. busy	BUSIER
8. deep	DEEPER	30. smart	SMARTER	52. crisp	CRISPER
9. rough	ROUGHER	31. high	HIGHER	53. bright	BRIGHTER
10. smooth	SMOOTHER	32. low	LOWER	54. dry	DRIER
11. quiet	QUIETER	33. long	LONGER	55. ugly	UGLIER
12. large	LARGER	34. clean	CLEANER	56. silly	SILLIER
13. soft	SOFTER	35. fresh	FRESHER	57. cute	CUTER
14. great	GREATER	36. new	NEWER	58. fat	FATTER
15. sharp	SHARPER	37. cheap	CHEAPER	59. narrow	NARROWER
16. thin	THINNER	38. few	FEWER	60. wide	WIDER
17. hot	HOTTER	39. rich	RICHER	61. firm	FIRMER
18. cold	COLDER	40. close	CLOSER	62. neat	NEATER
19. warm	WARMER	41. thick	THICKER	63. skinny	SKINNIER
20. cool	COOLER	42. near	NEARER	64. sad	SADDER
21. hard	HARDER	43. tough	TOUGHER	65. lazy	LAZIER
22. fast	FASTER	44. clear	CLEARER	66. dull	DULLER

COMPOSITION EXERCISE

Choose 10 adjectives which end with "er." Write a sentence with each.

1. _____
2. _____
3. _____
4. _____
5. _____
6. _____
7. _____
8. _____
9. _____
10. _____

Unit 33 cont'd →

Adjectives That Add "est"

To show the greatest form of comparison,
adjectives of one or two syllables add "est."

EXAMPLES: a. full, fuller, _fullest_   c. new, newer, _newest_
 b. sweet, sweeter, _sweetest_   d. dull, duller, _dullest_

 Write the greatest form of comparison for
each word.

1. small, smaller, _smallest_
2. short, shorter, **SHORTEST**
3. easy, easier, **EASIEST**
4. deep, deeper, **DEEPEST**
5. rough, rougher, **ROUGHEST**
6. wide, wider, **WIDEST**
7. quiet, quieter, **QUIETEST**
8. large, larger, **LARGEST**
9. soft, softer, **SOFTEST**
10. great, greater, **GREATEST**
11. sharp, sharper, **SHARPEST**
12. hot, hotter, **HOTTEST**
13. cold, colder, **COLDEST**
14. warm, warmer, **WARMEST**
15. fast, faster, **FASTEST**
16. busy, busier, **BUSIEST**
17. quick, quicker, **QUICKEST**
18. ugly, uglier, **UGLIEST**
19. fat, fatter, **FATTEST**
20. red, redder, **REDDEST**
21. early, earlier, **EARLIEST**
22. nice, nicer, **NICEST**
23. hard, harder, **HARDEST**
24. thick, thicker, **THICKEST**
25. fresh, fresher, **FRESHEST**

26. big, bigger, **BIGGEST**
27. tall, taller, **TALLEST**
28. slow, slower, **SLOWEST**
29. dark, darker, **DARKEST**
30. young, younger, **YOUNGEST**
31. old, older, **OLDEST**
32. smart, smarter, **SMARTEST**
33. kind, kinder, **KINDEST**
34. high, higher, **HIGHEST**
35. low, lower, **LOWEST**
36. long, longer, **LONGEST**
37. cheap, cheaper, **CHEAPEST**
38. few, fewer, **FEWEST**
39. close, closer, **CLOSEST**
40. near, nearer, **NEAREST**
41. cute, cuter, **CUTEST**
42. slim, slimmer, **SLIMMEST**
43. lazy, lazier, **LAZIEST**
44. sad, sadder, **SADDEST**
45. dull, duller, **DULLEST**
46. firm, firmer, **FIRMEST**
47. clear, clearer, **CLEAREST**
48. white, whiter, **WHITEST**
49. strong, stronger, **STRONGEST**
50. bright, brighter, **BRIGHTEST**

COMPOSITION EXERCISE

Choose 10 adjectives which end with "est." Write a sentence with each.

1. _____
2. _____
3. _____
4. _____
5. _____

6. _____
7. _____
8. _____
9. _____
10. _____

Adding "er" and "est" to Adjectives

To show comparison, an adjective of one or two syllables adds "er." Greatest comparison is shown by adding "est."

EXAMPLES:
  a. fat — fatter — fattest
  b. old — older — oldest
  c. young — younger — youngest
  d. late — later — latest

❋ Add "er" or "est" to each adjective. Watch out for changes in spelling.

	+ er	+ est			+ er	+ est
1. cold	colder	coldest	25. soon		SOONER	SOONEST
2. warm	WARMER	WARMEST	26. fast		FASTER	FASTEST
3. large	LARGER	LARGEST	27. quick		QUICKER	QUICKEST
4. big	BIGGER	BIGGEST	28. slow		SLOWER	SLOWEST
5. high	HIGHER	HIGHEST	29. long		LONGER	LONGEST
6. low	LOWER	LOWEST	30. weak		WEAKER	WEAKEST
7. soft	SOFTER	SOFTEST	31. full		FULLER	FULLEST
8. hard	HARDER	HARDEST	32. new		NEWER	NEWEST
9. easy	EASIER	EASIEST	33. old		OLDER	OLDEST
10. pretty	PRETTIER	PRETTIEST	34. sweet		SWEETER	SWEETEST
11. ugly	UGLIER	UGLIEST	35. safe		SAFER	SAFEST
12. straight	STRAIGHTER	STRAIGHTEST	36. strong		STRONGER	STRONGEST
13. green	GREENER	GREENEST	37. clean		CLEANER	CLEANEST
14. small	SMALLER	SMALLEST	38. fresh		FRESHER	FRESHEST
15. happy	HAPPIER	HAPPIEST	39. cheap		CHEAPER	CHEAPEST
16. sad	SADDER	SADDEST	40. rich		RICHER	RICHEST
17. thick	THICKER	THICKEST	41. close		CLOSER	CLOSEST
18. thin	THINNER	THINNEST	42. great		GREATER	GREATEST
19. tall	TALLER	TALLEST	43. sharp		SHARPER	SHARPEST
20. few	FEWER	FEWEST	44. deep		DEEPER	DEEPEST
21. short	SHORTER	SHORTEST	45. simple		SIMPLER	SIMPLEST
22. near	NEARER	NEAREST	46. busy		BUSIER	BUSIEST
23. kind	KINDER	KINDEST	47. bright		BRIGHTER	BRIGHTEST
24. nice	NICER	NICEST	48. dark		DARKER	DARKEST

COMPOSITION EXERCISE

Write a sentence with each of these adjectives.

1. sweet — sweeter — sweetest

_____

_____

2. happy — happier — happiest

_____

_____

3. tall — taller — tallest

_____

_____

4. big — bigger — biggest

_____

_____

Unit 34 cont'd ➡

Adjectives That Add "More"

To show comparison, most adjectives of two or
more syllables add the word "more."

EXAMPLES: a. You are intelligent.
I am _more intelligent_.

b. This is interesting.
That is _more interesting_.

 Fill in the blanks with adjectives of comparison.

1. This bike is expensive.
That bike is ___more expensive___ .

2. John Smith is famous.
Abe Lincoln is ___more famous___ .

3. Today is beautiful.
Tomorrow will be ___more beautiful___ .

4. My story is interesting.
Jay's story is ___more interesting___ .

5. A dog is intelligent.
People are ___more intelligent___ .

6. That tool is useful.
This tool is ___more useful___ .

7. Jason is forgetful.
His brother is ___more forgetful___ .

8. The show was terrible.
The ending was ___more terrible___ .

9. Rubies are valuable.
Diamonds are ___more valuable___ .

10. The weather today is threatening.
Yesterday was ___more threatening___ .

11. This is embarrassing.
Nothing could be ___more embarrassing___ .

12. Alex is polite.
He is ___more polite___ than you.

13. My work is important.
My friends are ___more important___ .

14. Sam is bashful.
His sister is ___more bashful___ .

15. The cake was delicious.
Your cake was ___more delicious___ .

16. The house was frightening.
The ghost was ___more frightening___ .

17. The first question was difficult.
The second was ___more difficult___ .

18. The truck was expensive.
The car was ___more expensive___ .

19. Our town is famous.
Paris is ___more famous___ .

20. The letter was interesting.
The picture was ___more interesting___ .

21. The tree looked decayed.
The house looked ___more decayed___ .

22. That was terrible.
This is ___more terrible___ .

23. The dinner was delicious.
The dessert was ___more delicious___ .

24. This stone is valuable.
That stone is ___more valuable___ .

COMPOSITION EXERCISE

Compare the items in each set. Then write a sentence which contains an adjective plus "more."

1. this chair...that chair

2. fruits...vegetables

3. chocolate...licorice

4. fried chicken...steak

5. rock music...country music

6. wool...cotton

7. tornado...hurricane

8. brothers...sisters

84

Adjectives That Add "Most"

To show the greatest comparison, most adjectives of two or more syllables add the word "most."

EXAMPLES: a. necessary, more necessary, <u>most necessary</u>
b. useful, more useful, <u>most useful</u>

 Fill in the blank with an adjective of greatest comparison.

1. My sister is intelligent.
   My brother is more intelligent.
   But, I am the <u>most intelligent</u>.

2. The dark room was frightening.
   The shadows were more frightening.
   The ghost was the <u>MOST FRIGHTENING</u>.

3. Yellow cake is delicious.
   Chocolate cake is more delicious.
   But, cherry cake is <u>MOST DELICIOUS</u>.

4. The show is interesting.
   The story was more interesting.
   Your secret is the <u>MOST INTERESTING</u>.

5. A penny is valuable.
   A nickel is more valuable.
   A dollar is the <u>MOST VALUABLE</u>.

6. Sarah is bashful.
   Debra is more bashful.
   Ann is the <u>MOST BASHFUL</u>.

7. Copper is expensive.
   Silver is more expensive.
   Gold is the <u>MOST EXPENSIVE</u>.

8. The history test was difficult.
   The English test was more difficult.
   The math test was the <u>MOST DIFFICULT</u>.

9. I am forgetful.
   My mom is more forgetful.
   But, my dad is the <u>MOST FORGETFUL</u>.

10. The weather is terrible.
    The thunder is more terrible.
    A tornado is the <u>MOST TERRIBLE</u>.

11. The man was polite.
    His wife was more polite.
    Their son was the <u>MOST POLITE</u>.

12. Paper and pencil are necessary.
    Books are more necessary.
    Learning is the <u>MOST NECESSARY</u>.

13. The gift was useful.
    Mom's gift was more useful.
    My aunt's gift was the <u>MOST USEFUL</u>.

14. Susan is beautiful.
    Karen is more beautiful.
    Lisa is the <u>MOST BEAUTIFUL</u>.

15. People are important.
    Friends are more important.
    A family is the <u>MOST IMPORTANT</u>.

16. Dan's clue was helpful.
    Sue's clue was more helpful.
    Terry's clue was the <u>MOST HELPFUL</u>.

COMPOSITION EXERCISE

List 10 adjectives that add "most." Write a sentence with each.

1. _____
2. _____
3. _____
4. _____
5. _____

6. _____
7. _____
8. _____
9. _____
10. _____

Unit 35 cont'd →

Adding "More" and "Most" to Adjectives

To show comparison, an adjective of two or more syllables adds "more." Greatest comparison is shown by adding "most."

EXAMPLES: a. important — more important — most important
            b. perfect — more perfect — most perfect

 Add "more" and "most" to each adjective.

1. expensive
   more expensive
   most expensive

2. appropriate
   MORE APPROPRIATE
   MOST APPROPRIATE

3. helpful
   MORE HELPFUL
   MOST HELPFUL

4. significant
   MORE SIGNIFICANT
   MOST SIGNIFICANT

5. wicked
   MORE WICKED
   MOST WICKED

6. selfish
   MORE SELFISH
   MOST SELFISH

7. beautiful
   MORE BEAUTIFUL
   MOST BEAUTIFUL

8. confident
   MORE CONFIDENT
   MOST CONFIDENT

9. attractive
   MORE ATTRACTIVE
   MOST ATTRACTIVE

10. valuable
    MORE VALUABLE
    MOST VALUABLE

11. precise
    MORE PRECISE
    MOST PRECISE

12. ruthless
    MORE RUTHLESS
    MOST RUTHLESS

13. wonderful
    MORE WONDERFUL
    MOST WONDERFUL

14. horrible
    MORE HORRIBLE
    MOST HORRIBLE

15. terrific
    MORE TERRIFIC
    MOST TERRIFIC

16. awkward
    MORE AWKWARD
    MOST AWKWARD

17. ignorant
    MORE IGNORANT
    MOST IGNORANT

18. intelligent
    MORE INTELLIGENT
    MOST INTELLIGENT

19. tragic
    MORE TRAGIC
    MOST TRAGIC

20. unimportant
    MORE UNIMPORTANT
    MOST UNIMPORTANT

21. recent
    MORE RECENT
    MOST RECENT

22. obedient
    MORE OBEDIENT
    MOST OBEDIENT

23. famous
    MORE FAMOUS
    MOST FAMOUS

24. correct
    MORE CORRECT
    MOST CORRECT

25. difficult
    MORE DIFFICULT
    MOST DIFFICULT

26. carefree
    MORE CAREFREE
    MOST CAREFREE

27. modern
    MORE MODERN
    MOST MODERN

28. glamorous
    MORE GLAMOROUS
    MOST GLAMOROUS

29. bashful
    MORE BASHFUL
    MOST BASHFUL

30. forgetful
    MORE FORGETFUL
    MOST FORGETFUL

31. polite
    MORE POLITE
    MOST POLITE

32. foolish
    MORE FOOLISH
    MOST FOOLISH

COMPOSITION EXERCISE

Compare these items.

1. a ruby — an emerald — a diamond

_____

_____

2. a book — a movie — a short story

_____

_____

_____

Comprehension Check

(A) Identify if the underlined word is a noun or a verb.

verb   1. He signed his name on the dotted line.

noun   2. The sign read 66 miles to Chicago.

noun   3. The call was placed from a pay phone.

verb   4. Someone called for Tom yesterday.

verb   5. We watch the show every Tuesday.

noun   6. I received a watch from my parents.

noun   7. His work is his life.

verb   8. It won't work without a battery.

verb   9. Everyone moved left.

noun   10. The move took four weeks.

noun   11. The train blew a signal.

verb   12. I trained my dog to fetch.

verb   13. Bart pushed the wrong button.

noun   14. It needs a push to get started.

verb   15. Someone signalled us to go.

noun   16. Hank waited for the green signal.

noun   17. I have no use for this.

verb   18. Jasper used my pen and paper.

verb   19. Hawkins will drive you home.

noun   20. Let's go for a drive.

(B) Underline the adjectives. Draw arrows to the words they modify.

1. Bentley preferred the blue one.

2. The next number will be mine.

3. Kelsey ate the chocolate mousse.

4. The history teacher is Mr. Marlowe.

5. Howard is the oldest player.

6. Eight students are absent today.

7. The children made mud pies.

8. You should try my spinach cake.

9. We still need thirty blankets.

10. Karen writes long essays.

11. The recipe calls for dill pickles.

12. Ms. Walters drives a yellow van.

13. Is that your final answer?

14. How do you like my new hat?

15. Mr. Davison has three sons.

16. Rock concerts are moneymakers.

17. She wore purple polish on her nails.

18. The corner lot is for sale.

19. Don't you like green slacks?

20. Cherry pies are easy to make.

21. I will see you Saturday night.

22. What is a black hole in space?

23. Margie sat in the third row.

24. Sad movies make me cry.

25. The city bus costs $2 to ride.

26. Pauline made an interesting speech.

27. All that's left is an empty jar.

28. Cameron bought a used car.

Test 7 cont'd

Comprehension Check (continued)

C Write the comparative and superlative forms of each adjective.

1. tall	taller	tallest	11. nice	nicer	nicest
2. sweet	sweeter	sweetest	12. beautiful	more beautiful	most beautiful
3. awkward	more awkward	most awkward	13. soft	softer	softest
4. loud	louder	loudest	14. high	higher	highest
5. wide	wider	widest	15. handsome	more handsome	most handsome
6. graceful	more graceful	most graceful	16. careful	more careful	most careful
7. thirsty	thirstier	thirstiest	17. expensive	more expensive	most expensive
8. large	larger	largest	18. short	shorter	shortest
9. fast	faster	fastest	19. pretty	prettier	prettiest
10. helpful	more helpful	most helpful	20. hopeless	more hopeless	most hopeless

D Compare these items or people.

1. math, English, and history
   English is my easiest subject.

2. an hour, a week, and a day
   A week is longer than an hour or a day.

3. dogs, cats, fish, and birds
   Fish are the quietest pets.

4. yellow and turquoise
   Yellow is prettier than turquoise.

5. train, jet, ship, and automobile
   Jet travel is the fastest.

6. elephants, horses, and camels
   Elephants are the biggest land animals.

7. breakfast, lunch, and dinner
   Dinner is my biggest meal.

8. a yacht, a rowboat, and a sailboat
   The yacht is the largest boat.

9. a parrot and a blackbird
   A parrot is more colorful than a blackbird.

10. Karen, Larry, Thomas, and Chris
   Karen is our tallest player.

11. a hamburger and a steak
   I like steak better than hamburgers.

12. diamonds, rubies, and emeralds
   Diamonds are the most expensive stones.

13. men and women
   Women are smarter than men.

14. rock, country, and classical music
   Classical music is the most soothing.

Write a paragraph comparing two of your favorite singers or bands. Underline the adjectives which show your comparison.

_____
_____
_____
_____
_____
_____
_____
_____
_____

Using Adjectives

Adjectives are words that describe. They may tell how many, what color, what kind, or which one.

EXAMPLES: a. The old man bought a new car.
The poor man bought a used car.

b. Two boys took a red bike.
Most boys took a 10-speed bike.

 Fill in each blank with an adjective.

1. Larry is my __youngest__ brother.
2. I left my __math__ book at home.
3. My grandfather is a __proud__ man.
4. He owns the __grocery__ store on Main.
5. The __new__ store will open on Monday.
6. Ken and I visited the __art__ museum.
7. __Several__ students attended the meet.
8. __Plastic__ toys are cheaper to buy.
9. A __blue__ car hit the mailbox.
10. Fred got a __speeding__ ticket.
11. The __yield__ sign had been run over.
12. __Two__ men worked on the roof.
13. Uncle Jeff drives an __old__ truck.
14. The __pickup__ truck parked behind me.
15. __Winter__ clothes are my favorite.
16. A __young__ police officer helped us.
17. The __scared__ child cried for her mother.
18. The doctor cured the __sick__ girl.
19. The Wilsons are my __new__ neighbors.
20. His __other__ neighbor is Capt. Lewis.
21. Her __best__ friend is from California.
22. All __ten__ horses jumped the fence.
23. A __wire__ fence is sturdier.
24. __Wood__ fences blend in with nature.
25. The __white__ fence needs repainting.

26. I have tickets to the __hockey__ game.
27. The __junior__ team won the championship.
28. My sister won the __essay__ contest.
29. She received a __silver__ trophy.
30. Our __nature__ club planned a hike.
31. The __science__ club is going with us.
32. The __next__ meeting is Saturday.
33. __Gym__ class is cancelled.
34. Mr. Richards is my __history__ teacher.
35. I have math __third__ period.
36. No one passed the __science__ test.
37. The __English__ assignment was easy.
38. Camden received a __new__ bike.
39. He wrecked his __green__ one.
40. The __birthday__ party is tomorrow.
41. I bought Lou a __leather__ hat.
42. __Twenty__ people have been invited.
43. It starts at __three__ o'clock.
44. Nancy made a __chocolate__ cake.
45. Betsy made __tuna__ sandwiches.
46. Roy will bring __fruit__ punch.
47. Can you bring some __corn__ chips?
48. It should be an __interesting__ party.
49. Jay and I spent __six__ hours studying.
50. I told you it was a __hard__ test.

COMPOSITION EXERCISE

Use each of these adjectives in a sentence.

(short)   1. _____
(nice)   2. _____
(orange) 3. _____
(three)   4. _____
(good)   5. _____

(sad)   6. _____
(new)   7. _____
(wild)   8. _____
(fat)   9. _____
(juicy)   10. _____

Unit 36 cont'd

Choosing Correctly Spelled Adjectives

An adjective is a word which tells which one, what kind, what color, or how many.

EXAMPLES:
which one:	The tall boy is Adam.
what kind:	Randy loves chocolate candy.
what color:	Jill wore a red beret.
how many:	I need ten pennies.

Complete each sentence with the adjective which is spelled correctly.

		(a)	(b)	(c)
1.	The whale is an __enormous__ animal.	enormus	enormous	enormis
2.	You have made an __EXCELLENT__ choice.	excellent	ekscellent	excellint
3.	Your story is very __INTERESTING__ .	inturesting	interresting	interesting
4.	The diamond is a __VALUABLE__ stone.	valluable	valuable	valuble
5.	Did you hear a __STRANGE__ noise?	strange	strainge	strang
6.	Mr. Cook is a __PROSPEROUS__ businessman.	prosperous	properus	prosperis
7.	This is not a __STRAIGHT__ line.	straght	straigt	straight
8.	The sunset was __BEAUTIFUL__ .	beutiful	beautiful	beautifel
9.	She is __HONEST__ and trustworthy.	honest	onest	honist
10.	That sounds __TERRIBLE__ !	terribul	terrible	terribel
11.	Quincy is my __YOUNGEST__ brother.	yungest	youngist	youngest
12.	Do you have a __LARGER__ size?	larger	largger	largeer
13.	The food was __DELICIOUS__ .	delishus	delicious	delecious
14.	Jean was __NERVOUS__ about the trial.	nervous	nerveous	nurvous
15.	Paul is a __TERRIFIC__ dancer.	terific	terrifik	terrific
16.	Many people are __DISCONTENT__ .	discontent	discontint	discontant
17.	We're all part of a __WINNING__ team.	wining	winning	winnin
18.	Katie always looks __CHEERFUL__ .	chearful	cheerful	cheerfull
19.	I need a __BROWN__ suitcase.	broun	browen	brown
20.	__TWENTY__ students were absent.	Twenty	Twinty	Twente
21.	I've never visited a __FOREIGN__ country.	foriegn	foreign	forun
22.	My parents were __FURIOUS__ .	furous	furrious	furious
23.	You can't see an __INVISIBLE__ man.	invisible	innvisible	invisibul
24.	The __VACANT__ lot has been sold.	vakant	vacant	vacent
25.	Newton was a __FAMOUS__ scientist.	famus	fammous	famous
26.	He collected __SEVENTEEN__ signatures.	seventeen	seventene	sevinteen
27.	My grandmother is a __WISE__ woman.	wize	wise	whise
28.	Fred lives in a __HAUNTED__ house.	haunted	hanted	hauntid
29.	The cars' lights were __BRIGHT__ .	brit	bright	brigt
30.	Tim is an __INTELLIGENT__ boy.	intelligent	inteligent	intelligant
31.	What is the __CORRECT__ answer?	corect	correct	coreck
32.	May I have a __DIFFERENT__ one?	diffrent	differint	different
33.	Pam baked a __CHOCOLATE__ cake.	choclate	chocolate	choklat
34.	Steve is in the __FOURTH__ grade.	fourth	forthe	foreth

Defining an Adverb

An adverb is a word that tells when,
where, or how.

EXAMPLES; a. *When will we meet again? We will meet tomorrow.*
b. *Where is my new bike? Your new bike is outside.*
c. *How does he work? Hank works quickly.*

 Write an adverb in the blank to make the answer
to the question complete. You may choose one
from the box.

wisely	yesterday	here	there	outside	quickly
truthfully	never	slowly	tomorrow	beautifully	immediately
out	inside	well	home	later	easily
early	carefully	nearby	away	now	today

1. When will you come home? I will come home ___ *later* ___.
2. When does the plane leave? The plane is leaving ___ NOW ___.
3. When does the show begin? The show will begin ___ TOMORROW ___.
4. When did Sam arrive? Sam arrived ___ EARLY ___.
5. When may I have it? You may have it ___ LATER ___.
6. When will you be sure? I'll ___ NEVER ___ be sure.
7. When did you buy that table? I bought the table ___ YESTERDAY ___.
8. When is her appointment? Her appointment is ___ TODAY ___.
9. When will we eat? We will eat ___ IMMEDIATELY ___.
10. Where did you put your hat? I put my hat ___ THERE ___.
11. Where did Mike go? Mike went ___ HOME ___.
12. Where did you park the car? I parked the car ___ HERE ___.
13. Where is the monkey? The monkey is ___ OUTSIDE ___.
14. Where are the horses running? The horses are running ___ AWAY ___.
15. Where does Kate live? Kate lives ___ NEARBY ___.
16. Where are we going? We are going ___ OUT ___.
17. Where is your mother? My mother is ___ INSIDE ___.
18. How did the turtle move? The turtle moved ___ SLOWLY ___.
19. How did they sing? They sang ___ BEAUTIFULLY ___.
20. How did George run? George ran ___ QUICKLY ___.

COMPOSITION EXERCISE

Write 12 sentences which contain adverbs.

1. _____
2. _____
3. _____
4. _____
5. _____
6. _____

7. _____
8. _____
9. _____
10. _____
11. _____
12. _____

Unit 37 cont'd →

Where to Find Adverbs

Adverbs are words that tell when, where, or how. They usually come close to verbs.

EXAMPLES:
   a. *Carrie went <u>downstairs</u>.*
   b. *Come <u>here</u> <u>immediately</u>.*
   c. *Mr. Carson waited <u>patiently</u>.*
   d. *<u>Suddenly</u> it was dark.*

 Underline the adverbs.

1. I <u>always</u> eat <u>slowly</u>.
2. The mail will come <u>soon</u>.
3. The puppy ran <u>outside</u>.
4. The plane landed <u>safely</u>.
5. The paper comes <u>daily</u>.
6. The spider moved <u>closer</u>.
7. You acted <u>foolishly</u>.
8. Bring your paper <u>here</u>.
9. Lisa cried <u>quietly</u>.
10. The class <u>finally</u> ended.
11. It occurred <u>recently</u>.
12. The circus leaves <u>tonight</u>.
13. He <u>quickly</u> hid the evidence.
14. I locked the doors <u>securely</u>.
15. He planned his attack <u>wisely</u>.
16. Mother came <u>immediately</u>.
17. The people shouted <u>angrily</u>.
18. <u>Lately</u> you've been rude.
19. My aunt left <u>yesterday</u>.
20. I will be <u>there</u>.
21. You must come <u>quickly</u>.
22. Thomas ran <u>upstairs</u>.
23. Come <u>inside</u>.
24. The hospital is <u>nearby</u>.
25. Chris works <u>carelessly</u>.
26. She <u>seldom</u> visits us.
27. The accident happened <u>suddenly</u>.
28. Why were you <u>late</u>?
29. I <u>usually</u> bring my own.
30. The lion roared <u>loudly</u>.
31. <u>Luckily</u> we arrived <u>safely</u>.
32. The choir sang <u>beautifully</u>.
33. Can you come <u>sooner</u>?
34. <u>Generally</u> we take checks.
35. Read the book <u>now</u>.
36. The coins rolled <u>everywhere</u>.
37. <u>Sometimes</u> you bother me.
38. The ship sailed <u>smoothly</u>.
39. School begins <u>tomorrow</u>.
40. Stack the books <u>neatly</u>.
41. She swims <u>gracefully</u>.
42. I had called her <u>earlier</u>.
43. The colors match <u>perfectly</u>.
44. Peter has <u>never</u> seen a parade.
45. They are <u>here</u>.
46. Dean sat <u>quietly</u> and waited.
47. Why did you run <u>away</u>?
48. The man was <u>badly</u> hurt.
49. Are you <u>always</u> this happy?
50. The dog ate <u>greedily</u>.

COMPOSITION EXERCISE

List 20 adverbs.

1. _____
2. _____
3. _____
4. _____
5. _____
6. _____
7. _____
8. _____
9. _____
10. _____
11. _____
12. _____
13. _____
14. _____
15. _____
16. _____
17. _____
18. _____
19. _____
20. _____

Adverbs That Tell When

An adverb may be a word that tells when.

EXAMPLES: a. I'll see you <u>tomorrow</u>.
                b. Cathy arrived <u>late</u>.
                c. <u>Finally</u>, the show was over.
                d. I <u>always</u> sit here.

Underline the adverbs that tell when.

1. She will come <u>tomorrow</u>.
2. It rained <u>yesterday</u>.
3. We will begin <u>now</u>.
4. I will see you <u>soon</u>.
5. The paper comes <u>daily</u>.
6. I <u>usually</u> feed the dog.
7. The bus is <u>late</u>.
8. You are too <u>early</u>.
9. The test is <u>today</u>.
10. Answer me <u>now</u>.
11. I <u>always</u> help my mom.
12. The show plays <u>tonight</u>.
13. The bell will ring <u>soon</u>.
14. <u>Sometimes</u> we play football.
15. You have a recital <u>tomorrow</u>.
16. <u>Suddenly</u> the rain stopped.
17. I heard it <u>again</u>.
18. It <u>never</u> snows in June.
19. My dog goes to bed <u>early</u>.
20. Kelly came home <u>late</u>.
21. The train <u>finally</u> came.
22. Diane <u>always</u> finishes.
23. It rained all day <u>yesterday</u>.
24. We will leave <u>soon</u>.
25. Go home <u>now</u>.
26. The show will begin <u>soon</u>.
27. Sandra <u>always</u> wins.
28. We will eat <u>early</u>.
29. The party is <u>tonight</u>.
30. You <u>always</u> try.
31. Bring your money <u>tomorrow</u>.
32. The ralley is scheduled <u>today</u>.
33. I must go <u>earlier</u>.
34. We <u>never</u> found the shoe.
35. Can't you come <u>sooner</u>?
36. We <u>usually</u> eat at six.
37. The man <u>finally</u> talked.
38. We will meet <u>again</u>.
39. The choir sang beautifully <u>today</u>.
40. Read your lesson <u>now</u>.
41. Come <u>early</u>.
42. I will see you <u>tonight</u>.
43. The doctor will arrive <u>soon</u>.
44. The radio has <u>never</u> worked.
45. The twins <u>always</u> fight.
46. <u>Sometimes</u> I help my dad.
47. Hand me your work <u>now</u>.
48. <u>Suddenly</u> I remembered.
49. My aunt is <u>always</u> talking.
50. School is out <u>today</u>.

COMPOSITION EXERCISE

List 28 adverbs that tell when.

1. _____
2. _____
3. _____
4. _____
5. _____
6. _____
7. _____
8. _____
9. _____
10. _____
11. _____
12. _____
13. _____
14. _____
15. _____
16. _____
17. _____
18. _____
19. _____
20. _____
21. _____
22. _____
23. _____
24. _____
25. _____
26. _____
27. _____
28. _____

Unit 38 cont'd

Adverbs That Tell Where

An adverb may be a word that tells where.

EXAMPLES: a. Susan is going <u>home</u>.   c. The man went <u>inside</u>.
          b. The birds flew <u>away</u>.   d. Jane is <u>upstairs</u>.

 Underline the adverbs that tell where.

1. Don't go <u>away</u>.
2. Bring the dog <u>here</u>.
3. I left the book <u>there</u>.
4. The team has gone <u>home</u>.
5. Come <u>closer</u>.
6. Did you go <u>anywhere</u>?
7. Ask her to come <u>inside</u>.
8. Take that frog <u>outside</u>.
9. Is the post office <u>nearby</u>?
10. The beans rolled <u>everywhere</u>.
11. Your room is <u>upstairs</u>.
12. We went shopping <u>downtown</u>.
13. The fish swam <u>away</u>.
14. The train is <u>here</u>.
15. I have been <u>nowhere</u>.
16. The balloon rose <u>higher</u>.
17. Won't you sit <u>down</u>?
18. The pain went <u>away</u>.
19. Let's sit <u>outside</u>.
20. The horse ran <u>away</u>.
21. Were you <u>there</u>?
22. Mom is <u>inside</u>.
23. Go <u>west</u>.
24. The car is getting <u>closer</u>.
25. Why don't you live <u>here</u>?
26. It is beautiful <u>outside</u>.
27. I want to go <u>everywhere</u>.
28. The shy kitten moved <u>closer</u>.
29. Thomas lives <u>nearby</u>.
30. Take the food <u>inside</u>.
31. Who lives <u>upstairs</u>?
32. The store is <u>downtown</u>.
33. I work <u>here</u>.
34. The mouse hurried <u>away</u>.
35. She is sitting <u>there</u>.
36. Jill wants to go <u>home</u>.
37. I can't find it <u>anywhere</u>.
38. Janet is <u>downstairs</u>.
39. Why don't you lie <u>down</u>?
40. Come <u>in</u>.
41. I have to hurry <u>home</u>.
42. Karen moved <u>away</u>.
43. The dog ran <u>outside</u>.
44. This bus goes <u>downtown</u>.
45. Show him <u>out</u>.
46. Gary lives <u>there</u>.
47. Take your friend <u>upstairs</u>.
48. We will stay <u>nearby</u>.
49. I will wait <u>here</u>.
50. We never go <u>anywhere</u>.

COMPOSITION EXERCISE

List 28 adverbs that tell where.

1. _____
2. _____
3. _____
4. _____
5. _____
6. _____
7. _____
8. _____
9. _____
10. _____
11. _____
12. _____
13. _____
14. _____
15. _____
16. _____
17. _____
18. _____
19. _____
20. _____
21. _____
22. _____
23. _____
24. _____
25. _____
26. _____
27. _____
28. _____

Choosing Correctly Spelled Adverbs Unit 39

An adverb is a word which shows when, where, why, or how.

EXAMPLES: a. Barry is leaving <u>today</u>.
b. You don't live <u>here</u>.
c. <u>Suddenly</u> it stormed.

 Complete each sentence with the adverb which is spelled correctly.

1. __*Sometimes*__ I argue with myself.
   (a) Sumtimes (b) Sometimes (c) Somtimes

2. Henry __**ALWAYS**__ wears that red cap.
   (a) always (b) allways (c) alsways

3. __**YESTERDAY**__ was Wednesday.
   (a) Yesturday (b) Yestirday (c) Yesterday

4. The front lock was fastened __**SECURELY**__.
   (a) sekurely (b) securly (c) securely

5. Paper was flying __**EVERYWHERE**__.
   (a) everwhere (b) everywhere (c) everywher

6. I __**OFTEN**__ wonder what happened to him.
   (a) ofen (b) often (c) offten

7. Please try to come __**EARLY**__.
   (a) early (b) urly (c) earley

8. Finish your work __**QUICKLY**__.
   (a) qwickly (b) quickly (c) kwickly

9. Adam has __**NEVER**__ been to Mexico.
   (a) never (b) niver (c) nevur

10. He was __**NOWHERE**__ to be found.
    (a) nowher (b) nowhere (c) no where

11. __**FINALLY**__ we gave up.
    (a) Finaly (b) Finally (c) Finnally

12. She smiled __**SADLY**__.
    (a) saddly (b) sadly (c) sadley

13. __**EAGERLY**__ Don accepted the proposal.
    (a) Eagerly (b) Egerly (c) Eagurly

14. Brad is __**FOREVER**__ asking questions.
    (a) forevir (b) forevor (c) forever

15. The mountain towered __**MAJESTICALLY**__.
    (a) majestically (b) magestically (c) majestikally

16. Mom waited __**PATIENTLY**__.
    (a) patently (b) patiently (c) patintly

17. I __**SINCERELY**__ regret my decision.
    (a) sincerely (b) sincerly (c) sincerelly

18. John __**CAREFULLY**__ lifted the box.
    (a) carfully (b) carefuly (c) carefully

19. I waited __**ANXIOUSLY**__ for the mail.
    (a) anxshusly (b) anxiously (c) anxiusly

20. Les __**USUALLY**__ drinks milk for lunch.
    (a) usually (b) ussualy (c) usualy

21. Spread the paint __**EVENLY**__.
    (a) evinly (b) evenly (c) evenlly

22. I'll call you __**TONIGHT**__.
    (a) tunight (b) tonit (c) tonight

23. She answered each one __**CORRECTLY**__.
    (a) korrectly (b) corectly (c) correctly

24. __**SUDDENLY**__ it began to rain.
    (a) Suddenly (b) Suddinly (c) Sudenly

25. Won't you come __**INSIDE**__?
    (a) innside (b) inside (c) insside

26. Your room is __**UPSTAIRS**__.
    (a) upstares (b) upstairz (c) upstairs

27. The boy __**SELDOM**__ speaks.
    (a) selldom (b) seldom (c) seldim

28. Step __**FORWARD**__.
    (a) forward (b) forword (c) forwerd

29. School begins __**TODAY**__.
    (a) tuday (b) todaey (c) today

30. Paul comes here __**FREQUENTLY**__.
    (a) frequently (b) freqwently (c) frequintly

31. The man spoke __**TACTLESSLY**__.
    (a) tactlessly (b) taklessly (c) tactlesly

32. You were __**DIRECTLY**__ responsible.
    (a) direkly (b) directly (c) directley

33. __**HOPEFULLY**__ it's not too late.
    (a) Hopefuly (b) Hopefully (c) Hopfully

34. __**CAUTIOUSLY**__ he opened the door.
    (a) Cautiously (b) Cautiusly (c) Cawtiously

Unit 39 cont'd →

Prepositions

Prepositions are words that show what relationship one word has to another.

EXAMPLES:
  a. *for James*   d. *with Eric*   g. *up the stairs*
  b. *in the house*   e. *over the hill*   h. *by herself*
  c. *to the rescue*   f. *among the ruins* i. *at school*

A Underline the prepositions.

1. of	26. nest
2. under	27. through
3. words	28. behind
4. in	29. ice
5. are	30. between
6. from	31. down
7. by	32. up
8. at	33. floor
9. crash	34. within
10. storm	35. above
11. around	36. is
12. for	37. except
13. Mike	38. ten
14. into	39. inside
15. number	40. table
16. over	41. without
17. to	42. flower
18. toward	43. music
19. head	44. outside
20. across	45. bank
21. after	46. out of
22. paper	47. in front of
23. on	48. George
24. ring	49. until
25. with	50. against

B Write a preposition in each blank.

1.	*in* the morning	26.	BETWEEN us
2.	FROM Alex	27.	ABOVE the clouds
3.	FOR an hour	28.	WITH her mother
4.	OVER the fence	29.	DOWN the road
5.	ACROSS the street	30.	UP the tree
6.	UNDER the house	31.	OUT OF my room
7.	AFTER class	32.	EXCEPT me
8.	OF the book	33.	INSIDE the box
9.	INTO the car	34.	FOR Janice
10.	ON my head	35.	UNDER the sofa
11.	BY the window	36.	ON the table
12.	WITH a friend	37.	DOWN the hill
13.	IN the chair	38.	AT noon
14.	AT the meeting	39.	ON time
15.	UNTIL January	40.	TO the edge
16.	OUTSIDE our home	41.	ACROSS the river
17.	AROUND the corner	42.	FROM the store
18.	TO Sam's house	43.	WITHOUT a doubt
19.	IN the hall	44.	BETWEEN the pages
20.	TOWARD the center	45.	UNTIL tomorrow
21.	AGAINST the door	46.	OVER the rainbow
22.	BEHIND his father	47.	IN your eye
23.	BY train	48.	WITH a pencil
24.	ON his nose	49.	BY Mark Twain
25.	WITHOUT help	50.	ON television

COMPOSITION EXERCISE

Use 24 prepositions from part A and write prepositional phrases.

1. _____	9. _____	17. _____
2. _____	10. _____	18. _____
3. _____	11. _____	19. _____
4. _____	12. _____	20. _____
5. _____	13. _____	21. _____
6. _____	14. _____	22. _____
7. _____	15. _____	23. _____
8. _____	16. _____	24. _____

The Conjunction

*Conjunctions are connecting words. Common
conjunctions are "and," "but," and "or."*

EXAMPLES: a. *The man is rich and famous.*   c. *Is Michael short or tall?*
              b. *Read the book, and write a report.*   d. *He aimed carefully but missed.*

In each blank write a conjunction.

1. Dave __and__ I will defend you.
2. Take a pen __AND__ pencil.
3. I ate not one __BUT__ six cakes.
4. Choose Karen __OR__ Doris.
5. Do you need Paul __OR__ me?
6. The show is on Tuesday __AND__ Friday.
7. Go home __OR__ stay here.
8. Not John __BUT__ Al is responsible.
9. Kay ran away __AND__ hid.
10. Is the dog a collie __OR__ a poodle?
11. We had lunch __BUT__ not dinner.
12. The boy pushed __AND__ pulled.
13. Was that Sue __OR__ Kate?
14. I can skate __AND__ swim.
15. Is she calling you __OR__ me?
16. Are they friends __OR__ enemies?
17. Will you bring apples __OR__ bananas?
18. Did she choose red __OR__ orange?
19. The river was wide __AND__ deep.
20. Answer yes __OR__ no.
21. I saw a zebra __AND__ an elephant.
22. Runners were on first __AND__ second.
23. You __AND__ his are pronouns.
24. Mr. James is old __BUT__ wise.
25. Your mom __AND__ dad must attend.
26. We must fight __OR__ surrender.
27. Diane __AND__ Steve are twins.
28. Did you __OR__ Jan see the accident?
29. Perry __AND__ Chris were elected.
30. It took Jay __AND__ Phil to hold him.
31. We had peas __AND__ carrots.
32. She is cute __BUT__ not pretty.
33. Ms. Kay brought pencils __AND__ paper.
34. I like math __AND__ science.
35. Did you invite Jack __OR__ Pam?
36. Pete __AND__ Lee tied for first place.
37. The water was cold __AND__ dirty.
38. We ate sandwiches __AND__ drank Cokes.
39. The baby yawned __AND__ fell asleep.
40. Candy is sweet, __BUT__ lemons are sour.
41. Yellow __AND__ green are my favorite colors.
42. Don __AND__ I are neighbors.
43. Bring me a hammer __AND__ a nail.
44. I have a brother __AND__ two sisters.
45. Am I invited __OR__ not?
46. Is the answer true __OR__ false?
47. Tim is small __BUT__ strong.
48. Do you want a fork __OR__ a spoon?
49. He opened the door __AND__ walked inside.
50. The advice was helpful __BUT__ unwanted.

COMPOSITION EXERCISE

Write two sentences with each of these conjunctions.

1. and

_____

_____

2. but

_____

_____

3. or

_____

_____

Unit 40 cont'd

Using "And" and "Or"

"And" and "or" are conjunctions. They join together two or more words or ideas.

EXAMPLES: a. this or that
              b. you and me
              c. pencil and paper
              d. true or false

 Write either "and" or "or" in each blank to make the sentence complete.

1. Dan __and__ Jan are twins.
2. Did you pick red __OR__ orange?
3. Do you want one __OR__ two?
4. I had cake __AND__ ice cream.
5. Answer true __OR__ false.
6. I have lived in Texas __AND__ Utah.
7. Ask George __AND__ Sara to come.
8. I need a hammer __AND__ nail.
9. Tell me now __OR__ never.
10. I have a dog, a cat, __AND__ a chicken.
11. Choose from box a, b, __OR__ c.
12. The dog was tired __AND__ hungry.
13. Open your eyes __AND__ ears.
14. Nouns are common __OR__ proper.
15. I ate bacon __AND__ eggs.
16. Is your bike yellow __OR__ red?
17. Did you pass __OR__ fail?
18. The winner will be Al __OR__ Gary.
19. You may print __OR__ write.
20. I always have butter __AND__ jelly.
21. Dennis __AND__ Jim are my friends.
22. Should we go north __OR__ south?
23. Wash your hands __AND__ face.
24. Was the test hard __OR__ easy?
25. Our flag is red, white, __AND__ blue.
26. Is Tim short __OR__ tall?
27. Mom __AND__ Dad are home.
28. Bring a pencil __AND__ paper.
29. I saw Mr. __AND__ Mrs. Lewis.
30. She will come by car __OR__ bus.
31. Are you coming __OR__ going?
32. We planted roses __AND__ daisies.
33. They are brother __AND__ sister.
34. Will you __OR__ won't you?
35. I will wear a hat __AND__ coat.
36. We had toast __AND__ jam.
37. Was the ending happy __OR__ sad?
38. We need milk __AND__ bread.
39. Did you buy apples __OR__ oranges?
40. Should we walk __OR__ ride?
41. Is __AND__ are are helping verbs.
42. I bought cookies __AND__ candy.
43. Was the show good __OR__ bad?
44. Everyone bring crayons __AND__ glue.
45. Do you live in town __OR__ in the country?
46. Sam __AND__ I ride the same bus.
47. Are your eyes brown __OR__ blue?
48. I want Joe __AND__ Jill to come.
49. Will you come today __OR__ tomorrow?
50. Tell me yes __OR__ no.

COMPOSITION EXERCISE

Write 6 sentences which contain "and" and 6 which contain "or."

and

1. _____
2. _____
3. _____
4. _____
5. _____
6. _____

or

1. _____
2. _____
3. _____
4. _____
5. _____
6. _____

Comprehension Check

Ⓐ Add the adjectives.

1. __Butterscotch__ pudding is my favorite.
2. We planted __pine__ trees in back.
3. __Six__ people have not registered.
4. The __blonde__ boy is named Ralph.
5. Do you have __eight__ pennies?
6. Our __baseball__ uniforms are gray.
7. __Math__ books are now on sale.
8. Do you like __fudge__ cakes?
9. I sent Julie a __birthday__ card.
10. He bought a __riding__ lawnmower.
11. We can pick up __sixty__ channels.
12. Jon prefers __country__ music to rock.
13. __Two__ halves make a whole.
14. The pie makes __four__ servings.
15. My sister drives a __red__ jeep.
16. The __old__ truck won't start.
17. Minnie misplaced her __house__ key.
18. Will you work this __algebra__ problem?
19. The __history__ exam is Thursday.
20. Where is your __science__ homework?

Ⓑ Underline the adverbs.

1. <u>Suddenly</u> it began to rain.
2. Can we go <u>home</u> <u>soon</u>?
3. Let's try the number <u>again</u>.
4. They <u>immediately</u> stopped the car.
5. We must <u>somehow</u> try to stop him.
6. It <u>always</u> works for Pamela.
7. The bus <u>never</u> comes before noon.
8. Suzanne worked the problem <u>easily</u>.
9. Norman will mow the lawn <u>Friday</u>.
10. <u>Now</u> the thing works.
11. You could have told me <u>sooner</u>.
12. The room <u>upstairs</u> is for rent.
13. Spread the icing <u>evenly</u>.
14. Brad couldn't meet with us <u>today</u>.
15. Should I turn <u>right</u> or <u>left</u>?
16. I met him <u>yesterday</u>.
17. Wesley began the speech <u>again</u>.
18. No one <u>ever</u> tells me anything.
19. <u>Lately</u> everything has gone wrong.
20. I'm hungry <u>now</u>!

Ⓒ Underline the adverb in each sentence. Then identify if it tells when or where.

___when___ 1. Jim is <u>always</u> considerate.
___where___ 2. Kelly sits <u>here</u> beside Jason.
___where___ 3. The puppy followed me <u>home</u>.
___when___ 4. Christi will <u>never</u> believe that.
___when___ 5. It will be delivered <u>tomorrow</u>.
___where___ 6. Someone lives <u>here</u>!
___where___ 7. The birds flew <u>away</u>.
___when___ 8. Theodore's cat <u>always</u> bites me.
___where___ 9. Go <u>north</u> to Wilkins Street.
___where___ 10. Put the map <u>inside</u>.
___where___ 11. The mouse scampered <u>across</u>.
___when___ 12. The paper comes <u>daily</u>.
___where___ 13. Stop at the light and turn <u>left</u>.
___when___ 14. <u>Now</u> we understand.
___when___ 15. Can you come <u>earlier</u> than Rex?
___where___ 16. The beans spilled <u>everywhere</u>.
___when___ 17. The police came <u>immediately</u>.
___where___ 18. Lonnie was <u>nowhere</u> to be seen.
___when___ 19. Tashia <u>usually</u> drinks water.
___where___ 20. It crawled <u>under</u> and waited.
___where___ 21. The mail fell <u>out</u>.
___when___ 22. Lionel asked her <u>first</u>.
___when___ 23. The report is published <u>monthly</u>.
___where___ 24. Julius set the box <u>there</u>.

Test 8 cont'd →

Comprehension Check (continued)

D Add the preposition to complete each phrase.

1. __under__ the door
   __in front ot__ the door
   __behind__ the door

2. __over__ Paul's head
   __on__ Paul's head
   __beside__ Paul's head

3. __from__ the country
   __to__ the country
   __in__ the country

4. __with__ you and me
   __between__ you and me
   __for__ you and me

5. __for__ your birthday
   __before__ your birthday
   __after__ your birthday

6. __with__ Andrew
   __without__ Andrew
   __except__ Andrew

7. __to__ Australia
   __from__ Australia
   __in__ Australia

8. __after__ math class
   __during__ math class
   __until__ math class

E Underline the prepositions.

1. Katherine walked to the mailbox.
2. I read the book by Scott.
3. Park your car behind that one.
4. Don't look inside the box yet.
5. No one wanted waffles for breakfast.
6. It looks like a giant octopus.
7. They sat at the window.
8. Meet me after the movie.
9. The look in his eyes was sadness.
10. Frank brought a copy for David.
11. The bird flew over our heads.
12. On her arm was a black arm band.
13. George eats ketchup with everything.
14. The song on the radio made me smile.
15. Stevie moved to Boston from Westport.

F Add the conjunctions.

1. Kenneth __and__ Jean ordered a pizza.
2. She will ask Harry __or__ Richard.
3. They talked __and__ laughed for hours.
4. Did anyone call __or__ come by?
5. Adam __and__ Elton sang a duet.
6. Would you rather have soup __or__ stew?
7. I'm taking journalism __and__ typing.
8. You __or__ I must warn him!
9. Should I choose Poe __or__ Twain?
10. Blake completed A, B, __and__ C.
11. Stanley __and__ Shirley are siblings.
12. You can have one __or__ the other.
13. Cards __and__ letters are welcome.
14. Answer yes __or__ no to these questions.
15. Who ate the cookies __and__ cupcakes?

Write a paragraph about travelling. Underline your prepositional phrases.

_____
_____
_____
_____
_____
_____
_____
_____
_____

Interjections!

An interjection is a word that expresses a very strong emotion. It is followed by an exclamation point.

EXAMPLES:
a. <u>Yes!</u> I want one.
b. <u>Help!</u> I fell down.
c. <u>Ouch!</u> You hit me.
d. <u>Gee!</u> That sounds great.

A Identify the interjections by placing an exclamation point after each one.

1. **OUCH!**	11. Three	21. Good!	31. Wait!
2. Sometimes	12. Oh!	22. Bah!	32. Fine!
3. Surprise!	13. Help!	23. Hurry!	33. Home
4. Tomorrow	14. Now	24. Always	34. Yes!
5. Rats!	15. Heavens!	25. Golly!	35. Go
6. My!	16. Everything	26. Find	36. Here
7. None	17. Stop!	27. Goodness!	37. Wow!
8. Hurrah!	18. Gosh!	28. Yesterday	38. Happy Birthday!
9. Gee!	19. Looking	29. Hey!	39. Soon
10. Well!	20. No!	30. Fishing	40. Alas!

B In each blank write an interjection.

1.	*Help!*	I'm drowning!	13.	OUCH!	That hurts.
2.	WAIT!	You left one.	14.	ALAS!	It's over.
3.	GEE!	That's terrific.	15.	HURRY!	He'll catch you.
4.	WOW!	What a game that was.	16.	NO!	You can't come.
5.	GOOD!	I'm glad you made it.	17.	HURRAY!	We won again.
6.	GEE!	Did you do this?	18.	WELL!	You could have told me.
7.	HEY!	You come back here.	19.	OH!	That's my foot.
8.	STOP!	I won't hurt you.	20.	GOSH!	I'm sorry.
9.	GOODNESS!	Is it that late?	21.	FINE!	How are you?
10.	YES!	I'd love to go.	22.	HEY!	I'm talking to you.
11.	HELP!	I'm hurt!	23.	HURRY!	It's getting late.
12.	BAH!	That was terrible.	24.	RATS!	We lost.

COMPOSITION EXERCISE

Choose 14 interjections from part A. Write a sentence with each.

1. _____
2. _____
3. _____
4. _____
5. _____
6. _____
7. _____
8. _____
9. _____
10. _____
11. _____
12. _____
13. _____
14. _____

Unit 41 cont'd

Adding Interjections

Interjections are words that express strong feelings. Exclamation points follow them.

EXAMPLES: a. <u>Rats!</u> I struck out.   c. <u>Hey!</u> Who are you?
           b. <u>Stop!</u> You'll get hurt.   d. <u>Wait!</u> I'll help you.

 In each blank write an interjection. Punctuate each interjection properly.

1. __Ouch!__ That hurts.
2. __WAIT!__ You forgot me.
3. __STOP!__ You can't do that.
4. __WOW!__ Did you see that?
5. __HEY!__ Who did this?
6. __BOY!__ He is strong.
7. __OH!__ How could you?
8. __WELL!__ Did you hear that?
9. __AH!__ That was a good meal.
10. __ALAS!__ We lost.
11. __HEAVENS!__ It's 5 o'clock.
12. __FINE!__ Now we can begin.
13. __NO!__ I won't help you.
14. __GEE!__ You're nice.
15. __WHY!__ It's for me.
16. __GOSH!__ We're late.
17. __MY!__ What a beautiful day this is.
18. __BAH!__ That's a silly idea.
19. __SURPRISE!__ I'm home.
20. __YES!__ I'd love to go.
21. __HUMBUG!__ I hate holidays.
22. __HURRY!__ It's raining again.
23. __RATS!__ I missed it.
24. __GOOD!__ He deserved it.
25. __HELP!__ I can't move.

26. __BAH!__ It tastes terrible.
27. __WELL!__ What can I do?
28. __YES!__ I made it.
29. __GOOD!__ Now we can eat.
30. __AH!__ That's a relief.
31. __NO!__ Don't come in here.
32. __SURPRISE!__ It's I.
33. __RATS!__ Report cards are today.
34. __BOY!__ This game is great.
35. __STOP!__ You're taking my car.
36. __OUCH!__ Be careful.
37. __OH!__ You don't mean that.
38. __HURRY!__ She'll see you.
39. __WAIT!__ I'm coming.
40. __HELP!__ I can't swim.
41. __MY!__ You've worked all day.
42. __GEE!__ I'm glad you came.
43. __HUMBUG!__ Thanksgiving is a bore.
44. __WHY!__ Here comes Terry.
45. __FINE!__ You did it perfectly.
46. __HEAVENS!__ What will we do?
47. __ALAS!__ She broke my heart.
48. __SEE!__ I can do it.
49. __HEY!__ You stop that.
50. __WOW!__ It's another home run.

COMPOSITION EXERCISE

Write 14 sentences that begin with interjections.

1. _____
2. _____
3. _____
4. _____
5. _____
6. _____
7. _____
8. _____
9. _____
10. _____
11. _____
12. _____
13. _____
14. _____

Identifying Parts of Speech

1. **noun** — *names a person, place, or thing*
   children   home   tree
2. **pronoun** — *takes place of a noun*
   I   you   us
3. **verb** — *shows action or state of being*
   read   am   add
4. **adjective** — *describes a noun*
   skinny   green   four
5. **adverb** — *tells when, where, or how*
   now   here   suddenly
6. **conjunction** — *connects*
   and   but   or
7. **interjection** — *shows strong feelings*
   Ouch!   Wait!   Help!
8. **preposition** — *shows word relationships*
   in   with   under

✳ **Identify the parts of each underlined word.**
N — noun   P — pronoun   V — verb   Adj. — adjective
ADV — adverb   CON — conjunction   INT — interjection   PR — preposition

N	1. The <u>house</u> was built in 1901.
P	2. <u>He</u> is the star player.
V	3. Dave <u>smashed</u> the vase.
ADJ	4. I bought a <u>yellow</u> hat.
ADV	5. Come <u>now</u>.
CON	6. You <u>and</u> I are going.
INT	7. <u>Wow</u>! What a game that was.
PR	8. Run <u>to</u> the house.
N	9. Josh is an <u>astronaut</u>.
ADJ	10. This is a <u>good</u> book.
P	11. <u>It</u> has stopped raining.
PR	12. Put the box <u>on</u> the floor.
CON	13. I ate not one <u>but</u> six pies.
INT	14. <u>Hurray</u>! We won.
P	15. <u>You</u> are in trouble.
CON	16. Paul <u>and</u> Isaac raced.
ADV	17. He <u>always</u> finishes first.
ADJ	18. The <u>second</u> car is on fire.
V	19. I <u>love</u> it.
N	20. These <u>vegetables</u> are fresh.
V	21. Don <u>pushed</u> the car.
V	22. I <u>am</u> Stephen.
CON	23. They were blue <u>and</u> white.

PR	24. The dog is <u>under</u> the porch.
CON	25. Choose Barry <u>or</u> me.
N	26. The <u>swing</u> is broken.
P	27. <u>I</u> need $30.00.
P	28. Where did <u>she</u> go?
N	29. <u>Bill</u> works for my dad.
V	30. Eve <u>fell</u> on the ice.
ADJ	31. That is a <u>dangerous</u> animal.
V	32. <u>Is</u> this yours?
INT	33. <u>Ouch</u>! You stuck me.
CON	34. Lee <u>and</u> George will help.
ADJ	35. We found an <u>old</u> trunk.
ADV	36. <u>Sometimes</u> I can't sleep.
V	37. The child is <u>crying</u> again.
P	38. Have <u>they</u> called yet?
N	39. The <u>trip</u> is postponed.
INT	40. <u>Well</u>! You could warn me.
ADJ	41. <u>My</u> sister has already gone.
PR	42. Take Gina <u>into</u> the kitchen.
V	43. I <u>will see</u> him Thursday.
N	44. <u>James</u> filled the box.
CON	45. She sings <u>and</u> dances.
ADV	46. Everyone must leave <u>now</u>.

COMPOSITION EXERCISE

List the 8 parts of speech. Then list one example for each part.

1. _____
2. _____
3. _____
4. _____

5. _____
6. _____
7. _____
8. _____

103

Unit 42 cont'd ➡

Changing Parts of Speech

Sometimes the same word can function as different parts of speech. It may have to take on additional prefixes and suffixes, but its part of speech is determined by its use in a sentence. For example, notice how the word "order" changes from a noun to a verb to an adjective in these three sentences:

noun: I gave you an order.
verb: Kevin did order the tuna salad.
adjective: Fill out the order blank.

 Identify the part of speech of each underlined word. Write "1" for noun, "2" for verb, and "3" for adjective.

1   1. A small crowd gathered around us.
3   2. I felt uncomfortable in the crowded room.
2   3. Ten people crowded into the elevator.

3   4. He is an escaped convict.
1   5. The prisoners planned their escape.
2   6. The man escaped on July 22.

2   7. The incident troubled Dan.
1   8. I think we're in trouble.
3   9. Jill gave me a troubled look.

3   10. The reward money was stolen.
2   11. The winner was rewarded a trophy.
1   12. The reward was fifty dollars.

1   13. Gilda has a good suggestion.
2   14. Mr. Price suggested we think it over.
3   15. Put your idea in the suggestion box.

2   16. Welcome our guests.
1   17. Tim was given a warm welcome.
3   18. Mother bought a new welcome mat.

2   19. Frank changed his mind again.
1   20. Everyone was ready for a change.
3   21. My change purse has a hole in it.

1   22. The scale is broken.
3   23. Isaac did a scale drawing.
2   24. Mark scaled the wall.

2   25. Eric promised to bring the book.
3   26. The deal sounds promising.
1   27. I never break a promise.

1   28. Call the police.
2   29. The army policed the area carefully.
3   30. I've never ridden in a police car.

1   31. Storms frighten me.
3   32. We slept in the storm cellar.
2   33. It stormed again last night.

2   34. Joan watered the flowers.
3   35. The water buffalo lives there.
1   36. The water was cool and refreshing.

2   37. The captain commanded his troops to stop.
3   38. The singer gave a command performance.
1   39. He disobeyed your command.

2   40. We surprised you.
3   41. Kelly gave Sue a surprise party.
1   42. This is a pleasant surprise!

2   43. She headed the ship for home.
3   44. Phil is the head officer.
1   45. Move your head to the right.

2   46. Ms. Young graded our tests.
1   47. Vera always makes good grades.
3   48. The teacher lost her grade book.

No-Words

A no-word is a word that means "no."

no	*none*	*never*	*no one*
nothing	*nowhere*	*not*	*nobody*

✱ **Fill in each blank with a no-word. Choose from the words listed in the example box.**

1. __No one__ came.
2. There are __NO__ answers.
3. I have __NONE__.
4. Sheila is __NOT__ home.
5. Jeff is __NEVER__ late.
6. __NOTHING__ was in the box.
7. He is __NOBODY__.
8. __NO ONE__ called.
9. We found __NOTHING__.
10. __NO ONE__ answered her.
11. The man could __NOT__ stay.
12. I am going __NOWHERE__.
13. Pat is __NOT__ my sister.
14. __NO ONE__ was there.
15. That is __NOT__ the answer.
16. __NOTHING__ was left.
17. We __NEVER__ go anywhere.
18. __NOBODY__ likes me.
19. I did __NOT__ see her.
20. Tom has __NO__ brothers.
21. __NOTHING__ can help.
22. The mail has __NOT__ come.
23. __NO ONE__ heard her.
24. I knew __NOTHING__ about it.
25. I could __NOT__ sleep.

26. I am __NOT__ going.
27. You __NEVER__ smile.
28. That is __NOT__ funny.
29. The dog was __NOWHERE__.
30. The man had __NONE__.
31. __NOBODY__ told us.
32. Roy is __NOT__ happy.
33. __NOBODY__ wants to go.
34. Jim __NEVER__ does his homework.
35. The bird could __NOT__ fly.
36. __NO__ answers were given.
37. __NOTHING__ tastes good.
38. He was __NOT__ invited.
39. There is __NO__ school today.
40. __NONE__ of you failed.
41. George does __NOT__ swim.
42. __NOTHING__ was found.
43. We have __NO__ money.
44. Fran is __NOT__ absent.
45. __NO ONE__ called you.
46. There is __NOTHING__ here.
47. I have __NEVER__ danced.
48. Jay could __NOT__ eat.
49. __NO ONE__ saw me leave.
50. We __NEVER__ go to the zoo.

COMPOSITION EXERCISE

Write 12 sentences which contain no-words.

1. _____
2. _____
3. _____
4. _____
5. _____
6. _____

7. _____
8. _____
9. _____
10. _____
11. _____
12. _____

Unit 43 cont'd

No-Words and Not-Words

A no-word is one that means "no." A not-word is a contraction made with a verb plus the word "not." Never use a no-word and a not-word in the same sentence.

EXAMPLES:
a. He wouldn't give none.
   He wouldn't give any.

b. The train ain't never on time.
   The train is never on time.

 Rewrite each sentence correctly.

1. I don't have none.
   I don't have any.

2. I could not find nothing.
   I could find nothing.

3. We didn't see nobody.
   We didn't see anyone.

4. Nothing never goes right.
   Nothing ever goes right.

5. I can't do nothing.
   I can't do anything.

6. I won't never tell.
   I will never tell.

7. It ain't nowhere.
   It isn't anywhere.

8. No one knows nothing.
   No one knows anything.

9. You don't never call.
   You never call.

10. Jake wouldn't talk to nobody.
    Jake wouldn't talk to anybody.

11. I don't see no lights.
    I don't see any lights.

12. There wasn't no one.
    There wasn't anyone.

13. No one never told me.
    No one ever told me.

14. It hasn't never worked.
    It has never worked.

15. He's not no doctor.
    He's not a doctor.

16. That man ain't no friend.
    That man is no friend.

17. It doesn't look no good.
    It doesn't look good.

18. I couldn't see no one.
    I couldn't see anyone.

19. This isn't no picnic.
    This isn't a picnic.

20. I'm not going nowhere.
    I'm not going anywhere.

21. There isn't none left.
    There isn't any left.

22. The decision wasn't no good.
    The decision was no good.

23. The dog won't never come back.
    The dog will never come back.

24. He ain't never on time.
    He is never on time.

COMPOSITION EXERCISE

Write 12 sentences which contain no-words or not-words.

1. _____
2. _____
3. _____
4. _____
5. _____
6. _____

7. _____
8. _____
9. _____
10. _____
11. _____
12. _____

Contractions

A contraction is two words joined as one. An apostrophe is used to show where letters have been left out.

EXAMPLES:
a. is + not = isn't
b. would + not = wouldn't

c. he + is = he's
c. will + not = won't

A Matching

e	1. I'm	a.	has + not
X	2. isn't	b.	he + is
S	3. aren't	c.	we + are
L	4. wasn't	d.	can + not
Q	5. weren't	e.	I + am
A	6. hasn't	f.	will + not
V	7. haven't	g.	could + not
D	8. can't	h.	you + are
P	9. don't	i.	I + had
J	10. didn't	j.	did + not
F	11. won't	k.	she + had
O	12. shouldn't	l.	was + not
T	13. wouldn't	m.	I + have
G	14. couldn't	n.	it + is
B	15. he's	o.	should + not
Y	16. she's	p.	do + not
U	17. he'd	q.	were + not
K	18. she'd	r.	we + had
N	19. it's	s.	are + not
H	20. you're	t.	would + not
C	21. we're	u.	he + had
R	22. we'd	v.	have + not
I	23. I'd	w.	they + are
W	24. they're	x.	is + not
M	25. I've	y.	she + is

B Write the contractions of the words in parentheses.

1. (I am) __I'm__ hungry.
2. (can not) I __CAN'T__ go.
3. (are not) You __AREN'T__ ready.
4. (he is) __HE'S__ fixing the car.
5. (we are) __WE'RE__ leaving.
6. (was not) That __WASN'T__ fair.
7. (will not) I __WON'T__ tell you.
8. (did not) They __DIDN'T__ answer.
9. (I had) __I'D__ seen the show.
10. (have not) We __HAVEN'T__ any money.
11. (it is) __IT'S__ over.
12. (is not) She __ISN'T__ coming.
13. (should not) You __SHOULDN'T__ do that.
14. (she had) __SHE'D__ cut her finger.
15. (we had) __WE'D__ stayed too long.
16. (would not) He __WOULDN'T__ move.
17. (were not) They __WEREN'T__ at home.
18. (has not) He __HASN'T__ called.
19. (could not) Dave __COULDN'T__ see him.
20. (do not) I __DON'T__ know.
21. (she is) __SHE'S__ unhappy.
22. (you are) __YOU'RE__ standing on me.
23. (I have) __I'VE__ finished.
24. (he had) __HE'D__ planned to go.
25. (they are) __THEY'RE__ outside.

COMPOSITION EXERCISE

Write 12 sentences which contain contractions.

1. _____
2. _____
3. _____
4. _____
5. _____
6. _____

7. _____
8. _____
9. _____
10. _____
11. _____
12. _____

Unit 44 cont'd ➡

What Is a Sentence?

A sentence is a group of words that expresses a complete thought.

EXAMPLES:
   a. I cannot hear you.
   b. She knows the secret.
   c. Sam goes swimming every day.
   d. This house is my home.

 Underline the complete sentences.

1. <u>Mother hates to cook.</u>
2. On the bus sitting.
3. <u>Everyone was angry</u>.
4. Around the corner.
5. If it doesn't work.
6. <u>No one is home.</u>
7. Or the ending.
8. <u>We collected sea shells</u>.
9. <u>The answers are correct</u>.
10. <u>The story is very sad</u>.
11. One at a time.
12. <u>The ocean is enormous</u>.
13. Until tomorrow.
14. In every state.
15. <u>Grandma will arrive tomorrow</u>.
16. Within an hour.
17. <u>The car moved slowly</u>.
18. During the movie.
19. Lisa, Angie, Sue, and I.
20. <u>They had already gone</u>.
21. <u>I will see you in the morning</u>.
22. Wearing my jacket.
23. <u>I met Bob at the party</u>.
24. Going to run away.
25. <u>My dad is a pilot</u>.
26. <u>The pictures were beautiful</u>.
27. <u>Here comes our teacher</u>.
28. Always the last one.
29. <u>I don't want to eat</u>.
30. Closing the windows.
31. Maybe not.
32. <u>We must leave quickly</u>.
33. A sure way.
34. <u>Tomorrow is the last day</u>.
35. <u>The policeman caught the robbers</u>.
36. Have been here.
37. Away from me.
38. In a long time.
39. <u>We are ready to begin</u>.
40. With a smile.
41. Against a brick wall.
42. <u>The wagon costs $20.00</u>.
43. <u>He planted the trees</u>.
44. <u>I will help you tomorrow</u>.
45. From your answers.
46. Sneezing and coughing.
47. <u>We want to buy a horse</u>.
48. Over the fence and under a car.
49. <u>Karen painted the picture</u>.
50. John, Alex, and Eric.

COMPOSITION EXERCISE

Write 12 sentences about hobbies.

1. _____
2. _____
3. _____
4. _____
5. _____
6. _____
7. _____
8. _____
9. _____
10. _____
11. _____
12. _____

Identifying Sentences

A sentence is a group of words that expresses a complete thought.

EXAMPLES: a. The equipment has arrived.
          b. The road was repaired.

c. Paul sounded furious.
d. Harriet has blue eyes.

 Underline the complete sentences.

1. Diane was chosen president.
2. A book fell from the shelf.
3. The children played hopscotch.
4. An angry bull.
5. There is a call for you.
6. Quietly walked away.
7. The music is too loud.
8. Without any help.
9. The clown made us laugh.
10. I pretended to be asleep.
11. Pushing and pulling.
12. She doesn't like us.
13. A bright light.
14. Six books on health.
15. Paul will win the contest.
16. An exciting ballgame.
17. The theft occurred yesterday.
18. He suffered a broken arm.
19. Took his son home.
20. Your questions are silly.
21. The jewels are fake.
22. Wanted to see Jan.
23. You have my permission.
24. Plants and shrubs.
25. I have confidence in you.

26. Watching and waiting.
27. Through the night.
28. The new plant is dying.
29. Baking all day.
30. This trailer is too small.
31. Sandy imagined a ghost.
32. Won't go away.
33. The wood burned slowly.
34. Candy is bad for your teeth.
35. He obeyed his orders.
36. Suddenly happened.
37. Tripped over the skates.
38. Charles opened the wrong door.
39. Right now.
40. The blanket is brown and green.
41. My homework is finished.
42. Groups of happy students.
43. Tammy stared at the animal.
44. Fished in the lake.
45. He was proud of his award.
46. Peter, Timothy, and Andy.
47. Sure to win.
48. We are interested in your plan.
49. The lot next door is vacant.
50. Because of the rain.

COMPOSITION EXERCISE

Write 12 complete sentences.

1. _____
2. _____
3. _____
4. _____
5. _____
6. _____

7. _____
8. _____
9. _____
10. _____
11. _____
12. _____

Unit 45 cont'd →

Word Order

Word order determines the sentence's meaning.

EXAMPLES: a. apples I picked
I picked apples.

b. you will I the show horse
I will show you the horse.

 Arrange the words so that each sentence's meaning is clear.

1. stopped bus quickly the
   The bus stopped quickly.

2. will horse Dave the buy
   Dave will buy the horse.

3. game I watching the was
   I was watching the game.

4. father knows my man that
   That man knows my father.

5. now 3 it o'clock is
   It is now 3 o'clock.

6. late you don't be
   Don't you be late.

7. huge are footprints the
   The footprints are huge.

8. will helper Mary choose a
   Mary will choose a helper.

9. under the the dog chair hid
   The dog hid under the chair.

10. a policeman our is neighbor
    Our neighbor is a policeman.

11. tomorrow the is picnic
    The picnic is tomorrow.

12. promised Jan come to
    Jan promised to come.

13. tree George climbed the
    George climbed the tree.

14. a he farmer is
    He is a farmer.

15. drew Lynn picture the
    Lynn drew the picture.

16. too long the is story
    The story is too long.

17. jumped frog the
    The frog jumped.

18. are the dirty dishes
    The dishes are dirty.

19. very lake is the deep
    The lake is very deep.

20. blooming the are roses
    The roses are blooming.

21. is food the delicious
    The food is delicious.

22. kites flew we our
    We flew our kites.

23. was the open gate
    The gate was open.

24. morning plane the the in leaves
    The plane leaves in the morning.

COMPOSITION EXERCISE

Write 8 sentences. Can you change the word order on any of your sentences?

1. _____

2. _____

3. _____

4. _____

5. _____

6. _____

7. _____

8. _____

110

Comprehension Check

Ⓐ Add the interjections.

1. _____Yea!_____ We scored a touchdown!
2. _____No!_____ It's starting to rain again.
3. _____Wait!_____ You forgot your coat.
4. _____Ouch!_____ That hurts!
5. _____Hey!_____ You can't go in there.

6. _____Help!_____ I can't swim!
7. _____Wow!_____ Did you see that jump?
8. _____Yes!_____ I want that job.
9. _____Listen!_____ Did you hear a knock?
10. _____Yuk!_____ That tastes awful.

Ⓑ Write a sentence for each of these situations. Begin each sentence with an interjection.

1. winning a trip to Los Angeles
   Yikes! I won the trip!

2. seeing a car accident
   Look out! They're going to hit!

3. making a 100 on a test
   Yeah! I did it!

4. getting a stereo for Christmas
   Wow! I got a stereo.

5. tasting burnt food
   Yuk! This food is burnt.

6. going to the dentist's office
   No! I won't go!

7. getting a shot at the doctor's office
   Ouch! I hate shots.

8. watching your favorite singer
   Oh! He's terrific.

9. falling down in the mud
   Oh no! I'm stuck in the mud.

10. seeing a ghost
    Help! It's a ghost!

Ⓒ Match each part of speech with its definition.

__b__ 1. noun
__f__ 2. pronoun
__e__ 3. verb
__h__ 4. adjective
__c__ 5. adverb
__d__ 6. preposition
__g__ 7. conjunction
__a__ 8. interjection

a. word that expresses strong emotion
b. word that names person, place, or thing
c. word that tells when or where or how
d. word that relates to other words in sentence
e. word that shows action or state of being
f. word that serves as noun substitute
g. word that connects
h. word that tells which one, what kind, how many, or what color

Ⓓ Identify the part of speech of each underlined word.

__adj.__ 1. Reggie wrote a good report.
__inter.__ 2. Hey! Don't do that again.
__verb__ 3. No one tried to stop us.
__noun__ 4. Put the mask on.
__conj.__ 5. I like to ski and to swim.
__prep.__ 6. Billy works at the drugstore.

__pron.__ 7. She can repair anything.
__adv.__ 8. Is Donna going home with you?
__noun__ 9. Jill wants to buy a motorcycle.
__verb__ 10. Ted slid into home.
__adv.__ 11. You must be there early.
__adj.__ 12. Brenda wore a plaid skirt.

Test 9 cont'd →

Comprehension Check (continued)

(E) **Underline the no-words and not-words.**

1. I <u>don't</u> like pizza or tacos.
2. Calvin <u>never</u> finishes what he starts.
3. The train will <u>not</u> arrive on schedule.
4. <u>Doesn't</u> he look familiar?
5. <u>Nobody</u> answered our ad.

6. I have <u>nothing</u> to say to you.
7. <u>No one</u> knew what to do next.
8. There <u>weren't</u> any more cookies.
9. <u>Isn't</u> that animal a gnu?
10. James does <u>not</u> have a motorcycle.

(F) **Rewrite each sentence correctly.**

1. I don't have no more.
   I don't have any more.

2. Jackie didn't want none.
   Jackie didn't want any.

3. It don't never leave on time.
   It never leaves on time.

4. We shouldn't never have told her.
   We should never have told her.

5. The clock isn't no alarm clock.
   The clock is not an alarm clock.

6. They hardly never come here.
   They hardly ever come here.

7. I can't do nothing right.
   I can't do anything right.

8. Sam didn't talk to nobody.
   Sam didn't talk to anyone.

9. He's not nowhere to be found.
   He's nowhere to be found.

10. We don't never do nothing.
    We never do anything.

(G) **Arrange each set of words into a sentence.**

1. tuna made Candace sandwiches the
   Candace made the tuna sandwiches.

2. Wednesday will on it rain
   It will rain on Wednesday.

3. the twice rung has doorbell
   The doorbell has rung twice.

4. heard slam I a door
   I heard a door slam.

5. all Lucy the answers knew
   Lucy knew all the answers.

6. a to I write have letter
   I have to write a letter.

7. Joey in put the the box closet
   Joey put the box in the closet.

8. fixed Mr. the car Denton
   Mr. Denton fixed the car.

9. his notes studied Alfred
   Alfred studied his notes.

10. your you camera forgot
    You forgot your camera.

Write a paragraph about things you dislike to do. Underline the no-words and not-words.

_____
_____
_____
_____
_____
_____

112

Changing Word Order

Word order is very important to a sentence's meaning. If you change the word order, you change the meaning.

Notice how word order affects the meaning of this sentence.
  My uncle plays the flute. The flute plays my uncle.

Even though we did not use any additional words or leave out any words, we have a completely different meaning in the second sentence.

Now let's change the word order in this sentence:
  Wilma read a poem by Keats. Keats read a poem by Wilma.

Although the second makes more sense than the one used in the first example, we still have a completely different meaning.

 Change the word order in each sentence, and write the new sentence on the blank.

1. The cat tried to catch the goldfish.
   The goldfish tried to catch the cat.

2. The frog turned into a handsome prince.
   The handsome prince turned into a frog.

3. The father scolded his son.
   The son scolded his father.

4. Roger owes Harry $1,000.
   Harry owes Roger $1,000.

5. Kim borrowed a book from Terry.
   Terry borrowed a book from Kim.

6. Wes copied from Thurmond.
   Thurmond copied from Wes.

7. The monkey chased the lion up a tree.
   The lion chased the monkey up a tree.

8. Isaac bought the puppy a collar.
   The puppy bought Isaac a collar.

9. The animal bit Rudy on the nose.
   Rudy bit the animal on the nose.

10. Arnie was frightened by the ghost.
    The ghost was frightened by Arnie.

11. The collie barked at the stranger.
    The stranger barked at the collie.

12. Kelly loaned Paula her book.
    Paula loaned Kelly her book.

13. Nancy purchased the car from Mr. Delzt.
    Mr. Delzt purchased the car from Nancy.

14. Janet lives next door to Aaron.
    Aaron lives next door to Janet.

15. Rob threw Louis into the lake.
    Louis threw Rob into the lake.

16. Sylvia voted for Debbie.
    Debbie voted for Sylvia.

17. Sam plays the piano better than Chris.
    Chris plays the piano better than Sam.

18. The barn is behind the house.
    The house is behind the barn.

19. The mother carried the baby upstairs.
    The baby carried the mother upstairs.

20. Liz is older than Aunt Sally.
    Aunt Sally is older than Liz.

21. The judge ordered Dean to be quiet.
    Dean ordered the judge to be quiet.

22. The car hit a pole.
    The pole hit a car.

23. I found the money under the rug.
    I found the rug under the money.

24. Ginger smiled at William.
    William smiled at Ginger.

25. Vicki saw Francis take the money.
    Francis saw Vicki take the money.

26. The witch became a beautiful princess.
    The beautiful princess became a witch.

27. Sterling Heights is a suburb of Detroit.
    Detroit is a suburb of Sterling Heights.

28. William went to college at Rutford.
    Rutford went to college at William.

Unit 46 cont'd ⟶

Arranging Words into Sentences

A sentence is a group of words that expresses a complete thought. Words in a sentence must come in a definite order so that the meaning is clear.

EXAMPLES: a. is favorite green color my
  Green is my favorite color.
  b. don't ghosts I in believe
  I don't believe in ghosts.

 Arrange each set of words into a sentence.

1. finally speech over his was
   His speech was finally over.

2. understand I the couldn't man
   I couldn't understand the man.

3. hour make sixty an minutes
   Sixty minutes make an hour.

4. never at she laughs jokes my
   She never laughs at my jokes.

5. delivers John after newspapers school
   John delivers newspapers after school.

6. umbrella I in car left my the
   I left my umbrella in the car.

7. Lynn history lesson studying is her
   Lynn is studying her history lesson.

8. contest won the Chris essay
   Chris won the essay contest.

9. ordered bowl soup Joe a of chicken
   Joe ordered a bowl of chicken soup.

10. your I advice need
    I need your advice.

11. did we our together homework
    We did our homework together.

12. usually at home Mr. lunch eats Redd
    Mr. Redd usually eats lunch at home.

13. meeting next Monday the is night
    The next meeting is Monday night.

14. bird nest built the a our in tree
    The bird built a nest in our tree.

15. not purple match and do green
    Purple and green do not match.

16. bike flat my tire has a
    My bike has a flat tire.

17. important is an education
    An education is important.

18. went her to Cheryl visit aunt
    Cheryl went to visit her aunt.

19. piano I'm lessons taking
    I'm taking piano lessons.

20. egg I the dropped the on floor
    I dropped the egg on the floor.

21. trouble I you think in are
    I think you are in trouble.

22. weighs the box pounds four
    The box weighs four pounds.

23. want job I a airport the at
    I want a job at the airport.

24. honest dependable is and Ben
    Ben is honest and dependable.

25. knock door was there a the on
    There was a knock on the door.

26. rain it will tomorrow
    It will rain tomorrow.

27. Patty keep secret a cannot
    Patty cannot keep a secret.

28. movie everyone the enjoyed
    Everyone enjoyed the movie.

29. noon the melted snow by
    The snow melted by noon.

30. list here is of a members the
    Here is a list of the members.

31. Ed another cake wants of piece
    Ed wants another piece of cake.

32. family a week spent the Mexico in
    The family spent a week in Mexico.

Subjects Plus Verbs

Every sentence must include a subject and a verb.

EXAMPLES: missing subject: *Hit a home run.*

missing verb: *The new player.*

What is missing from each sentence? Write "S" if there is no subject. Write "V" is there is no verb.

V	1.	This trip beautiful.
S	2.	Ran like the wind.
S	3.	Moved to the next row.
V	4.	The blue and white car.
S	5.	Will yell at you.
S	6.	Follows me home.
V	7.	The shy little boy.
V	8.	My sister and brother.
S	9.	Told me to stay here.
V	10.	The soft music.
V	11.	A large empty box.
S	12.	Likes to ski.
S	13.	Fixed the car.
S	14.	Are moving to the country.
V	15.	A shiny car quickly.
V	16.	The old man always.
S	17.	Sat on the wet bench.
S	18.	Comes every day.
V	19.	The last day of school.
S	20.	Wanted to buy my bike.
S	21.	Were crushed flat.
V	22.	The tall boy early.
S	23.	Hits me on the arm.
V	24.	A letter and a package.
S	25.	Is driving the school bus.

S	26.	Were making a mess.
V	27.	A sad smile.
V	28.	An interesting book.
S	29.	Found the answer.
S	30.	Has already gone.
V	31.	The last girl in line.
V	32.	Thursday a rainy day.
V	33.	A school bus home.
S	34.	Was looking everywhere.
S	35.	Gave an easy test.
V	36.	Everyone in the class.
S	37.	Caught the ball.
V	38.	A green frog nearby.
S	39.	Is snowing in New York.
V	40.	A man with a cane.
S	41.	Is listening to the rain.
S	42.	Are waiting for me.
V	43.	A brown and white dog.
V	44.	An empty basket.
S	45.	Took him for a walk.
S	46.	Sang a sad song.
V	47.	Six students from our class.
S	48.	Pulled his wagon home.
V	49.	A long and boring story.
V	50.	Grandpa and I.

COMPOSITION EXERCISE

Rewrite 12 of the incomplete sentences from today's exercise. Add either a subject or a verb.

1. _____

2. _____

3. _____

4. _____

5. _____

6. _____

7. _____

8. _____

9. _____

10. _____

11. _____

12. _____

Unit 47 cont'd →

Avoiding Sentence Fragments

A fragment is a part of a sentence that does not express a complete thought.

EXAMPLES: fragment: *Found a home.*
             complete: *The puppy found a home.*

✳ **Underline the sentence fragments.**

1. <u>Next to the grocery store</u>.
2. Today is Thursday.
3. <u>In the hallway</u>.
4. <u>When I see you again</u>.
5. Someone broke the window.
6. <u>Over that mountain</u>.
7. I wish I had a horse.
8. <u>At the end of the line</u>.
9. <u>To see you soon</u>.
10. <u>Lisa, Danny, and Tony</u>.
11. We visited my grandmother.
12. Let's sit on the bench.
13. Someone left a coat.
14. I took the cookies to school.
15. <u>Through the mail</u>.
16. We were watching the show.
17. <u>With her family to the zoo</u>.
18. <u>When it rains</u>.
19. That man is my uncle.
20. <u>Eating her breakfast</u>.
21. <u>On your head</u>.
22. <u>Making a mess</u>.
23. The man waited in his car.
24. <u>At three o'clock</u>.
25. <u>All six of us</u>.
26. The plane is leaving.
27. <u>Down the road a mile</u>.
28. <u>On the left side</u>.
29. We ate hot dogs.
30. I collect old coins.
31. <u>Under the bridge</u>.
32. <u>Between you and me</u>.
33. <u>For your birthday</u>.
34. We laughed at the clown.
35. Jason walked to the store.
36. <u>For the next two years</u>.
37. The bus will be late.
38. <u>Because it will</u>.
39. <u>Toward the center</u>.
40. School is closed today.
41. I dropped my sandwich.
42. <u>Since you can't go</u>.
43. Mom watched us leave.
44. We fed the animals.
45. The birds have flown south.
46. <u>Beyond the stars</u>.
47. <u>Extra nice</u>.
48. Lynn is not hungry.
49. <u>A place to stay</u>.
50. They won the game.

COMPOSITION EXERCISE

Choose 12 fragments from today's exercise. Rewrite them into complete sentences.

1. _____
2. _____
3. _____
4. _____
5. _____
6. _____
7. _____
8. _____
9. _____
10. _____
11. _____
12. _____

The Fragment

A fragment does not contain either a subject or verb or both. It is an incomplete thought.

EXAMPLES:

missing subject:	*Was watching cartoons.*	
missing verb:	*My father.*	
missing both:	*On television.*	
complete:	*My father was watching cartoons on television.*	

 In each blank write which sentence part is missing. Use "S" for subject, "V" for verb, or "B" for both.

S	1.	Suddenly left.
V	2.	An untimely delay.
B	3.	Without a warning.
S	4.	Suggested the idea.
V	5.	The skeleton in the closet.
V	6.	The cruel man.
S	7.	Singing "Yankee Doodle."
B	8.	Through the window.
B	9.	By the willow tree.
S	10.	Pulled his wagon home.
V	11.	A fluffy white rabbit.
S	12.	Formed a circle.
B	13.	Toward the middle.
S	14.	Conquered the people.
B	15.	Behind the station.
S	16.	Stood in the doorway.
S	17.	Found the stolen jewels.
B	18.	In the evening.
V	19.	The team's new coach.
V	20.	A fierce wind.
S	21.	Chose the blue jacket.
B	22.	To another town.
S	23.	Urged him to stay.
B	24.	Around three o'clock.
V	25.	Twenty-five guests.

B	26.	At the corner.
S	27.	Ran four miles.
V	28.	Wisdom and courage.
B	29.	After the show.
V	30.	A tight budget.
S	31.	Defended his country.
B	32.	Up the hill.
V	33.	A descriptive poem.
S	34.	Pledge my trust.
V	35.	A penalty against us.
B	36.	With her brother.
B	37.	Under the table.
S	38.	Vanished into thin air.
V	39.	The deadline for the contest.
V	40.	A luxury for kings.
B	41.	Over the rainbow.
V	42.	Greed and gossip.
S	43.	Sent a message.
V	44.	A black parachute.
B	45.	Inside the envelope.
B	46.	On the rocking chair.
S	47.	Combined his forces.
V	48.	A lonely soldier.
S	49.	Balanced the budget.
B	50.	In front of you.

COMPOSITION EXERCISE

Correct 10 of the fragments in today's exercise.

1. _____

2. _____

3. _____

4. _____

5. _____

6. _____

7. _____

8. _____

9. _____

10. _____

117

Unit 48 cont'd

Dividing a Run-On Sentence

A run-on sentence occurs when two or more sentences are joined without any punctuation.

EXAMPLES: a. *It has been a long day / I am tired.*
              b. *The table broke / Jack was sitting on it.*

 Use a slash mark (/) to show where each run-on sentence should be divided.

1. I came too early/no one had arrived.
2. The strong wind blew/the leaves covered the yard.
3. I walked through the snow/I am freezing.
4. The dog barked/the thief ran away quickly.
5. She couldn't see me/it was very dark outside.
6. The birds ate the seeds/then they flew away.
7. I chased the grasshopper/I couldn't catch him.
8. We missed our bus/we slept too long.
9. Sherry rang the doorbell/no one answered.
10. I am leaving now/don't try to stop me.
11. Clean your room/it is a mess.
12. Help me move this chair/my pen fell behind it.
13. The ghost came closer/we were too scared to move.
14. Don't break the mirror/you'll have bad luck.
15. Carl sold his bike/he wants to borrow mine.
16. Tomorrow is my birthday/we are having a party.
17. Mom bought the lamps/they were on sale.
18. The shoes are too small/I can't wear them.
19. It's time to leave/put away your books.
20. The money is in my coat/bring it to me.
21. George is my neighbor/he is a lawyer.
22. Everyone enjoyed the show/it was great.
23. My pencil is broken/may I use yours?
24. The old man is tired/he needs to rest.
25. Let's walk to school today/it is a beautiful morning.

COMPOSITION EXERCISE

Write 5 sentences about a superstition you do/don't believe. Be sure to divide your sentences with the proper punctuation.

_____

_____

_____

_____

The Run-On Sentence

A *run-on sentence is one that consists of two or more sentences joined together without punctuation.*

EXAMPLES: a. *Mr. Carter is our President/he is from Georgia.*

b. *The new boy is Tom Kise/he moved here from Utah.*

 Use a slash mark (/) to separate the run-on sentences into two or more complete sentences. Rewrite them correctly.

1. Kevin likes to fish his brother likes to camp they go to the mountains every weekend.
   Kevin likes to fish. His brother likes to camp. They go to the mountains every weekend.

2. The little boy is greedy he ate all of the cookies he didn't share them with anyone.
   The little boy is greedy. He ate all of the cookies. He didn't share them with anyone.

3. Our new house is in the country it is very pretty I hope you will visit me soon I would like that very much.
   Our new house is in the country. It is very pretty. I hope you will visit me soon. I would like that very much.

4. Our game had to be postponed two of our best players couldn't play one had the measles the other one broke his leg.
   Our game had to be postponed. Two of our best players couldn't play. One had the measles. The other one broke his leg.

5. Your advice was very helpful I am trying to follow it.
   Your advice was very helpful. I am trying to follow it.

6. My brother has an unusual hobby he raises aardvarks they are interesting animals he sells them too not many people have an aardvark for a pet.
   My brother has an unusual hobby. He raises aardvarks. They are interesting animals. He sells them too. Not many people have an aardvark for a pet.

7. My family loves the outdoors last weekend we went on a hike we camped under the stars all of us hated to go home.
   My family loves the outdoors. Last weekend we went on a hike. We camped under the stars. All of us hated to go home.

8. Lisa is going to the zoo she likes to watch the monkeys they are funny animals.
   Lisa is going to the zoo. She likes to watch the monkeys. They are funny animals.

9. The tornado swept through the town it destroyed many things.
   The tornado swept through the town. It destroyed many things.

10. I am writing a novel it is about a girl and her dog they run away from home to find adventure I haven't decided how the story will end yet.
    I am writing a novel. It is about a girl and her dog. They run away from home to find adventure. I haven't decided how the story will end yet.

11. Our class visited the Grand Canyon we listened to our echoes we took many pictures.
    Our class visited the Grand Canyon. We listened to our echoes. We took many pictures.

12. Mr. Parsons is my neighbor he owns the bakery I love to go there and visit him he always gives me a sample.
    Mr. Parsons is my neighbor. He owns the bakery. I love to go there and visit him. He always gives me a sample.

13. The telephone rang it was for Karen Karen was not here I took the message.
    The telephone rang. It was for Karen. Karen was not here. I took the message.

14. Tomorrow is my birthday I will be sixteen years old will you come to my party?
    Tomorrow is my birthday. I will be sixteen years old. Will you come to my party?

Unit 49 cont'd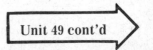

What Is a Run-On Sentence?

A run-on sentence occurs when two or more
sentences are joined without any punctuation.

EXAMPLES: run-on: I always come here it is my favorite spot it is so peaceful.
           corrected: I always come here. It is my favorite spot. It is so peaceful.

❋ If each sentence is a run-on, write " r " in the blank. If it
is not, write "c" in the blank.

r	1.	Do you like the color I do.	C	16. The woman is a teacher.
C	2.	I am almost finished.	R	17. How old are you I am eleven years old.
C	3.	This cake is delicious.		
R	4.	How did you do it it is working again.	R	18. The bird flew out of his cage we tried to catch him.
R	5.	Did you take my hat I can't find it anywhere.	R	19. The bell rang we went home.
			C	20. The music is too loud. It hurts my ears.
C	6.	Someone saw us. I'm sure they did.	R	21. I found the book it belongs to me now.
C	7.	Now I remember him. He owns the store.	C	22. The people were angry. They wanted a change.
R	8.	We found our dog he had run away.	C	23. This man is ill. We must help him.
C	9.	Will you help me fix it?	R	24. I met him he's a doctor.
R	10.	The whistle blew it always blows at noon.	R	25. Read this book it is very interesting.
R	11.	This car is too small all of us can't go.	R	26. Our vacation begins tomorrow I can't wait.
C	12.	We saw the rainbow. The storm was over.	C	27. Where are you going? I want you to stay.
R	13.	Karen is my sister she is older than I.	C	28. Did you see a black cat?
C	14.	You are not old enough to get a job.	R	29. You're hurt let me help you.
R	15.	I like you you're nice.	R	30. Jan called for you you weren't home.

COMPOSITION EXERCISE

Choose 8 of the run-on sentences from today's exercise. Write these sentences correctly.

1. _____
2. _____
3. _____
4. _____
5. _____
6. _____
7. _____
8. _____

Finding the Subject

The subject is what the sentence is all about.
Usually it will come before the verb.

EXAMPLES: a. The <u>weather</u> is terrible.   c. The <u>picture</u> looks beautiful.
           b. <u>Mike</u> called his sister.   d. His <u>actions</u> were rude.

✸   **Underline the subject of each sentence.**

1. Your <u>brother</u> broke the window.
2. The <u>train</u> will be here soon.
3. <u>Jane</u> sat on the steps.
4. This <u>house</u> scares me.
5. <u>Penny</u> finished the story.
6. My favorite <u>movie</u> is "King Kong."
7. The <u>money</u> belongs to Kathy.
8. <u>Mrs. Benton</u> lives next door.
9. This <u>plant</u> needs special care.
10. The <u>fish</u> is a shark.
11. His <u>answer</u> is no.
12. <u>Laura</u> knows the secret.
13. Our <u>club</u> meets on Thursday.
14. <u>Jane</u> copied the sentences.
15. <u>You</u> have finished too early.
16. This <u>pen</u> doesn't write.
17. The <u>book</u> was interesting.
18. A <u>monkey</u> followed me home.
19. The <u>trip</u> must be postponed.
20. That <u>building</u> is very old.
21. The <u>account</u> is closed.
22. <u>Donna</u> stepped on the bug.
23. The <u>money</u> is safe now.
24. The <u>dog</u> is a collie.
25. <u>Mark</u> is ill.
26. The <u>skeleton</u> fell out of the closet.
27. <u>We</u> repeated the pledge.
28. The <u>suggestion</u> was rejected.
29. <u>Dan</u> announced the winners.
30. The <u>penalty</u> is too harsh.
31. The <u>remedy</u> is working.
32. <u>Connie</u> will stay here.
33. The <u>class</u> worked together.
34. <u>He</u> raised his hand.
35. <u>Onions</u> made me cry.
36. <u>Susan</u> decorated the room.
37. <u>They</u> asked for you.
38. His <u>speech</u> was excellent.
39. The <u>question</u> was difficult.
40. The <u>game</u> is over.
41. <u>I</u> made the mess.
42. The <u>ghosts</u> vanished.
43. <u>Jill</u> forgot her shoes.
44. The <u>grass</u> needs cutting.
45. The <u>frog</u> chased me.
46. The <u>paint</u> was spilled on the rug.
47. <u>We</u> followed the footprints.
48. <u>Cathi</u> arrived at noon.
49. Two <u>men</u> argued.
50. That <u>man</u> is a coward.

COMPOSITION EXERCISE

Write 10 sentences in which the subject comes before the verb.

1. _____
2. _____
3. _____
4. _____
5. _____
6. _____
7. _____
8. _____
9. _____
10. _____

Unit 50 cont'd

Simple Subjects

A simple subject is who or what the sentence is talking about. It may be a noun or pronoun.

EXAMPLES: a. The <u>spinach</u> was delicious.   c. <u>Ann</u> wrote the play.
         b. The <u>car</u> hit a pole.   d. The <u>wheel</u> was bent.

A Underline the simple subjects.

1. The <u>clue</u> helped.
2. The <u>ground</u> was muddy.
3. <u>Jason</u> bit my hand.
4. <u>I</u> wrote the answers.
5. The <u>mouse</u> was scared.
6. Our <u>house</u> is brick.
7. <u>We</u> made a list.
8. The <u>movie</u> was good.
9. <u>John</u> went home.
10. The <u>clock</u> ticked loudly.
11. The <u>police</u> came.
12. The <u>park</u> is closed today.
13. The <u>bus</u> is yellow.
14. Our <u>class</u> went on a picnic.
15. <u>Cotton</u> is white.
16. The <u>story</u> is too long.
17. The <u>sky</u> is blue.
18. <u>Nancy</u> is from California.
19. The <u>train</u> was empty.
20. The <u>mermaid</u> swam away.
21. <u>Peter</u> pushed the button.
22. <u>Mary</u> caught a fish.
23. The <u>candle</u> burned slowly.
24. <u>We</u> saw the accident.
25. <u>Mike</u> was chosen to go.

B In each blank write a word which will be the subject of the sentence.

1. The ___bottle___ broke.
2. ___DAD___ was angry.
3. The ___WINDOW___ was open.
4. The ___ROOM___ was large.
5. The ___DOGS___ barked.
6. The ___CANDY___ was too sweet.
7. ___BARBRA___ is my sister.
8. ___WE___ built the house.
9. The ___WIND___ blew.
10. The ___MOVIE___ is over.
11. ___FIGHTING___ is bad.
12. The ___QUESTION___ was simple.
13. My ___BIKE___ was stolen.
14. ___I___ wore a sweater.
15. The ___CAT___ broke the lamp.
16. ___PAUL___ hid in the closet.
17. The ___MONEY___ is missing.
18. ___BEN___ moved the table.
19. ___JUDY___ spilled the milk.
20. My ___EYES___ are blue.
21. A ___TREE___ fell on our house.
22. The ___TRUCK___ pulled the car.
23. ___BOZO___ won the race.
24. The ___FISH___ got away.
25. My ___AUNT___ lives in Florida.

COMPOSITION EXERCISE

Write 12 sentences. Underline the simple subject in each sentence.

1. _____
2. _____
3. _____
4. _____
5. _____
6. _____
7. _____
8. _____
9. _____
10. _____
11. _____
12. _____

Comprehension Check

Ⓐ Rearrange each set of words into a logical sentence.

1. The car chased the dogs.
   The dogs chased the car.

2. The ladder climbed Arnold.
   Arnold climbed the ladder.

3. Hazel bit the spider on her hand.
   The spider bit Hazel on her hand.

4. Joe put the pocket in his money.
   Joe put the money in his pocket.

5. Tie the knots in ribbons.
   Tie the ribbons in knots.

6. I heard the television on the news.
   I heard the news on the television.

7. The fox ran away from the rabbit.
   The rabbit ran away from the fox.

8. The piano played a song on Ted.
   Ted played a song on the piano.

9. Ray put the horse on the saddle.
   Ray put the saddle on the horse.

10. Voice your raise.
    Raise your voice.

Ⓑ Connect possible subjects with possible verbs. Then write a short sentence.

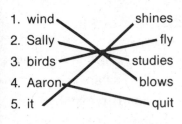

1. wind — shines
2. Sally — fly
3. birds — studies
4. Aaron — blows
5. it — quit

The wind blows.
Sally studies.
Birds fly.
Aaron quit.
It shines.

11. bees — breaks
12. dogs — will win
13. Dale — sting
14. they — bark
15. glass — met

Bees sting.
Dogs bark.
Dale will win.
They met.
Glass breaks.

6. puppy — squeal
7. we — laugh
8. pigs — followed
9. phone — waited
10. I — rang

The puppy followed.
We laugh.
Pigs squeal.
The phone rang.
I waited.

16. Ann — forgot
17. mouse — hid
18. fish — jump
19. kangaroos — blink
20. lights — smell

Ann forgot.
The mouse hid.
Fish smell.
Kangaroos jump.
Lights blink.

Ⓒ Why are each of these sentences fragments?

1. The house on the corner of Main and Holt. — *lacks verb*
2. Swam across the lake quickly. — *lacks subject*
3. Opened the box marked "Surprise." — *lacks subject*
4. Louisa and her mother today. — *lacks verb*
5. A blue shirt with yellow stripes. — *lacks verb*
6. In the room next to the kitchen. — *lacks subject and verb*
7. A call from your Aunt Agnes. — *lacks verb*
8. Ran into the room screaming. — *lacks subject*
9. The last train to Baltimore. — *lacks verb*
10. Held his breath. — *lacks subject*
11. Someone with a deep voice. — *lacks verb*
12. For the officer in charge. — *lacks subject and verb*
13. The woman with the red hat. — *lacks verb*
14. Sang the baby to sleep. — *lacks subject*

Test 10 cont'd →

Comprehension Check (continued)

D Divide each set of run-on sentences. Rewrite them correctly.

1. I ran to the mailbox to see if they had come but they hadn't when would I receive my tickets I had ordered them three weeks ago the concert was next week what if they wouldn't arrive on time.

    I ran to the mailbox to see if they had come, but they hadn't. When would I receive my tickets? I had ordered them three weeks ago! The concert was next week. What if they wouldn't arrive on time?

2. Saturday before the concert came, I reached into the mailbox they were there I couldn't believe it I would guard these tickets with my life.

    Saturday before the concert came, I reached into the mailbox. They were there! I couldn't believe it. I would guard these tickets with my life!

E Underline the subjects.

1. The <u>judge</u> listened carefully.
2. <u>Kathy</u> exercises every day.
3. <u>Washington</u> was the first President.
4. <u>Rudy</u> examined the paper.
5. The hot <u>fudge</u> was delicious.
6. The <u>mouse</u> hurried under the chair.
7. This <u>show</u> is ridiculous.
8. <u>No one</u> volunteered.
9. <u>Steve</u> joined the Army.
10. The <u>music</u> was too loud.
11. <u>You</u> should have been there.
12. The <u>thief</u> was my cat Bradley.
13. Our <u>vacation</u> has been postponed.
14. The <u>cake</u> is tonight's dessert.
15. <u>Lucas</u> acts silly.

F Supply the subjects.

1. *Kangaroos* live in Australia.
2. Your *report* was very interesting.
3. *Vera* reads poetry by Frost.
4. My *fork* is bent.
5. *Judy* made a B on her speech.
6. The *necklace* was made of brass.
7. The *tour* of the city was fun.
8. *Joel* knows all about it.
9. Mark's *eyes* are blue.
10. The *bus* is always late on Tuesday.
11. *Ava* caught the biggest fish.
12. The *chili* was hot.
13. The *telephone* rang three times.
14. *Don* works after school.
15. The *candle* burned brightly.

Write a paragraph about your favorite family member. Underline the subject of each sentence.

_____
_____
_____
_____
_____
_____
_____
_____
_____
_____

Nouns Used as Subjects

The subject is who or what the sentence
is about. A noun names a person, place,
or thing.

EXAMPLES: a. The _breeze_ feels cool.   c. Your _smile_ is beautiful.
            b. _Jill_ wants to be a pilot.   d. This _room_ smells like a fish.

   In each blank write a noun (common or proper)
which will serve as the subject of the sentence.

1. My __pencil__ fell on the floor.
2. Your __HANGER__ tore my coat.
3. The __FLOWERS__ smell good.
4. __FRANK__ is a soldier.
5. That __MAN__ told us to leave.
6. __LYNN__ visited Mr. Collins.
7. The __STORE__ sells hardware.
8. The __MONEY__ is due today.
9. A __BIRD__ flew into our classroom.
10. This __STORY__ is frightening.
11. Sam's __PROJECT__ is finished.
12. __JILL__ gave Donna the prize.
13. The __TEACHER__ waited for an answer.
14. The __MOUSE__ ran across the street.
15. His __NAME__ is Jackson.
16. An __ORANGE__ is my favorite fruit.
17. __TIM__ bought the basket.
18. The __FAMILY__ moved to Omaha.
19. __MARCIA__ saw the accident.
20. A __THIEF__ took my radio.
21. My __HOUSE__ is not home.
22. The __KITTEN__ needs a new home.
23. The __ANSWER__ is incorrect.
24. __SUE__ was sent to the office.
25. That __BOY__ forgot his hat.

26. The __RULE__ was necessary.
27. __CANDY__ is my sister.
28. The __LIE__ has been forgotten.
29. A __SNAKE__ bit me.
30. The __OWNER__ showed me the room.
31. Your __UNCLE__ left for Toledo.
32. The __ROBINS__ built a nest in our tree.
33. The __CLASS__ wrote a play.
34. __PETE__ pushed the wrong button.
35. The __CLUB__ will meet tonight.
36. The __BELL__ rang three times.
37. __JUDY__ found a valuable coin.
38. The __PEOPLE__ elected him treasurer.
39. My __AUNT__ speaks French.
40. The __FISH__ tastes salty.
41. __BILLY__ broke the new vase.
42. The __ARTIST__ painted my portrait.
43. A __LIE__ is seldom good.
44. The __PARACHUTE__ did not open.
45. __HOCKEY__ is a great sport.
46. The __SONG__ was perfect.
47. The __MYSTERY__ has been solved.
48. The __MONSTER__ destroyed the city.
49. The shy __GIRL__ was embarrassed.
50. __MOM__ listened to us.

COMPOSITION EXERCISE

Write 12 sentences which have nouns as subjects.

1. _____
2. _____
3. _____
4. _____
5. _____
6. _____

7. _____
8. _____
9. _____
10. _____
11. _____
12. _____

Unit 51 cont'd ➡

The Understood Subject "You"

Most commands contain the understood subject "you." (It is not written in the sentence.)

EXAMPLES: a. *Write a short sentence.*   c. *Open your mouth.*

                b. *Draw a straight line.*   d. *Kill the spider!*

 Underline the sentences which contain the understood subject "you."

1. Give me your hand.
2. The film is about glass.
3. Show her your pictures.
4. Come here.
5. I can't find my sweater.
6. Finish your dinner.
7. Kay lives on Reed Street.
8. Persuade him to come.
9. Call your parents.
10. Explain yourself.
11. This hat is too large.
12. The rabbit ate carrots for lunch.
13. Replace the bulb.
14. Decide on the one you want.
15. No one will see you.
16. Forget the idea.
17. This flower is beautiful.
18. Listen to this riddle.
19. There are too many numbers.
20. Measure the room.
21. Surround the house.
22. She is an actress.
23. Your map is torn.
24. Begin now.
25. Tell her I am leaving.
26. We know the answers.
27. Postpone the meeting.
28. Consult a dictionary.
29. Pam will mail the letter.
30. Defend your rights.
31. The tape doesn't stick.
32. He wants to go home.
33. Combine the two numbers.
34. I am not able to come.
35. Climb the ladder.
36. Suggest a new method.
37. Invite Dorothy too.
38. State the problem.
39. Dana is going to England.
40. The show begins at six o'clock.
41. Clear the table.
42. Include a stamp.
43. The painting was done by Keith.
44. The bullet missed the target.
45. Match the pieces.
46. I am mixing the paints.
47. Think about your answer.
48. Leave me alone.
49. My friend lives in Chicago.
50. Sign on the bottom line.

COMPOSITION EXERCISE

Write 12 sentences which have understood subjects.

1. _____
2. _____
3. _____
4. _____
5. _____
6. _____
7. _____
8. _____
9. _____
10. _____
11. _____
12. _____

Compound Subjects

Sentences may have more than one subject. These subjects are joined together with "and," "or," or "but."

EXAMPLES: a. *Jack and Al are our leaders.*
  b. *A pen or a pencil is necessary.*
  c. *Karen and I are friends.*
  d. *My aunt and uncle live in Ohio.*

  Underline the compound subjects.

1. One boy and two girls were selected.
2. Pears and peaches were served.
3. Baseball and football are sports.
4. Don or Steve is guilty.
5. The man and woman ate lunch.
6. A bike and a wagon were stolen.
7. Tim and Mark were absent.
8. Not Joe but I will attend.
9. A monkey and a zebra escaped.
10. Mom and Dad gave their permission.
11. Peas and carrots are good for you.
12. The boys and girls enjoyed the circus.
13. The bread and butter are on the table.
14. The soup and sandwiches were ready.
15. Jim and Ernie caught the chicken.
16. The money and keys are on the table.
17. Jake and I fished all day.
18. Lee and Gary are my brothers.
19. The windows and doors were locked.
20. The cake and ice cream were delicious.
21. Andy and I went home.
22. The mop and broom are in the closet.
23. Ted and Pam are leaving.
24. Food and drink will be served.
25. Your shoes and socks are muddy.
26. Diamonds and rubies are jewels.
27. Dogs and cats are not allowed.
28. She and I have the same teacher.
29. You or Tim will have to go.
30. Swimming and skiing are fun.
31. The mayor and the judge were present.
32. Tom and Bob will help you.
33. Bread and water make a poor meal.
34. Susan and Chris are from Kansas.
35. Mr. Sims and I had a long talk.
36. A bus and a red car hit the sign.
37. You or I will tell her.
38. Your friends and neighbors are here.
39. George or Ken will help us.
40. His hat and coat are missing.
41. These apples and bananas are good.
42. The television and radio do not work.
43. Jack and Connie ran to the river.
44. The paper and books were wet.
45. The hammer and nails lay on the porch.
46. Cards and letters were in the box.
47. Willie and Rex built the cage.
48. My brother and sister argue often.
49. Kelly and John are waiting outside.
50. Houston and Chicago are big cities.

COMPOSITION EXERCISE

Write 12 sentences which contain compound subjects.

1. _____
2. _____
3. _____
4. _____
5. _____
6. _____
7. _____
8. _____
9. _____
10. _____
11. _____
12. _____

Unit 52 cont'd

Using Compound Subjects

Sentences which have more than one subject have compound subjects. These subjects are connected with conjunctions.

EXAMPLES: a. <u>Sue</u> and <u>Chris</u> came early.   c. <u>He</u> and <u>I</u> share the room.
           b. The <u>dog</u> and <u>cat</u> are fighting.   d. <u>You</u> and <u>Jim</u> will win.

   In each blank write a noun or pronoun which will serve as a subject.

1. <u>Mom</u> and <u>Dad</u> came to the meeting.
2. The <u>RIVERS</u> and <u>LAKES</u> are polluted.
3. The <u>BOYS</u> and <u>GIRLS</u> were cheering.
4. <u>KNIVES</u> and <u>FORKS</u> are on the table.
5. <u>JOHN</u> and <u>ERIC</u> will be leaving.
6. <u>PEN</u> and <u>PAPER</u> lay on her desk.
7. The <u>MAP</u> and <u>MONEY</u> were stolen.
8. A <u>SKELETON</u> or a <u>GHOST</u> will appear.
9. <u>GEORGIA</u> and <u>TEXAS</u> are in the South.
10. <u>GINA</u> and <u>I</u> planted the tree.
11. The <u>DEN</u> and <u>BEDROOM</u> are blue.
12. <u>MIKE</u> and <u>TOD</u> are proper nouns.
13. <u>JOHN</u> and <u>JOSH</u> are responsible.
14. My <u>SOCKS</u> and <u>SHOES</u> were clean.
15. The <u>MAN</u> and <u>WOMAN</u> argued.
16. <u>SHERRY</u> and <u>KATE</u> weren't invited.
17. The <u>COWS</u> and <u>PIGS</u> have been fed.
18. <u>LESTER</u> and <u>I</u> were tired.
19. <u>BEN</u> and <u>BRAD</u> are here.
20. <u>JAKE</u> or <u>LOU</u> will finish last.
21. A <u>CARD</u> and <u>PACKAGE</u> are in the box.
22. <u>MOM</u> and <u>I</u> went to town.
23. The <u>ICE</u> and <u>SNOW</u> were messy.
24. <u>AL</u> and <u>IVAN</u> made a deal.
25. The <u>MATH</u> and <u>ENGLISH</u> are easy.

26. <u>DOGS</u> and <u>CATS</u> make good pets.
27. <u>EGGS</u> and <u>MILK</u> spilled on the floor.
28. The <u>PEARS</u> and <u>APPLES</u> are ripe.
29. <u>YOU</u> and <u>I</u> are not friends.
30. <u>DISHES</u> and <u>GLASSES</u> were broken.
31. The <u>LIONS</u> and <u>TIGERS</u> were asleep.
32. <u>JUDY</u> or <u>MARY</u> will be elected.
33. The <u>LEAVES</u> and <u>GRASS</u> are green.
34. <u>LEROY</u> and <u>GARY</u> painted the fence.
35. Her <u>HAIR</u> and <u>EYES</u> are brown.
36. The <u>BACON</u> and <u>TOAST</u> were burnt.
37. His <u>HAT</u> and <u>COAT</u> are missing.
38. <u>DON</u> and <u>I</u> had a fight.
39. The <u>MOVIE</u> and <u>CARTOONS</u> were funny.
40. <u>BUSES</u> and <u>TRAINS</u> are usually late.
41. The <u>WIND</u> and <u>RAIN</u> ruined my crop.
42. The <u>APPLES</u> and <u>PEACHES</u> were rotten.
43. The <u>FLOOR</u> and <u>CHAIRS</u> were wet.
44. The <u>FENCE</u> and <u>BARN</u> are being painted.
45. <u>SATURDAY</u> and <u>SUNDAY</u> are busy days.
46. <u>MOLLY</u> and <u>DOT</u> were crying.
47. The <u>CAR</u> and <u>TRUCK</u> are silver.
48. <u>JUAN</u> and <u>LOUIS</u> are good friends.
49. <u>JULY</u> and <u>AUGUST</u> are hot months.
50. <u>NICK</u> and <u>ROY</u> were on television.

COMPOSITION EXERCISE

Write a sentence using each set of words as a compound subject.

(soup and sandwiches) 1. _____

(David and Alan) 2. _____

(shouts and cheers) 3. _____

(cows and horses) 4. _____

(orchids and roses) 5. _____

(Cindy and Adam) 6. _____

Statements

A statement is a sentence that gives information and ends with a period.

EXAMPLES: a. *My eyes are blue.*
b. *Sammy is visiting us.*
c. *The house is for sale.*
d. *I studied all day.*

 Answer each question with a statement.

1. What is your name?
   My name is Christi.

2. How old are you?
   I am twelve years old.

3. What color is your hair?
   My hair is black.

4. Do you have any brothers?
   I have three brothers.

5. Do you have any sisters?
   I don't have any sisters.

6. What do you want to be?
   I would like to be an actor.

7. Who is your teacher?
   Mrs. Simmons is my teacher.

8. Who is your best friend?
   My best friend is Mike.

9. What is your neighbor's name?
   Mr. Fisher is our neighbor.

10. What school do you attend?
    Our school is Westside Elementary.

11. In what city do you live?
    I live in Burbank.

12. In what state do you live?
    Burbank is in California.

13. What sports do you like?
    I like tennis and hockey.

14. Do you know how to swim?
    I know how to swim.

15. Do you have any pets?
    Keets is my pet rat.

16. Do you like spinach?
    I hate spinach.

17. How do you get to school?
    I ride the bus to school.

18. What room are you in?
    This is room 302.

19. Do you know George?
    George sits next to me.

20. Who is your principal?
    Our principal is Ms. Granger.

21. Do you like liver?
    Liver is delicious.

22. What will you eat for lunch?
    Today we are having spaghetti.

23. What do you like to do?
    I like to go camping.

24. What is your favorite subject?
    My favorite subject is English.

COMPOSITION EXERCISE

Write 12 statements about school.

1. _____
2. _____
3. _____
4. _____
5. _____
6. _____

7. _____
8. _____
9. _____
10. _____
11. _____
12. _____

Unit 53 cont'd

Making a Statement

A statement is a sentence which gives information.

EXAMPLES: a. I love to travel.
             b. Kathy is not here.
             c. She and I are friends.
             d. I know the man.

 Underline the statements.

1. The weather is cold.
2. I wish I could go.
3. Joshua is absent today.
4. Whenever.
5. I tried to warn you.
6. Maybe never.
7. The radio is too loud.
8. I knocked on the door.
9. Someone has been here.
10. The mountain was beautiful.
11. In a while.
12. I caught the ball.
13. No one saw the mermaid.
14. Passed quickly.
15. My shoes are gone.
16. Without a word.
17. I could hear the voices.
18. The ghost was friendly.
19. We watched the game.
20. She bought a watch.
21. Immediately.
22. I believed his story.
23. She knew Paul and Jake.
24. That man.
25. I must finish my work.
26. Pulling a wagon.
27. The shy girl smiled.
28. My mom drove the bus.
29. We couldn't find anyone.
30. All of us.
31. Now and always.
32. It rained again.
33. They moved to Utah.
34. Very suddenly.
35. We worked all night.
36. Two students from our class.
37. This is too tight.
38. The farm was enormous.
39. We saw nothing.
40. More than we had.
41. Let's play outside.
42. Dan waited for Dale.
43. I can't stay here.
44. David is never late.
45. A short story.
46. Two men with glasses.
47. Steve is my neighbor.
48. Too long and narrow.
49. We arrived on time.
50. Everything is closed.

COMPOSITION EXERCISE

Write 12 statements.

1. _____
2. _____
3. _____
4. _____
5. _____
6. _____
7. _____
8. _____
9. _____
10. _____
11. _____
12. _____

Questions

A question is a sentence that asks something and ends with a question mark.

EXAMPLES: a. Have you been sleeping?
 b. Did anyone answer the phone?
 c. Where is Cooper Avenue?
 d. What should we do?

 Use the information given in the statement and write a question.

1. The amendment passed.
   Did the amendment pass?

2. I know how to speak French.
   Do you know how to speak French?

3. The train will be late.
   Will the train be on time?

4. The weather was beautiful.
   How was the weather?

5. Sylvester is my pet frog.
   Who is Sylvester?

6. Mr. Wilson is the owner.
   Is Mr. Wilson the owner?

7. Your mom called this morning.
   Did anyone call?

8. Wes took the bicycle.
   Who took the bicycle?

9. It was an opossum.
   What was it?

10. Someone knocked on the door.
    Did someone knock on the door?

11. I will ride the bus home.
    How will you get home?

12. These boxes are heavy.
    Are the boxes heavy?

13. Charles is my cousin.
    Is Charles your cousin?

14. We will begin on Monday.
    When will we begin?

15. It is three o'clock.
    What time is it?

16. He lives on Burton Street.
    Where does he live?

17. This coat is not mine.
    Is this your coat?

18. Your brother is upstairs.
    Where is my brother?

19. His name is Joseph.
    What is his name?

20. I don't feel well.
    Do you feel well?

21. We rode the Ferris wheel.
    What did you do?

22. The blue team won.
    Which team won?

23. Gina was in the play.
    Was Gina in the play?

24. Cathy bought a new book.
    What did Cathy buy?

COMPOSITION EXERCISE

Write 12 questions.

1. _____
2. _____
3. _____
4. _____
5. _____
6. _____

7. _____
8. _____
9. _____
10. _____
11. _____
12. _____

Unit 54 cont'd

Asking a Question

A question is a sentence that asks something.
It ends with a question mark (?).

EXAMPLES: a. How many brothers do you have?
            b. What is the date?
            c. Where do you live?

 Rewrite each sentence into a question.

1. I am ten years old.
How old are you?

2. I want to go to the zoo.
Where do you want to go?

3. My teacher is Ms. Murdock.
Who is your teacher?

4. This bike costs $85.00.
What is the price of this bike?

5. This animal is an aardvark.
What animal is this?

6. The store is closed.
Is the store open?

7. Jason loves to ski.
Does Jason like to ski?

8. My birthday is in June.
When is your birthday?

9. I have been to Mexico.
Have you been to Mexico?

10. My sister's name is Tina.
What is your sister's name?

11. Joan is my best friend.
Who is your best friend?

12. I finished my homework.
Did you finish your homework?

13. I was born in Phoenix.
Where were you born?

14. Today is Thursday.
What day is it?

15. I am hungry.
Are you hungry?

16. My mom is a lawyer.
What does your mom do?

17. The package came today.
When did the package come?

18. Monday is the deadline.
When is the deadline?

19. I want to be a doctor.
What do you want to be?

20. Eric opened the window.
Who opened the window?

21. The dog belongs to me.
Whose dog is this?

22. Mr. Carson called you.
Did Mr. Carson call?

23. We rode horses.
What did you do today?

24. I enjoyed the movie.
Did you enjoy the movie?

COMPOSITION EXERCISE

Write 12 questions about school.

1. _____
2. _____
3. _____
4. _____
5. _____
6. _____

7. _____
8. _____
9. _____
10. _____
11. _____
12. _____

Commands

A command is a sentence that tells someone to do something. It ends with a period.

EXAMPLES:
a. *Close the door.*
b. *Tell us a joke.*
c. *Call me at noon.*
d. *Look at the ocean.*

✳ Underline the commands.

1. Come to my house.
2. Listen to me.
3. Stewart is the best player.
4. Put the book down.
5. Carry the package for me.
6. Throw George the ball.
7. I made this for you.
8. Be quiet.
9. The trip begins tomorrow.
10. Find those keys now.
11. Tell me the answer.
12. I will help you finish.
13. Move your feet.
14. Your shoes are muddy.
15. Come in here.
16. Hide these in the closet.
17. Where did you go?
18. Open the windows.
19. Eat your breakfast.
20. No one saw me.
21. Answer my question.
22. Fix the car.
23. Leave me alone.
24. Follow these footprints.
25. Call a taxi.
26. Show me the way home.
27. Make up your mind.
28. My dog is sick.
29. I will mow the lawn.
30. Don't open your eyes.
31. Here are the keys.
32. Sit on the couch.
33. Order our dinner.
34. Give Sarah the money.
35. I am fishing.
36. Read this letter.
37. Comb your hair.
38. Does this belong to you?
39. Look at this picture.
40. Your home is beautiful.
41. The nest was empty.
42. Wash the dishes.
43. Cut the ribbon.
44. Choose the one you want.
45. Stop crying.
46. Is she your sister?
47. Turn off the lights.
48. I read the book.
49. Water the garden.
50. Bring me the paper.

COMPOSITION EXERCISE

Write 12 commands.

1. _____
2. _____
3. _____
4. _____
5. _____
6. _____
7. _____
8. _____
9. _____
10. _____
11. _____
12. _____

Unit 55 cont'd →

Giving Commands

A command is a sentence that gives orders. It ends with a period.

EXAMPLES: a. *Unlock the front door.* c. *Take the dog for a walk.*
  b. *Tell George to leave.* d. *Talk to me.*

 Change each statement to a command.

1. I will close the windows.
   Close the windows.

2. We voted yes.
   Vote yes.

3. He ended his speech with a joke.
   End the speech with a joke.

4. I must finish my history report.
   Finish your history report.

5. The garden has been watered.
   Water the garden.

6. Kim left us alone.
   Leave us alone.

7. We can walk to school.
   Walk to school.

8. I moved the chair in here.
   Move the chair in here.

9. You should not touch the set.
   Don't touch the set.

10. Everyone listened to the music.
    Listen to the music.

11. He drew us a map.
    Draw us a map.

12. Sam turned the radio on.
    Turn the radio on.

13. Carl polished the trophy.
    Polish the trophy.

14. The man fixed the leaky faucet.
    Fix that leaky faucet.

15. You should buy a new car.
    Buy a new car.

16. The dog brought Dad the paper.
    Bring Dad the paper.

17. I sat on the new sofa.
    Sit on the sofa.

18. Susan filled the glasses with milk.
    Fill the glasses with milk.

19. I'll help you set the table.
    Help me set the table.

20. You should call your mother.
    Call your mother.

21. The fence needs painting.
    Paint the fence.

22. He will find us a seat.
    Find us a seat.

23. You can take the book home.
    Take the book home.

24. I will wait for you outside.
    Wait for me outside.

COMPOSITION EXERCISE

Write 12 commands which tell someone to do things around the house.

1. _____ 7. _____

2. _____ 8. _____

3. _____ 9. _____

4. _____ 10. _____

5. _____ 11. _____

6. _____ 12. _____

Comprehension Check

Test 11

A Complete each sentence with a noun that functions as the subject.

1. The _____plane_____ for Germany leaves soon.
2. _____Jim_____ is looking forward to going.
3. The _____mountains_____ are tall and majestic.
4. The _____people_____ are friendly.
5. The _____buildings_____ are old and stately.
6. _____Austria_____ is a beautiful place.
7. My _____uncle_____ lives in Amsterdam.
8. The _____trip_____ will last three weeks.
9. A _____bus_____ will take us to the airport.
10. Your _____luggage_____ is too heavy.

11. The _____show_____ begins at six o'clock.
12. _____Comedies_____ are my favorite shows.
13. _____Laughter_____ is good medicine.
14. _____Bill Cosby_____ is my favorite comedian.
15. The _____house_____ was built in 1879.
16. The _____windows_____ came from France.
17. The _____rugs_____ came from Persia.
18. My _____grandmother_____ lived in the house.
19. The _____news_____ shocked everyone.
20. _____Hank_____ had won the election.

B Place an "x" beside each sentence which contains an understood subject.

_x_ 1. Listen to my new album.
_x_ 2. Show Barbara the picture.
____ 3. It uses too much oil.
_x_ 4. Hold out your hand.
____ 5. The winds destroyed the flowers.
_x_ 6. Don't sit on the park bench.
_x_ 7. Cook the spaghetti tomorrow.
____ 8. I must have an answer now.
_x_ 9. Enter the contest before June 6.
_x_ 10. Finish your homework first.

C Write 10 sentences which contain understood subject.

1. _Write your name here._
2. _Look through the telescope._
3. _Open your eyes._
4. _Send me a postcard._
5. _Pour him a glass of water._
6. _Tell Kevin the joke._
7. _Go home and find it._
8. _Park the car behind the gym._
9. _Don't set the glass on it._
10. _Move your feet._

D Underline the compound subjects.

1. <u>Kelsey</u> and <u>Robert</u> left Saturday morning.
2. My <u>dogs</u> and <u>cats</u> get along splendidly.
3. <u>You</u> and <u>I</u> should review for the test together.
4. <u>Strawberry</u> and <u>chocolate</u> are my favorite flavors.
5. <u>Dr. Johnson</u> and <u>Mrs. Reeves</u> are the chaperones.
6. <u>Joanne</u> and <u>Marcia</u> always know where I am.
7. The <u>moon</u> and <u>stars</u> only reflect light from the sun.
8. <u>Lawrence</u> and <u>Howard</u> practice two hours every day.
9. The <u>telephone</u> and <u>television</u> are out of order.
10. <u>Hamburgers</u> and <u>French fries</u> is Kip's favorite lunch.
11. <u>Flour</u> and <u>sugar</u> were spilled everywhere.
12. <u>Jessica</u> and <u>Daniel</u> wanted to be partners.

135

Test 11 cont'd

Comprehension Check (continued)

E Write a statement about each of these subjects.

1. your favorite author
   Stephen King is my favorite author.

2. the animals in the zoo
   Monkeys are popular zoo animals.

3. choosing classes for next year
   I am taking algebra next year.

4. working during the summer
   Hank works as a mechanic.

5. the house at the corner
   The house at the corner is for sale.

6. the people of Denmark
   The people of Denmark speak Danish.

7. a popular singer
   Whitney Houston is a popular singer.

8. economical cars
   Economical cars are usually uncomfortable.

F Write a question about each of these subjects.

1. a newcomer's name
   What is her name?

2. speaking a foreign language
   Do you speak Spanish?

3. a test in history
   Was the history test hard?

4. the topic of a term paper
   What are you writing about?

5. directions to Welch Boulevard
   Which way is Welch Boulevard?

6. eating Chinese food
   Do you like to eat Chinese food?

7. going to the class party
   Are you going to the class party?

8. finding Rick's phone number
   What is Rick's phone number?

G Write a command about each of these subjects.

1. writing a letter to Kate
   Write Kate a letter.

2. a cut on your hand
   Wash the cut on your hand.

3. making a peanut-butter sandwich
   Make me a peanut-butter sandwich.

4. cleaning the basement
   Clean the basement first.

5. parking your car
   Park your car in the garage.

6. buying groceries
   Buy milk and bread.

7. choosing a new watch
   Choose another watch.

8. reading a book
   Read this book for your report.

Write a paragraph about choosing an automobile. Use at least one statement, one question, and one command.

_____

_____

_____

_____

_____

_____

_____

Exclamations

An exclamation is a sentence that expresses strong emotion and ends with an exclamation point.

EXAMPLES:
a. Look out for that car!
b. Who's going to make me!
c. Stop your crying!
d. It belongs to me!

 If the sentence is an exclamation, end it with an exclamation point. If not, use a period.

1. Watch out for the bull!
2. It begins next week.
3. I had a great time.
4. Don't you yell at me!
5. We will be home at noon.
6. He's gone!
7. Don't leave me here alone!
8. I will introduce them.
9. No, it's mine!
10. Please change your clothes.
11. We won!
12. This is my last class.
13. Take your medicine.
14. I don't want to see you!
15. I'm sure of it.
16. They're beautiful!
17. He's after me!
18. Micky pulled my hair again.
19. Don't lie to me!
20. My sister takes ballet.
21. The police are coming.
22. I saw you do it!
23. Sam is responsible.
24. She's the one!
25. I'm warning you!

26. Mr. West wants to see you.
27. Don't touch the stone!
28. Leave her alone!
29. I am going to school.
30. Get out of here!
31. He took my purse!
32. We can paint the fence tomorrow.
33. I am ready to go.
34. Run quickly!
35. My uncle lives with us.
36. Please wait for me.
37. It tastes awful!
38. I love it!
39. Lana bought a new bike.
40. Go away!
41. My dog barked all night.
42. I didn't order anything.
43. Catch that ball!
44. Hide in the closet!
45. What a game that was!
46. The ocean was beautiful.
47. He's hurt!
48. Martin is my cousin.
49. My throat is sore.
50. Who do you think you are!

COMPOSITION EXERCISE

Write 12 exclamations.

1. _____
2. _____
3. _____
4. _____
5. _____
6. _____

7. _____
8. _____
9. _____
10. _____
11. _____
12. _____

Unit 56 cont'd

Sentences That Show Feelings

Sentences that show strong feelings are called exclamations. They end with exclamation points.

EXAMPLES: a. It's a winner!   c. I passed the test!
           b. I'm drowning!   d. What was that!

 Underline the exclamations.

1. <u>Run for your life!</u>
2. The clown made us laugh.
3. <u>The house is on fire!</u>
4. <u>I'm drowning!</u>
5. Is Johnny home?
6. Our vacation starts tomorrow.
7. <u>Stop that man!</u>
8. <u>Here comes our bus!</u>
9. <u>We're lost!</u>
10. <u>I told you the truth!</u>
11. We are going fishing.
12. Can you read this?
13. <u>He's stealing my bike!</u>
14. The house was empty.
15. <u>I found him!</u>
16. Mary was chosen.
17. <u>It's a home run!</u>
18. <u>I hate it!</u>
19. <u>This is terrible!</u>
20. This soup is too hot.
21. <u>It's mine!</u>
22. What are you doing?
23. <u>I'm scared!</u>
24. <u>He's here!</u>
25. <u>We won the game!</u>

26. It's time to go home.
27. <u>Get out of here!</u>
28. Are we having a test?
29. <u>Don't touch that flower!</u>
30. <u>We did it!</u>
31. We traveled by jet.
32. The bus had a flat tire.
33. <u>You broke my watch!</u>
34. What's for dinner?
35. <u>I'm freezing!</u>
36. <u>I want it now!</u>
37. <u>Don't yell at me!</u>
38. I saw you at the show.
39. <u>I can't see!</u>
40. How did you know?
41. <u>Call an ambulance!</u>
42. <u>He's after us!</u>
43. <u>I want to go home!</u>
44. Here is her address.
45. <u>We made it!</u>
46. <u>Hold on!</u>
47. I want a chocolate one.
48. <u>That plane's going to crash!</u>
49. <u>I'm sorry!</u>
50. Today is Monday.

COMPOSITION EXERCISE

Write 12 exclamations you might hear when a house is on fire.

1. _____
2. _____
3. _____
4. _____
5. _____
6. _____

7. _____
8. _____
9. _____
10. _____
11. _____
12. _____

Reviewing the Four Types of Sentences

1. **Statements** are sentences that give information.
   I want a bike.
2. **Questions** are sentences that ask something.
   Who are you?
3. **Commands** are sentences that tell someone to do something.
   Write your name.
4. **Exclamations** are sentences that show strong feelings.
   There's a fire!

 Identify each of the following sentences. Write "s" for "statement," "q" for "question," "c" for "command," and "e" for "exclamation."

s	1. Dad and I went fishing.		E	24. She's drowning!
Q	2. Did you catch anything?		Q	25. Which one is mine?
E	3. I've got one!		S	26. I need a pencil.
C	4. Give me a hand.		S	27. Donna was crying.
S	5. I told our secret.		S	28. The puppy was lonely.
S	6. Sara lives next door.		C	29. Bring me the book.
Q	7. When did he call?		S	30. I like to camp.
C	8. Tie your shoelaces.		C	31. Give me a clue.
E	9. Run quickly!		Q	32. Who is that woman?
S	10. We bought a barn.		E	33. Help me!
Q	11. Is Gary home?		S	34. I found a quarter.
Q	12. What is your name?		Q	35. Have you seen my coat?
E	13. The house is on fire!		Q	36. When will you come?
E	14. Call the police!		Q	37. Is that a camel?
S	15. The man fixed our sink.		E	38. You killed it!
S	16. Cathi is a doctor.		E	39. I passed the test!
C	17. Eat your spinach.		C	40. Read this sentence.
C	18. Answer me.		S	41. The door is locked.
C	19. Clean your shoes.		C	42. Finish your homework.
Q	20. Why are they leaving?		S	43. The lights are beautiful.
E	21. My watch is gone!		Q	44. Do you have a sister?
Q	22. Where is Whitten Street?		E	45. We won!
S	23. This book is interesting.		E	46. It's snowing!

COMPOSITION EXERCISE

Write two examples of each kind of sentence.

1. statements
   _____
   _____

2. questions
   _____
   _____

3. commands
   _____
   _____

4. exclamations
   _____
   _____

139

Unit 57 cont'd

Distinguishing Between Four Types of Sentences

1. **Statements give information.**
   I like going to school.
2. **Questions ask something.**
   Is this your book?
3. **Commands give orders.**
   Write your name and number.
4. **Exclamations show strong feelings.**
   He's getting away!

✳ **Write "s" for statement, "q" for question, "c" for command, and "e" for exclamation.**

S	1. My friend is visiting me.	
Q	2. May I talk to Lynn?	
E	3. Stop that man!	
C	4. Bring me your paper.	
C	5. Sit here with me.	
S	6. George wants to eat now.	
Q	7. Where is my letter?	
E	8. Get out of my way!	
C	9. Wait for Chris.	
Q	10. Did you buy any peanut butter?	
S	11. The movie starts tomorrow.	
S	12. Your fee is too high.	
Q	13. What was that noise?	
Q	14. Do you like Jane?	
S	15. This river is too dirty.	
C	16. Mail the letter for me.	
S	17. Billie caught a fish.	
Q	18. Where are you?	
E	19. He saw me!	
Q	20. How did you find me?	
S	21. The team was ready to go.	
E	22. Let's hide!	
S	23. The meeting will be Thursday.	
Q	24. Who told you my name?	
C	25. Don't tell him I'm here.	

Q	26. What is the penalty?
E	27. Help me!
S	28. The men are working.
Q	29. Why can't you come?
Q	30. Who made the cake?
C	31. Check your answers.
E	32. The bear is after me!
S	33. We watched the panda.
Q	34. Will the bus come soon?
S	35. Sarah will wait for you.
C	36. Give Louis the newspaper.
Q	37. Is it raining again?
E	38. Look out for that car!
S	39. Your aunt teaches math.
Q	40. Did you throw the ball?
S	41. The trip lasted two days.
C	42. Button your coat.
E	43. She's coming!
Q	44. Will you give her a message?
S	45. Sandra is the treasurer.
S	46. He will carry our bags.
C	47. Meet me in the morning.
Q	48. What will you do?
S	49. My window was broken.
Q	50. How did you recognize me?

COMPOSITION EXERCISE

Write one of each kind of sentence for each situation.

1. a perfect test score

_____

_____

_____

2. a tornado

_____

_____

_____

Punctuating the Four Types of Sentences

1. **Statements end with periods.**
2. **Questions end with question marks.**
3. **Commands end with periods.**
4. **Exclamations end with exclamation points.**

EXAMPLES:
  a. *I bought a kite.*
  b. *Is she pretty?*
  c. *Find the answer.*
  d. *I love it!*

 Punctuate the following sentences.

1. The house is yellow .
2. Did the phone ring ?
3. My bike was stolen !
4. Write him a letter .
5. Comb your hair .
6. Where is everyone ?
7. What did you buy ?
8. Should I tell her ?
9. I must go soon .
10. Skating is fun .
11. Wear a coat .
12. He's hurt !
13. Are you telling me the truth ?
14. I couldn't find him .
15. Go to your room .
16. What have I done ?
17. I put it on the table .
18. Irene will stay here .
19. The work is finished .
20. Throw the ball .
21. May I go now ?
22. This is a good show .
23. Here they are !
24. The table is too large .
25. Are you a policeman ?

26. Do your homework .
27. You're hurting me !
28. We watched the planes .
29. Would you wait for me ?
30. Why is Dennis absent ?
31. Is the clue helpful ?
32. It's a ghost !
33. The fish is hungry .
34. Today is Thursday .
35. Which room is yours ?
36. Hold this for me .
37. Buy me an ice-cream cone .
38. We rode the subway .
39. I hate you !
40. I'm bleeding!
41. I painted my bike .
42. Are you going ?
43. Who told you ?
44. Make a chocolate pie .
45. That was my mother .
46. We lost the game .
47. What is the problem ?
48. Is this a true story ?
49. You'll miss the bus !
50. Ask me a question .

COMPOSITION EXERCISE

Write 10 sentences. Identify the punctuation used with each sentence.

1. _____
2. _____
3. _____
4. _____
5. _____
6. _____
7. _____
8. _____
9. _____
10. _____

Unit 58 cont'd

Punctuating Sentences

1. A statement ends with a period.
   I'm hungry for tacos.
2. A question ends with a question mark.
   Would you help me?
3. A command ends with a period.
   Open the door for Bart.
4. An exclamation ends with an exclamation point.
   He's hurt!

 Punctuate each sentence properly.

1. I can't tell you.
2. Who is that man?
3. You're hurting my arm.
4. Apologize.
5. My decision is final.
6. Why are you crying?
7. Don't sit on my hat.
8. It's a tornado!
9. The dam has burst!
10. Was that the reason?
11. Take this paper to the office.
12. Who told you that?
13. Your shoes are too big.
14. Save my place.
15. It will discourage her.
16. He's going to crash!
17. Did you find him?
18. Is it snowing again?
19. Wave at him.
20. The lot next door is vacant.
21. You made it!
22. Will you listen to me?
23. I know a solution.
24. Close the lid tightly.
25. Don't confuse me.

26. I'm stuck!
27. He was hiding under the porch.
28. Is Sarah home?
29. What can I do?
30. Bring your parents too.
31. Sandy can't see you now.
32. Where did he go?
33. I didn't do it!
34. Are you Don's brother?
35. Sing us a song.
36. The game is finally over.
37. We're lost!
38. What made you say that?
39. Don't talk to me now.
40. Bears hibernate in winter.
41. Which one is Lucy's?
42. Ignore him.
43. We must postpone our plans.
44. You hit me!
45. Did anyone find my pen?
46. The weather is terrible.
47. I can't reach you!
48. Sit down and listen.
49. Everyone went home.
50. When did the accident happen?

COMPOSITION EXERCISE

Write two sentences which end with question marks, two which end with exclamation points, and four which end with periods.

1. _____
2. _____
3. _____
4. _____

5. _____
6. _____
7. _____
8. _____

The Simplest Sentences (N-V)

The simplest sentence is the N-V pattern.
It consists of a subject and a verb.

EXAMPLES: a. The dog talks.   c. The bus came.
           b. Dad shouted.   d. Jason called.

 Underline each subject once and each verb twice.

1. The music played.
2. The children sang.
3. George ran.
4. I am.
5. The box fell.
6. Mary called.
7. Fish swim.
8. The dog barked.
9. The cat meowed.
10. Birds fly.
11. The noise stopped.
12. The bell rang.
13. Dean smiled.
14. The paper burned.
15. I tried.
16. They left.
17. Connie laughed.
18. The mail came.
19. The people shouted.
20. Larry cried.
21. The ice cream melted.
22. The ghost disappeared.
23. The man answered.
24. The door opened.
25. The frog jumped.

26. Our team won.
27. The egg broke.
28. The ship sank.
29. The dog sat.
30. The wind blew.
31. Turtles crawl.
32. Everyone saw.
33. She heard.
34. The snow fell.
35. He walked.
36. Dan followed.
37. They lost.
38. The rabbit hopped.
39. Mom drove.
40. Karen fell.
41. The cat scratches.
42. They moved.
43. The camel slept.
44. The sun shines.
45. My dog steals.
46. The child played.
47. The cow mooed.
48. Lucy knows.
49. The show began.
50. We helped.

51. Ann sneezed.
52. We waited.
53. I passed.
54. We listened.
55. Gary went.
56. The man turned.
57. The water froze.
58. They arrived.
59. The phone rang.
60. Susan answered.
61. The balloon rose.
62. The story ended.
63. The kangaroo jumped.
64. The milk spilled.
65. The candle burned.
66. The tree died.
67. The kitten drank.
68. We hurried.
69. The boy rested.
70. The glass broke.
71. The table moved.
72. A knife cuts.
73. The leaves fell.
74. My hand hurts.
75. The roses bloomed.

COMPOSITION EXERCISE

Write 18 sentences which follow the N-V pattern.

1. _____
2. _____
3. _____
4. _____
5. _____
6. _____

7. _____
8. _____
9. _____
10. _____
11. _____
12. _____

13. _____
14. _____
15. _____
16. _____
17. _____
18. _____

Unit 59 cont'd

The Basic Sentence Pattern

The N-V sentence pattern is the simplest
sentence. It contains a subject and a verb.
EXAMPLES: a. The truth hurts.   c. Ted understood.
            b. The dog growled.   d. My plan failed.

A Supply the noun or noun substitute which will
serve as each subject.

1. The ___leaves___ were burning.
2. __SAMMY__ forgot.
3. The __GLASS__ broke.
4. The __DISHES__ are dried.
5. The __WHEELS__ are turning.
6. __MOTHER__ called.
7. The __PUPPY__ obeyed.
8. The __ARMY__ surrendered.
9. The __WATER__ evaporated.
10. The __DAMAGE__ was estimated.
11. Your car's __HORN__ is blowing.
12. __CATHI__ belongs here.
13. __I__ approve.
14. The __MISSION__ is accomplished.
15. The __SHIP__ is sinking.
16. The __TRUCK__ was damaged.
17. The __PEOPLE__ were exiled.
18. The __PAINT__ is peeling.
19. Your __VOTE__ counts.
20. The __FUNDS__ are depleted.
21. The __MAN__ was deceived.
22. The __REPORT__ was completed.
23. The __LION__ leaped.
24. The __BILL__ has been paid.
25. The __HOUSE__ is condemned.

B Supply the verbs.

1. Lee ___danced___.
2. The glass __WAS FILLED__.
3. The thunder __RUMBLED__.
4. The bell __WILL RING__ soon.
5. This pen __WRITES__.
6. The farmer __RELAXED__.
7. Two cars __COLLIDED__.
8. The mouse __SCAMPERED__ away.
9. The balloons __ROSE__.
10. The grass __GROWS__.
11. Our team __WON__.
12. The snake __COILED__.
13. The frog __JUMPED__.
14. The ice __MELTED__.
15. The ball __BOUNCED__ against the car.
16. The job __WAS TAKEN__.
17. The town __CELEBRATED__.
18. A new remedy __WAS DISCOVERED__.
19. We __SLEPT__.
20. The shadow __APPEARED__.
21. Diana __COUGHED__.
22. The kitten __MEOWED__.
23. The papers __BURNED__.
24. The thief __RAN__.
25. The volcano __ERUPTED__.

COMPOSITION EXERCISE

Write 18 N-V sentences about animals.

1. _____
2. _____
3. _____
4. _____
5. _____
6. _____

7. _____
8. _____
9. _____
10. _____
11. _____
12. _____

13. _____
14. _____
15. _____
16. _____
17. _____
18. _____

The N-V Pattern

A sentence that follows the N-V Pattern contains
a subject and a verb.

EXAMPLES: a. Christy walked home.
            b. The car will start now.

c. Your friend is leaving.
d. The moccasins fit.

 Underline the noun once and the verb twice.

1. The jewels sparkle in the sunlight.
2. The ghost vanished before our eyes.
3. The bleach spilled on the floor.
4. Babies cry.
5. Dick was confused.
6. The amendment passed by one vote.
7. The game was delayed.
8. Joseph transferred.
9. Gossip is discouraged.
10. The trip was cancelled.
11. Mr. Peters cares about us.
12. You were expected yesterday.
13. The bullet missed.
14. The voyage ended in tragedy.
15. The incident occurred here.
16. We pretended.
17. Joshua was convinced.
18. The telephone is ringing.
19. The sisters argued.
20. That plane will crash.
21. Your father is waiting.
22. The funds were spent foolishly.
23. Sammy sneezed.
24. He ran into the door.
25. A rainbow appeared.

26. The meeting was postponed again.
27. Frank hesitated.
28. Finally the parachute opened.
29. The atomic bomb exploded.
30. The book was published.
31. Bears hibernate.
32. The balance has been paid.
33. Our guests arrived early.
34. The game has begun.
35. The remedy worked immediately.
36. Suzanne passed.
37. The money was misplaced.
38. The problem is solved.
39. The banker retired.
40. Paul disapproves of him.
41. The hikers rested.
42. The car license has expired.
43. The pieces matched perfectly.
44. That clown is crying.
45. Sarah will help.
46. The fish swam down the river.
47. Tony sings.
48. The noises stopped.
49. I will drive.
50. The court adjourned until noon.

COMPOSITION EXERCISE

Write 18 N-V sentences about people.

1. _____
2. _____
3. _____
4. _____
5. _____
6. _____

7. _____
8. _____
9. _____
10. _____
11. _____
12. _____

13. _____
14. _____
15. _____
16. _____
17. _____
18. _____

Unit 60 cont'd

Diagramming the N-V Sentence

The N-V sentence consists of a simple subject and its verb. It is diagrammed as follows:

(subject) | (verb)

Notice the position of this line. It separates the subject and verb.

 Diagram these N-V sentences on the lines provided.

1. No one responded.

No one | responded

2. Melanie has changed.

Melanie | has changed

3. Suzanne confessed.

Suzanne | confessed

4. Do you swim?

you | Do swim

5. Mice scamper.

Mice | scamper

6. Joey coughed.

Joey | coughed

7. I won!

I | won

8. Mother listened.

Mother | listened

9. Will Terry remember?

Terry | Will remember

10. It broke.

It | broke

11. We danced.

We | danced

12. Monkeys chatter.

Monkeys | chatter

13. Has it rung?

it | Has rung

14. Jennifer will drive.

Jennifer | will drive

Comprehension Check

A Write an exclamation about each of these subjects.

1. getting a shot at the doctor's
   I don't want a shot!

2. a house on fire
   Call the fire department!

3. a bull chasing you
   The bull is after me!

4. getting a tooth pulled
   It's going to hurt!

5. slamming the door on your foot
   It hit my foot!

6. winning a million dollars
   I won a million dollars!

7. seeing your favorite rock star
   I saw Rick Springfield!

8. making all A's
   I did it!

9. falling out of a boat
   Yikes! I can't swim!

10. seeing a ghost
    It's a ghost!

B Identify the kinds of sentences.

1 - statement   **2 - question**   **3 - command**   **4 - exclamation**

_1_ 1. The special for today is soup.
_2_ 2. What have you decided?
_3_ 3. Don't forget to bring your uniform.
_4_ 4. It's too late for that!
_1_ 5. It always rains on Thursday.
_1_ 6. I made tuna salad for lunch.
_2_ 7. How will we know the time?
_2_ 8. Are you going to the game?
_3_ 9. Copy these problems.
_3_ 10. Help Hillary clean the kitchen.
_4_ 11. Catch him!
_4_ 12. Someone, help me!
_3_ 13. Wear your glasses.
_1_ 14. Her birthday is September 29.
_2_ 15. When did you see her last?

_4_ 16. Will you stop talking!
_1_ 17. Theo will mow the lawn Friday.
_2_ 18. Where does Laura live?
_3_ 19. Drive me to school.
_2_ 20. Is Larry taking French too?
_4_ 21. Drive on your side of the road!
_1_ 22. The music is soothing.
_3_ 23. Answer yes or no.
_2_ 24. Have you bought anything?
_1_ 25. The picnic is Saturday.
_1_ 26. Chris will play the lead.
_3_ 27. First brush your teeth.
_4_ 28. Why did you do that!
_2_ 29. Who was that?
_1_ 30. Everything is finished.

C Punctuate these sentences.

1. I told you I didn't like it!
2. The brochure is free.
3. We visited the zoo and the park.
4. How do you attach the pedals?
5. Clean the floor with this.
6. Do you think it will work?
7. No one even missed you!
8. Answer the door.
9. We're having chicken and dressing.
10. Smell the roses.
11. Read this note from Dana.
12. When will we see you again?
13. Isaac sent his mother daisies.
14. You promised not to tell!
15. We have been rehearsing our lines.
16. Is that all?

Test 12 cont'd

Comprehension Check (continued)

D **Identify the parts of each N-V sentence.**

1. The **N** windows **V** rattled.
2. **N** I believe **V** in me.
3. Two **N** men **V** argued.
4. The **N** meat **V** sizzled.
5. **N** Adam **V** left at two.
6. The **N** frog **V** jumped.
7. **N** Jessica **V** yawned.

8. The **N** coins **V** rolled everywhere.
9. **N** We will **V** hurry.
10. The **N** turtle **V** crawled away.
11. **N** Cabot **V** fell off.
12. My **N** finger **V** hurts.
13. The **N** glue **V** dried quickly.
14. **N** Terri **V** smiled.

E **Diagram these N-V sentences.**

1. The sun shines.

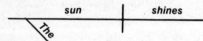

2. Leslie cried.

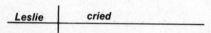

3. The fire burned.

4. Roscoe sneezed.

5. We danced.

6. Randy sighed.

7. The snow melted.

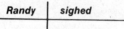

8. The tooth ached.

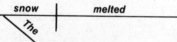

9. Fish swim.

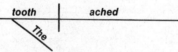

10. The clock ticked.

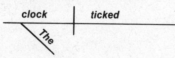

11. The twig snapped.

12. Julia called.

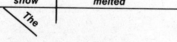

13. Mrs. Duncan paused.

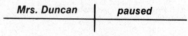

14. No one listened.

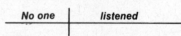

15. The color will change.

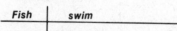

Write a paragraph about city life vs. country life. Use at least two N-V sentences.

Diagramming Compound Subjects

The N-V sentence may consist of a compound subject and its verb.
It is diagrammed as follows:

* Diagram these N-V sentences which contain compound subjects.

1. Kate and Allie laughed.

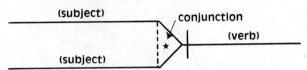

2. Jake and Ernie will help.

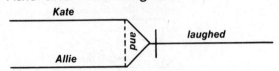

3. Ed, Dave, and Phil worked.

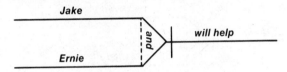

4. You or I must win.

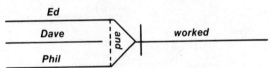

5. Either Anne or Bob will call.

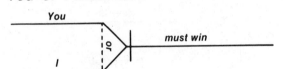

6. Deb and Jan shivered.

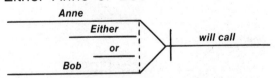

7. Chris or Richard can go.

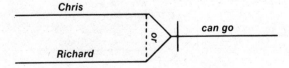

8. A, B, and C were done.

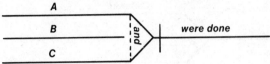

9. Lillian and I hiked.

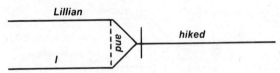

10. Either Wes or Kay must sign.

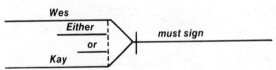

11. Barry, James, and Tim overslept.

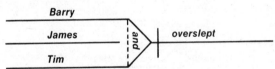

12. Neither Rex nor Jill smiled.

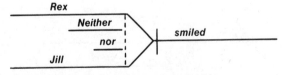

13. Brenda and Greg are reading.

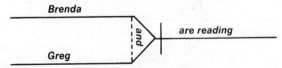

14. Horace and Lea practiced.

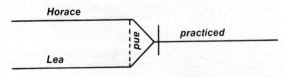

149

Unit 61 cont'd

Diagramming Compound Verbs

The N-V sentence may consist of a simple subject and its compound verb. It is diagrammed as follows:

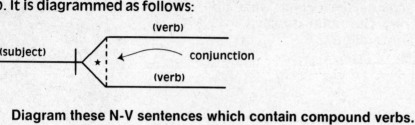

Diagram these N-V sentences which contain compound verbs.

1. Can he read or write?

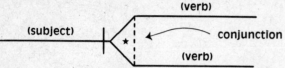

2. Paula dusted and mopped.

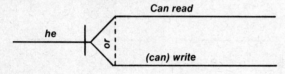

3. Did you argue or fight?

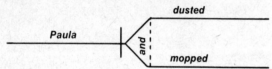

4. It walks and talks.

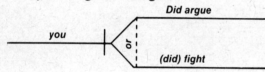

5. Vera tripped, fell, and cried.

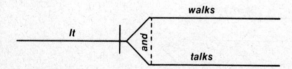

6. I swim and ski.

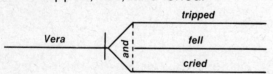

7. Jerry studied but failed.

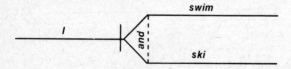

8. Should we walk or ride?

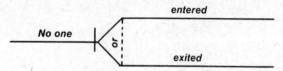

9. No one entered or exited.

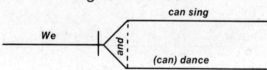

10. We can sing and dance.

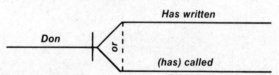

11. Has Don written or called?

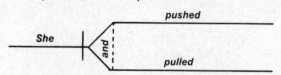

12. She pushed and pulled.

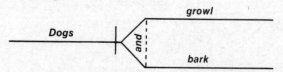

13. Dogs growl and bark.

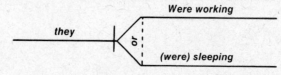

14. Were they working or sleeping?

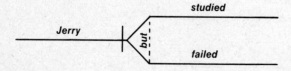

150

Diagramming Adjectives

An adjective is a word that tells **which one**, **what color**, **what kind**, or **how many**. An adjective may modify the noun (subject) in a N-V sentence. An adjective is diagrammed as follows:

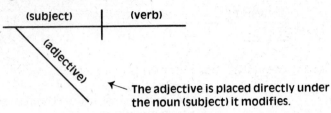

← The adjective is placed directly under the noun (subject) it modifies.

 Diagram these sentences on the lines provided.

1. Four glasses broke.

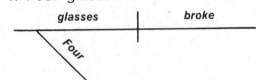

2. Concerned citizens vote.

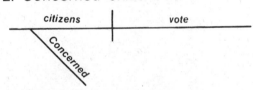

3. Energetic people exercise.

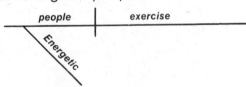

4. One balloon popped.

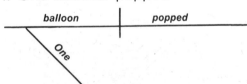

5. Boiling water burns.

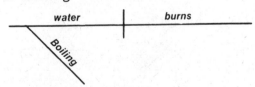

6. Silly girls giggle.

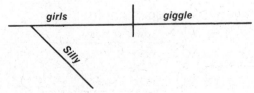

7. Two men argued.

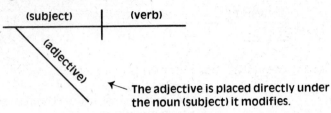

8. Cool breezes refresh.

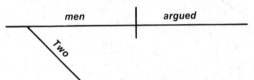

9. Smart students study.

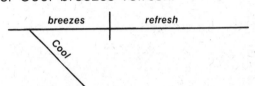

10. Eight phones rang.

11. Twenty persons applied.

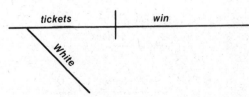

12. White tickets win.

151

Unit 62 cont'd

Diagramming Adverbs

An adverb is a word that tells when, where, why, or how. An adverb may modify the verb in a N-V sentence. An adverb is diagrammed as follows:

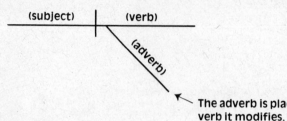

The adverb is placed directly under the verb it modifies.

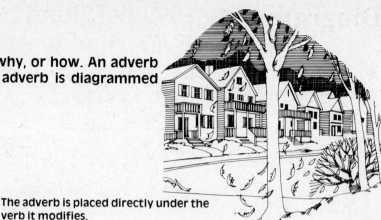

* **Diagram these sentences on the lines provided.**

1. I went home.

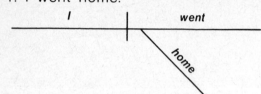

2. Calvin ran away.

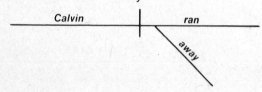

3. It rings constantly.

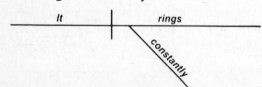

4. No one ever calls.

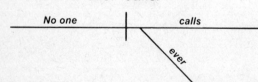

5. Robert never studies.

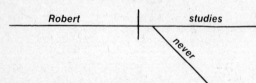

6. They arrived early.

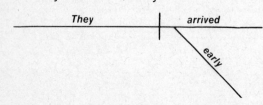

7. Wanda lives here.

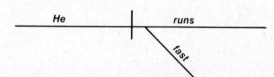

8. Dorothy knocked again.

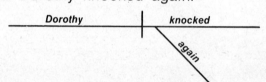

9. He runs fast.

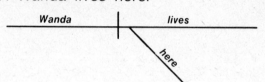

10. Barbara passed easily.

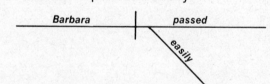

11. We walked slowly.

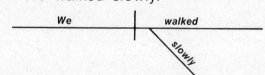

12. Harriet called twice.

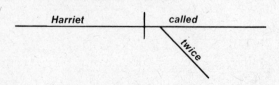

152

Diagramming Prepositional Phrases Which Function as Adverbs

A N-V sentence may contain a prepositional phrase which functions as an adverb. It is diagrammed as follows:

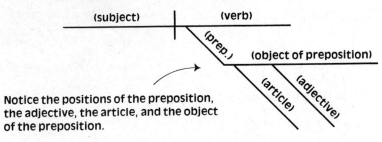

Notice the positions of the preposition, the adjective, the article, and the object of the preposition.

A meeting is at three.

✳ Diagram these sentences on the lines provided.

1. Louis sat in Dad's chair.

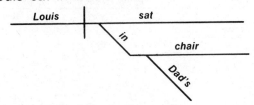

2. They moved to New Orleans.

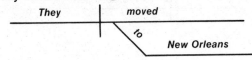

3. The money was found in a cave.

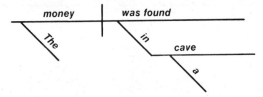

4. A meeting is planned at three.

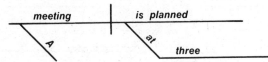

5. Tom rested at the coffee shop.

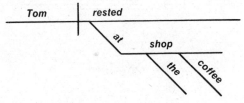

6. The cat crawled behind the bookcase.

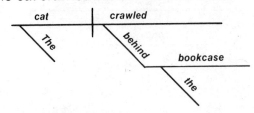

7. We met at a dance.

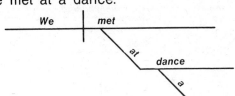

8. Wait by the old mill.

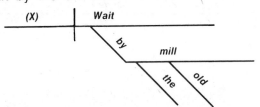

9. Someone stood beside the car.

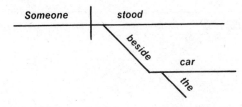

10. Janice looked up at the clouds.

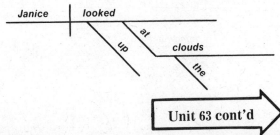

Unit 63 cont'd

Diagramming Prepositional Phrases Which Function as Adjectives

A N-V sentence may contain a prepositional phrase which functions as an adjective. It is diagrammed as follows:

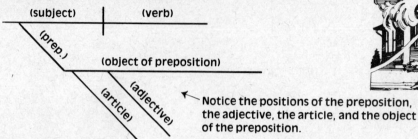

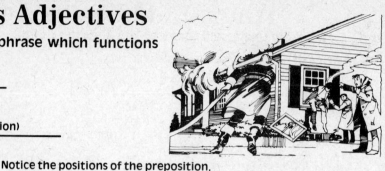

Notice the positions of the preposition, the adjective, the article, and the object of the preposition.

 Diagram these sentences on the lines provided.

1. The puppy in the pet shop barked.

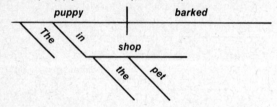

2. The money on the table disappeared.

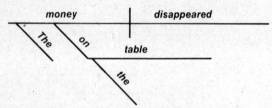

3. The plane from Miami landed.

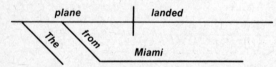

4. The man in the uniform left.

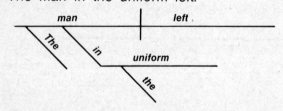

5. Students with their homework went home.

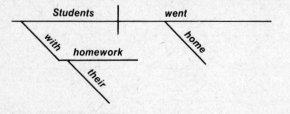

6. The mayor of Chicago arrived.

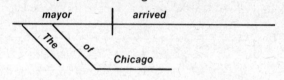

7. Houses on Main Street were damaged.

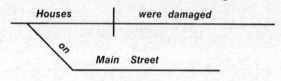

8. The woman behind the counter smiled.

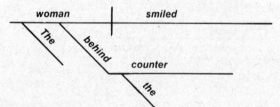

9. Books by King sell.

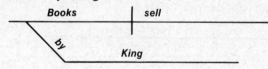

10. A woman with a French accent called.

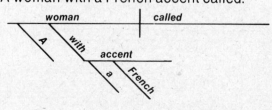

Diagram these sentences on the lines provided.

1. Look at the picture.

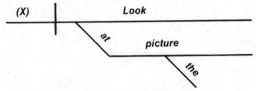

2. Katherine sings and dances.

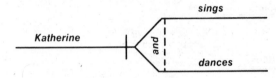

3. Zeke hurried home.

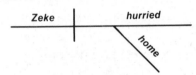

4. Three students tied.

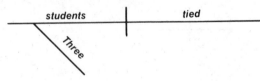

5. Do you remember?

6. Rock back and forth.

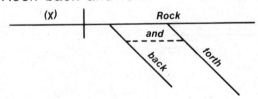

7. You work too hard.

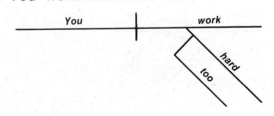

8. The train always arrives late.

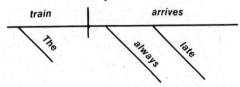

9. The cat meowed.

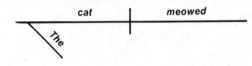

10. The house on the corner burned.

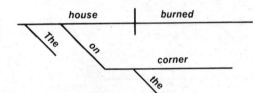

11. Brad and I agree.

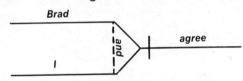

12. Get out!

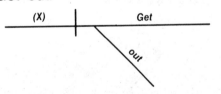

13. The new car shines.

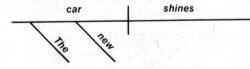

14. A black and white van stopped.

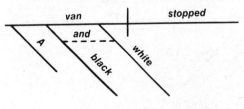

155

Unit 64 cont'd

Diagram Practice

 Diagram these sentences on the lines provided.

1. Chris called here yesterday.

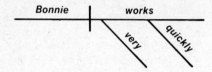

2. Bonnie works very quickly.

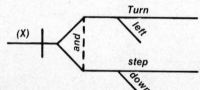

3. Turn left and step down.

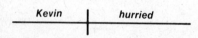

4. Kevin hurried.

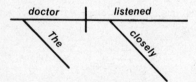

5. The doctor listened closely.

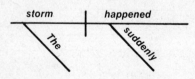

6. The storm happened suddenly.

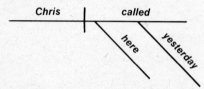

7. Two yellow ballooons popped.

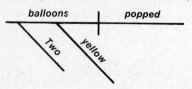

8. The mouse ran under the couch.

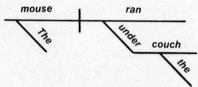

9. Aaron and Barry studied.

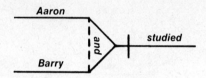

10. What happened here?

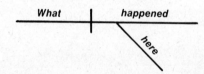

11. His right leg hurts.

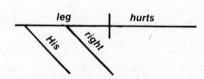

12. The first call wins.

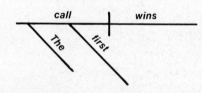

13. Go home.

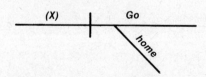

14. Are we leaving today or tomorrow?

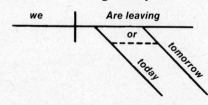

The Direct Object

A direct object is a noun or pronoun that follows the verb and answers the question "who" or "what."

EXAMPLES: a. *I received a letter.*
  b. *She knows my name.*
  c. *Dave likes bananas.*
  d. *Our class built a dollhouse.*

 Underline the direct objects.

1. I hit the ball.
2. He took the money.
3. Jay broke the glass.
4. Mark drives a red car.
5. She closed the door.
6. We rang the bell twice.
7. I found my shoes.
8. The cat drank the milk.
9. James told the secret.
10. Everyone watched the clown.
11. I need a straw.
12. Grandma brought ice cream.
13. Dad cut the grass.
14. Louis read my book.
15. My family owns a farm.
16. Mr. Sims asked the questions.
17. I liked the story.
18. He always wears a hat.
19. The puppy followed me.
20. We raised the flag.
21. Al forgot his coat.
22. The comedian told a joke.
23. Tammy likes Michael.
24. I caught the frog.
25. I want a hamburger.

26. Tim brushed his teeth.
27. We planted a garden.
28. The artist drew my picture.
29. Mom filled the basket.
30. You pushed the button.
31. Eve wrote the letter.
32. My dad bought a car.
33. I heard noises.
34. The monkey took the banana.
35. I did my homework.
36. Cathi picked the flowers.
37. The man built our house.
38. Vicki opened the window.
39. I answered the phone.
40. We took a math test.
41. The dog bit my leg.
42. Walt crossed the street.
43. Diane pushed the button.
44. We climbed the tree.
45. I found the answer.
46. Nancy tasted the soup.
47. I cleaned my room.
48. Jill carried the bucket.
49. The child pulled a wagon.
50. I dropped my book.

COMPOSITION EXERCISE

Write 5 sentences which contain direct objects that answer "who" and 5 that answer "what."

who

1. _____
2. _____
3. _____
4. _____
5. _____

what

1. _____
2. _____
3. _____
4. _____
5. _____

Unit 65 cont'd →

Where to Find Direct Objects

*Direct objects are nouns or pronouns that follow the
verb and answer the question "who" or "what."*

EXAMPLES: a. Gail speaks <u>French</u>.   c. I know the <u>answers</u>.

   b. He killed the <u>snake</u>.   d. Lee opened the <u>windows</u>.

 Underline the direct objects.

1. Ann filled the <u>glasses</u> with water.
2. Felix closed the <u>door</u>.
3. The thief took my <u>watch</u>.
4. I pushed the <u>button</u>.
5. Jamie cut the <u>strings</u>.
6. Mom sang a <u>lullaby</u>.
7. The man ate his <u>supper</u>.
8. Ray bought a new <u>car</u>.
9. Everyone heard the <u>news</u>.
10. The puppy is following <u>me</u>.
11. The child spilled the <u>milk</u>.
12. Dave picked the <u>flowers</u>.
13. He likes <u>me</u>.
14. Joey needs his <u>bike</u>.
15. This monkey hates <u>bananas</u>.
16. I earned the <u>money</u>.
17. We enjoyed the <u>hike</u>.
18. Their team won the <u>game</u>.
19. Grandpa owns this <u>land</u>.
20. Connie caught the <u>fish</u>.
21. Our class is planting a <u>garden</u>.
22. Mom bought a new <u>stove</u>.
23. I need a <u>ride</u>.
24. The cowboy saddled his <u>horse</u>.
25. I haven't any <u>homework</u>.
26. Andy mowed the <u>lawn</u>.
27. No one wanted <u>dessert</u>.
28. I took your <u>advice</u>.
29. The wind blew the <u>leaves</u>.
30. The men pushed the <u>car</u>.
31. The horses jumped the <u>fence</u>.
32. I washed the <u>dishes</u>.
33. The city condemned the <u>building</u>.
34. Dad cut the <u>firewood</u>.
35. My mom plays the <u>drums</u>.
36. I joined the <u>club</u>.
37. We made the <u>gifts</u>.
38. George set up the <u>tent</u>.
39. Our class visited a <u>farm</u>.
40. I broke my <u>nose</u>.
41. Kathy dropped her <u>fork</u>.
42. You used my <u>towel</u>.
43. The birds built a <u>nest</u>.
44. The man stopped the <u>car</u>.
45. We raised the <u>flag</u>.
46. You can keep the <u>kitten</u>.

COMPOSITION EXERCISE

Write 12 sentences which contain direct objects.

1. _____
2. _____
3. _____
4. _____
5. _____
6. _____
7. _____
8. _____
9. _____
10. _____
11. _____
12. _____

Comprehension Check

(A) Diagram these sentences.

1. Casey understood.

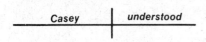

2. Morey and I laughed.

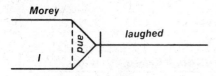

3. The dogs barked and growled.

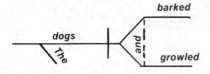

4. The blue team won.

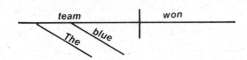

5. Julian left early.

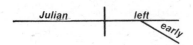

6. The family moved to Ohio.

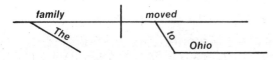

7. The actors rehearse daily.

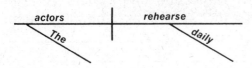

8. Someone with a deep voice called.

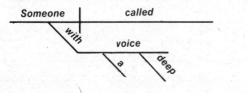

9. Johnny waited for the bus.

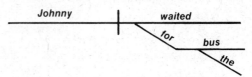

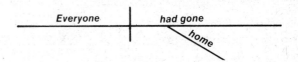

10. Everyone had gone home.

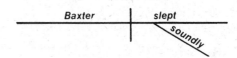

11. Baxter slept soundly.

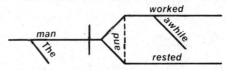

12. The man worked awhile and rested.

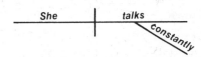

13. She talks constantly.

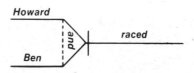

14. Howard and Ben raced.

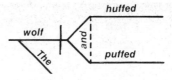

15. The wolf huffed and puffed.

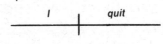

16. I quit!

159

Test 13 cont'd

Comprehension Check (continued)

(B) Identify each part of these N-V sentences.

1. The boy ran outside. _The-article, boy-N, ran-V, outside-adverb_
2. The train whistle blew. _The-article, train-adj., whistle-N, blew-V_
3. Simpson hurried to school. _Simpson-N, hurried-V, to school-prep. phrase_
4. Isaac waited patiently. _Isaac-N, waited-V, patiently-adverb_
5. You can win easily. _You-N, can win-V, easily-adverb_
6. The blue truck sold first. _The-article, blue-adj., truck-N, sold-V, first-adverb_
7. Olson paused. _Olson-N, paused-V_
8. The flag flew proudly. _The-article, flag-N, flew-V, proudly-adverb_
9. Anna answered politely. _Anna-N, answered-V, politely-adverb_
10. The train from Butte arrived. _The-article, train-N, from Butte-prep. phrase, arrived-V_
11. They waited until dark. _They-N, waited-V, until dark-prep. phrase_
12. Someone shouted. _Someone-N, shouted-V_
13. The girl in the hall fainted. _The-article, girl-N, in the hall-prep. phrase, fainted-V_
14. Nancy finished last. _Nancy-N, finished-V, last-adverb_
15. Dyanna walked to the door. _Dyanna-N, walked-V, to the door-prep. phrase_
16. It hurts! _It-N, hurts-V_
17. The rain has stopped. _The-article, rain-N, has stopped-V_
18. Nothing happened to it. _Nothing-N, happened-V, to it-prep. phrase_
19. Suddenly it exploded. _Suddenly-adverb, it-N, exploded-V_
20. Seven people voted. _Seven-adj., people-N, voted-V_

(C) Underline the direct objects.

1. Julio drives a black <u>convertible</u>.
2. My cousin plays professional <u>baseball</u>.
3. She delivers <u>newspapers</u> after school.
4. Jack listed the <u>inventory</u>.
5. The mayor cut the <u>ribbon</u>.
6. I made a pineapple <u>cake</u>.
7. You broke my favorite <u>vase</u>.
8. I'll answer the <u>telephone</u>.
9. Christine plays the <u>piano</u>.
10. We can trust <u>him</u>.
11. The water covered the <u>yard</u>.
12. Liz made the top <u>score</u>.
13. Nick crossed the <u>bridge</u> carefully.
14. Stars lit the <u>sky</u>.
15. Everyone watched the <u>game</u>.
16. Lynn rides a <u>pinto</u>.

Write a paragraph about allowances. How much should an allowance be? Should you get an allowance? Why do you need an allowance? Use at least three N-V sentences. Underline them.

_____
_____
_____
_____
_____
_____
_____

Adding Direct Objects

Direct objects are nouns that follow the verb
and answer the question "who" or "what."

EXAMPLE: a. *Our dog bit the <u>mailman</u>.*   c. *She introduced her <u>parents</u>.*
              b. *Danny chews <u>gum</u>.*   d. *We watched the <u>show</u>.*

 In each blank supply a noun which will serve as a direct object.

1. Sue received a __letter__.
2. Jake lost his __RING__.
3. Our class entered the __CONTEST__.
4. You must sign the __PAPER__.
5. She told the __TRUTH__.
6. He examined my __TEETH__.
7. Mrs. Cain will ring the __BELL__.
8. My mom made this __DRESS__.
9. No one ate the __PIE__.
10. We expected __SNOW__.
11. I smeared the __PAINT__.
12. Dad solved our __PROBLEM__.
13. He took your __ADVICE__.
14. You have my __PERMISSION__.
15. I forgot your __NAME__.
16. Sandy needs a __STRAW__.
17. Mr. Foster made the __DECISION__.
18. The farmer plowed his __FIELD__.
19. The woman bought a __LICENSE__.
20. I paid the __BILL__.
21. Our team played a good __GAME__.
22. Karen helped __SALLY__.
23. Mom prepared a __SNACK__.
24. She explained her __ANSWER__.
25. Mike caught the first __FISH__.
26. Everyone heard the __ECHO__.
27. James broke the __PENCIL__.
28. I saw a __MERMAID__.
29. We found a __SKELETON__.
30. The storm destroyed the __GARDEN__.
31. The comedian told a __JOKE__.
32. Dean dropped the __BALL__.
33. My dog eats __GRAPES__.
34. The monkey climbed the __LADDER__.
35. The dean will ask the __QUESTIONS__.
36. We planted the __TREES__.
37. Tom delivered the __MESSAGE__.
38. They invited our __CLASS__.
39. It includes your __TAXES__.
40. Eric turned the __KNOB__.
41. I trust __CHARLIE__.
42. The coach timed the __RACES__.
43. Sarah cut the __CAKE__.
44. He owns the __STORE__.
45. Paul wants a __BOX__.
46. Al carried the __PACKAGES__.
47. My uncle builds __HOUSES__.
48. I replaced the __LID__.
49. George missed the __TARGET__.
50. We postponed our __TRIP__.

COMPOSITION EXERCISE

Write 12 sentences which contain nouns used as direct objects.

1. _____
2. _____
3. _____
4. _____
5. _____
6. _____
7. _____
8. _____
9. _____
10. _____
11. _____
12. _____

Unit 66 cont'd

Compound Direct Objects

A direct object is a noun that follows the verb and answers the question "who" or "what." It may be compound.

EXAMPLES: a. They served <u>cookies</u> and <u>punch</u>.   c. I chose <u>George</u> and <u>Al</u>.
                  b. Tim likes <u>math</u> and <u>science</u>.   d. We had <u>pizza</u> and <u>ice cream</u>.

  Underline the compound direct objects.

1. I invited <u>Sam</u> and <u>Alice</u>.
2. The man told <u>James</u> and <u>me</u>.
3. He wants <u>clothes</u> and <u>money</u>.
4. Terry has a <u>bike</u> and a <u>car</u>.
5. Mom made a <u>cake</u> and a <u>pie</u>.
6. Wes caught two <u>fish</u> and a <u>frog</u>.
7. I sent a <u>letter</u> and a <u>card</u>.
8. Cory visited his <u>aunt</u> and <u>uncle</u>.
9. She misplaced her <u>pen</u> and <u>paper</u>.
10. I love my <u>mom</u> and <u>dad</u>.
11. Ken plays <u>football</u> and <u>hockey</u>.
12. I miss <u>Sandy</u> and <u>Jill</u>.
13. You must eat <u>fruits</u> and <u>vegetables</u>.
14. We rode a <u>train</u> and a <u>ship</u>.
15. He fixed the <u>sink</u> and the <u>bathtub</u>.
16. Kay lost her <u>socks</u> and <u>shoes</u>.
17. They moved the <u>table</u> and a <u>lamp</u>.
18. Bring the <u>forks</u> and <u>spoons</u>.
19. Joe built the <u>house</u> and the <u>barn</u>.
20. The class elected <u>Phil</u> and <u>me</u>.
21. Felix collects <u>coins</u> and <u>stamps</u>.
22. We read <u>poems</u> and <u>riddles</u>.
23. Sam lost his <u>coat</u> and <u>gloves</u>.
24. I found a <u>rabbit</u> and a <u>turtle</u>.
25. Jan planted <u>onions</u> and <u>carrots</u>.
26. Ann bought <u>balloons</u> and <u>hats</u>.
27. You count the <u>nickels</u> and <u>dimes</u>.
28. We watched the <u>movie</u> and <u>cartoons</u>.
29. He measured the <u>doors</u> and <u>windows</u>.
30. I have two <u>cats</u> and four <u>dogs</u>.
31. Jason spilled his <u>food</u> and <u>drink</u>.
32. You will need a <u>pillow</u> and a <u>blanket</u>.
33. Tina picked <u>daisies</u> and <u>roses</u>.
34. We heard a <u>scream</u> and an <u>echo</u>.
35. I saw <u>Peter</u> and <u>Danny</u>.
36. Sara cooked <u>lunch</u> and <u>dinner</u>.
37. Dad has two <u>cars</u> and a <u>truck</u>.
38. We drew <u>circles</u> and <u>squares</u>.
39. They painted the <u>walls</u> and <u>ceiling</u>.
40. I love <u>candy</u> and <u>ice cream</u>.
41. You should take a <u>raincoat</u> and <u>boots</u>.
42. He doesn't have <u>clothes</u> or <u>money</u>.
43. James brought the <u>chips</u> and <u>ice</u>.
44. This house needs a <u>door</u> and <u>window</u>.
45. Mr. Cobb painted the <u>fence</u> and <u>gate</u>.
46. I trusted <u>Jerry</u> and <u>Susan</u>.
47. We imagined <u>ghosts</u> and <u>witches</u>.
48. Turn in your <u>paper</u> and <u>books</u>.
49. Stan will bring the <u>table</u> and <u>chairs</u>.
50. He needs a <u>bath</u> and clean <u>clothes</u>.

COMPOSITION EXERCISE

Write 8 sentences which contain nouns used as compound direct objects.

1. _____
2. _____
3. _____
4. _____
5. _____
6. _____
7. _____
8. _____

Using Compound Direct Objects

Sentences which have more than one direct object have compound direct objects. These direct objects are connected with conjunctions.

EXAMPLES:
a. She cleaned the house and barn.
b. I need you and Thomas.
c. Bring pencil and paper.
d. He moved the table and chairs.

✱ In each blank write a noun or pronoun which will serve as a direct object.

1. George plays the _piano_ and _guitar_.
2. Karen brought _FRUIT_ and _PIE_.
3. The boy had _MILK_ and _COOKIES_.
4. My dad fixes _CARS_ and _TRUCKS_.
5. Steve took our _NICKELS_ and _DIMES_.
6. We need _MILK_ and _EGGS_.
7. I have a _BROTHER_ and a _SISTER_.
8. Mr. Lewis chose _KAY_ and _MARY_.
9. Dad wants a _HAMMER_ and _NAIL_.
10. She broke the _WINDOW_ and _LAMP_.
11. Build a _HOUSE_ and _PEN_.
12. I hurt my _ARM_ and _LEG_.
13. I can drive a _CAR_ or a _TRUCK_.
14. We saw _GHOSTS_ and _WITCHES_.
15. Lou heard a _ROAR_ and a _SCREAM_.
16. I expected _FELIX_ and _OSCAR_.
17. You water the _ONIONS_ and _PEAS_.
18. Wash your _FACE_ and _HANDS_.
19. We collected _FOOD_ and _CLOTHES_.
20. I finished my _HOMEWORK_ and _CHORES_.
21. Gary picked _GRAPES_ and _BERRIES_.
22. Dad likes _FOOTBALL_ and _BASEBALL_.
23. Don't eat the _BACON_ and _PANCAKES_.
24. Ignore _PATTY_ and _DAVID_.
25. I know her _HEIGHT_ and _WEIGHT_.
26. We had _LIVER_ and _ONIONS_.
27. I invited _ERIC_ and _BILL_ Lance.
28. He has a _TIGER_ and a _MONKEY_.
29. Call _PERRY_ and _MARTY_.
30. It will take _DIMES_ and _QUARTERS_.
31. She washed the _WALLS_ and _FLOORS_.
32. Wear a _HAT_ and _COAT_.
33. I hear _LAUGHING_ and _SINGING_.
34. We climbed _FENCES_ and _TREES_.
35. Thomas ate a _HAMBURGER_ and _FRIES_.
36. We ate _LUNCH_ and _DINNER_ at home.
37. Don't tell _BRENDA_ or _KITTY_.
38. The cowboy rides _HORSES_ and _BULLS_.
39. Mom is cooking _CHICKEN_ and _RICE_.
40. Bring a _BRUSH_ and _COMB_.
41. We caught _SPIDERS_ and _GRASSHOPPERS_.
42. Write _STATEMENTS_ and _QUESTIONS_.
43. Drink _MILK_ and _WATER_.
44. I take _MUSIC_ and _ART_.
45. Answer _TRUE_ or _FALSE_.
46. Discourage _GOSSIP_ and _GREED_.
47. He stole the _MONEY_ and _JEWELS_.
48. Mr. Ford owns _HOUSES_ and _STORES_.
49. Include your _NAME_ and _ADDRESS_.
50. We visited _ARIZONA_ and _UTAH_.

COMPOSITION EXERCISE

Write 8 sentences which contain compound direct objects joined by "and" or "or."

1. _____
2. _____
3. _____
4. _____
5. _____
6. _____
7. _____
8. _____

Unit 67 cont'd →

The N-V-N Pattern

The N-V-N pattern contains a direct object.

EXAMPLES: a. I solved the mystery.
           b. Eric told a lie.

c. Mark told the principal.
d. The rain hit the window.

 Draw one line under the subject, two lines under the verb, and one line under the direct object to show the N-V-N pattern.

1. I mailed the letter.
2. We trusted you.
3. Mr. Kent built the house.
4. Allison made the candy.
5. I bit my lip.
6. The principal hired the man.
7. Kevin delivers newspapers.
8. Deb fed the birds.
9. The dog chewed my shoes.
10. You must buy a license.
11. My uncle owns six horses.
12. The fire burned my finger.
13. Gina caught a mouse.
14. Mr. Fisher called you.
15. Martin killed the spider.
16. A dog caused the accident.
17. Kelly and I played "Clue."
18. Tammy is giving a party.
19. I counted the money.
20. Our family loves camping.
21. She writes poetry.
22. We will need ten balloons.
23. He heard your voice.
24. I finished the assignment.
25. The rabbit wants a carrot.

26. Mr. Sims postponed the meeting.
27. They know the password.
28. Mia is wearing moccasins.
29. I have located the problem.
30. Art will fix the flat.
31. I spent my allowance.
32. The officer found the jewels.
33. We climbed the mountain.
34. Donna won a prize.
35. My brother lost his wallet.
36. Larry likes math.
37. We crossed the river.
38. The wind destroyed the flowers.
39. I received an invitation.
40. The squirrel climbed the tree.
41. Dave will carry the box.
42. I brushed my teeth.
43. Sharon noted the changes.
44. He understands Spanish.
45. Mother baked a cake.
46. Alice brought the keys.
47. We won the battle.
48. Bob hurt his foot.
49. You are spilling the milk.
50. Mrs. Jackson set the deadline.

COMPOSITION EXERCISE

Write 10 sentences that follow the N-V-N pattern.

1. _____
2. _____
3. _____
4. _____
5. _____

6. _____
7. _____
8. _____
9. _____
10. _____

N-V-N Sentences

The N-V-N pattern consists of a subject, a verb, and a direct object.

EXAMPLES: a. Dad bought a boat.   c. I received a letter.
           b. Bill hurt his arm.   d. Mike kicked the ball.

 Underline the sentences that follow the N-V-N pattern.

1. We planted a garden.
2. Mom drives a car.
3. The letter came today.
4. The telephone rang.
5. It needs water.
6. Sarah broke the television.
7. We washed the windows.
8. Mark is not coming.
9. I lost my money.
10. The clown cried.
11. The fire burned our trees.
12. We crossed the river.
13. The wind was blowing.
14. We bought the license.
15. The voyage ended.
16. Paul dropped the lamp.
17. This pen writes.
18. I could hear an echo.
19. The rain stopped.
20. I brushed my teeth.
21. The car blocked the road.
22. The sack broke.
23. The bird built a nest.
24. The boy confessed.
25. The kitten followed me.

26. They left early.
27. The birds ate the seeds.
28. The food disappeared.
29. Dad read the newspaper.
30. I told our secret.
31. The boat sailed.
32. The horse pulled the sleigh.
33. Nancy called.
34. You carry the basket.
35. I need a spoon.
36. Dave caught a rabbit.
37. The monkey slept.
38. The man escaped.
39. Kathy set the table.
40. The owner locked the door.
41. George plays the drums.
42. I need more room.
43. We walked away.
44. No one answered.
45. Jane helped her mother.
46. The house was surrounded.
47. Fran made the decision.
48. She repeated her question.
49. We saw the lights.
50. The problem is solved.

COMPOSITION EXERCISE

Write 12 N-V-N sentences.

1. _____
2. _____
3. _____
4. _____
5. _____
6. _____

7. _____
8. _____
9. _____
10. _____
11. _____
12. _____

Unit 68 cont'd

Identifying N-V and N-V-N Patterns

The N-V pattern consists of a subject and a verb. The N-V-N pattern consists of a subject, a verb, and a direct object.

EXAMPLES: N-V sentences:
    a. The horses galloped.
    b. Carlton understands.

N-V-N sentences:
    a. We washed the car.
    b. Dad read the paper.

 Write N-V or N-V-N in each blank.

N-V	1. The fire burned.		N-V-N	26. I wrote a sentence.
N-V-N	2. The man caught a fish.		N-V-N	27. Jean told a joke.
N-V	3. The whistle blew.		N-V-N	28. They ate chicken.
N-V-N	4. She broke my pencil.		N-V	29. The puppy cried.
N-V	5. The woman screamed.		N-V-N	30. We will sing a song.
N-V-N	6. I found a pen.		N-V	31. Mary is moving.
N-V	7. The zoo was closed.		N-V	32. The train stopped.
N-V-N	8. I bought an apple.		N-V-N	33. The dog chewed my shoe.
N-V-N	9. I fixed the car.		N-V	34. Birds fly.
N-V	10. The door slammed.		N-V-N	35. John made a mess.
N-V-N	11. I need two chairs.		N-V-N	36. We named the rabbit.
N-V	12. The road ended.		N-V	37. It rained.
N-V-N	13. Jane ran a touchdown.		N-V	38. The lion roared.
N-V-N	14. I ride a bike.		N-V	39. The fish smelled.
N-V	15. The dog waited.		N-V-N	40. He milked the cows.
N-V	16. The glass broke.		N-V	41. The baby smiled.
N-V-N	17. Tim hit the ball.		N-V-N	42. We found a clue.
N-V	18. The men are leaving.		N-V-N	43. The cow ate the hay.
N-V-N	19. I like hamburgers.		N-V	44. The coward ran.
N-V-N	20. Alice set the table.		N-V	45. The movie began.
N-V	21. I will walk.		N-V	46. We hurried home.
N-V	22. Worms crawl.		N-V-N	47. She told the truth.
N-V-N	23. He robbed the bank.		N-V-N	48. Dad took our picture.
N-V-N	24. I watered the garden.		N-V	49. The apples are falling.
N-V	25. My watch has stopped.		N-V-N	50. I mailed the letter.

COMPOSITION EXERCISE

Write 5 N-V sentences and 5 N-V-N sentences.

N-V

1. _____
2. _____
3. _____
4. _____
5. _____

N-V-N

1. _____
2. _____
3. _____
4. _____
5. _____

Diagramming N-V-N Sentences

The **N-V-N** sentence consists of a subject, a transitive verb, and a direct object. It is diagrammed as follows:

| (subject) | (verb) | (direct object) |

Notice the position of this line.

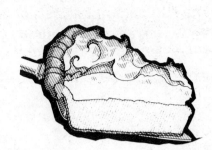

 Diagram these sentences on the lines provided.

1. Henry likes history.

| Henry | likes | history |

2. You made a mess.

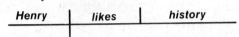

3. His brother owns the place.

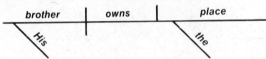

4. Jules ordered fish.

| Jules | ordered | fish |

5. Ed sold the house.

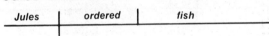

6. I have a pencil.

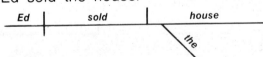

7. James chose B.

| James | chose | B |

8. Tony read the lesson.

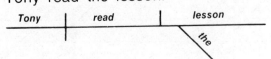

9. We passed the exam.

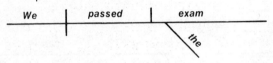

10. Someone took my book.

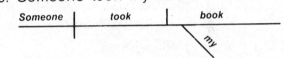

11. I mailed the package.

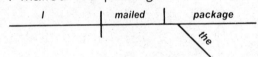

12. The boy burned his finger.

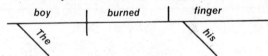

13. The police questioned Ben.

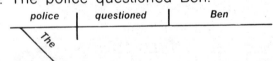

14. No one saw us.

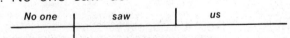

15. Have you finished the paper?

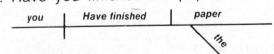

16. It makes six servings.

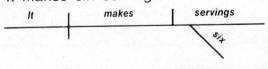

Unit 69 cont'd

Diagramming Adjectives and N-V-N Sentences

An adjective may modify the subject or the direct object of the N-V-N sentence. It is diagrammed as follows:

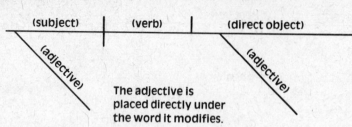

(subject) | (verb) | (direct object)

(adjective)   (adjective)

The adjective is placed directly under the word it modifies.

 Diagram these sentences on the lines provided.

1. Steve brought a blue cap.

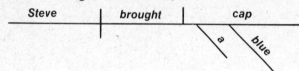

2. An old man made this bench.

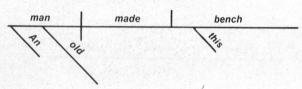

3. They changed the travel date.

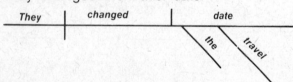

4. The clerk charged the old prices.

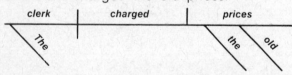

5. Margie baked a chocolate cake.

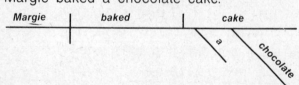

6. Many students volunteered their Saturdays.

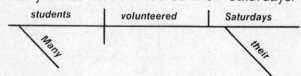

7. The tall girl plays basketball.

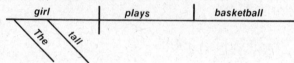

8. I opened another jar.

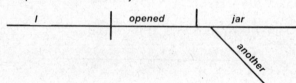

9. Ellen needs more time.

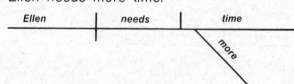

10. The woman told a sad story.

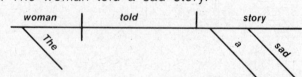

11. Do you like funny movies?

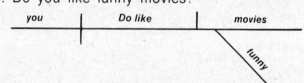

12. The detective found no helpful clues.

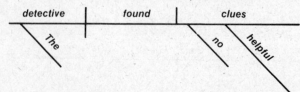

168

Diagramming Adverbs and N-V-N Sentences

An adverb may modify the transitive verb in the N-V-N sentence.
It is diagrammed as follows:

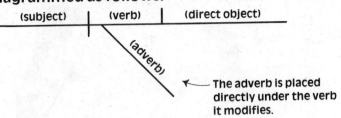

| (subject) | (verb) | (direct object) |

(adverb)

← The adverb is placed directly under the verb it modifies.

 Diagram these sentences on the lines provided.

1. The family always buys Brand X.

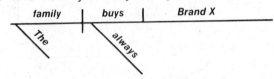

2. I usually read mystery novels.

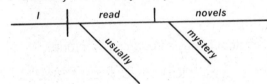

3. I took the package upstairs.

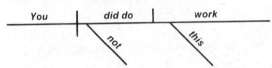

4. Dick answered the question correctly.

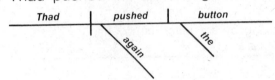

5. Les fixed the motor easily.

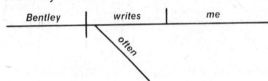

6. Sheila tried it once.

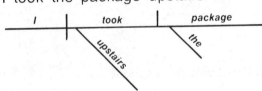

7. Thad pushed the button again.

8. You did not do this work.

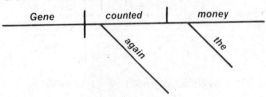

9. Bentley writes me often.

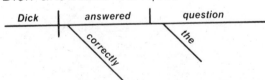

10. Dan solved the puzzle easily.

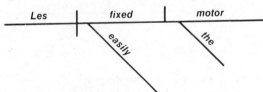

11. Gene counted the money again.

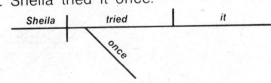

12. I rented the room downstairs.

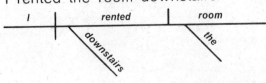

Unit 70 cont'd

Diagramming N-V-N Sentences with Prepositional Phrases

A prepositional phrase may modify the subject, the transitive verb, or the direct object of the N-V-N sentence. It is diagrammed as follows:

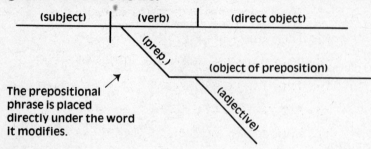

The prepositional phrase is placed directly under the word it modifies.

✳ Diagram these sentences on the line provided.

1. The dog by the fence bit my hand.

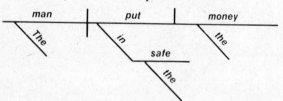

2. Her cousin wore a hat with blue stripes.

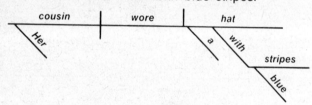

3. The man put the money in the safe.

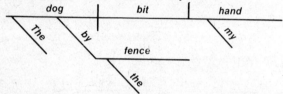

4. I decorated the room in green.

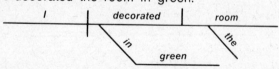

5. Did you recognize the man with Charles?

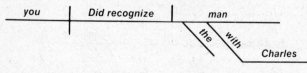

6. I travelled Europe in June.

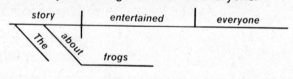

7. The story about frogs entertained everyone.

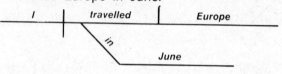

8. Bob put a worm on the hook.

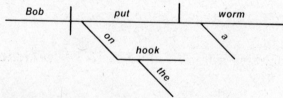

9. Tanya took the bus to Dallas.

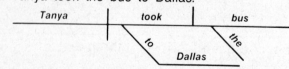

10. We planned the trip to the beach.

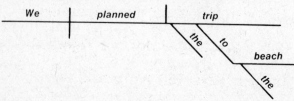

Comprehension Check

(A) **Underline the direct objects.**

1. I bought a <u>ticket</u> to Hawaii.
2. We flew a <u>jet</u> from Los Angeles.
3. We rented a <u>house</u> on the beach.
4. Rick and I took surfing <u>lessons</u>.
5. We rode the <u>waves</u> all day.
6. Rick learned <u>sailing</u> too.
7. We love the <u>sunshine</u>.
8. Tomorrow we'll visit the <u>volcano</u>.
9. Then we'll see native <u>dancers</u>.
10. We'll take a <u>boat</u> to Oahu.
11. Rick and I love <u>vacations</u>.
12. They read the <u>brochure</u> carefully.
13. The Tates sold their <u>house</u>.
14. Karen needs <u>help</u> with her bags.
15. The trip costs <u>$1200</u>.
16. Arnold followed <u>us</u>.
17. Lou drove the <u>car</u> to the airport.
18. He met <u>us</u> there.
19. John took our <u>bags</u> to the car.
20. I planned our next <u>trip</u>.

(B) **Place an "x" beside each sentence which contains a compound direct object.**

__x__ 1. Tonight we are having spaghetti and salad.
__x__ 2. My family watched a movie and the news.
__x__ 3. Samuel ordered ice cream and cake.
_____ 4. Janet dropped the heavy box on her foot.
__x__ 5. We still need potato chips and pickles for the picnic.
_____ 6. The teacher assigned two chapters for tomorrow.
__x__ 7. Sharon received flowers and candy from George.
__x__ 8. The dog stole my shoes and my cap.
_____ 9. They can take the bus to the museum.
__x__ 10. I'm taking literature and German next semester.

(C) **Identify each part of these N-V-N sentences.**

1. Cynthia wrote the best essay.
   N   *V*   *N*

2. Mr. Hawkins had hired Franklin.
   N   *V*   *N*

3. The contestant chose the box.
      N   *V*   *N*

4. I had dinner with Dr. Martin.
   N V   *N*

5. The man delivered the magazines.
     N   *V*   *N*

6. Bob plays football for the Tigers.
  N   *V*   *N*

7. The job pays $50 per week.
     N   *V*   *N*

8. Candace read the book last night.
  N   *V*   *N*

9. Jill didn't bring an umbrella.
  N   *V*   *N*

10. We can play Monopoly.
   N   *V*   *N*

11. I made an appointment for three.
  N V   *N*

12. The people voted "yes."
     N   *V*   *N*

13. Bonnie met Jackie at school.
  N   *V*   *N*

14. My cousin drives a jeep.
    N   *V*   *N*

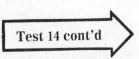 Test 14 cont'd

Comprehension Check (continued)

(D) Place an "x" beside each N-V-N sentence.

_X_ 1. I caught a fish with a worm.
_X_ 2. Dave caught one too.
___ 3. We fish every Saturday.
_X_ 4. Mom cooks our fish for us.
_X_ 5. She fries them.
_X_ 6. I love fried fish and cornbread.
___ 7. It is good!
_X_ 8. Mom never eats fish.
_X_ 9. She doesn't like the smell.
_X_ 10. Once she went fishing with us.

_X_ 11. She caught the first fish.
___ 12. She fell out of the boat.
_X_ 13. The fish chased her.
_X_ 14. It bit her arm.
___ 15. She screamed.
_X_ 16. Then she grabbed the fish.
_X_ 17. She hit him on the head.
___ 18. The fish gave up.
_X_ 19. She threw the fish in the boat.
_X_ 20. She has hated fish ever since.

(E) Diagram these N-V-N sentences.

1. Carlos gave a good speech.

| Carlos | gave | speech |
a / good

2. My cat likes popcorn.

| cat | likes | popcorn |
My

3. Someone moved the furniture.

| Someone | moved | furniture |
the

4. Blake needs our friendship.

| Blake | needs | friendship |
our

5. Wesley hates cauliflower.

| Wesley | hates | cauliflower |

6. We worked the problems easily.

| We | worked | problems |
easily / the

7. Close the door.

| (X) | Close | door |
the

8. I made the cookies for Hester.

| I | made | cookies |
the / for Hester

9. The aardvark eats ants.

| aardvark | eats | ants |
The

10. Do you speak Italian?

| you | Do speak | Italian |

Write a paragraph about something you would like to change. Use at least three N-V-N sentences.

_____
_____
_____
_____
_____
_____
_____
_____

When a Noun Follows a Linking Verb

A noun that follows a linking verb renames the
subject of the sentence.

EXAMPLES: a. *The prize is a collie.*   c. *The man was a policeman.*
                b. *You are the leader.*   d. *Ted and I were the winners.*

  In each blank write a noun that renames
the subject.

1. Her name is _____ *Susan* _____ .
2. Sarah is a __SECRETARY__ .
3. The room was a __DISASTER__ .
4. Karen is a __SOLDIER__ .
5. That story is __GOSSIP__ .
6. My parents are __LAWYERS__ .
7. The tuna is a __FISH__ .
8. The story was a __MYSTERY__ .
9. We were __MEMBERS__ .
10. These shoes are __MOCCASINS__ .
11. Maggie is a __NURSE__ .
12. My friend was a __POLICEMAN__ .
13. The principal is my __AUNT__ .
14. The building is a __HOSPITAL__ .
15. Our play is a __COMEDY__ .
16. The sentence was a __QUESTION__ .
17. Dolls are __TOYS__ .
18. An almanac is a __BOOK__ .
19. My brother is the __PILOT__ .
20. George and Peter are __TWINS__ .
21. That woman is my __MOTHER__ .
22. Sally was the __QUEEN__ .
23. My dog is a __POODLE__ .
24. The clown is __JAMIE__ .
25. Nancy and I are __FRIENDS__ .

26. Seymour is my __RABBIT__ .
27. An apple is a __FRUIT__ .
28. These flowers are __DAISIES__ .
29. Leroy was my __NEIGHBOR__ .
30. The woman is a __PLUMBER__ .
31. Alice is your __SISTER__ .
32. This tool is a __WRENCH__ .
33. The jewels were __DIAMONDS__ .
34. The cellar is our __DUNGEON__ .
35. Carrots are __VEGETABLES__ .
36. I am a __STUDENT__ .
37. The coin is a __PENNY__ .
38. This liquid is __WATER__ .
39. The animal was a __RACCOON__ .
40. My grandfather is the __OWNER__ .
41. The bird was a __ROBIN__ .
42. Lester is a __FROG__ .
43. This room is our __DEN__ .
44. The snake is my __PET__ .
45. Our guest speaker was a __WRITER__ .
46. Mr. Brown is our __PRINCIPAL__ .
47. She is a __WITCH__ .
48. You are the __MERMAID__ .
49. My teacher was __MISS COX__ .
50. Charlie is my __AARDVARK__ .

COMPOSITION EXERCISE

Write 10 sentences which contain nouns that follow linking verbs.

1. _____
2. _____
3. _____
4. _____
5. _____

6. _____
7. _____
8. _____
9. _____
10. _____

Unit 71 cont'd →

The N-LV-N Pattern

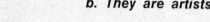

The N-LV-N pattern contains a linking verb followed by a noun that renames the subject.

EXAMPLES: a. *Mr. Owens is a pilot.*   c. *This house is my home.*
           b. *They are artists.*   d. *I am a teacher.*

 Underline each noun that follows a linking verb and renames a subject.

1. My dad is a lawyer.
2. The book is an almanac.
3. He was my neighbor.
4. Mrs. Erin is my aunt.
5. Susan was the winner.
6. The frog is my pet.
7. George was our leader.
8. The number is twelve.
9. My story is the truth.
10. Pam and Sue are my sisters.
11. That noise is an echo.
12. The animal is my friend.
13. These sandwiches are our lunch.
14. Al and Tom were enemies.
15. The basement is our jail.
16. These trees are pines.
17. That lady is Mrs. Horton.
18. This fruit is an orange.
19. James and Tom were farmers.
20. The drink is a Pepsi.
21. He was a cowboy.
22. Jewels are a luxury.
23. Our captain is Mr. Connors.
24. I am a scout.
25. The woman is a fake.
26. Her brother was the artist.
27. This flower is a rose.
28. Mark was our president.
29. The man is a thief.
30. Those birds are robins.
31. The movie is a comedy.
32. The judge was my uncle.
33. Alex is a mouse.
34. This room is the office.
35. Lions are wild animals.
36. Peter is a clown.
37. Those men are soldiers.
38. The coin is a quarter.
39. This plant is a cactus.
40. The pen is a Bic.
41. I am the treasurer.
42. That fish was a shark.
43. John is a guest.
44. Nursing is a good career.
45. The game was football.
46. The pan is a skillet.
47. Jack and I are classmates.
48. This building is a hospital.
49. The man is a famous actor.
50. Our show was a disaster.

COMPOSITION EXERCISE

Write 12 N-LV-N sentences.

1. _____
2. _____
3. _____
4. _____
5. _____
6. _____
7. _____
8. _____
9. _____
10. _____
11. _____
12. _____

Diagramming the N-LV-N Sentence

A N-LV-N sentence consists of a subject, a linking verb, and a predicate noun which renames the subject. It is diagrammed as follows:

(subject) | (linking verb) \ (predicate noun)

Notice how this line slants.

✱ **Diagram these sentences on the lines provided.**

1. Arnold is my friend.

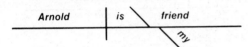

2. Lucy was secretary.

3. It is a timer.

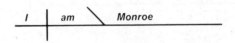

4. You will be boss.

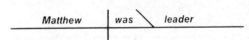

5. Is it the answer?

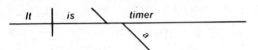

6. The owner is Mr. Waddell.

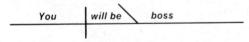

7. We are the winners!

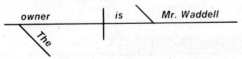

8. He became king.

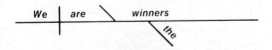

9. I am Monroe.

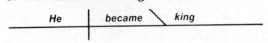

10. Matthew was leader.

11. The banker is my neighbor.

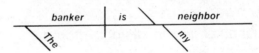

12. It is the end.

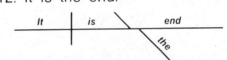

13. You are a thief!

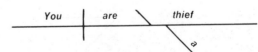

14. This is chaos!

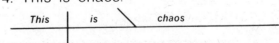

15. The sandwich is my dinner.

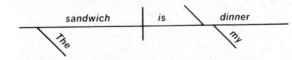

16. Rita is her cousin.

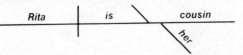

Unit 72 cont'd ▶

Diagramming Adjectives and N-LV-N Sentences

An adjective may modify the subject or the predicate noun of a N-LV-N sentence. It is diagrammed as follows:

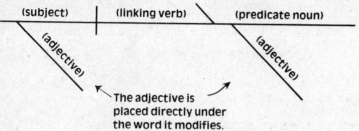

The adjective is placed directly under the word it modifies.

 Diagram these sentences on the lines provided.

1. The tall boy is an athlete.

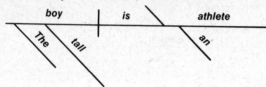

2. The blonde girl is Karen.

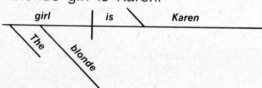

3. Susan's mother is the district attorney.

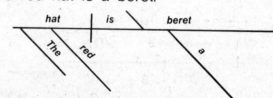

4. The old man was my grandfather.

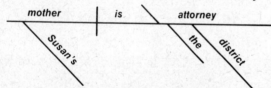

5. Dyanna is the new secretary.

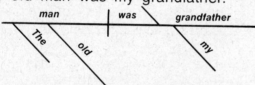

6. The first deadline is Monday.

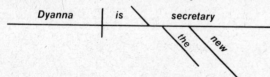

7. These men are outlaws.

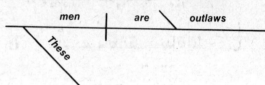

8. Eric is a good student.

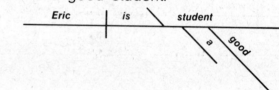

9. The red hat is a beret.

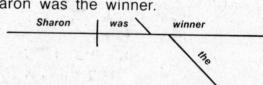

10. Sharon was the winner.

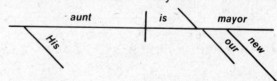

11. His aunt is our new mayor.

12. Six big dogs were the culprits.

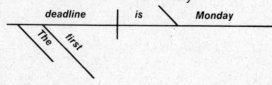

176

Diagramming Adverbs and N-LV-N Sentences

An adverb may modify the linking verb of a N-LV-N sentence. It is diagrammed as follows:

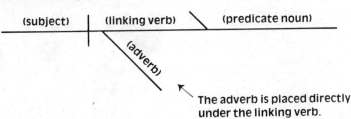

(subject) | (linking verb) \ (predicate noun)

(adverb)

The adverb is placed directly under the linking verb.

 Diagram these sentences on the lines provided.

1. He was supervisor then.

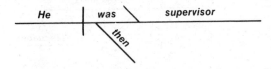

2. Paula has never been a leader.

3. Howard was always the captain.

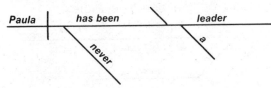

4. Yesterday I was the boss.

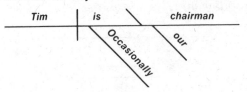

5. That building has never been a store.

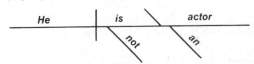

6. Mr. Hill is still the best plumber.

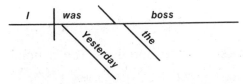

7. Glenn will always be a child.

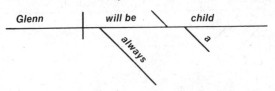

8. Occasionally Tim is our chairman.

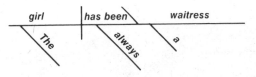

9. He is not an actor.

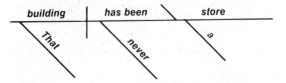

10. The girl has always been a waitress.

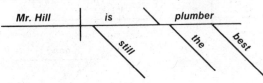

11. My bicycle is now a racer.

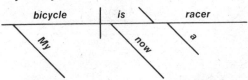

12. Someday you may be the President.

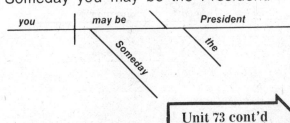

Unit 73 cont'd

Diagramming N-LV-N Sentences
with Prepositional Phrases

A prepositional phrase may modify the subject, the linking verb, or the predicate noun of the N-LV-N sentence. It is diagrammed as follows:

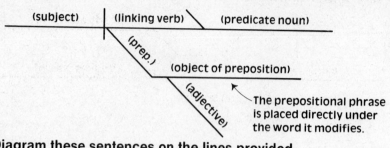

(subject) | (linking verb) \ (predicate noun)

(prep.)

(object of preposition)

(adjective)

The prepositional phrase is placed directly under the word it modifies.

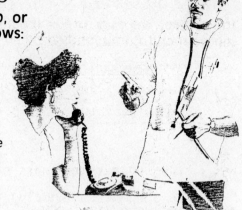

 Diagram these sentences on the lines provided.

1. The building on the left is Congress.

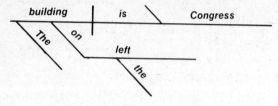

2. On Monday Judy is a cashier.

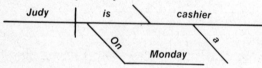

3. Arnold is my cousin from Ohio.

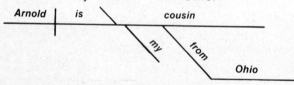

4. The assistant to Dr. Adams is Brenda.

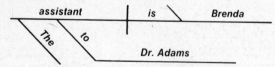

5. In the morning he will be the governor.

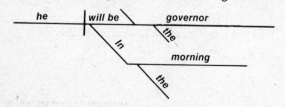

6. George is a student of languages.

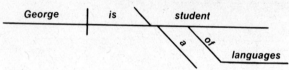

7. The dog on the porch is Pigley.

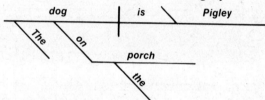

8. The senator from Nebraska is his uncle.

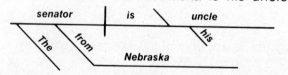

9. The house on the corner is Tom's home.

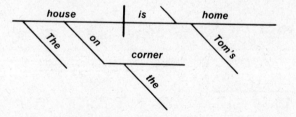

10. Jim was leader of the gang.

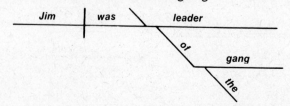

Diagramming N-LV-N Sentences with Compounds

The subject, verb, or predicate noun of a N-LV-N sentence may be compounded. Compounds are diagrammed as follows:

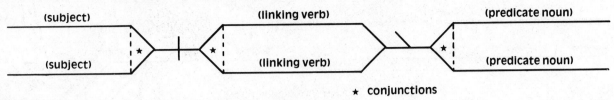

★ conjunctions

 Diagram these sentences on the lines provided.

1. Bob and Benny are brothers.

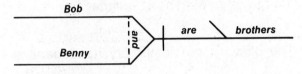

2. The answers are A and C.

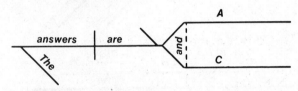

3. Eric is and always has been a good student.

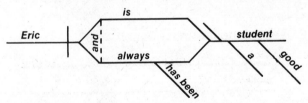

4. Was he a captain or a colonel?

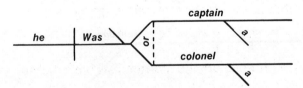

5. Sandra and Kim became nurses.

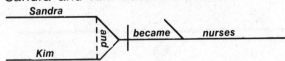

6. The owners are a lawyer and an accountant.

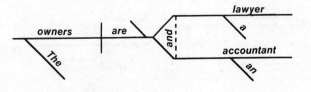

7. The prizes are money and a car.

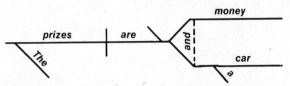

8. Larry and Adam are rivals.

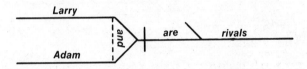

9. Kate is now and always will be my friend.

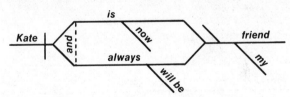

10. The man is a liar and thief.

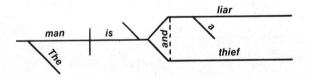

11. Chuck and Jason are roommates.

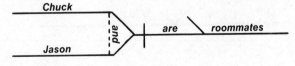

12. Was Kevin or David the artist?

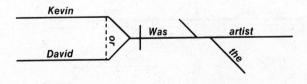

Unit 74 cont'd

N-LV-N Sentence Diagrams

Diagram these sentences.

1. Stephen was Romeo.

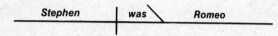

2. The dog is not a pedigree.

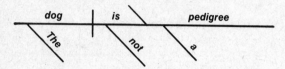

3. Lou and Jean are twins.

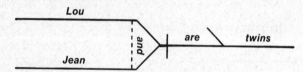

4. The woman is the pilot.

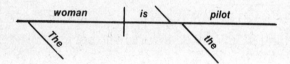

5. Was he an actor or a writer?

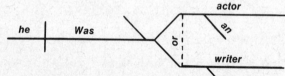

6. Lisa was the only volunteer.

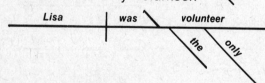

7. Now he is the owner.

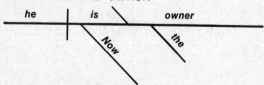

8. Dr. Barker was the defense attorney.

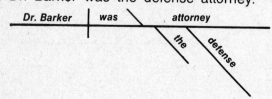

9. Georgia is a southern state.

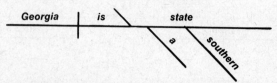

10. Poindexter is my cat.

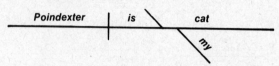

11. The office is our temporary headquarters.

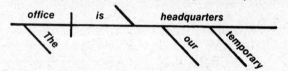

12. Ruth will always be best player.

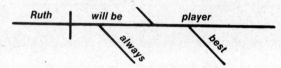

13. The piano is an antique.

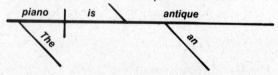

14. Johnathan will be the announcer.

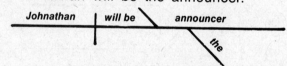

15. Rick is never the leader.

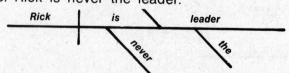

16. You and I are partners.

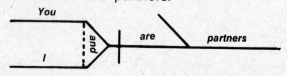

When an Adjective Follows a Linking Verb

An adjective that follows a linking verb describes the subject of the sentence.

EXAMPLES:
a. *The bear is <u>hungry</u>.*
b. *They are <u>greedy</u>.*
c. *Our homework was <u>easy</u>.*
d. *The men were <u>tired</u>.*

✱ In each blank write an adjective that describes the subject.

1. Mary is ___tall___.
2. Her hair is __BLONDE__.
3. The puppy is __BLACK__.
4. The meal was __DELICIOUS__.
5. The people were __ANGRY__.
6. Your aunt is __UPSET__.
7. His eyes are __BLUE__.
8. The dress is too __SMALL__.
9. The music was __RELAXING__.
10. Our fight was __SILLY__.
11. Ted is __SLEEPY__.
12. The flowers were __YELLOW__.
13. The witch is __WICKED__.
14. The kitten is __CUTE__.
15. The owners are __RICH__.
16. The spears were __SHARP__.
17. The fence is too __HIGH__.
18. Your face is __DIRTY__.
19. Our school is __NEW__.
20. An apple is __ROUND__.
21. The floors are __WET__.
22. The sick man was __WEAK__.
23. A window was __OPEN__.
24. The milk is __SOUR__.
25. The news was __SAD__.
26. He was __RUDE__.
27. This breeze is __CHILLY__.
28. It was __FALSE__.
29. The lights are too __BRIGHT__.
30. We were __CONFIDENT__.
31. The child is __BASHFUL__.
32. The dog was __ALERT__.
33. That sentence is __AWKWARD__.
34. Alex was __BRAVE__.
35. Those answers are __CORRECT__.
36. These scissors are __USELESS__.
37. You are __IMPORTANT__.
38. The grass is __GREEN__.
39. The boxes were __SQUARE__.
40. Katie is __TALL__.
41. The color is too __DARK__.
42. The baby bird is __TINY__.
43. The old woman was __KIND__.
44. The eggs were __ROTTEN__.
45. The rain was __COLD__.
46. The trip is __DANGEROUS__.
47. The job was __IDEAL__.
48. The clues were __HELPFUL__.
49. The punishment is __CRUEL__.
50. This exercise is __EASY__.

COMPOSITION EXERCISE

Write 12 sentences which contain adjectives that follow linking verbs.

1. _____
2. _____
3. _____
4. _____
5. _____
6. _____
7. _____
8. _____
9. _____
10. _____
11. _____
12. _____

Unit 75 cont'd

The N-LV-Adj. Pattern

The N-LV-Adj. pattern contains a linking verb followed by an adjective that describes the subject.

EXAMPLES:
a. The rooms were cold.
b. His face was green.
c. I am short.
d. Sally is helpless.

✳ Underline each adjective that follows a linking verb and describes the subject.

1. The storm was terrible.
2. The poem is nonsense.
3. The statements were true.
4. These jewels are valuable.
5. The comedian was funny.
6. Our show was silly.
7. She is nice.
8. The rooms are large.
9. Her answers were uncertain.
10. The melons are ripe.
11. Your idea is better.
12. The people are noisy.
13. Her nose is red.
14. An actress is glamorous.
15. The kitchen was clean.
16. I am thirsty.
17. The spoons were silver.
18. Highways are dangerous.
19. The roast is tender.
20. The clown is sad.
21. Dave is smart.
22. That joke was stupid.
23. The glasses are full.
24. They were poor.
25. My dog is obedient.
26. The kitchen is clean.
27. The buildings are old.
28. Candy is sweet.
29. My mother is beautiful.
30. The table was square.
31. Paul was tired.
32. The dog is healthy.
33. Your clothes are dry.
34. The package was open.
35. This water is muddy.
36. Your reasons are important.
37. The birds were hungry.
38. This painting is perfect.
39. This rope is strong.
40. The puppy was lonely.
41. This plant is healthy.
42. The movie was boring.
43. Richard is shy.
44. This room is different.
45. Dad was proud.
46. That dog is mean.
47. The call was important.
48. Sharon was polite.
49. The book is interesting.
50. Your manners are terrible.

COMPOSITION EXERCISE

Write 12 N-LV-Adj. sentences.

1. _____
2. _____
3. _____
4. _____
5. _____
6. _____
7. _____
8. _____
9. _____
10. _____
11. _____
12. _____

Comprehension Check

A Underline the nouns.

1. movie
2. bicycle
3. shiny
4. Michael
5. seem
6. automobile
7. newest
8. school
9. Kathy
10. happy
11. class
12. Jennifer
13. window
14. wider
15. language
16. were
17. Ramon
18. rocky
19. traveler
20. into

B Underline the linking verbs.

1. is
2. points
3. will be
4. seems
5. washes
6. am
7. believe
8. became
9. took
10. were
11. walks
12. become
13. was
14. looks
15. skate
16. appear
17. carried
18. are
19. seem
20. hide

C Identify each part of these N-LV-N sentences.

    N   LV   N
1. The island is now a resort.

    N   LV   N
2. Football is a contact sport.

    N   LV   N
3. Andrea was Ronald's coach.

    N LV   N
4. It is now four o'clock.

    N   LV N
5. Tonight's supper is sandwiches.

    N   LV   N
6. "Cosby" is his favorite show.

    N   LV   N
7. You will be our guide.

    N   LV N
8. The room upstairs is a disaster.

    N   LV   N
9. Marvin is the boy next to Ken.

    N   LV   N
10. Theodore was a turtle.

    N   N LV   N
11. Harriet and I were captains.

    N   LV   N
12. That area will be the playground.

    N   LV   N
13. Jillian became a good cook.

    N   LV   N
14. The result was chaos.

    N LV   N
15. He is a volunteer.

    N   LV   N
16. The river is the boundary.

    N   LV   N
17. James is the leader of the gang.

    N   LV   N
18. Karin was the top gymnast.

    N LV   N
19. We were guests of Dr. Owens.

    N   LV N
20. The highest grade was 84.

D Write 10 N-LV-N sentences about members of your family.

1. *My mother is an accountant.*
2. *She is my best friend.*
3. *My father is a banker.*
4. *He is a good listener.*
5. *My parents are Saturday golfers.*
6. *Joan is my sister.*
7. *Jim is my brother.*
8. *They are my siblings.*
9. *We are a happy family.*
10. *I am the youngest member.*

Test 15 cont'd →

Comprehension Check (continued)

E Explain why each of these sentences follow the N-LV-N pattern.

1. These animals are weasels.
2. You are the new champion.
3. Cameron was the guilty one.
4. Dr. Hubbert is a friend of mine.
5. That building was the Justice Complex.
6. Reginald is an excellent dancer.
7. My birthday is November 20.
8. The clock is an antique.
9. Dyanna became a dentist.
10. Ms. Harris is Alfred's mother.

"weasels" renames "animals"
"champion" renames "you"
"one" renames "Cameron"
"friend" renames "Dr. Hubbert"
"Justice Complex" renames "building"
"dancer" renames "Reginald"
"November 20" renames "birthday"
"antique" renames "clock"
"dentist" renames "Dyanna"
"mother" renames "Ms. Harris"

F Diagram these N-LV-N sentences.

1. Lisa is the smartest student.

| Lisa | is | student |

the / smartest

2. Alice became our tutor.

| Alice | became | tutor |

our

3. This room will be your office.

| room | will be | office |

This / your

4. Wilbur was the pitcher.

| Wilbur | was | pitcher |

the

5. The answer is yes.

| answer | is | yes |

The

6. Capt. Stewart was chief officer.

| Capt. Stewart | was | officer |

chief

7. Lionel is his partner.

| Lionel | is | partner |

his

8. Brandon was our first choice.

| Brandon | was | choice |

our / first

9. The boy in blue is Mitchell.

| boy | is | Mitchell |

The / in / blue

10. Erica will be the teacher today.

| Erica | will be | teacher |

today / the

Write a short paragraph describing you as a student. Use at least two N-LV-N sentences.

Diagramming N-LV-Adj. Sentences

A N-LV-Adj. sentence consists of a subject, a linking verb, and a predicate adjective which describes the subject. It is diagrammed as follows:

(subject) | (linking verb) \ (predicate adjective)

Notice how this line slants.

 Diagram these sentences on the lines provided.

1. Margie seems happy.

Margie | seems \ happy

2. He became nervous.

He | became \ nervous

3. Wally looks exhausted.

Wally | looks \ exhausted

4. It was fantastic!

It | was \ fantastic

5. You are lazy.

You | are \ lazy

6. I am afraid.

I | am \ afraid

7. It sounds painful.

It | sounds \ painful

8. Are you sure?

you | Are \ sure

9. We were ready.

We | were \ ready

10. Donnie sounds hoarse.

Donnie | sounds \ hoarse

11. Mrs. Carlson looks upset.

Mrs. Carlson | looks \ upset

12. Jennifer feels unwanted.

Jennifer | feels \ unwanted

13. She became ill.

She | became \ ill

14. You are wrong.

You | are \ wrong

15. Wesley is busy.

Wesley | is \ busy

16. They were polite.

They | were \ polite

Unit 76 cont'd

Diagramming Adjectives and N-LV-Adj. Sentences

An adjective may modify the subject of a N-LV-Adj. sentence. It is diagrammed as follows:

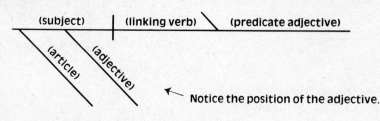

(subject) | (linking verb) \ (predicate adjective)

(article) (adjective)

Notice the position of the adjective.

 Diagram these sentences on the lines provided.

1. The last one is mine.

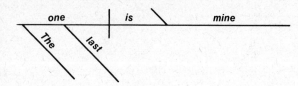

one | is \ mine
The / last

7. Our new car is red.

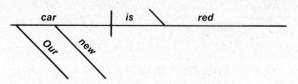

car | is \ red
Our / new

2. Your other hat is blue.

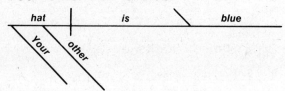

hat | is \ blue
Your / other

8. The fourth question was hard.

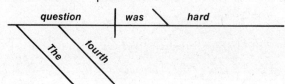

question | was \ hard
The / fourth

3. The old house looks haunted.

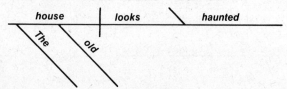

house | looks \ haunted
The / old

9. The back door was unlocked.

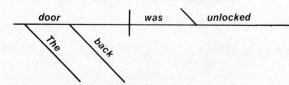

door | was \ unlocked
The / back

4. Two people are absent.

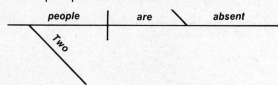

people | are \ absent
Two

10. My last grade was terrible.

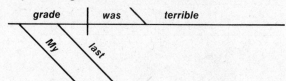

grade | was \ terrible
My / last

5. The math test was easy.

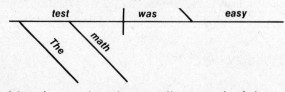

test | was \ easy
The / math

11. The green one is tighter.

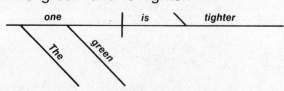

one | is \ tighter
The / green

6. Mom's apple pie smells wonderful.

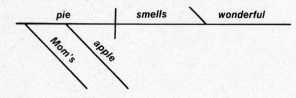

pie | smells \ wonderful
Mom's / apple

12. Six workers will be retired.

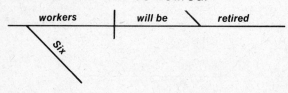

workers | will be \ retired
Six

186

Diagramming Adverbs and N-LV-Adj. Sentences

An adverb may modify the linking verb of a N-LV-Adj. sentence. It is diagrammed as follows:

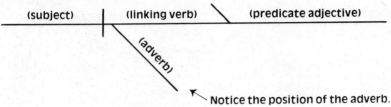

Notice the position of the adverb.

✻ Diagram these sentences on the lines provided.

1. She always acts disgusted.

2. Miss Donohue is usually nice.

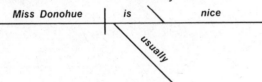

3. The car is never clean.

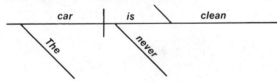

4. Someday you will be strong.

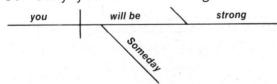

5. Eventually Sherry became ill.

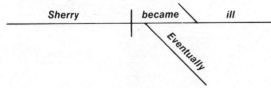

6. The house looks nice now.

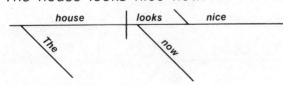

7. Kathy's appearance is seldom messy.

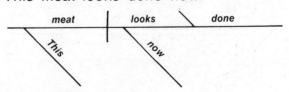

8. He always acts sleepy.

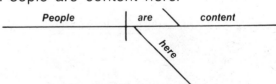

9. Has she always been sickly?

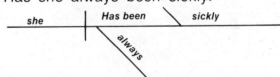

10. People are content here.

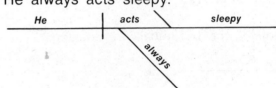

11. This meat looks done now.

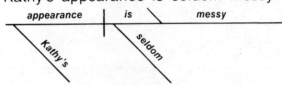

12. He seems angry today.

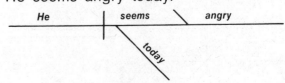

Unit 77 cont'd →

Diagramming N-LV-Adj. Sentences with Compounds

The subject, verb, or predicate adjective of a N-LV-Adj. sentence may be compounded. Compounds are diagrammed as follows:

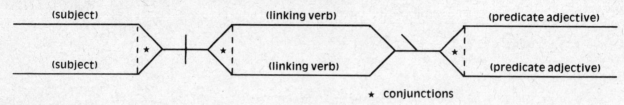

★ conjunctions

 Diagram these sentences on the lines provided.

1. He and I are careful.

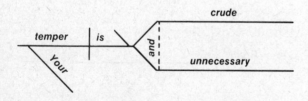

2. Football and basketball are exciting.

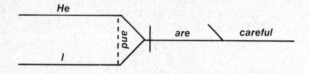

3. Your temper is crude and unnecessary.

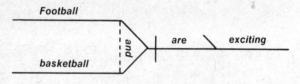

4. Cookies and milk taste delicious.

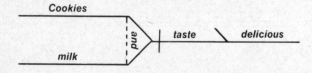

5. Are you healthy or ill?

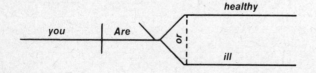

6. The meal smells and looks delicious.

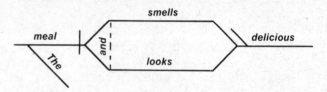

7. The sky was dark and dreary.

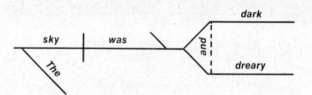

8. Amanda is and always will be beautiful.

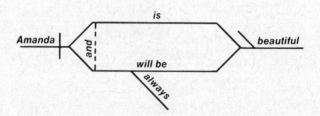

9. Keith is intelligent and handsome.

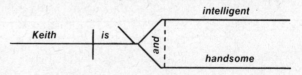

10. Cars are fun but dangerous.

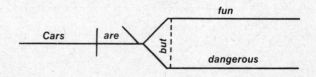

Diagramming N-LV-Adj. Sentences with Prepositional Phrases

A prepositional phrase may modify the subject, the linking verb, or the predicate adjective of the N-LV-Adj. sentence. It is diagrammed as follows:

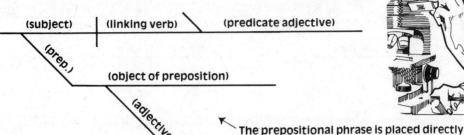

The prepositional phrase is placed directly under the word it modifies.

✱ Diagram these sentences on the lines provided.

1. I am excited about school.

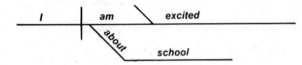

2. The top of his car is blue.

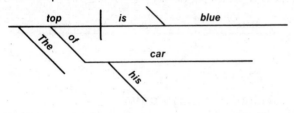

3. The questions in algebra were complex.

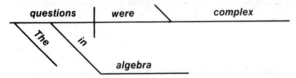

4. Ricky is tired of football.

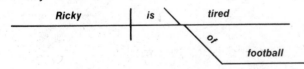

5. The food at that restaurant tastes bad.

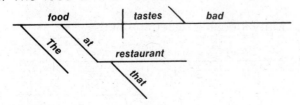

6. The man in the gray jacket is secretive.

7. The people at the office are strange.

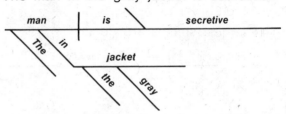

8. The book about seals was interesting.

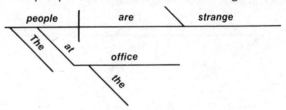

9. Is this type of news bad?

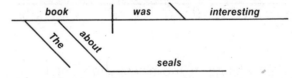

10. Paul is tired of working.

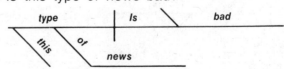

Unit 78 cont'd

N-LV-Adj. Sentence Diagrams

  Diagram these sentences.

1. Both questions are complicated.

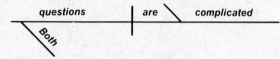

2. The big man was hungry.

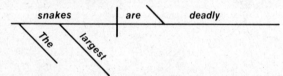

3. The largest snakes are deadly.

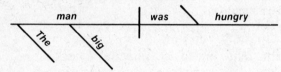

4. The air is warmest here.

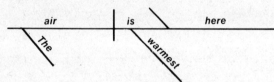

5. Monroe looks guilty.

6. The clouds in the sky are beautiful.

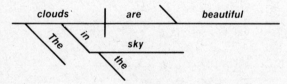

7. The first cake was best.

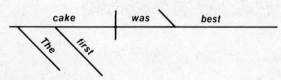

8. Most people are careful.

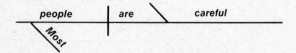

9. The answers were revealing.

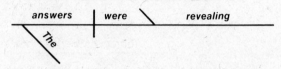

10. The smell was damp and musty.

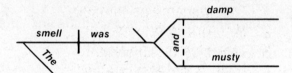

11. The king usually appears content.

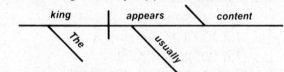

12. Mark acts tired.

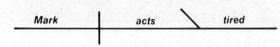

13. Samuel is always grumpy.

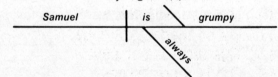

14. The sign was blue with silver letters.

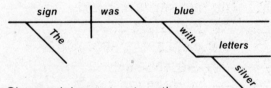

15. She and I are trustworthy.

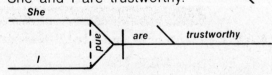

16. Mary became disenchanted.

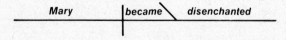

Comparing the N-LV-N and N-LV-Adj. Patterns

The **N-LV-Adj.** pattern contains a linking verb followed by an adjective that describes the subject. The **N-LV-N** pattern contains a linking verb followed by a noun that renames the subject.

EXAMPLES: **N-LV-Adj.** sentences:
a. The poem is silly.
b. The sets are complete.

N-LV-N sentences:
a. Pam is a secretary.
b. She was a good singer.

✱ In each blank write 1 if the sentence follows the N-LV-Adj. pattern or 2 if the sentence follows the N-LV-N pattern.

1	1. The woman was famous.		1	26. Peter was rude.
2	2. Mr. Kirk is my teacher.		1	27. The story is false.
1	3. This clue is significant.		2	28. My father is the owner.
2	4. Math is an easy subject.		1	29. The questions were simple.
1	5. My shirt is blue.		1	30. Janie is bashful.
1	6. Your answers are important.		2	31. Our guest is a comedian.
1	7. The room is too large.		1	32. These problems are difficult.
2	8. The song is a lullaby.		1	33. The floor is dirty.
1	9. Your paper was excellent.		2	34. The man is my neighbor.
1	10. The boxes were empty.		1	35. The paint was too thin.
2	11. My grandfather was a farmer.		2	36. The sentence is an exclamation.
1	12. The clowns were funny.		2	37. Josh is my friend.
2	13. Twain was a writer.		1	38. The water was cold.
2	14. Her sister is a nurse.		2	39. We are your helpers.
1	15. The wagon is red.		1	40. The answers were correct.
1	16. The man was polite.		1	41. The knife is sharp.
1	17. My brother was furious.		2	42. Dave is my brother.
2	18. This room is our den.		1	43. The food was delicious.
2	19. Bob is a proper noun.		1	44. The picture is crooked.
1	20. The crowns are gold.		1	45. My muscles are sore.
2	21. The monkey is my pet.		2	46. Greg is an artist.
1	22. The grapes are sour.		2	47. That building is our gym.
1	23. That elephant is enormous.		1	48. The butterfly is beautiful.
1	24. They are valuable.		2	49. Her friend is a pilot.
1	25. The candy is too sweet.		2	50. Kevin is my pal.

COMPOSITION EXERCISE

Write 4 N-LV-Adj. sentences and 4 N-LV-N sentences.

N-LV-Adj.

1. _____
2. _____
3. _____
4. _____

N-LV-N

1. _____
2. _____
3. _____
4. _____

Unit 79 cont'd

Sentence Patterns

The four basic sentence patterns are N-V, N-V-N,
N-LV-Adj., and N-LV-N.

EXAMPLES:
N-V	Our bus arrived.
N-V-N	Chris mowed the lawn.
N-LV-Adj.	Franklin is greedy.
N-LV-N	You are a good student.

Identify the sentence pattern of each sentence.

N-V	1. The water is running.	
N-V-N	2. I wrote a song.	
N-LV-ADJ	3. The house is beautiful.	
N-LV-N	4. Alex is a lawyer.	
N-V-N	5. We need a clue.	
N-LV-ADJ	6. This film is interesting.	
N-LV-N	7. They are twins.	
N-V	8. My uncle sneezed.	
N-LV-ADJ	9. Brad is forgetful.	
N-V-N	10. I opened the package.	
N-V	11. The rain stopped.	
N-V	12. The bullet missed.	
N-V-N	13. Karen won the contest.	
N-V	14. The game ended in a tie.	
N-LV-N	15. That car is a Chevrolet.	
N-V	16. The bells rang.	
N-LV-ADJ	17. Tony was ill.	
N-LV-ADJ	18. Their voices were spooky.	
N-LV-N	19. The lady is a mechanic.	
N-V	20. The wind was blowing.	
N-V-N	21. Eric approved our plans.	
N-LV-ADJ	22. Your ideas are different.	
N-V-N	23. He expects an answer.	
N-V	24. Someone screamed.	
N-LV-ADJ	25. Everyone was happy.	

N-V-N	26. The clock struck twelve.
N-LV-N	27. This object is a parachute.
N-LV-ADJ	28. The results are fantastic.
N-V-N	29. We accomplished our goal.
N-V	30. The lightning flashed.
N-LV-N	31. Mr. Adams is a plumber.
N-V-N	32. I heard a crash.
N-LV-ADJ	33. The money is safe.
N-V	34. No one moved.
N-V	35. The army has surrendered.
N-V-N	36. The officer arrested the thief.
N-LV-N	37. Your mother was my coach.
N-V-N	38. Dave fixed the leak.
N-V-N	39. The class is taking an exam.
N-LV-ADJ	40. The room was empty.
N-LV-ADJ	41. She is intelligent.
N-LV-ADJ	42. The equipment was heavy.
N-LV-ADJ	43. The decision is satisfactory.
N-V	44. Fire burns.
N-V-N	45. Phil lost the ball.
N-V-N	46. I voiced a no.
N-V-N	47. Ben dropped the books.
N-V	48. The license had expired.
N-LV-N	49. Dee is our guest.
N-V-N	50. Amy found a quarter.

COMPOSITION EXERCISE

Write two examples for each sentence pattern.

1. N-V

_____

_____

2. N-V-N

_____

_____

3. N-LV-Adj.

_____

_____

4. N-LV-N

_____

_____

What Are Indirect Objects?

An indirect object is a noun or pronoun that comes between the verb and the direct object. It answers the question "to whom" or "for whom."

EXAMPLES: a. Gene told <u>Lee</u> the story.
            b. I gave <u>her</u> the address.
            c. She asked <u>him</u> a question.
            d. He handed <u>Tom</u> the paper.

✳ In each blank write a noun or pronoun which will serve as the indirect object.

1. The policeman gave __*Mack*__ a ticket.
2. Mom fed __US__ our dinner.
3. I will give __DAN__ the key.
4. She taught __US__ a poem.
5. Lucas read the __CLASS__ a story.
6. Jason bought __TIM__ a present.
7. The dog gave __ME__ a scare.
8. My sister showed __JOE__ her ring.
9. Dad bought our __FAMILY__ a car.
10. She offered __CORY__ a cookie.
11. Mr. Conrad asked __HER__ a question.
12. I threw the __TEACHER__ the ball.
13. The manager told the __POLICE__ a lie.
14. My uncle will show __HIM__ the room.
15. Toni sang the __BABY__ a lullaby.
16. I will feed the __MOUSE__ some cheese.
17. Eric gave __THEM__ the answers.
18. We wrote our __PRINCIPAL__ a letter.
19. Mom offered __HIM__ a drink.
20. Dad read __US__ the note.
21. He loaned __ME__ a dime.
22. I found the __BIRD__ a home.
23. Jill fed the __RABBIT__ some lettuce.
24. He handed __CARL__ his report card.
25. I gave __YOU__ my opinion.

26. Our class sent __JILL__ a card.
27. I showed __HIM__ my work.
28. Pass __TONY__ the bread.
29. Jan fed the __KITTEN__ some milk.
30. Mom made __HIM__ a hat.
31. We told __THEM__ the scores.
32. Mark threw __FRANK__ a pass.
33. Mr. Jones drew __KEVIN__ a map.
34. We gave __BETH__ a party.
35. I will loan __KIM__ the money.
36. The man left __ME__ a note.
37. Cindy wrote __BRENDA__ a letter.
38. Alice brought the __HORSE__ an apple.
39. The coach taught __US__ the rules.
40. I told the __MAN__ my address.
41. Pat will make __GREG__ a belt.
42. Mrs. Smith gave __YOU__ the book.
43. Liz found the __MAN__ a seat.
44. The mailman handed __MOM__ a package.
45. Don gave __ME__ his pen.
46. He asked __HER__ the directions.
47. I ordered __PAULA__ a hamburger.
48. Mom taught __US__ a lesson.
49. Diane will show __YOU__ the way.
50. The teacher gave __US__ our assignment.

COMPOSITION EXERCISE

Write 5 sentences which contain nouns used as indirect objects and 5 which contain pronouns used as indirect objects.

nouns	pronouns
1. _____	1. _____
2. _____	2. _____
3. _____	3. _____
4. _____	4. _____
5. _____	5. _____

Unit 80 cont'd →

Where to Find Indirect Objects

Indirect objects come between the verb and the direct object.

EXAMPLES: a. Loan <u>me</u> a dollar.   c. Jan baked <u>Dave</u> a cake.
            b. He bought <u>Sandy</u> a new watch.   d. He will find <u>us</u> a taxi.

  Underline the indirect objects.

1. Mom gave <u>me</u> a spanking.
2. Alex sent <u>Cindy</u> a card.
3. Kevin threw <u>Don</u> the ball.
4. The man sold <u>us</u> the house.
5. Connie offered <u>me</u> some gum.
6. He showed <u>Paul</u> the map.
7. Dad bought my <u>brother</u> a horse.
8. I owe <u>you</u> a quarter.
9. Throw <u>me</u> an apple.
10. My aunt taught <u>us</u> music.
11. She brought <u>him</u> his lunch.
12. You must give <u>Kay</u> the rings.
13. Find <u>her</u> a pencil.
14. I asked the <u>lady</u> her name.
15. Harry can tell <u>you</u> the story.
16. They bought <u>Ken</u> a gift.
17. Dana made the <u>dog</u> a coat.
18. My uncle sent <u>me</u> a painting.
19. Mom will fix <u>us</u> a snack.
20. I brought <u>you</u> a pie.
21. We gave the <u>dog</u> a bath.
22. The man threw the <u>lion</u> his dinner.
23. The magician showed <u>us</u> a trick.
24. Karla presented <u>Pam</u> the prize.
25. Rodney owes <u>me</u> a favor.
26. Patty told her <u>mom</u> the truth.
27. James loaned <u>Dad</u> the money.
28. I asked the <u>teacher</u> a question.
29. Dee wrote her <u>friend</u> a letter.
30. Mr. Carson taught the <u>class</u> a riddle.
31. I made <u>Tom</u> a shirt.
32. Kim will loan <u>you</u> a dime.
33. Steve bought his <u>mother</u> a purse.
34. He sold <u>me</u> the book.
35. I gave <u>them</u> some advice.
36. The comedian told <u>us</u> a joke.
37. Lynn presented <u>Joe</u> the trophy.
38. Show <u>Mr. Cook</u> your picture.
39. The woman gave the <u>boy</u> the change.
40. I will make <u>you</u> a sandwich.
41. He brought <u>Penny</u> the mail.
42. Lonnie will buy <u>me</u> the horse.
43. Kenny offered the <u>lady</u> his seat.
44. Mike owes <u>Darrel</u> a new hat.
45. Tammy showed <u>us</u> the cave.
46. I told <u>you</u> our reasons.
47. Bring <u>me</u> the newspaper.
48. We fed the <u>birds</u> popcorn.
49. Ben gave the old <u>man</u> his sandwich.
50. I sent <u>Betty</u> an invitation.

COMPOSITION EXERCISE

Write 12 sentences which contain indirect objects.

1. _____
2. _____
3. _____
4. _____
5. _____
6. _____
7. _____
8. _____
9. _____
10. _____
11. _____
12. _____

Comprehension Check

A **Underline the linking verbs.**

1. <u>is</u>
2. <u>looks</u>
3. counts
4. hit
5. <u>are</u>
6. <u>were</u>
7. <u>appears</u>
8. put
9. mixed
10. <u>sound</u>
11. studied
12. <u>am</u>
13. made
14. <u>tastes</u>
15. <u>seem</u>
16. will
17. <u>became</u>
18. <u>smells</u>
19. <u>was</u>
20. opens

B **Underline the adjectives.**

1. <u>sweet</u>
2. practice
3. <u>neat</u>
4. <u>delicious</u>
5. <u>pretty</u>
6. chair
7. <u>green</u>
8. pattern
9. <u>taller</u>
10. <u>salty</u>
11. <u>large</u>
12. dinner
13. <u>odd</u>
14. reason
15. <u>unhappy</u>
16. set
17. <u>cheap</u>
18. <u>complete</u>
19. quickly
20. <u>helpless</u>

C **Complete each N-LV-Adj. sentence with an adjective.**

1. The water was too _____*hot*_____.
2. Lillian is _____*confident*_____.
3. I am _____*content*_____.
4. The music was _____*wonderful*_____.
5. Angela is not _____*clumsy*_____.
6. The news was _____*upsetting*_____.
7. He feels _____*rejected*_____.
8. The sign looks _____*crooked*_____.
9. Your ears are too _____*small*_____.
10. It is _____*difficult*_____.
11. The ribbons are _____*yellow*_____.
12. Melanie seems _____*excited*_____.
13. Roger acted _____*nervous*_____.
14. My cat is very _____*shy*_____.
15. Paulette looks _____*beautiful*_____.
16. The questions were _____*hard*_____.
17. That sounds _____*terrible*_____.
18. Neta became _____*depressed*_____.
19. The clock was _____*noisy*_____.
20. Carter smells _____*good*_____.

D **Identify the parts of these N-LV-Adj. sentences.**

1. The reporter was nervous.
       N   LV   Adj.
2. The water felt cool.
       N   LV   Adj.
3. I am very happy.
     N LV   Adj.
4. This soup smells awful.
       N   LV   Adj.
5. Benjamin is too tall.
       N   LV   Adj.
6. The puppies are cute.
       N   LV   Adj.
7. The speech sounds interesting.
       N   LV   Adj.
8. The cake tastes too sweet.
       N   LV   Adj.
9. Lucia became angry.
       N   LV   Adj.
10. The movie was frightening.
        N   LV   Adj.
11. Katherine seems sure of herself.
        N   LV   Adj.
12. Stephen will be careful.
        N   LV   Adj.
13. The people were proud.
        N   LV   Adj.
14. Harry is quiet.

Test 16 cont'd →

Comprehension Check (continued)

E Diagram these N-LV-Adj. sentences.

1. The child was lost.

child | was \ lost
The

6. I am positive.

I | am \ positive

2. The test was easy.

test | was \ easy
The

7. The weather is humid.

weather | is \ humid
The

3. You were fantastic!

You | were \ fantastic

8. This answer is correct.

answer | is \ correct
This

4. Henry is old-fashioned.

Henry | is \ old-fashioned

9. Your idea sounds terrific.

idea | sounds \ terrific
Your

5. Johnathan is too young.

Johnathan | is \ young
too

10. Bonnie was very helpful.

Bonnie | was \ helpful
very

F Identify the (1) N-LV-N and (2) N-LV-Adj. sentences.

_1_ 1. Georgia was the winner.
_2_ 2. Customers are always right.
_1_ 3. Jackie was a waitress.
_1_ 4. That room is the den.
_2_ 5. It looks great!
_2_ 6. The surface feels rough.
_2_ 7. The house is too old.
_1_ 8. Ramsey became a doctor.
_2_ 9. Carson was ready.
_1_ 10. Drew is my assistant.

_2_ 11. You are funny.
_2_ 12. The boat is not safe.
_2_ 13. Hillary looks worried.
_2_ 14. The ocean was calm.
_1_ 15. Ken will be Santa Claus.
_2_ 16. A smile is beautiful.
_1_ 17. The reward is $600.
_2_ 18. Lucy seemed anxious.
_1_ 19. Diane plays Ophelia.
_1_ 20. The store is a bakery.

Write a paragraph describing your favorite season. Tell why you like it best. Use at least three N-LV-Adj. sentences.

_____

_____

_____

_____

_____

_____

Nouns Used as Indirect Objects

An indirect object is a noun that comes between the action verb and the direct object. It answers the question "to whom" or "for whom."

EXAMPLES:
a. Linda sent <u>Judy</u> a note.
b. We gave <u>Ms. Jones</u> a watch.
c. He showed the <u>child</u> the toy.
d. I paid the <u>man</u> a dollar.

＊ In each sentence underline the indirect object.

1. Lisa made <u>Tom</u> a cake.
2. I wrote my <u>friend</u> a letter.
3. Joe gave the <u>monkey</u> a banana.
4. I threw <u>Al</u> the football.
5. Dick fed the <u>dog</u> a bone.
6. I showed <u>Dave</u> a picture.
7. Dr. Jones told the <u>nurse</u> everything.
8. She left the <u>man</u> some food.
9. Kay will tell the <u>class</u> the news.
10. We bought <u>Dad</u> a pipe.
11. Donna loaned <u>Pete</u> a dime.
12. I took the <u>team</u> some water.
13. She read the <u>children</u> a story.
14. They gave the <u>elephant</u> a peanut.
15. Chris handed <u>Dennis</u> the book.
16. We paid the <u>owner</u> the money.
17. I will give <u>Tim</u> the prize.
18. Mom will give the <u>child</u> a toy.
19. The teacher gave the <u>class</u> a test.
20. I left the <u>mouse</u> some cheese.
21. Ben will throw <u>Clare</u> the ball.
22. She wrote the <u>company</u> a letter.
23. Joan fed the <u>baby</u> his lunch.
24. I gave the <u>horse</u> a carrot.
25. He built his <u>family</u> a house.
26. I told <u>Paul</u> the answer.
27. Dee showed the <u>man</u> a map.
28. Mom gave the <u>baby</u> a bath.
29. I brought <u>Sam</u> his coat.
30. The man sent <u>Betty</u> a card.
31. I loaned my <u>brother</u> my bike.
32. Dad bought <u>Mom</u> a car.
33. Nancy bought the <u>cat</u> a collar.
34. We will tell the <u>police</u> our story.
35. I fed the <u>bear</u> a fish.
36. We left <u>Santa</u> an orange.
37. Don handed <u>Bill</u> a hammer.
38. I told the <u>teacher</u> the truth.
39. He will show <u>Ted</u> the cave.
40. We fed the <u>rabbits</u> lettuce.
41. I will make <u>Sue</u> a hat.
42. Eric will write his <u>grandpa</u> the news.
43. Chris will buy the <u>kitten</u> a bed.
44. I loaned the <u>girl</u> my book.
45. Eve fed the <u>cows</u> some hay.
46. I will show the <u>class</u> a film.
47. I brought <u>Mona</u> a chair.
48. You left <u>Kim</u> your shoes?
49. Dad gave <u>George</u> a haircut.
50. I drew <u>Jason</u> a map.

COMPOSITION EXERCISE

Write 12 sentences which contain nouns as indirect objects.

1. _____
2. _____
3. _____
4. _____
5. _____
6. _____
7. _____
8. _____
9. _____
10. _____
11. _____
12. _____

Unit 81 cont'd →

Pronouns Used as Indirect Objects

An indirect object is a pronoun that comes between the action verb and the direct object. It answers the question "to whom" or "for whom."

EXAMPLES: a. You gave <u>me</u> that hat.   c. I sent <u>her</u> the roses.
           b. I will tell <u>you</u> a story.   d. Jay bought <u>me</u> a hot dog.

✳ In each blank write a pronoun which will serve as the indirect object.

1. Sharon told __him__ a secret.
2. Grandma gave __ME__ a cookie.
3. The teacher showed __US__ a puzzle.
4. Mom made __THEM__ a cake.
5. I bought __HER__ a present.
6. Tim wrote __HIM__ a letter.
7. I fed __HIM__ his cereal.
8. We brought __THEM__ the mail.
9. Lynn read __US__ the answers.
10. Don gave __HER__ a ring.
11. Tony showed __ME__ the way.
12. I found __YOU__ a house.
13. She told __US__ a lie.
14. The sailor gave __THEM__ a clue.
15. Sue brought __YOU__ a Coke.
16. She handed __ME__ a fork.
17. Dale told __HIM__ nothing.
18. She read __ME__ the letter.
19. Terry sent __ME__ a card.
20. Mom will give __HER__ some milk.
21. Eric will tell __YOU__ the reason.
22. I will loan __HER__ a dollar.
23. We sent __HIM__ the package.
24. I will leave __YOU__ a note.
25. The teacher gave __US__ a test.
26. I threw __HIM__ the ball.
27. Tina bought __ME__ a shirt.
28. Fran loaned __HIM__ the money.
29. I took __HIM__ his paper.
30. Gary read __US__ his report.
31. The comedian told __US__ a joke.
32. I drew __HER__ a picture.
33. Wanda will sing __THEM__ a song.
34. George paid __HIM__ the money.
35. The policeman gave __ME__ a ticket.
36. The clown threw __US__ some candy.
37. Don handed __ME__ the money.
38. I will show __YOU__ the room.
39. Bonnie left __HIM__ his watch.
40. The man sent __HER__ a flower.
41. I will feed __YOU__ your lunch.
42. Al wrote __HER__ a poem.
43. Dad bought __ME__ a new bike.
44. Molly showed __ME__ the photo.
45. The lady gave __US__ an order.
46. I will read __YOU__ the titles.
47. Our class is buying __HER__ a gift.
48. Kate brought __ME__ a book.
49. I wrote __THEM__ a note.
50. I told __HER__ a secret.

COMPOSITION EXERCISE

Write 12 sentences which contain pronouns as indirect objects.

1. _____
2. _____
3. _____
4. _____
5. _____
6. _____
7. _____
8. _____
9. _____
10. _____
11. _____
12. _____

Diagramming N-V-IO-DO Sentences

The N-V-IO-DO sentence consists of a subject, a transitive verb, an indirect object, and a direct object. It is diagrammed as follows:

| (subject) | (verb) | (indirect object) | (direct object) |

Notice the positions of these lines.

 Diagram these sentences on the lines provided.

1. He gave us the answers.

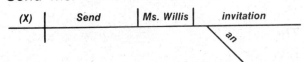

7. Show Carl the map.

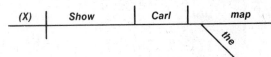

2. Send Ms. Willis an invitation.

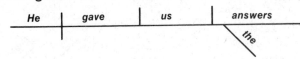

8. Betty wished us good luck.

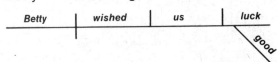

3. Chris will lend Paul the money.

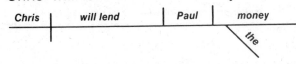

9. Bring me the newspaper.

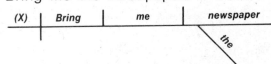

4. Feed the cat milk.

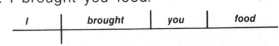

10. I brought you food.

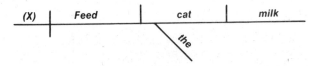

5. Joey awarded Sam the certificate.

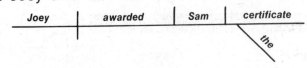

11. I will ask Lucy the way.

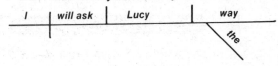

6. He sent me the papers.

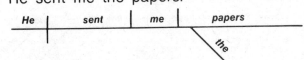

12. We read them the contract.

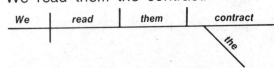

Unit 82 cont'd

Diagramming Adjectives and N-V-IO-DO Sentences

An adjective may modify the subject, the indirect object, or the direct object of a N-V-IO-DO sentence. It is diagrammed as follows:

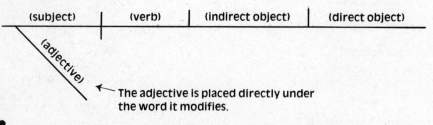

| (subject) | (verb) | (indirect object) | (direct object) |

(adjective)

← The adjective is placed directly under the word it modifies.

 Diagram these sentences on the lines provided.

1. John sent Howard the largest package.

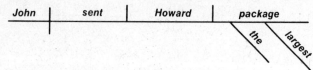

John | sent | Howard | package / the / largest

7. Prepare him the final copy.

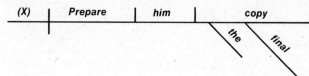

(X) | Prepare | him | copy / the / final

2. He took the big dog a bone.

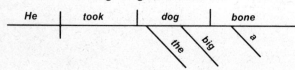

He | took | dog / the / big | bone / a

8. I wrote her a long letter.

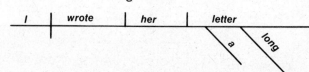

I | wrote | her | letter / a / long

3. Sarah paid the rug cleaner his bill.

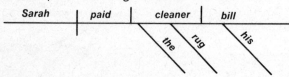

Sarah | paid | cleaner / the / rug | bill / his

9. The young waiter served the teenagers a pizza.

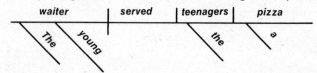

waiter / The / young | served | teenagers / the | pizza / a

4. Sam gave her a new watch.

Sam | gave | her | watch / a / new

10. Show me your best move.

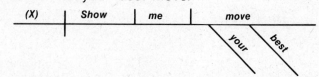

(X) | Show | me | move / your / best

5. He asked her the last answer.

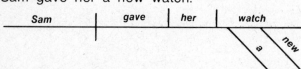

He | asked | her | answer / the / last

11. Can you deliver him five cases?

you | Can deliver | him | cases / five

6. Pam brought them marble bags.

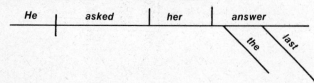

Pam | brought | them | bags / marble

12. Chris cooked Lanny an entire meal.

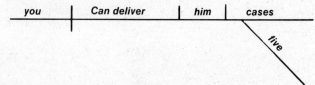

Chris | cooked | Lanny | meal / an / entire

Diagramming Adverbs and N-V-IO-DO Sentences

An adverb may modify the transitive verb of the N-V-IO-DO sentence. It is diagrammed as follows:

(subject) | (verb) | (indirect object) | (direct object)

(adverb)

The adverb is placed under the verb it modifies.

✱ Diagram these sentences on the lines provided.

1. I always take Mrs. Ritchie her medicine.

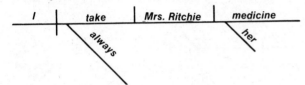

2. Take him the message now!

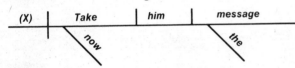

3. Roberta baked us a pie today.

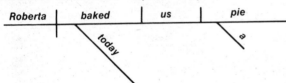

4. Ask me the question again.

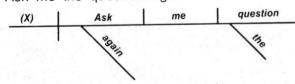

5. Mr. Kimmey told them the answers twice.

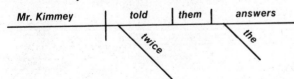

6. I gave her the gift early.

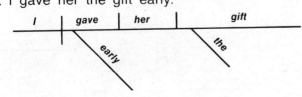

7. He always gives her a headache.

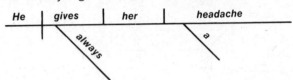

8. Don't show them the letter.

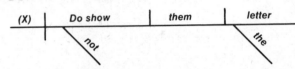

9. Brandon tells his brother a story every night.

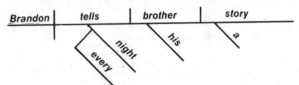

10. They will bring us the furniture tomorrow.

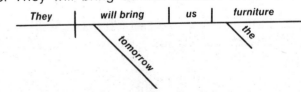

11. She'll take them supper tonight.

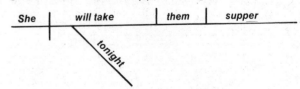

12. James seldom writes Tom notes.

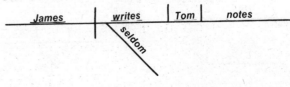

Unit 83 cont'd

Diagramming N-V-IO-DO Sentences with Compounds

The subject, verb, indirect object, or direct object of the N-V-IO-DO sentence may be compounded. Compounds are diagrammed as follows:

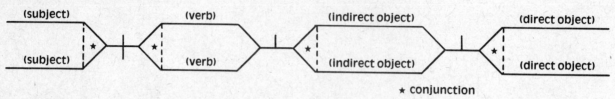

★ conjunction

 Diagram these sentences on the lines provided.

1. Eric and Shea won her the prize.

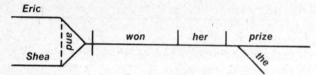

2. Kim prepared Elise and Choya a meal.

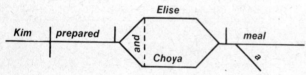

3. Gene bought Dad the tools and parts.

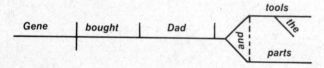

4. Issue Bob and Phil two uniforms.

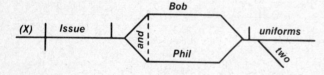

5. Get them food and drinks.

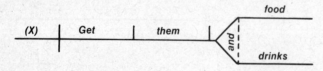

6. He and I taught them tricks.

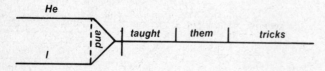

7. Tell David and Sue both stories.

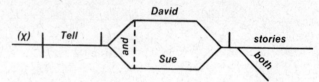

8. Mr. Chambers sold them food and medicine.

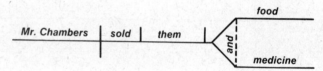

9. Laura and Cherry showed Mrs. Carson their work.

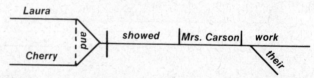

10. They fixed him and her frozen dinners.

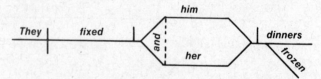

11. He pronounced them man and wife.

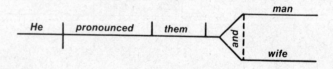

12. Read Sam and John the book.

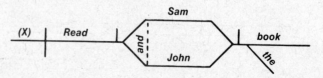

202

Diagram these sentences on the lines provided.

1. Take the boy by the window the message.

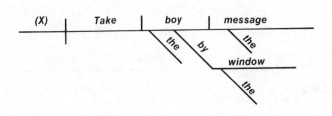

2. Give me the answer to the question.

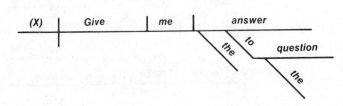

3. I made myself a hamburger with mustard.

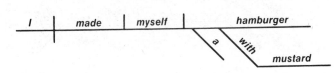

4. Both women in the shop bought themselves nice dresses.

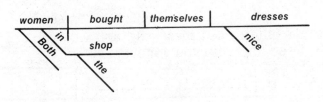

5. Feed them the box of cereal.

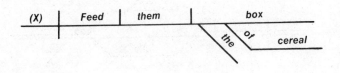

6. Tim took Sarah a present for Christmas.

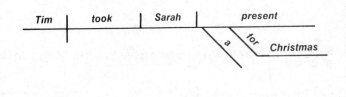

7. They wrote Noble a letter from Memphis.

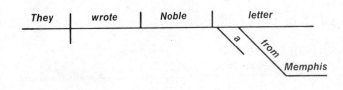

8. Mrs. Carter gave J.D. a look of malice.

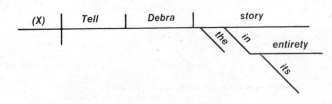

9. Tell Debra the story in its entirety.

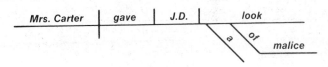

10. Lonnie brought the customer the order of fries.

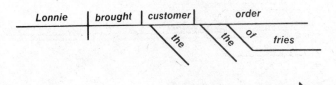

Unit 84 cont'd

N-V-IO-DO Sentence Diagrams

 Diagram these sentences.

1. Give David the money.

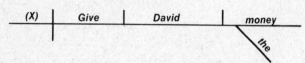

2. She gave him a gift of purest gold.

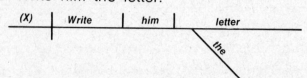

3. Sheila designed them a new home.

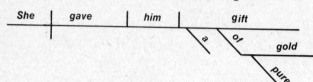

4. Sometimes Terry delivers us pizza.

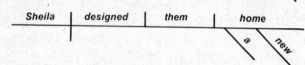

5. Donna and Amy will find us the key.

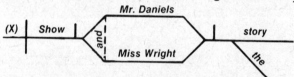

6. Don't tell him the stories anymore.

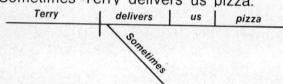

7. Pass Dad the salt.

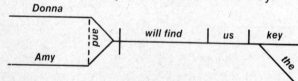

8. A stranger brought us the picture.

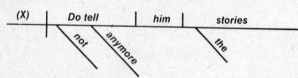

9. Write him the letter.

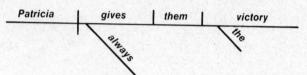

10. Patricia always gives them the victory.

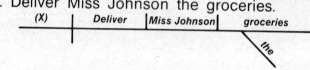

11. Show Mr. Daniels and Miss Wright the story.

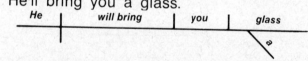

12. Deliver Miss Johnson the groceries.

13. He'll bring you a glass.

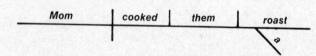

14. Mom cooked them a roast.

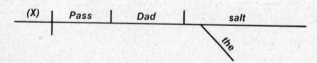

15. Feed the dog the leftovers.

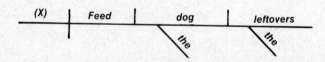

16. Fix me Chinese food for dinner.

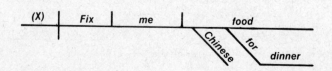

Practice with Objects

A direct object follows the verb and answers the question "who" or "what." An indirect object comes between the verb and the direct object and answers "to whom" or "for whom."

EXAMPLES: direct objects: *a. I answered the questions.*
                          b. The wind blew the leaves.

   indirect objects: *a. Mr. Cupp gave us candy.*
                      b. I told Bob the story.

 Write "DO" if the underlined word is a direct object. Write "IO" if the underlined word is an indirect object.

_DO_	1. Tom broke the <u>window</u>.		_IO_	26. I gave the <u>dog</u> a bath.
_IO_	2. She gave <u>me</u> a cookie.		_DO_	27. Susan bought a <u>chair</u>.
_DO_	3. I saw the <u>bridge</u>.		_IO_	28. Lee brought <u>you</u> a cake.
_DO_	4. I ate the <u>banana</u>.		_DO_	29. Ted wants a <u>hammer</u>.
_IO_	5. I showed <u>Jan</u> the present.		_DO_	30. I read the <u>book</u>.
_IO_	6. Eva bought <u>me</u> a hat.		_DO_	31. Danny pushed the <u>door</u>.
_IO_	7. Sherry told <u>us</u> a story.		_IO_	32. The man gave <u>Sara</u> a dollar.
_DO_	8. Dave moved the <u>chair</u>.		_IO_	33. Karen gave <u>him</u> the car.
_DO_	9. I hate <u>peanuts</u>.		_IO_	34. I will show <u>you</u> the way.
_DO_	10. The comedian told a <u>joke</u>.		_DO_	35. I fed the <u>baby</u>.
_DO_	11. I cleaned my <u>room</u>.		_IO_	36. You showed <u>me</u> the paper.
_DO_	12. We built a <u>clubhouse</u>.		_DO_	37. Dad fixed the <u>roof</u>.
_IO_	13. Mom made <u>you</u> a cake.		_IO_	38. Kay read the <u>class</u> a poem.
_DO_	14. Cleo dropped the <u>fish</u>.		_IO_	39. Jack sent <u>me</u> a letter.
_DO_	15. We jumped the <u>fence</u>.		_DO_	40. Karen drives a <u>truck</u>.
_IO_	16. I gave <u>you</u> a pen.		_DO_	41. The farmer plowed the <u>field</u>.
_IO_	17. Liz told <u>Dee</u> our secret.		_DO_	42. I heard <u>music</u>.
_DO_	18. The thief took our <u>jewels</u>.		_IO_	43. We gave <u>them</u> the money.
_DO_	19. She opened the <u>box</u>.		_IO_	44. Wanda gave the <u>dog</u> a bone.
_DO_	20. The cat pulled the <u>string</u>.		_DO_	45. Nancy found her <u>presents</u>.
_DO_	21. Vicki hit a <u>home run</u>.		_IO_	46. I gave <u>Gus</u> the book.
_DO_	22. Ellen called the <u>police</u>.		_IO_	47. I made <u>George</u> a sandwich.
_DO_	23. Mom closed the <u>garage</u>.		_IO_	48. Dad brought <u>me</u> the paper.
_DO_	24. Billy lost the <u>key</u>.		_DO_	49. Our class won the <u>contest</u>.
_IO_	25. I wrote <u>Alex</u> a letter.		_DO_	50. Everyone passed the <u>test</u>.

COMPOSITION EXERCISE

Write 4 sentences which contain direct objects and 4 which contain indirect objects.

direct objects	indirect objects
1. _____	1. _____
2. _____	2. _____
3. _____	3. _____
4. _____	4. _____

Unit 85 cont'd

Identifying Sentence Parts

1. **Subject** — *tells who or what sentence is about*
   The <u>parachute</u> opened.
2. **Verb** — *shows action or state of being*
   Al <u>presented</u> the awards. Jack <u>is</u> late.
3. **Direct Object** — *answers "who" or "what"*
   Lisa speaks <u>German</u>.
4. **Indirect Object** — *answers "to whom" or "for whom"*
   He bought <u>me</u> a pizza.
5. **Predicate Adjective** — *describes subject*
   Steven is <u>furious</u>.
6. **Predicate Noun** — *renames subject*
   The winner is <u>Roscoe</u>.

✳ Identify the underlined words. Write "S" for subject, "V" for verb, "DO" for direct object, "IO" for indirect object, "PA" for predicate adjective, and "PN" for predicate noun.

S	1. The <u>rain</u> watered the garden.		DO	20. That cat climbed the <u>tree</u>.
V	2. Mr. West <u>stopped</u> the car.		S	21. <u>It</u> is too late now.
DO	3. I picked the <u>flowers</u>.		PN	22. The cat is a <u>Siamese</u>.
IO	4. Give <u>us</u> the directions.		S	23. The <u>goldfish</u> was hungry.
PA	5. She is <u>beautiful</u>.		PA	24. He was <u>happy</u>.
PN	6. Carl was the <u>speaker</u>.		IO	25. Mr. Owens told <u>her</u> a riddle.
V	7. It <u>sounds</u> awful.		DO	26. I misplaced the <u>hammer</u>.
IO	8. I will find <u>you</u> a home.		PN	27. Your hat is a <u>derby</u>.
PN	9. The lady is an <u>actress</u>.		V	28. Ben <u>disapproved</u>.
S	10. The <u>voyage</u> ended in France.		PN	29. She is a <u>mermaid</u>.
PA	11. Wanda was <u>sad</u>.		S	30. The <u>game</u> was exciting.
PN	12. I am the best <u>player</u>.		DO	31. Mrs. Box presented the <u>award</u>.
V	13. We <u>received</u> a warning.		DO	32. Tie the <u>ribbon</u>.
IO	14. She brought <u>Mike</u> a cola.		PN	33. You are a <u>ghost</u>.
DO	15. He signed his <u>name</u>.		V	34. The car <u>was damaged</u>.
S	16. The <u>festival</u> begins tomorrow.		IO	35. Max owes <u>me</u> a nickel.
V	17. Her temperature <u>is</u> normal.		S	36. The <u>apple</u> fell from the tree.
PN	18. Eric was our <u>captain</u>.		PA	37. The carrots are <u>raw</u>.
IO	19. I sent <u>him</u> the bill.		DO	38. I like <u>people</u>.

COMPOSITION EXERCISE

Write an example for each of these sentence parts.

1. subject

   _____

2. verb

   _____

3. direct object

   _____

4. indirect object

   _____

5. predicate adjective

   _____

6. predicate noun

   _____

206

Comprehension Check

(A) Answer these questions.

1. Roger sent Marie the roses.
   What was sent? __roses__
   To whom were they sent? __Marie__

2. Mr. Baker gave me the key.
   What was given? __key__
   To whom was it given? __me__

3. She made Chris a chocolate pie.
   What was made? __pie__
   For whom was it made? __Chris__

4. The man fed the dog a biscuit.
   What was fed? __biscuit__
   To whom was it fed? __dog__

5. Kenneth read Margie the letter.
   What was read? __letter__
   To whom was it read? __Margie__

6. I showed Beverly the map.
   What was shown? __map__
   To whom was it shown? __Beverly__

7. Dr. Sands brought Bob the bicycle.
   What was brought? __bicycle__
   To whom was it brought? __Dr. Sands__

8. Barry wrote Tim the news.
   What was written? __news__
   To whom was it written? __Tim__

9. Theo prepared us our lunch.
   What was prepared? __lunch__
   For whom was it prepared? __us__

10. Paul told you our secret.
    What was told? __secret__
    To whom was it told? __you__

(B) Underline the indirect objects.

1. Karin asked Deb the question.
2. Sandy will make you a sandwich.
3. Capt. Leo showed them the paper.
4. The doctor ordered me a shot.
5. Kris fed the horses hay.
6. Miriam sent Jan a picture.
7. Mrs. Thatcher read us her poem.
8. Give Robert another book.
9. I bought Linda a scarf.
10. Ted picked Barb some flowers.

(C) Identify the parts of these N-V-IO-DO sentences.

1. I told you the whole story.
   N V IO DO

2. Ms. Atkins read us the rules.
   N V IO DO

3. Someone wrote him this note.
   N V IO DO

4. Roxanne bought Carol an album.
   N V IO DO

5. Tess showed me her new car.
   N V IO DO

6. We fed the pigeons bread crumbs.
   N V IO DO

7. The officer gave James a ticket.
   N V IO DO

8. Aunt Clara sent Alan some jelly.
   N V IO DO

9. I made Phil these cookies.
   N V IO DO

10. The clerk sold Jeff two shirts.
    N V IO DO

11. Don asked Rodney the problem.
    N V IO DO

12. No one told me the news.
    N V IO DO

13. Lou will give Eddie the message.
    N V IO DO

14. She mailed him the package.
    N V IO DO

Test 17 cont'd →

Comprehension Check (continued)

D Diagram these N-V-IO-DO sentences.

1. Deborah read Jill a story.

Deborah	read	Jill	story

a

2. I told him the truth!

I	told	him	truth

the

3. Send me another picture.

(x)	Send	me	picture

another

4. Lionel wrote her a song.

Lionel	wrote	her	song

a

5. We sent Hank a card.

We	sent	Hank	card

a

6. Julia will buy them the supplies.

Julia	will buy	them	supplies

the

7. The man asked Mark the directions.

man	asked	Mark	directions

The / the

8. Connie showed Brad the scores.

Connie	showed	Brad	scores

the

9. Lynn kept Ralph a copy.

Lynn	kept	Ralph	copy

a

10. I made you a cake.

I	made	you	cake

a

E Identify the underlined sentence parts.

ind. obj.	1.	Serena gave <u>Bradley</u> the money.
verb	2.	The woman <u>lives</u> on Murdock Street.
dir. obj.	3.	Kelsey wrote his <u>sister</u> about the party.
subject	4.	<u>Wayne</u> moved here from Miami, Florida.
verb	5.	The van <u>parked</u> too close to the edge.
dir. obj.	6.	Nicholas wants a new <u>motorcycle</u>.
verb	7.	Something <u>is</u> wrong with my telephone.
ind. obj.	8.	I will tell the <u>class</u> our new assignment.

Write a paragraph about a surprise you are planning for someone. Use at least one N-V-IO-DO sentence.

_____

_____

_____

_____

_____

_____

Capitals

We know some words always begin with capital letters, such as our names and the names of our friends; but suppose the teacher told us to write about the dark ages. Is the **d** a capital letter? Is **ages** capitalized? A quick look in the dictionary shows us the preferred way is to capitalize both words.

A Some of the words below should be spelled beginning with capital letters. Some should not. In the blanks write the words or names correctly. Use your dictionary for help.

1. andrew jackson __Andrew Jackson__

2. elephant __elephant__

3. monday __Monday__

4. negro __Negro__

5. democrat __Democrat__

6. dog __dog__

7. poison ivy __poison ivy__

8. television __television__

9. baptist church __Baptist Church__

10. calendar __calendar__

11. month __month__

12. christ __Christ__

13. january __January__

14. chrysler __Chrysler__

15. car __car__

16. ocean __ocean__

17. empire state building __Empire State Building__

18. mother's day __Mother's Day__

B In the space below write five sentences using the list of words given. Be sure to capitalize the words correctly. Use your dictionary for help.

HENRY   THANKSGIVING
STRAWBERRIES   BOY SCOUTS
HOLIDAY   COLOR
WEDNESDAY   IRISH

1. _____

2. _____

3. _____

4. _____

5. _____

Unit 86 cont'd

Capitalizing Names and "I"

Proper nouns are always capitalized. The word "I" is always capitalized.

EXAMPLES: a. My name is Danny.   c. He lives in Kansas.
b. I was born in May.   d. You and I will go.

 Underline the words which should be capitalized.

1. That man is mr. jackson.
2. Mom gave sarah a dime.
3. We crossed the atlantic ocean.
4. We could ask mrs. johnson.
5. She and i are friends.
6. Have you seen the gulf of mexico?
7. We saw tammy and mike.
8. Tell paul to come here.
9. My sister's name is tara.
10. Are you going to sue's party?
11. He is talking to carrie.
12. My brother goes to winthrop high school.
13. We live in texas.
14. My home is in illinois.
15. The child was born in april.
16. The rocky mountains are beautiful.
17. The bull chased bob and me.
18. This train goes to new york.
19. We bought it at sears.
20. She lives on thurmon street.
21. Here comes larry's mother.
22. We swam in the mississippi river.
23. Let's go to central park.
24. Finally i solved the problem.
25. My teacher is mrs. perkins.
26. This is jill's desk.
27. The call was from memphis.
28. This is kay minson.
29. We will visit the detroit zoo.
30. Call jim.
31. This is where i live.
32. My friend lives in chicago.
33. Dad and i cut the grass.
34. We are going to yellowstone park.
35. My dog's name is ginger.
36. The school is on finch street.
37. She invited jack and willie.
38. Is that ms. peterson?
39. The lawyer is john taylor.
40. Everyone ordered dr. pepper.
41. Don't tell george.
42. The next street is cedar drive.
43. This bike belongs to thomas.
44. The man was from denver.
45. You're sitting in al's chair.
46. Do i know you?
47. The man is going to boston.
48. We bought this car last july.
49. She and i went to hawaii.
50. School is out in june.

COMPOSITION EXERCISE

Write two sentences which contain the word "I" and ten which contain proper nouns.

1. _____
2. _____
3. _____
4. _____
5. _____
6. _____
7. _____
8. _____
9. _____
10. _____
11. _____
12. _____

Beginning Sentences with Capitals

A sentence always begins with a capital letter.

EXAMPLES: a. I would like to go.
b. When will they arrive?
c. Sit in the chair.
d. Have you met Chris?

 Underline the sentences which are written correctly.

1. The train left early.
2. The moon looks beautiful.
3. mom left me a note.
4. He comes here every day.
5. i told you everything.
6. We made the cake.
7. Eric swims better than I.
8. do you know John?
9. tell him I'm home.
10. Mr. Owens lives there.
11. That man is a pilot.
12. She is very unhappy.
13. would someone help me?
14. I tried to tell you.
15. dean stopped talking.
16. are you afraid to go?
17. No one could see me.
18. i fell on the stairs.
19. your bike looks great.
20. Is he your brother?
21. When will you know?
22. My mom is not home.
23. the fish got away.
24. Do you like turtles?
25. maybe we can help.

26. how did you find it?
27. This room is too small.
28. stand over there.
29. jean hurt her arm.
30. The slide is too hot.
31. i want to see him.
32. She bought the dog.
33. My horse ran away.
34. Take me with you.
35. It is too early.
36. did you hear anything?
37. i'm afraid of ghosts.
38. The sky is getting darker.
39. move your books.
40. Where should we go?
41. a voice called softly.
42. These shoes are too big.
43. write the answer.
44. i wish you would come.
45. was that all?
46. everyone was quiet.
47. Did you pass the test?
48. this math is easy.
49. Mr. Kent is a good teacher.
50. Give me the paper.

COMPOSITION EXERCISE

Choose 12 of the incorrectly written sentences from today's lesson. Rewrite them correctly.

1. _____
2. _____
3. _____
4. _____
5. _____
6. _____

7. _____
8. _____
9. _____
10. _____
11. _____
12. _____

Unit 87 cont'd

Capitalizing Titles

To write a title correctly, capitalize the first and last words and all other words except short prepositions, conjunctions, and articles.

EXAMPLES: a. **The Long Green**   c. **The Two Worlds of Davy Blount**
       b. **Uncle Robert's Secret**   d. **Under the Haystack**

 Underline the words which should be capitalized.

1. the adventures of huckleberry finn
2. the hiding place
3. the dark is rising
4. bigfoot
5. the return of the twelves
6. robinson crusoe
7. the learning tree
8. lord of the flies
9. the seventh cross
10. a lion in winter
11. a tale of two cities
12. the adventures of tom sawyer
13. catch-22
14. salem's lot
15. the house of seven gables
16. and then there were none
17. life under the sea
18. the bell jar
19. roots
20. alice in wonderland
21. the eagle has landed
22. i am third
23. the queen's confessions
24. the sound and the fury
25. the summer of little rain

26. sister carrie
27. land of midnight sun
28. photography made simple
29. the power and the glory
30. eye of the needle
31. song of bernadette
32. the art of writing letters
33. an american tragedy
34. let there be thorns
35. dancing for the stage
36. the thorn birds
37. valley of no return
38. first on the moon
39. treasure island
40. travelling abroad
41. the longest yard
42. the robe
43. a man for all seasons
44. deathwork
45. the lost horizon
46. when all else fails
47. the power and the glory
48. patton
49. murder, she wrote
50. war of the worlds

COMPOSITION EXERCISE

Rewrite 12 of the above titles correctly.

1. _____
2. _____
3. _____
4. _____
5. _____
6. _____

7. _____
8. _____
9. _____
10. _____
11. _____
12. _____

Capitalization in Titles

When writing a title, capitalize the first word, the last word, and all other words except short prepositions, conjunctions, and articles.

EXAMPLES: a. "Winds from the North"
           b. To Catch a Thief
           c. Night Riders and Blue Moons

A Explain why each word is or is not capitalized.

1. Gone with the Wind _____ Gone - first word; with - short preposition; the - article; Wind - last word

2. Ashanti to Zulu _____ Ashanti - first word; to - short preposition; Zulu - last word

3. Portrait of Ivan _____ Portrait - first word; of - short preposition; Ivan - last word

4. "The Raven" _____ The - first word; Raven - last word

5. Watership Down _____ Watership - first word; Down - last word

6. "Trees" _____ Trees - single-word title

7. The Man Without a Country _____ The - first word; Man - important word; Without - long preposition; a - article; Country - last word

8. "On Top of Old Smokey" _____ On - first word; Top - important word; of - short preposition; Old - important word; Smokey - last word

9. Stories by Mark Twain _____ Stories - first word; by - short preposition; Mark - important word; Twain - last word

10. Land of the Lost _____ Land - first word; of - short preposition; the - article; Lost - last word

11. "Down in the Valley" _____ Down - first word; in - short preposition; the - article; Valley - last word

12. The Prince and the Pauper _____ The - first word; Prince - important word; and - conjunction; the - article; Pauper - last word

B Underline the words which should be capitalized.

1. "star spangled banner"
2. robinson crusoe
3. pride and prejudice
4. "the wizard of oz"
5. "look over the rainbow"
6. for those who love
7. doctor zhivago
8. "hold fast your dreams"

9. "the road not taken"
10. animal farm
11. "the yak"
12. a cry in the night
13. holocaust
14. the painted bird
15. a farewell to arms
16. the cat who went to heaven

213

Unit 88 cont'd

When to Capitalize a Word

Capital letters are used when
1. *the word is a proper noun,*
2. *the word begins a sentence,*
3. *the word begins a quote,*
4. *the word is "I."*

EXAMPLES: a. *July is a hot month.*   c. *Lewis and I made the team.*
           b. *My grandparents live in Omaha.*   d. *The door is open.*

✱ **Underline the words which should be capitalized.**

1. theo and i are studying.
2. our class is going outside.
3. paul said, "this is my mother."
4. i will help if i can.
5. pam and ted live there.
6. my aunt is visiting us.
7. "how are you?" she asked.
8. when is the play?
9. i live next door.
10. detroit is in michigan.
11. pete, chris, and tom are waiting.
12. her house is on kim circle.
13. i want a pepsi.
14. the doorbell rang.
15. the army crossed the river.
16. mrs. lawrence gave it to me.
17. cathi and i rode horses.
18. she attends st. paul's academy.
19. dick said, "i'll be there."
20. cindy and connie sat on the fence.
21. the stream is polluted.
22. the witch scares me.
23. charlotte has lived in england.
24. i waited to see you.
25. that's a silly commercial.
26. we went to the beach.
27. dad and i fished all day.
28. my cousins live in nebraska.
29. this is the hudson river.
30. jamie knows my sister.
31. "please come in," said ken.
32. it is a beautiful day.
33. did you meet dr. martin?
34. the old house is haunted.
35. mr. and mrs. green are here.
36. i will tell mark and sheila.
37. if laurie calls, talk to her.
38. "dinner is ready!" mom called.
39. the dog growled at us.
40. i am watching donald duck.
41. "where is the leak?" the plumber asked.
42. the party is tuesday.
43. "don't tell him," she begged.
44. he and i discussed it.
45. mom made a lemon cake.
46. the kitten sat in the window.
47. my birthday is in january.
48. his sister's name is donna.
49. mickey mouse is my favorite.
50. we stayed in miami.

COMPOSITION EXERCISE

Write two examples to illustrate each part of the rule.

1. proper nouns
   _____
   _____

2. beginning sentences
   _____
   _____

3. beginning quotes
   _____
   _____

4. word "I"
   _____
   _____

214

Capitalization Practice

Always capitalize the following:

1. **a proper noun**
   Sandra White

2. **the word "I"**
   I love to ski.

3. **a title used before a name**
   This is Dr. Adamson.

4. **the first word of a sentence**
   The decorations were blue.

5. **the first word of a quotation**
   Kim asked, "Is it raining?"

 Underline the words which should be capitalized.

1. i have always wanted to go to paris.
2. lewis and i have been friends for years.
3. how did you get in here?
4. we must hurry.
5. my teacher is ms. fielder.
6. sally stopped at the store.
7. drink your orange juice.
8. why can't we stay awhile?
9. martha is my guest.
10. did you go by the post office?
11. "i'm too tired," moaned charlie.
12. lt. peters would like to talk to you.
13. someone has opened my letter.
14. did you spend all of your money?
15. jim's birthday is in february.
16. it is ten degrees below zero!
17. how much does an elephant weigh?
18. "that's impossible!" exclaimed sam.
19. this is pat and allen sommers.
20. nancy and i are watching television.
21. did dr. mills go to school in london?
22. where are your gloves?
23. this train is going to boston.
24. edna warned, "look out for that car!"
25. walter wants a career in law.

26. is mr. jamison coming to the play?
27. no one is supposed to know that.
28. we are going to the airport.
29. bob asked, "what happened here?"
30. the deadline is thursday.
31. i need two dozen eggs.
32. "open the door!" yelled tom.
33. everyone likes mrs. west.
34. the owner is capt. martin.
35. i can't remember ann's address.
36. kim has to practice her singing.
37. "sit there," ordered the man.
38. i thought you were still at home.
39. we took a vacation to california.
40. dan has three tickets to the game.
41. i want to climb mt. everest!
42. you will always be welcome here.
43. jean cried, "can't you do anything?"
44. look to your left.
45. the next meeting is on wednesday.
46. the united states is my home.
47. mr. green asked, "is this your book?"
48. my mother speaks german.
49. i am hungry.
50. we moved to ohio in november.

COMPOSITION EXERCISE

Write 12 sentences. Underline the capitalized words.

1. _____
2. _____
3. _____
4. _____
5. _____
6. _____

7. _____
8. _____
9. _____
10. _____
11. _____
12. _____

Unit 89 cont'd

Addressing Someone — the Comma

Use the comma to set off the name of the person you are addressing.

EXAMPLES:
  a. *Ernie, tell us a joke.*
  b. *What did you say, Pete?*
  c. *Your mother is here, Carl.*
  d. *Frank, did you call me?*

 Place commas where needed.

1. John, are you coming to my party?
2. Sally, you must tell me.
3. Yes, Keith, I saw you.
4. May I have a cookie, Mom?
5. Jenny, I can't hear you.
6. How are you, Paul?
7. Kay, have you talked to Tom?
8. Well, Jill, how was school?
9. Come in, Nick.
10. Mr. Davis, I need your help.
11. I'm talking to you, Chris.
12. Jan, you'll miss the bus.
13. Mrs. Wilson, is this correct?
14. It's beautiful, Karen.
15. What's wrong, Dana?
16. Dr. Drake, this is Jean.
17. I'm too tired, Wayne.
18. I will see you tomorrow, Kevin.
19. Doug, I'm sorry.
20. Yes, Kenny, it's for you.
21. Answer the phone, Andy.
22. What happened, Dad?
23. Louise, are you coming?
24. Who was at the door, Deb?
25. Gwen, will you hurry please?
26. We're leaving, Adam.
27. Sit down, Dr. Cookson.
28. Mr. Owens, may we talk to you?
29. Liz, finish your homework.
30. Leave me alone, Eric.
31. Now, Lynn, let's eat.
32. Rick, are you hungry?
33. Get in the car, Judy.
34. Why were you late, Mark?
35. Listen to the song, Brad.
36. Jerry, will you bring me a rope?
37. Is Pat angry, Dean?
38. Mr. Cooper, I'm your neighbor.
39. No, Laurie, you can't go.
40. Mom, I'm home.
41. Who is she, Marcia?
42. Wait until Thursday, Sue.
43. Mrs. Hawk, it's your turn.
44. Willie, we must find it.
45. Joan, the plane has landed.
46. I'm scared, Perry.
47. Jack, where have you been?
48. No, Mrs. Winters, she's not here.
49. Ann, she's waiting.
50. That's not true, Alex.

COMPOSITION EXERCISE

Write 12 sentences which contain names in direct address.

1. _____
2. _____
3. _____
4. _____
5. _____
6. _____
7. _____
8. _____
9. _____
10. _____
11. _____
12. _____

Commas Used in Dates

A comma is used to separate the day and year but not usually the month and year.

EXAMPLES:
a. *June 30, 1800*   c. *August 1701*   e. *December 1950*
b. *February 25, 1977*   d. *September 1, 1911*   f. *May 16, 1923*

A Place commas where needed.

1. Jan. 1, 1990
2. April 4, 1842
3. Nov. 1599
4. Aug. 14, 1979
5. May 1830
6. June 13, 1922
7. June 1897
8. Dec. 1949
9. March 19, 1961
10. Nov. 27, 1970
11. April 1991
12. Feb. 14, 1900

13. Dec. 2001
14. April 5, 1991
15. May 1980
16. Feb. 1403
17. Nov. 15, 1901
18. March 1, 1976
19. July 1921
20. Aug. 11, 1957
21. Oct. 1980
22. Jan. 1801
23. Sept. 19, 1979
24. May 1941

25. August 1912
26. July 29, 1840
27. March 19, 1973
28. Dec. 1985
29. July 1737
30. Nov. 1987
31. Oct. 7, 1951
32. Jan. 19, 1879
33. April 12, 1708
34. May 21, 1700
35. Sept. 1999
36. Feb. 1929

37. June 27, 1896
38. April 1500
39. Dec. 18, 1953
40. June 1575
41. Sept. 1588
42. Feb. 1977
43. Aug. 1978
44. March 1993
45. May 1492
46. Oct. 1602
47. Nov. 1856
48. July 4, 1776

B Place commas where needed.

1. Today is April 16, 1982.
2. Yesterday was April 15, 1982.
3. Tomorrow will be April 17, 1982.
4. I was born October 7, 1969.
5. The date is November 5, 1987.
6. We moved in June 1980.
7. They will arrive May 10, 1979.
8. The war began in August 1987.
9. I will graduate in May 1990.
10. My sister was born in March 1971.

11. The movie was made in July 1950.
12. Our vacation is in December 1988.
13. Were you there in August 1975?
14. My mom was born May 1, 1945.
15. We lived there in November 1967.
16. The house was built in May 1918.
17. The offer expires July 10, 1981.
18. It happened in September 1900.
19. The car was built in January 1949.
20. August 21, 1988 is the deadline.

COMPOSITION EXERCISE

Write 16 sentences which contain dates.

1. _____
2. _____
3. _____
4. _____
5. _____
6. _____
7. _____
8. _____

9. _____
10. _____
11. _____
12. _____
13. _____
14. _____
15. _____
16. _____

Unit 90 cont'd →

Commas Used to Separate Cities and States

Use a comma between the city and state.

EXAMPLES: a. *Memphis, Tennessee* c. *Philadelphia, Pennsylvania*
b. *Newark, New Jersey* d. *Los Angeles, California*

A Place commas where needed.

1. We live in San Francisco, California.
2. Atlanta, Georgia, is a big city.
3. Sue visited Nashville, Tennessee.
4. The next town is Columbus, Ohio.
5. It is hot in Miami, Florida.
6. They are from Muncie, Indiana.
7. Karen went to Topeka, Kansas.
8. She was born in Las Vegas, Nevada.
9. My home is Richmond, Virginia.
10. Have you been to Houston, Texas?
11. Jack is from Flint, Michigan.
12. Louisville, Kentucky, is my next stop.
13. Palmer, Alaska, is a cold place to live.
14. We stayed in Salt Lake City, Utah.
15. Portland, Oregon, is too far away.
16. Let's go to St. Louis, Missouri.
17. Chicago, Illinois, is a busy place.
18. We moved here from Yuma, Arizona.
19. Seattle, Washington, is our last stop.
20. Home is in Helena, Montana.

B Place commas where needed.

1. Fresno, California
2. Salem, Oregon
3. Jackson, Michigan
4. Butte, Montana
5. Reno, Nevada
6. Des Moines, Iowa
7. Plains, Georgia
8. Bangor, Maine
9. Fairbanks, Alaska
10. Hot Springs, Arkansas
11. Hannibal, Missouri
12. Roanoke, Virginia
13. Dayton, Ohio
14. Tulsa, Oklahoma
15. Wichita, Kansas
16. Tampa, Florida
17. Trenton, New Jersey
18. Dallas, Texas
19. Boise, Idaho
20. Ogden, Utah
21. Denver, Colorado
22. Charlotte, North Carolina
23. Frankfort, Kentucky
24. Biloxi, Mississippi
25. Oahu, Hawaii
26. Albany, New York
27. Carlsbad, New Mexico
28. Monroe, Louisiana
29. Tucson, Arizona
30. Mobile, Alabama
31. Laramie, Wyoming
32. Gary, Indiana
33. New Haven, Connecticut
34. Madison, Wisconsin
35. Lincoln, Nebraska
36. Duluth, Minnesota

COMPOSITION EXERCISE

Write 16 sentences which contain the names of cities and states.

1. _____
2. _____
3. _____
4. _____
5. _____
6. _____
7. _____
8. _____
9. _____
10. _____
11. _____
12. _____
13. _____
14. _____
15. _____
16. _____

Comprehension Check

(A) Underline the writing situations which require capitals.

1. <u>the name of your best friend</u>
2. <u>the name of your aunt</u>
3. the name of things you wear
4. <u>the first word of a sentence</u>
5. the last word of a sentence
6. the name of an animal
7. <u>the word "I"</u>
8. <u>the first word of a question</u>
9. <u>the name of your home town</u>
10. the name of a color

11. the word "cake"
12. <u>the name of a specific river</u>
13. <u>the first word of a book title</u>
14. the word "and" in a title
15. the word "you"
16. <u>the name of your pet beagle</u>
17. <u>the name of your math book</u>
18. <u>the last word of a song title</u>
19. <u>the first word of a quotation</u>
20. <u>any important word of a title</u>

(B) Explain why each word is capitalized.

1. The house on First Street is for sale. *first word of sentence/proper noun*
2. Betsy and Rick moved to New York City. *first word of sentence/proper nouns*
3. A meeting is set for next Thursday. *first word of sentence/proper noun*
4. Mr. Owens and I are neighbors. *first word of sentence/proper noun/word "I"*
5. Steve said, "The book was checked out." *first word of sentence/proper noun/ first word of quotation*
6. The show is a big success. *first word of sentence*
7. Your uncle will visit us next week. *first word of sentence*
8. "Walking is good exercise," she corrected. *first word of quotation*
9. You and I will travel first to Paris. *first word of sentence/ word "I"/proper noun*
10. The newspaper is running another ad. *first word of sentence*
11. Tell Marci to meet me at the library. *first word of sentence/proper noun*
12. The mailman usually comes at two. *first word of sentence*
13. He asked again, "Is David working at Swenson's?" *first word of sentence/ first word of quotation/proper nouns*
14. The package was trimmed with blue ribbons. *first word of sentence*
15. Jena is a wonderful dancer. *first word of sentence/proper noun*

(C) Underline the words in each title which should be capitalized.

1. <u>ashanti</u> to <u>zulu</u>
2. <u>animal</u> <u>farm</u>
3. <u>gone</u> with the <u>wind</u>
4. "<u>hail</u> to the <u>chief</u>"
5. the <u>story</u> of <u>tarzan</u>
6. <u>robinson</u> <u>crusoe</u>
7. "<u>ten</u> <u>little</u> <u>indians</u>"

8. <u>red</u> <u>badge</u> of <u>courage</u>
9. the <u>brain</u>
10. the <u>learning</u> <u>tree</u>
11. <u>huckleberry</u> <u>finn</u>
12. "<u>the</u> <u>road</u> <u>not</u> <u>taken</u>"
13. <u>lord</u> of the <u>flies</u>
14. the <u>dead</u> <u>zone</u>

15. <u>jane</u> <u>eyre</u>
16. "<u>shades</u> of <u>gray</u>"
17. <u>catch</u>-22
18. "<u>amazing</u> <u>grace</u>"
19. <u>roget's</u> <u>thesaurus</u>
20. <u>a</u> <u>cry</u> in the <u>night</u>
21. the <u>president's</u> <u>lady</u>

Test 18 cont'd

Comprehension Check (continued)

D **Underline the words which should be capitalized.**

1. the woman replied, "i was born in paris."
2. he and i have known each other for years.
3. how did you recognize the man?
4. we are reading *hamlet* in english.
5. "may i help you?" the clerk asked.
6. sweden is a beautiful country.
7. lisa told bobby all about it.
8. the news will be on in ten minutes.
9. refer to *webster's dictionary*.
10. the fishing trip is next saturday.
11. thomas bought a new jacket.
12. reuben's birthday is in march.
13. we'll watch *death of a salesman*.
14. mr. hogan owns an oldsmobile.
15. "the rest was easy," she sighed.
16. "rita and les are here," he announced.
17. the train stops first in chicago.
18. melanie whispered, "who is he?"
19. answer the phone on the third ring.
20. "i can't answer that," nick said.
21. charles drove the truck home.
22. the money is counterfeit.
23. may i speak with dr. baker?
24. they have traveled all over the world.
25. no one has ever been to saturn.

E **Place commas where needed.**

1. Have you ever been to Mobile, Alabama?
2. Andy was born October 12, 1976.
3. Look, Robert, there's the ship now.
4. We'll drive to Atlanta, Georgia.
5. Louise, must you go so soon?
6. They met on September 16, 1985.
7. My cousin lives in Phoenix, Arizona.
8. The answer, Deidre, is on page 71.
9. My parents married on May 20, 1969.
10. Sally, do you know the combination?
11. We are visiting Los Angeles, California.
12. It happened on June 7, 1984.
13. Jetta, have you seen Ken today?
14. Our next stop is Butte, Montana.
15. No, Alice, we don't have enough time.
16. Christmas is fun, isn't it, James?
17. His birthdate is February 1, 1958.
18. Jane's family moved to Dallas, Texas.
19. I want to go to Memphis, Tennessee.
20. Yes, Chris, you made the team.

Write a paragraph about your favorite novel, poem, or song. Tell why you like it and why you would/would not recommend it to others. Remember to capitalize your sentences correctly.

_____
_____
_____
_____
_____
_____
_____
_____

When Commas Follow "Yes" and "No"

When "yes" or "no" begins a sentence, use a comma to separate it from the remainder of the sentence.

EXAMPLES: a. **Yes, I saw the plane.**   c. **No, I don't know him.**
            b. **No, he's not my brother.**   d. **Yes, I brought the gift.**

A Place commas where needed.

1. Yes, I did my homework.
2. No, I can't come to the party.
3. No, she isn't here.
4. Yes, I'll tell her the news.
5. Yes, it works perfectly.
6. No, it's not too late.
7. No, she couldn't come.
8. Yes, I want a blue one.
9. Yes, the radio is mine.
10. No, no one told me.
11. Yes, I love it.
12. No, today is Saturday.

B Answer each question with a sentence that begins with "yes" or "no."

1. May I go?
   Yes, you may go.

2. Is that an aardvark?
   Yes, that's an aardvark.

3. Did you pass the test?
   Yes, I passed the test.

4. Can you help me?
   Yes, I can help you.

5. Is your aunt here?
   No, my aunt isn't here.

6. Do you live here?
   No, I don't live here.

7. Have you seen this show?
   Yes, I've seen this show.

8. Was the light on?
   Yes, the light was on.

9. Did the train stop?
   No, the train didn't stop.

10. Have they arrived?
    No, they haven't arrived.

11. Do you hear anything?
    No, I don't hear anything.

12. Is this yours?
    Yes, this is mine.

13. Did you bring it?
    No, I didn't bring it.

14. Are you ready to go?
    Yes, I am ready to go.

15. May I have one?
    Yes, you may have one.

16. Is today Wednesday?
    Yes, today is Wednesday.

17. Has George been here?
    No, George hasn't been here.

18. Did the bus leave?
    Yes, the bus left.

COMPOSITION EXERCISE

Write 12 sentences which begin with either "yes" or "no."

1. _____
2. _____
3. _____
4. _____
5. _____
6. _____
7. _____
8. _____
9. _____
10. _____
11. _____
12. _____

Unit 91 cont'd

Commas in a Series

Commas (,) are used to separate words in a series.

EXAMPLES: a. *Mom bought chocolate, vanilla, and strawberry ice cream.*
b. *My dad plays basketball, football, and field hockey.*

 Place commas where needed.

1. I like apples,pears,and bananas.
2. John,Tony,and Phil are absent.
3. They read poems,stories,and books.
4. I study math,history,and English.
5. She needs scissors,glue,and a pen.
6. We planted beans,lettuce,and carrots.
7. I invited Jason,Mary,and Diane.
8. A noun names a person,place,or thing.
9. I own a car,a truck,and a bus.
10. Adverbs tell when,where,or how.
11. Mom,Dad,and I are leaving.
12. The zoo has camels,bears,and giraffes.
13. I like monkeys,lions,and zebras.
14. You,he,and it are pronouns.
15. I have a dog,a cat,and a parrot.
16. I have been to Texas,Utah,and Florida.
17. I saw Sandy,Dee,and Paula.
18. We picked tomatoes,beans,and squash.
19. Mike,Sara,and I went to the circus.
20. There,their,and they're sound alike.
21. He sold peanuts,popcorn,and candy.
22. I save pennies,dimes,and nickels.
23. The balloons were red,yellow,and green.
24. You told Liz,Ann,and Sherry.
25. Should I go north,south,east,or west?
26. We made cookies,cakes,and pies.
27. We visited Chicago,New York,and Detroit.
28. I rode a boat,a train,and a plane.
29. Lisa,Jill,and Dana are my friends.
30. I bought a hat,a coat,and a shirt.
31. I found a penny,a key,and a pin.
32. I ate a hot dog,popcorn,and candy.
33. Jack,Eric,and Rich were there.
34. I received a letter,a card,and a package.
35. Sam,Eddie,and Mark came to see you.
36. It was about a boy,a horse,and a dog.
37. Apples,pears,and peaches are fruits.
38. I speak English,French,and German.
39. Eric plays football,baseball,and hockey.
40. Mom works Monday,Thursday,and Friday.
41. I see a rabbit,a turkey,and a fox.
42. I like to swim,to ski,and to camp.
43. Kay,Pam,and Sally were at the party.
44. Do you want beef,pork,or chicken?
45. Teachers,parents,and students were there.
46. He has lived in Maine,Georgia,and Ohio.
47. We will need a hoe,a rake,and a shovel.
48. I chose Mike,Dan,and Alex.
49. I collect rocks,coins,and stamps.
50. The flag is red,white,and blue.

COMPOSITION EXERCISE

Write a sentence using each set of words as a series.

1. potatoes / rice / noodles

_____

2. land / air / sea

_____

3. Dave / Jill / Rex / Liz

_____

4. Monday / Tuesday / Wednesday

_____

Dividing Words in a Series — the Comma

Use a comma to separate words in a series.

EXAMPLES:
a. *I chose Deana, Lee, and Cory.*
b. *He collects leaves, coins, and rocks.*
c. *Rich, Dan, and I will finish.*
d. *The house, barn, and fence burned.*

 Place a comma where needed.

1. My team is Joey, Alex, and me.
2. Wes needs shoes, socks, and a tie.
3. Jason, Sue, and I were chosen.
4. They swam, fished, and hiked.
5. We picked cherries, apples, and pears.
6. He wrote poems, stories, and books.
7. Roses, daisies, and marigolds are flowers.
8. She served steak, potatoes, and peas.
9. I have lived in Kansas, Ohio, and Texas.
10. We will see zebras, camels, and monkeys.
11. Kelly, Gina, and Dawn want to see you.
12. Kate, Bo, and I planned a picnic.
13. We washed walls, windows, and doors.
14. Robins, swallows, and sparrows are birds.
15. I can cook, sew, and clean.
16. He eats, sleeps, and watches television.
17. Mom needs sugar, milk, and eggs.
18. Is it a pond, a lake, or a river?
19. Was the dog a collie, a poodle, or a mutt?
20. Tell Carl, Louis, and Billy.
21. We had cake, doughnuts, and pie.
22. Show Ken, Bill, and Al the bike.
23. He pushed, pulled, and tugged.
24. I take math, history, and English.
25. I lost my keys, money, and umbrella.
26. We studied the sun, moon, and stars.
27. I enjoy walking, talking, and laughing.
28. He's traveled by bus, car, and plane.
29. Charles, Steve, and Paul are brothers.
30. Jo sings, dances, and plays the piano.
31. He found the cards, letters, and gifts.
32. I want to be a pilot, a soldier, or a ranger.
33. She knows English, French, and German.
34. My aunt, uncle, and cousins visited us.
35. Ernie, Bert, and Sam were invited.
36. We are having chicken, rice, and beans.
37. He was absent Monday, Tuesday, and Friday.
38. I have a radio, a television, and a phone.
39. He told jokes, riddles, and stories.
40. Mom, Dad, and I watched the game.
41. Call Ernest, Andy, and Larry.
42. Work numbers 4, 6, and 8.
43. June, July, and August are summer months.
44. We studied nouns, pronouns, and verbs.
45. Utah, Nevada, and Arizona are in the West.
46. Marty, Vicki, or Seth will be the winner.
47. Would you like coffee, tea, or milk?
48. Bring knives, forks, and spoons.
49. She can add, subtract, and divide.
50. Let's count the pennies, nickels, and dimes.

COMPOSITION EXERCISE

Write 8 sentences which contain words in a series.

1. _____
2. _____
3. _____
4. _____
5. _____
6. _____
7. _____
8. _____

Unit 92 cont'd

The Comma to Introduce Quotes

Use a comma to separate the quote
from the speaker.

EXAMPLES: a. *Anna shouted, "He's guilty!"*   c. *"No," said Frank, "we must proceed."*
         b. *"The man is shrewd," said Ben.*   d. *Sam asked, "What did he say?"*

 Place a comma where needed.

1. Gina said, "It was easy."
2. "Why," Steve asked, "didn't you?"
3. "I am the winner," he announced.
4. He asked, "Is this your room?"
5. Tom thought, "He's angry."
6. "Write to me," Mr. Williams said.
7. Eric cried, "Watch out!"
8. "The deadline," she said, "is today."
9. Jill cried, "Don't leave me!"
10. "You heard me," Mother said.
11. Wes shouted, "You stop that!"
12. "I love the summer," Dot sighed.
13. Jim exclaimed, "You're the thief!"
14. Pam cried, "I love it!"
15. "You're too greedy," said Adam.
16. "Estimate the cost," the man said.
17. Theo asked, "Where is Church Park?"
18. Molly cried, "It's a skeleton!"
19. He announced, "Mission accomplished."
20. "I'm innocent," Arnie repeated.
21. Barb said, "I want ice cream."
22. "Bring me the book," Liz said.
23. Suzanne exclaimed, "It's beautiful!"
24. "Wait here," Dee said.
25. Alice shouted, "That's mine!"
26. "I will," she answered.
27. Ken asked, "Is it over yet?"
28. "I'm tired," Bob repeated.
29. "Yes," he said, "my name is Don."
30. "I know the story," said Louis.
31. "Please," he begged, "don't tell Mom."
32. "Stay here," Carl ordered.
33. Holly thought, "They know."
34. "He's my dog," said the boy.
35. Walt said, "Be there at 6."
36. "Look at me," said Gladys.
37. Perry announced, "This is my home."
38. The doctor said, "Take this medicine."
39. "The guests are here," Ted said.
40. The man asked, "Are you from Texas?"
41. "I see him," she said.
42. George answered, "I did it."
43. "The moon," she sighed, "is beautiful."
44. "Watch this," said Jason.
45. Dad said, "Clean your room."
46. Dave asked, "Who is she?"
47. "It's cold in here," said Kim.
48. "Talk to me," Joe ordered.
49. Mike asked, "Can't you do it?"
50. "I'm a rich man," he boasted.

COMPOSITION EXERCISE

Write 6 sentences which contain quotes.

1. _____
2. _____
3. _____
4. _____
5. _____
6. _____

Using a Period

Use a period:
 (1) at the end of a statement
      I will write the code.
 (2) at the end of a command
      Open the door slowly.
 (3) at the end of most abbreviations
      Capt. Nest is my uncle.

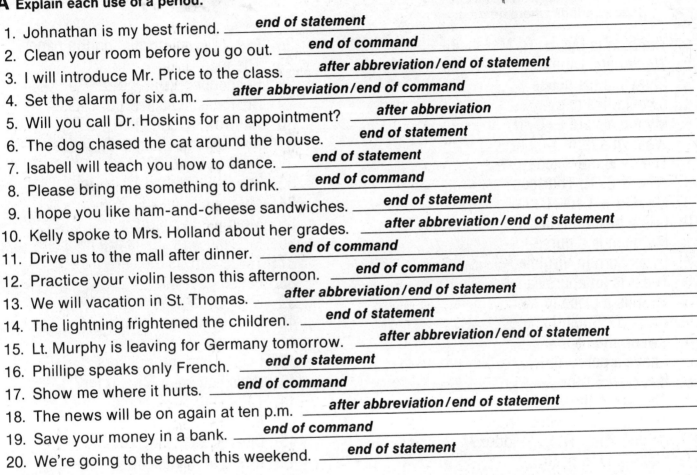

A Explain each use of a period.

1. Johnathan is my best friend. _____ *end of statement* _____
2. Clean your room before you go out. _____ *end of command* _____
3. I will introduce Mr. Price to the class. _____ *after abbreviation / end of statement* _____
4. Set the alarm for six a.m. _____ *after abbreviation / end of command* _____
5. Will you call Dr. Hoskins for an appointment? _____ *after abbreviation* _____
6. The dog chased the cat around the house. _____ *end of statement* _____
7. Isabell will teach you how to dance. _____ *end of statement* _____
8. Please bring me something to drink. _____ *end of command* _____
9. I hope you like ham-and-cheese sandwiches. _____ *end of statement* _____
10. Kelly spoke to Mrs. Holland about her grades. _____ *after abbreviation / end of statement* _____
11. Drive us to the mall after dinner. _____ *end of command* _____
12. Practice your violin lesson this afternoon. _____ *end of command* _____
13. We will vacation in St. Thomas. _____ *after abbreviation / end of statement* _____
14. The lightning frightened the children. _____ *end of statement* _____
15. Lt. Murphy is leaving for Germany tomorrow. _____ *after abbreviation / end of statement* _____
16. Phillipe speaks only French. _____ *end of statement* _____
17. Show me where it hurts. _____ *end of command* _____
18. The news will be on again at ten p.m. _____ *after abbreviation / end of statement* _____
19. Save your money in a bank. _____ *end of command* _____
20. We're going to the beach this weekend. _____ *end of statement* _____

B Place periods where needed.

1. Dr. Miles asked Mike and Arnold.
2. I watched the movie four times.
3. Pour the milk and water.
4. It is supposed to rain today.
5. Wash the car first.
6. Louis chose to stay at home.
7. My father is Col. Hoban.
8. Christi needs our help.
9. Water the garden every day.
10. The police arrived quickly.
11. Bring a loaf of bread too.
12. Someone left the door unlocked.
13. Pam has beautiful brown eyes.
14. Mr. Sawyer travels by train.
15. It is time to go home.
16. Help me finish these chores.
17. Mr. and Mrs. Wright want to see you.
18. They adopted six children.
19. Nancy wants to be a singer.
20. Let's go to lunch.

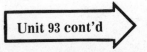 Unit 93 cont'd

When to Use a Period

Use a period (a) at the end of a statement, (b) at the end of a command, (c) after an abbreviation, and (d) after an initial.

EXAMPLES:
(statement)	I am a student.
(command)	Move the books.
(abbreviation)	This is Dr. Morgan.
(initial)	His name is J.T. Maddox.

✱ Place periods where needed.

1. The man is Mr. H. G. Marshall.
2. We left at 11 a.m.
3. Show me his house.
4. I would like to go.
5. My initials are L. C. N.
6. We own a farm.
7. The deadline is today.
8. Who is C. K. Thurmon?
9. My dad is Capt. Davis.
10. It is a beautiful day.
11. My mom is a nurse.
12. I was born in Virginia.
13. Tues. is an abbreviation.
14. Find us a place to sit.
15. Dr. G. L. Smith is here.
16. Sweep the floor.
17. I have a pet turtle.
18. It is now 6 p.m.
19. Sit next to the window.
20. This is Paul A. Winslow.
21. Do you know R. P. Maddox?
22. I learned the poem.
23. My teacher is Mrs. Duncan.
24. The party begins at 7 p.m.
25. The town was deserted.
26. F. L. C. was printed on the paper.
27. The man is ill.
28. School begins at 8 a.m.
29. Dr. Paulson visited our class.
30. Answer my question.
31. My name is Thomas B. Jones.
32. I live in the U. S. A.
33. The fish weighed 10 lb. 6 oz.
34. My boss is Alex E. Kelly.
35. Meet me at 5 p.m.
36. Mr. and Mrs. Sans are here.
37. Three a.m. is too early.
38. Finish your milk.
39. Capt. Thiel was angry.
40. The trip was wonderful.
41. Open the door for me.
42. I can't find my scissors.
43. Have you seen Mr. Porter?
44. Take your book home.
45. Mr. Turner wants to see you.
46. Did you say P.M. Vox?
47. It is now 3:15 p.m.
48. Fill the glasses with tea.
49. The field is muddy.
50. Have you met Dr. and Mrs. North?

COMPOSITION EXERCISE

Write 12 sentences which show uses of the period.

1. _____
2. _____
3. _____
4. _____
5. _____
6. _____
7. _____
8. _____
9. _____
10. _____
11. _____
12. _____

When Are Periods Needed?

Use a period after a statement or command and after most abbreviations and a person's title.

EXAMPLES:
a. You may use this one.
b. Try to convince Mom.
c. It is now 2 p.m.
d. Dr. H. R. Morgan will attend.

 Use periods where needed.

1. This is Dr. Stevens.
2. He arrived at 8 p.m.
3. Did you see Capt. Richards?
4. Watch this pass.
5. The room was empty.
6. Sgt. Phillips is in here.
7. This is J. P. Whitman.
8. Don't close your books.
9. The President made a speech.
10. I waited for Mrs. Danforth.
11. Close your mouth.
12. The time is 11 a.m.
13. Steve is not coming.
14. The game is being postponed.
15. Mr. Lewis is looking for us.
16. Feb. is the abbreviation for February.
17. I don't understand this.
18. Ask him your question.
19. At 3 p.m. the doors will open.
20. Curtis is very tired.
21. Lt. Davis is from Hawaii.
22. The deadline is 8 p.m.
23. Consult your dictionary.
24. The dog obeys my orders.
25. The ocean is very large.
26. Take your report card home.
27. I need a new pencil.
28. The map fell on the floor.
29. Mr. and Mrs. King live next door.
30. E. C. Thomas is the owner.
31. The plan is hopeless.
32. May I talk with Dr. Cook?
33. Let's sit by the window.
34. You have an obligation.
35. E. E. Marshall was elected.
36. I am going to win.
37. Mr. Harris is the watchman.
38. Jill decided to stay.
39. Give me some advice.
40. Capt. Jones is my mother.
41. My name is C. J. Koff.
42. I never said that.
43. Your room is a mess.
44. The dungeon was cold and damp.
45. Mrs. Worth graded my test.
46. Susan is my oldest sister.
47. Give me a hint.
48. Wear your jeans.
49. The show begins at 6 p.m.
50. May I introduce Dr. Stroud?

COMPOSITION EXERCISE

Write 12 sentences which illustrate the use of the period.

1. _____
2. _____
3. _____
4. _____
5. _____
6. _____
7. _____
8. _____
9. _____
10. _____
11. _____
12. _____

Unit 94 cont'd →

The Question Mark

The question mark (?) is used to end a sentence that asks something.

EXAMPLES: a. Have you seen Arnie?   c. Is this all you've done?
             b. Why don't we share?   d. Where is his home?

 If the sentence is a question, end it with a question mark. If not, use a period.

1. When is the deadline?
2. I must leave before noon.
3. Who opened this window?
4. May I go now?
5. Did you call her?
6. Eric believed the story.
7. Where is George?
8. I wish Mark were here.
9. The clouds are beautiful.
10. Is the water cold?
11. Which one is Nancy's?
12. Let's ride horses.
13. What is wrong?
14. Were you asleep?
15. Who took my chair?
16. Drink your orange juice.
17. Jason saw Jill do it.
18. When will we eat?
19. Johnny is next.
20. Did you mail my letter?
21. Which color do you like?
22. Please hold this for me.
23. Will you listen to me?
24. How are you?
25. What have you done?

26. That is good news.
27. Why can't I go?
28. Will you come along?
29. Sit here and wait for him.
30. Did he watch the game?
31. Steve will be home soon.
32. Are they late again?
33. Why didn't you tell me?
34. What did I do?
35. I'm too tired to play.
36. When is your birthday?
37. Pam isn't in her room.
38. How did you know?
39. Does Felix like me?
40. Keith made this for you.
41. Tell Tim to call me.
42. How can we help?
43. The dog is hungry.
44. Is he angry?
45. Why didn't you wait for me?
46. What took you so long?
47. I spoke to Mrs. Freeman.
48. Did anyone call?
49. Who is your teacher?
50. I'm glad it's over.

COMPOSITION EXERCISE

Write 12 sentences which illustrate the use of the question mark.

1. _____
2. _____
3. _____
4. _____
5. _____
6. _____
7. _____
8. _____
9. _____
10. _____
11. _____
12. _____

The Exclamation Point

The exclamation point is used after an interjection and a sentence that shows a strong emotion.

EXAMPLES:
a. *Ouch! That hurts.*
b. *Don't come in here!*
c. *Stop that car!*
d. *Wow! That's great.*

 Use exclamation points and periods as needed.

1. You're hurting my arm!
2. Hurry! He's leaving.
3. Wait! I'm coming.
4. It's a touchdown!
5. He bit me!
6. Oh! I didn't hear you.
7. We were here first!
8. Gee! You're lucky.
9. I hate spinach!
10. Don't shoot!
11. You broke my lamp!
12. Stop! You'll hurt yourself.
13. Don't you dare!
14. He's in trouble!
15. Ouch! That's my finger.
16. You can't go in there!
17. Hurrah! We're winning.
18. Look at that car!
19. No! It will burn.
20. It's going to crash!
21. I need your help!
22. Yes! We'll do it.
23. Great! I knew he would.
24. I'm not yelling!
25. Hey! Don't touch that.
26. No! It belongs to me.
27. Run faster!
28. Don't touch the stove!
29. Surprise! It's me.
30. See! I told you.
31. We won the championship!
32. Leave me alone!
33. Hey! I saw that.
34. Why! It's beautiful.
35. Don't! He's my brother.
36. Call the fire department!
37. Come quickly!
38. He's the thief!
39. Wow! It's the ocean.
40. It's a perfect match!
41. Marty fell in the lake!
42. They're here!
43. Hi! I'm Susan Brown.
44. No! It's not true.
45. I waited for two hours!
46. Terrific! It's working.
47. Ouch! You hit me.
48. I'm telling you the truth!
49. Wow! This game is terrific.
50. I'm trying to hurry!

COMPOSITION EXERCISE

Write 12 sentences which illustrate the use of the exclamation point.

1. _____
2. _____
3. _____
4. _____
5. _____
6. _____
7. _____
8. _____
9. _____
10. _____
11. _____
12. _____

Unit 95 cont'd

Using the Apostrophe in Contractions

A contraction is two words combined by leaving out some of the letters. An apostrophe represents the omitted letters.

EXAMPLES:
a. had + not = hadn't
b. she + has = she's
c. did + not = didn't
d. I + have = I've
e. of the clock = o'clock
f. what + is = what's

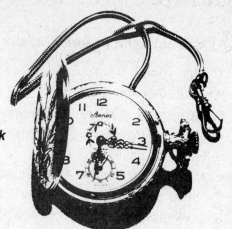

A Combine the two words, and write the contraction in the blank.

1. can + not = _can't_
2. would + not = WOULDN'T
3. he + is = HE'S
4. did + not = DIDN'T
5. you + will = YOU'LL
6. I + am = I'M
7. she + had = SHE'D
8. we + have = WE'VE
9. do + not = DON'T
10. have + not = HAVEN'T
11. they + have = THEY'VE
12. is + not = ISN'T
13. we + are = WE'RE
14. I + have = I'VE
15. were + not = WEREN'T
16. they + had = THEY'D
17. are + not = AREN'T
18. you + have = YOU'VE
19. I + had = I'D
20. could + not = COULDN'T
21. you + are = YOU'RE
22. I + will = I'LL
23. has + not = HASN'T
24. it + is = IT'S

B Complete the sentences with contractions.

1. _I'm_ sure we can do it.
2. _HE'S_ not mad at you.
3. You _SHOULDN'T_ talk like that.
4. _DON'T_ move or _I'LL_ shoot.
5. _SHE'D_ already gone home.
6. _AREN'T_ you finished yet?
7. I _HAVEN'T_ told anyone.
8. We _WEREN'T_ ready to play.
9. Lonnie _DIDN'T_ ask me.
10. _THEY'RE_ not my friends.
11. _IT'S_ too late now.
12. _YOU'RE_ not going in there.
13. James _WON'T_ help me.
14. _WE'RE_ going to Salt Lake City.
15. It _HASN'T_ rained in two months.
16. I _CAN'T_ wait any longer.
17. Sally _ISN'T_ feeling well.
18. It _WASN'T_ my fault.
19. _I'VE_ made up my mind.
20. You _AREN'T_ trying.

COMPOSITION EXERCISE

Write 12 sentences which contain contractions.

1. _____
2. _____
3. _____
4. _____
5. _____
6. _____
7. _____
8. _____
9. _____
10. _____
11. _____
12. _____

230

Comprehension Check

Test 19

A Explain each use of the comma.

1. Yes, I think it will work.
2. Jetta, Connie, and I went to Memphis today.
3. Larry replied, "The wind will be the determining factor."
4. Tell me, David, why you are always late.
5. No, the results will not be in until Thursday.
6. My aunt moved here from Columbus, Ohio.
7. We are having fried chicken, potato salad, and slaw.
8. Jackie asked, "Whom did you vote for?"
9. Yes, everything is all set for the fair.
10. The launch is set for September 23, 1988.
11. Corinne, Adam, and Steve are running for treasurer.
12. Give the apples, bananas, and plums to Walter.
13. She whispered, "May I please go now?"
14. We can take a train to Portland, Oregon.
15. Next semester I'm taking English, history, and algebra.

following "yes" or "no"
dividing words in a series
introducing a quote
setting off a name in address
following "yes" or "no"
separating city and state
dividing words in a series
introducing a quote
following "yes" or "no"
separating day and year
dividing words in a series
dividing words in a series
introducing a quote
separating city and state
dividing words in a series

B Explain each use of the period.

1. I saw Cameron at the mall this morning.
2. Have you met Dr. Winston?
3. Ask Leslie to bring the Monopoly game.
4. The house on Elm Street is still for sale.
5. Is he R. J. Hawkins?
6. Listen to the conclusion again.
7. Did you tell Capt. Stephens about it?
8. Why did Mrs. Thompson say that to you?
9. The money will be spent on food for the poor.
10. Make me a peanut-butter sandwich.
11. Everything was just as we left it.
12. Felix trusts your advice.
13. Will you speak to Mr. Hyatt by Monday?
14. I think Barton is handsome.
15. Wait for me in the hall.

after statement
after abbreviation
after command
after statement
after initials
after command
after abbreviation
after abbreviation
after statement
after command
after statement
after statement
after abbreviation
after statement
after command

C Write each contraction correctly.

1. is'not — *isn't*
2. your'e — *you're*
3. would'nt — *wouldn't*
4. were' — *we're*
5. can'not — *can't*

6. 'oclock — *o'clock*
7. its's — *it's*
8. aren'ot — *aren't*
9. wasnt' — *wasn't*
10. wo'nt — *won't*

11. did'nt — *didn't*
12. youl'l — *you'll*
13. wev'e — *we've*
14. haveno't — *haven't*
15. theyr'e — *they're*

231

Test 19 cont'd

Comprehension Check (continued)

D Explain the end punctuation of each sentence.

1. No one suspected Jeremy of cheating. *period after statement*
2. When will you begin the trip home? *question mark after question*
3. Set these dishes on the table by the door. *period after command*
4. The car is rolling into the river! *exclamation point after exclamation*
5. I called the plumber about the leak. *period after statement*
6. Andrew spends too much money on clothes. *period after statement*
7. How could you have believed him! *exclamation point after exclamation*
8. What did Reuben say to Mr. Henderson? *question mark after question*
9. Look both ways before crossing. *period after command*
10. Surely you knew that! *exclamation point after exclamation*
11. That truck is too big for this driveway. *period after statement*
12. How will we be able to control it? *question mark after question*
13. Sit down and close your mouth! *exclamation point after exclamation*
14. The weather seems warmer this afternoon. *period after statement*
15. What time do we eat? *question mark after question*

E Punctuate these sentences correctly.

1. I'll wait by the water fountain.
2. Annette, where have you been?
3. Kim loves picnics, parades, and fairs.
4. Yes, I have known Ted for years.
5. Hank, James, and Ed are here.
6. The spider bit me!
7. Stand beside Christopher.
8. Sam said, "Jesse is my partner."
9. I want to visit Holland, Michigan.
10. Shirley and Rick are absent.
11. What can I do to help?
12. Open your books to page 148.
13. Look for a red brick house.
14. Betsy received a new motorcycle.
15. Look out for that car!
16. Who is responsible for this program?
17. Turn left on Monroe Avenue.
18. It happened on June 16, 1980.
19. No, you can't go with me.
20. Is it working now?

Write a paragraph about your favorite television show. Why is it your favorite?

_____

_____

_____

_____

_____

_____

_____

Writing Titles of Books

The title of a book is always underlined.

EXAMPLES:
  a. *Joey really enjoyed* <u>Letters from the Earth</u>*.*
  b. *Don't choose* <u>The Warriors</u>*.*
  c. *Ask for* <u>Crackerjack Detective</u>*.*
  d. *Have you read* <u>Ten Little Indians</u>*?*

 Underline the book titles correctly.

1. Kevin brought you <u>The Mill on the Floss</u>.
2. Stan bought <u>Tom Sawyer</u>.
3. I am now reading <u>Chief's Ransom</u>.
4. <u>Music Man</u> is a very good book.
5. Bring me a copy of <u>Gone with the Wind</u>.
6. Where did you get <u>The Jury</u>?
7. <u>A Guide to Wushu</u> is Rick's book.
8. Last week he read <u>Of Mice and Men</u>.
9. <u>The Hiding Place</u> was interesting.
10. Bob's report is on <u>The Road West</u>.
11. <u>Writing Good Letters</u> is very helpful.
12. <u>If There Be Thorns</u> is on my desk.
13. <u>Learning French</u> will be our text.
14. I wrote <u>Cooking with Garlic</u>.
15. Ed borrowed <u>Winter's Revenge</u>.
16. <u>King's Crown</u> is about Henry VIII.
17. <u>Jo's Boys</u> is a classic.
18. Steinbeck wrote <u>The Grapes of Wrath</u>.
19. I finally finished <u>War and Peace</u>.
20. Ben is reading <u>Yellow Canyon</u>.
21. <u>The Great Stone Face</u> is a mystery.
22. I read <u>Dear Anna</u> last summer.
23. <u>To Kill a Mockingbird</u> is on the list.
24. Is <u>The Cave of Delphi</u> a good one?
25. Has he read <u>Dawn of Fear</u>?
26. <u>Metamagical Themas</u> sounds awful.
27. <u>Legends of Man</u> was a big book.
28. No one had read <u>The Furies</u>.
29. Ned chose <u>The Eagle Has Landed</u>.
30. I had already read <u>Bigfoot</u>.
31. <u>Two Years Before the Mast</u> was boring.
32. <u>The Seventh Cross</u> is Betsy's book.
33. Help me find <u>Arrow to the Sun</u>.
34. Read <u>The Prince and the Pauper</u>.
35. <u>Echoes from the Past</u> is checked out.
36. I want to read <u>Snare of the Hunter</u>.
37. I don't recommend <u>The Shining</u>.
38. <u>I Am Third</u> was sad.
39. Everyone had read <u>Animal Farm</u>.
40. <u>Silas Marner</u> is by George Elliot.
41. Who wrote <u>A Tale of Two Cities</u>?
42. Why don't you read <u>Camille</u>?
43. <u>The Old Man and the Sea</u> is good.
44. <u>The Titans</u> is missing.
45. Here's a copy of <u>Call to Glory</u>.
46. Is that <u>Secret of the Andes</u>?
47. Everyone had to read <u>America</u>.
48. <u>Flying High</u> is about aviation.
49. Alex will read us part of <u>Royalty</u>.
50. My first choice was <u>The Dream</u>.

COMPOSITION EXERCISE

Write 10 sentences which contain titles of books.

1. _____
2. _____
3. _____
4. _____
5. _____

6. _____
7. _____
8. _____
9. _____
10. _____

Unit 96 cont'd

Underlining Titles of Books

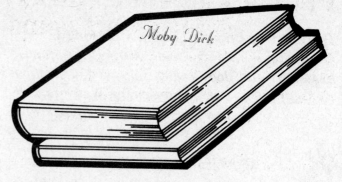

The title of a book is always underlined.

EXAMPLES:
  a. I am reading <u>Roots</u>.
  b. Jim likes <u>The Sun Also Rises</u>.
  c. Have you read <u>Pet Sematary</u>?
  d. <u>The Wayward Bus</u> is a good book.

 Underline the book titles correctly.

1. I want to read <u>Tom Sawyer</u>.
2. Have you read <u>Robinson Crusoe</u>?
3. <u>The Robe</u> is a good book.
4. Steve read <u>Walden</u>.
5. Did you finish <u>Moby Dick</u>?
6. <u>The Jungle Book</u> was funny.
7. My report is on <u>Billy the Kid</u>.
8. My brother is reading <u>Sherlock Holmes</u>.
9. <u>The Diary of Anne Frank</u> is good.
10. May I borrow the <u>College Thesaurus</u>?
11. <u>Holocaust</u> is my favorite.
12. Did they like <u>The Survivors</u>?
13. I cannot find <u>Exodus</u>.
14. <u>The Cathedral</u> has a good plot.
15. I bought him <u>A Guide to Hiking</u>.
16. <u>Little Men</u> is a good choice.
17. Mom bought me <u>American Legends</u>.
18. I loved <u>The Agony and the Ecstasy</u>.
19. May I read <u>In Harm's Way</u>?
20. <u>Catch 22</u> is a war novel.
21. Who wrote <u>East of Eden</u>?
22. I found a copy of <u>Sybil</u>.
23. <u>The Story of Tarzan</u> is his favorite.
24. Mr. Perry suggested <u>Greek Myths</u>.
25. <u>The Wizard</u> is a comedy.
26. Did you read <u>Jane-Emily</u>?
27. I enjoyed <u>Petals on the Wind</u>.
28. May I borrow <u>Lord of the Flies</u>?
29. Twain wrote <u>Huckleberry Finn</u>.
30. <u>Christine</u> was scary.
31. My sister read <u>The Bell Jar</u>.
32. I am looking for <u>Treblinka</u>.
33. Has anyone read <u>The Brain</u>?
34. <u>Flowers in the Attic</u> is sad.
35. Suzanne will report on <u>Jane Eyre</u>.
36. I really liked <u>Jaws</u>.
37. Barbara bought <u>Night Shift</u>.
38. <u>Brian's Song</u> made me cry.
39. She reported on <u>Frankenstein</u>.
40. Use your <u>Webster's Dictionary</u>.
41. You should read <u>Death on the Nile</u>.
42. Last night I began <u>Centennial</u>.
43. The teacher read us <u>Sounder</u>.
44. <u>The Thorn Birds</u> is checked out.
45. The new book is <u>The Equalizer</u>.
46. I will bring the <u>Gem Finder</u>.
47. <u>An American Tragedy</u> is an old book.
48. Tom gave me <u>Fiddler on the Roof</u>.
49. Will you read <u>In Cold Blood</u>?
50. I always enjoy <u>Grimm's Fairy Tales</u>.

COMPOSITION EXERCISE

List 10 of your favorite book titles.

1. _____
2. _____
3. _____
4. _____
5. _____
6. _____
7. _____
8. _____
9. _____
10. _____

Putting Quotation Marks Around
Titles of Poems and Songs

Quotation marks are used around the titles
of poems and songs.

EXAMPLES: a. I read "The Butterfly."

b. Do you like "The Peacock"?

c. We sang "My Bonnie."

d. "Alley Cat" is a fast song.

 Put quotation marks (" ") where needed.

Poems

1. We read "Work Horses."
2. Do you know "The Little Turtle"?
3. "The Butterfly" is a pretty poem.
4. "The Little Snail" is a sad poem.
5. Sarah likes "Dawn."
6. My favorite is "The Grasshopper."
7. Let's read "Christoper Columbus."
8. I will recite "Stars over Norway."
9. "The Journey" is a beautiful poem.
10. I love "The Frog and I."
11. Jan wrote "Last Night."
12. I can't find "Two by Two."
13. "A Sad Tale" is in our book.
14. I copied "Monkey in a Zoo."
15. Look at the poem "Annabel Lee."
16. Mary recited "King's Ransom."
17. "Running Free" is excellent.
18. Our class studied "Ginger."
19. "Our Ghost" was a scary poem.
20. "Little Fishes" is a funny poem.
21. Our teacher read us "Mystery Bird."
22. "The Moon in August" is a good poem.
23. I love to read "The Raven."
24. "Jabberwocky" is by Lewis Carroll.

Songs

25. "Sandman's Near" is a pretty song.
26. We will sing "Home on the Range."
27. I know "Blue-Bells of Scotland."
28. Who wrote "Rain on the Roof"?
29. Was that "The Long Trail"?
30. Let's sing "Good King Wenceslas."
31. I don't like "Baseball Days."
32. Chris is singing "Toy Soldiers."
33. At Christmas we sing "Silent Night."
34. "Melanie" is a sad song.
35. I sang "Make a Wish."
36. Jenny wrote "Here Today."
37. Our last song is "Auf Wiedersehen."
38. "Chicago" is one of my favorites.
39. This song is called "Mindy."
40. I suggest we sing "Old Kentucky Home."
41. I never heard the song "Sandy."
42. "Camptown Races" is an old favorite.
43. Do you know "Marching Home"?
44. Her favorite song is "Sunshine."
45. "My Bonnie" is an old song.
46. We will play and sing "Alley Cat."
47. Let's sing "Happy Birthday."
48. "Vaya Con Dios" is a beautiful song.

COMPOSITION EXERCISE

List 5 of your favorite poems and 5 of your favorite songs.

poems	songs
1. _____	1. _____
2. _____	2. _____
3. _____	3. _____
4. _____	4. _____
5. _____	5. _____

Unit 97 cont'd →

Quotation Marks Around Titles

When writing the title of a poem or song, place quotation marks around it.

EXAMPLES:
   a. *Everyone sang "Michael."*
   b. *Let's read "My Thumb."*
   c. *"Jabberwocky" is a silly poem.*
   d. *He wrote "Moonlight."*

 Place quotation marks where needed.

1. She wrote "Sounds at Midnight."
2. "My Big Brother" is a sad poem.
3. Let's sing "Down the River."
4. I liked "Waiting for Daddy."
5. He sang "Whistle While You Work."
6. "Going Home" is my favorite.
7. I know "Toy Soldiers."
8. "The Wind" is a beautiful poem.
9. May I read "Dawn"?
10. He wrote "The Open Window."
11. I can't find "Color Me Blue."
12. Sing "Apples of Gold."
13. No one read "Trails."
14. "The Peacock" is Joe's favorite.
15. "Sandman" was everyone's choice.
16. Copy "Walking on the Beach."
17. She doesn't know "The Hero."
18. Is "Farming" a long poem?
19. Jack is writing "On the Wall."
20. Recite "The People."
21. "Friendship" was Kate's favorite.
22. Do you know "The Willow Tree"?
23. Yesterday I read "Candy."
24. Who sang "The Fiddler"?
25. "Mr. Owl" is easy to read.
26. Karen will sing "Starlight."
27. I am writing "Crossing the River."
28. Did you read "Mindy"?
29. "The Spider" was a good poem.
30. Here is "The Haunted House."
31. "Blue Eyes" is a sad song.
32. Everyone has read "The Elephant."
33. "A Coward" was funny.
34. I love to sing "Tammy."
35. "In the Jungle" is by Cookson.
36. "Morning" is on page 32.
37. My mother wrote "Asleep."
38. Our choir sang "School Days."
39. Sing "The Witch's Song."
40. "The Snake" is silly.
41. Our assignment is "Our Town."
42. "The Lion and Me" made me happy.
43. The poem "Me" is about Jill.
44. Stevens wrote "My World."
45. "Tugboat" had a happy ending.
46. May we sing "Raindrops"?
47. Everyone must read "Sharing."
48. "Flying High" is about airplanes.
49. Alex will read us "Saturday."
50. "Today" is her favorite song.

COMPOSITION EXERCISE

Write 10 sentences which contain titles of poems or songs.

1. _____
2. _____
3. _____
4. _____
5. _____
6. _____
7. _____
8. _____
9. _____
10. _____

Quotation Marks — Conversation

Place quotation marks (" ") around the exact words of a speaker.

EXAMPLES: a. "I made the team," John cried happily.
b. Dad said, "I hope you made good grades."

 Place quotation marks where needed.

1. The woman yelled," Who are you? "
2. "I want to go home," he cried.
3. "That man in the red car is my father," said Johnny.
4. "Did you see anyone leave the room?"she asked.
5. Lisa said,"I thought you had left with Tom."
6. "You may go now,"she said.
7. The nurse announced,"The doctor will see you now."
8. "Help me!"she cried.
9. "That man is a thief!"the woman screamed.
10. Mother asked,"Where are you two going now?"
11. "I tried to warn you about it," Sam said.
12. "You are late again," Dad said angrily.
13. The policeman asked,"Where is your home?"
14. "Won't someone believe me?" the girl begged.
15. "See you tomorrow," he called.

16. "I saw the man leave," he repeated.
17. The girl cried,"I'm not guilty!"
18. "That's not true!"he shouted.
19. Thomas said,"It was too dark to see anyone."
20. "Did you know him very well?" I asked.
21. "Go to your room immediately!" Mother ordered.
22. Jake asked,"Where did you hide the money?"
23. "Is this all that's left of the cake?"she asked.
24. The old man yelled,"I'll get you for this!"
25. "Clean this room," she ordered.
26. "Did you enjoy the party Terry gave?"he asked.
27. "Why don't we buy her a hat,"Tim suggested.
28. "The house is in a mess," she cried.
29. "I can't wait," he yelled.
30. "Who did it?"Sarah asked.

COMPOSITION EXERCISE

Write 8 sentences which illustrate the use of quotation marks around speakers' words.

1. _____
2. _____
3. _____
4. _____
5. _____
6. _____
7. _____
8. _____

Unit 98 cont'd

Quotation Marks Around Exact
Words of a Speaker

*Use quotation marks around the exact
words of the speaker.*

EXAMPLES: a. "Wow!" exclaimed Jim.
          b. "No," said Lou, "he isn't home."
          c. Pete asked, "Where did you go?"
          d. "I'm sorry," Deb said.

 Place quotation marks where needed.

1. Alice said, "It's time to go."
2. "I want to help you," Mom said.
3. "Hurry!" Carla shouted.
4. The man yelled, "I'll get you!"
5. He turned and said, "It's too late."
6. "Why," asked Kim, "is it my fault?"
7. "Bring the mail," he called.
8. "I love you," said Donna.
9. "Tomorrow," said Ted, "we'll finish."
10. "Wait!" Becky yelled.
11. "Dinner is served," he announced.
12. "Is Luke your brother?" Kay asked.
13. Lisa called, "Is that you, Chris?"
14. "Read it," she ordered.
15. "Let us go," we begged.
16. Mary asked, "Would you come?"
17. "Is this all?" Keith asked.
18. "Is it safe?" she whispered.
19. "Speak louder," the teacher said.
20. Bozo asked, "May I come too?"
21. "Drink your milk," she ordered.
22. "I dropped it!" Mindy cried.
23. Sara said, "Your dad is here."
24. "Wonderful!" she exclaimed.
25. "Yes," said Jan, "I'll take it."
26. "Someday you'll understand," he said.
27. "Where is it?" Sandy asked.
28. "The house was empty," Jay reported.
29. "Stop him!" the lady screamed.
30. Sue cried, "He's hurt!"
31. "Don't touch it," my sister warned.
32. "Please don't," she begged.
33. "Dad's home," I called.
34. "Let's eat early," Connie said.
35. Wanda asked, "Who is Sylvester?"
36. I suggested, "Let's paint it orange."
37. "We won!" the team shouted.
38. "It's good to be home," said Phil.
39. "Was that the bus?" asked John.
40. "I'm coming," she called.
41. "It's not your turn," he argued.
42. Andy called, "Where are you?"
43. "It's dark in here!" cried Nancy.
44. Ernie said, "Let's go to town."
45. "Who opened the door?" asked Bob.
46. "What is it?" I asked.
47. "It's not fair," he pouted.
48. Christy asked, "Is it for me?"
49. "Take one," she said.
50. The man warned, "Don't come in."

COMPOSITION EXERCISE

Write a conversation you and a friend might have about what you'll do Saturday.

_____

_____

_____

_____

_____

_____

_____

Punctuation Marks

The period is used at the end of statements, commands, and most abbreviations.

The exclamation point is used after interjections and exclamations.

The question mark is used after questions.

The comma is used with words in a series and nouns in direct address.

EXAMPLES:
a. Sherry, where have you been?
b. Mr. Dent left yesterday.
c. See you at 9 a.m.
d. Hey! Watch the game.

✳ Place periods, exclamation points, question marks, and commas where needed.

1. Did you see that sign?
2. I'm doing my homework.
3. Are you sure?
4. You can't do that!
5. Close your eyes.
6. Stop! The dog will bite you.
7. Dr. Winters lives there.
8. Linda, will you help me?
9. My name is not Theresa.
10. It began at 6 p.m.
11. Steve, Eric, and Joe play ball.
12. The leaves turned brown.
13. Ouch! I bumped into the chair.
14. Would you like some candy?
15. John, where is my coat?
16. The bus is leaving!
17. Make a wish.
18. The house is sold.
19. School begins at 8 a.m.
20. Let's take a walk.
21. Is that Capt. Wright?
22. Hey! Who did this?
23. My brother is studying.
24. Wait! We'll look again.
25. He took apples, pears, and plums.
26. I found it, Richard.
27. The monkey is following me.
28. Here come Sue, Pat, and Kay.
29. When is your vacation?
30. You come back here!
31. Give me the book.
32. Sally, he's not there.
33. Have we met?
34. Tomorrow is March 4.
35. Mr. and Mrs. Johnson moved.
36. I need paper, pen, and ink.
37. Take a nap.
38. Wow! We made it.
39. Who said that?
40. Ernie, is this yours?
41. The balls were red, white, and blue.
42. Has Doug been here?
43. Swimming is fun.
44. Here I am!

COMPOSITION EXERCISE

Write two examples for each of these marks of punctuation.

1. period

_____

_____

2. exclamation point

_____

_____

3. question mark

_____

_____

4. comma

_____

_____

Unit 99 cont'd ➜

What Is a Word?

A word is a group of letters or sounds which stands for something or communicates an idea.

EXAMPLES: a. awetr *spells* water
 b. mpeyt *spells* empty
 c. efnec *spells* fence
 d. repytt *spells* pretty

 Unscramble the letters to make a word.

1. itme	*time*	
2. fsto	*soft*	
3. utrck	*truck*	
4. ivrre	*river*	
5. nghti	*night*	
6. ayd	*day*	
7. cwonl	*clown*	
8. ascls	*class*	
9. omor	*room*	
10. clcko	*clock*	
11. barbti	*rabbit*	
12. epople	*people*	
13. nsoei	*noise*	
14. ttleur	*turtle*	
15. ofnud	*found*	
16. chrhuc	*church*	
17. armfre	*farmer*	
18. nmaial	*animal*	
19. wfoler	*flower*	
20. uaot	*auto*	
21. ssteri	*sister*	
22. bbya	*baby*	
23. ncilpe	*pencil*	
24. ppaer	*paper*	
25. okob	*book*	

26. cta	*act*	
27. kbie	*bike*	
28. asgrs	*grass*	
29. nwki	*wink*	
30. ucle	*clue*	
31. slinet	*silent*	
32. emlno	*melon*	
33. rtpi	*trip*	
34. ilsly	*silly*	
35. inocme	*income*	
36. lcaeot	*locate*	
37. onet	*note*	
38. oontacr	*cartoon*	
39. ssper	*press*	
40. rriaev	*arrive*	
41. nscak	*snack*	
42. cllhiy	*chilly*	
43. tlneat	*talent*	
44. hwpi	*whip*	
45. smplei	*simple*	
46. wlero	*lower*	
47. rsuelt	*result*	
48. qreuas	*square*	
49. cbuci	*cubic*	
50. mteer	*meter*	

51. abskte	*basket*	
52. boye	*obey*	
53. hleaht	*health*	
54. alghu	*laugh*	
55. intkh	*think*	
56. plseae	*please*	
57. olsve	*solve*	
58. edcdie	*decide*	
59. ssimnig	*missing*	
60. ousmaf	*famous*	
61. fnlliay	*finally*	
62. ured	*rude*	
63. mcael	*camel*	
64. mpac	*camp*	
65. montuina	*mountain*	
66. ffflyu	*fluffy*	
67. gdera	*grade*	
68. snnteece	*sentence*	
69. lleps	*spell*	
70. wonre	*owner*	
71. plceoi	*police*	
72. tepelnoeh	*telephone*	
73. mvoei	*movie*	
74. oudns	*sound*	
75. dwro	*word*	

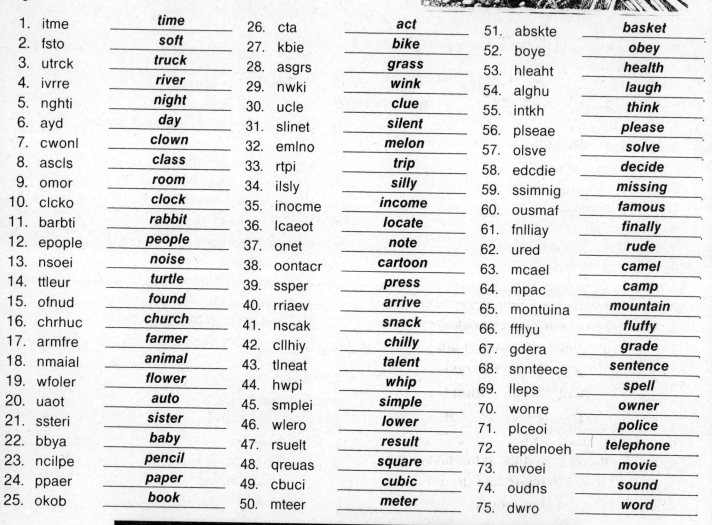

COMPOSITION EXERCISE

Choose 12 words from today's exercise. Write a sentence with each.

1. _____
2. _____
3. _____
4. _____
5. _____
6. _____
7. _____
8. _____
9. _____
10. _____
11. _____
12. _____

Unscrambling Letters to Make Words

The letters which make a word are arranged in a definite order.

EXAMPLES:
- a. tnaeru *spells* nature
- b. nynuf *spells* funny
- c. eephntla *spells* elephant
- d. ryusfole *spells* yourself
- e. snauuul *spells* unusual
- f. demlia *spells* mailed

A Arrange each set of letters to make a word.

1. saetnb	*absent*	21. ecpae	PEACE	41. ntnlue	TUNNEL
2. esepla	ASLEEP	22. sviti	VISIT	42. cweelom	WELCOME
3. spstro	SPORTS	23. fofcie	OFFICE	43. rkmeat	MARKET
4. wldro	WORLD	24. wblo	BLOW	44. srmat	SMART
5. bcani	CABIN	25. cvoie	VOICE	45. wonre	OWNER
6. wdmsio	WISDOM	26. nmalro	NORMAL	46. usllayu	USUALLY
7. thghtuo	THOUGHT	27. fsokl	FOLKS	47. otgsh	GHOST
8. rrwead	REWARD	28. pttooa	POTATO	48. ctsere	SECRET
9. daegr	GRADE	29. uenssl	UNLESS	49. theors	OTHERS
10. weelj	JEWEL	30. ryruh	HURRY	50. gynou	YOUNG
11. aihtb	HABIT	31. oprsime	PROMISE	51. gmica	MAGIC
12. sstdeer	DESSERT	32. tcreen	CENTER	52. eyoujrn	JOURNEY
13. zoend	DOZEN	33. cfta	FACT	53. poplee	PEOPLE
14. tquei	QUIET	34. sreano	REASON	54. stcale	CASTLE
15. etclos	CLOSET	35. rshea	SHARE	55. fela	FLEA
16. outblr	TROUBLE	36. tmcha	MATCH	56. tlounei	OUTLINE
17. memsur	SUMMER	37. ndaec	DANCE	57. slinad	ISLAND
18. rnoht	THORN	38. wnse	NEWS	58. wntire	WINTER
19. shfferi	SHERIFF	39. mnerub	NUMBER	59. betask	BASKET
20. unhert	HUNTER	40. gdeui	GUIDE	60. hgrynu	HUNGRY

B Here are some really tough ones. Arrange the letters to make words.

1. vtenadeur	*adventure*	9. soloenem	LONESOME	17. ffeidernt	DIFFERENT
2. tvseelioni	TELEVISION	10. rlleumba	UMBRELLA	18. nsoeenns	NONSENSE
3. cvtnioaa	VACATION	11. exresiec	EXERCISE	19. caonitdue	EDUCATION
4. dsdnlyue	SUDDENLY	12. tinesingret	INTERESTING	20. tonuqesi	QUESTION
5. wdfluoenr	WONDERFUL	13. rmmeeerb	REMEMBER	21. eioafvrt	FAVORITE
6. ffltdiicu	DIFFICULT	14. sioniced	DECISION	22. vyigeerthn	EVERYTHING
7. aistrtgh	STRAIGHT	15. prgroma	PROGRAM	23. eaarfstkb	BREAKFAST
8. ewapnpers	NEWSPAPER	16. btphaael	ALPHABET	24. lllyaesb	SYLLABLE

Unit 100 cont'd

Your Alphabet

The vowels are a e i o u and sometimes y.

The consonants are b c d f g h j k l m n p q r s t v w x y z

A Write a vowel in each blank.

1. _A_ct
2. m_I_nd
3. c_O_zy
4. _A_rriv_E_
5. n_O_t_E_
6. sh_Y_
7. m_I_ss
8. f_O_ll_O_w
9. st_E_p
10. br_A_g
11. w_O_rry
12. s_E_cr_E_t

13. cl_E_ _A_r
14. r_U_d_E_
15. w_I_nk
16. f_O_rg_E_t
17. pr_E_t_E_nd
18. r_E_s_U_lt
19. n_O_ _I_s_E_
20. d_I_ff_E_r
21. l_A_w
22. _E_v_E_nt
23. _I_ll
24. f_I_n_A_lly

25. str_A_ng_E_
26. tr_I_p
27. h_I_k_E_
28. pr_O_p_E_r
29. s_I_mpl_E_
30. wh_I_p
31. m_E_l_O_n
32. f_A_ls_E_
33. t_A_bl_E_t
34. br_A_v_E_
35. _U_nk_I_nd
36. s_I_gn_A_l

B Write a consonant in each blank.

1. _c_a_r_e
2. _W_ _H_a_T_
3. _M_o_N_ey
4. ea_T_
5. _B_elie_V_e
6. _L_iqui_D_
7. a_S_ _K_ed
8. _S_ai_D_
9. o_F_ _F_ice
10. _R_oo_M_
11. o_F_ _F_
12. _S_ee

13. _R_ain
14. _F_oolis_H_
15. a_R_ _R_ive
16. _G_ _R_eat
17. _P_erfec_T_
18. _H_i_D_e
19. _F_u_N_ny
20. _T_ _H_in
21. _R_esul_T_
22. _R_easo_N_
23. _G_uess
24. _N_one

25. _S_ome_T_hing
26. a_P_ _P_ear
27. _V_alue
28. a_L_ike
29. _G_ _R_ound
30. lum_B_er
31. _L_o_W_er
32. confe_S_ _S_
33. stu_P_id
34. _W_ _R_iter
35. co_M_ _M_on
36. _R_eplace

COMPOSITION EXERCISE

List the vowels and write a word that begins with each.

1. _____   3. _____   5. _____

2. _____   4. _____   6. _____

List the 21 consonants and write a word that begins with each.

1. _____   7. _____   12. _____   17. _____

2. _____   8. _____   13. _____   18. _____

3. _____   9. _____   14. _____   19. _____

4. _____   10. _____   15. _____   20. _____

5. _____   11. _____   16. _____   21. _____

6. _____

Comprehension Check

(A) Underline the book titles.

1. Jane Austen wrote <u>Emma</u>.
2. <u>When Worlds Collide</u> is fascinating.
3. <u>Tom Swift</u> entertained me.
4. Did you understand <u>The Dollmaker</u>?
5. <u>National Velvet</u> was made into a movie.
6. <u>The Wonderful Year</u> is one of my favorites.
7. <u>Drums</u> was an impressive story.
8. I learned a great deal from <u>The Good Earth</u>.
9. <u>My Antonia</u> is on my list.
10. My favorite adventure is <u>The Sea Hunt</u>.
11. <u>Lord Jim</u> has strong characters.
12. Edna Ferber's book, <u>Giant</u>, is also a movie.
13. <u>Johnny Tremain</u> covers the Revolutionary War period.
14. I read <u>Hot Rod</u> when I was twelve.
15. <u>Blackboard Jungle</u> made me think.
16. One classic is <u>The Scarlet Letter</u>.
17. Does <u>Brave New World</u> predict our future?
18. <u>Strawberry Girl</u> tells an interesting story.
19. Thurber wrote <u>Many Moons</u> and <u>Thirteen Clocks</u>.
20. <u>All-American</u> is about my favorite sport.

(B) Put the poem titles in quotation marks.

1. I missed the point of "Lord Randal."
2. "Dust of Snow" made me feel cold.
3. "November Night" gave a good description.
4. Robert Frost's poem, "Birches," has been carefully studied.
5. "Skating" is full of pretty images.
6. I read "The Tiger" to my sister.
7. "The Blind Girl" was so sad.
8. I liked the silly poem, "Jabberwocky."
9. "Jesse James" told a true story.
10. We liked the message of "The Patriot."

(C) Put the song titles in quotation marks.

1. Have you ever heard "Nellie Bly"?
2. "All Through the Night" is a lovely lullaby.
3. We sang "Silent Night" at the play.
4. "Puff the Magic Dragon" was a popular folk song.
5. I'm tired of hearing "Row, Row, Row Your Boat."
6. Ray Charles sang "Georgia."
7. "Moonlight Sonata" is a classic.
8. "Yellow Submarine" is a fantasy.
9. "Oh, Susannah" was sung on the frontier.
10. He sang the "Hawaiian Wedding Song."

(D) Place quotation marks around each speaker's exact words.

1. "I saw the burglar run!" he cried.
2. "Do you have enough money?" Jim asked.
3. "We took a picture of the snake," said Tim.
4. "You missed your bus," Mom complained.
5. "I'll call you Sunday," Gail promised.
6. "Can you," Marie asked, "finish this?"
7. "Do you want tuna salad?" asked the waitress.
8. "There's my billfold!" yelled Bob.
9. Mother ordered, "Shut the door now!"
10. Melissa cried, "I don't understand!"
11. Chris asked, "Have you seen my notebook?"
12. "Please do this again," she repeated.
13. "I'm not going to tell you again," Phil warned.
14. "We'll see," Rona promised, "when Jack arrives."
15. "Don't leave yet," Marty begged.
16. "You don't like me," the little girl pouted.
17. The director whispered, "Close the curtain."
18. "Your dinner," Gene reported, "burned."
19. Bill suggested, "Let's copy the page."
20. "I'll be back soon," Matt called.
21. "Yes!" John exclaimed, "I understand!"
22. "The vase is broken!" Keith cried.
23. "Why," Sean asked, "do you want to know?"
24. "Please be seated," requested the speaker.
25. The announcer cried, "Welcome to the show!"
26. "Can you come, too?" Mary asked.
27. The baby screamed, "Billy hit me!"
28. "Go, team, go!" the cheerleaders yelled.
29. Lynn called, "Is that your book, Thomas?"
30. "Wednesday," Gil promised, "we'll have pizza."
31. "Kindly step to the rear," requested the bus driver.
32. "Can we come out now?" the children whined.

Test 20 cont'd

Comprehension Check (continued)

E **Place a period, exclamation point, or question mark after each sentence.**

1. Carry this pack.
2. Does Marla have any pets?
3. Do you know how to swim?
4. Play the record now, please.
5. What a wonderful sight!
6. She has three sisters.
7. Is it raining?
8. The film is too old to use.
9. I like rock music.
10. Stop that noise now!
11. Your tie is crooked.
12. Tina must make a choice.
13. I think the dog ate my hamburger.
14. Did Sherry place the order?
15. Look at these old pictures.
16. Her jewelry sparkles.
17. We built a new house.
18. Stop the car immediately!
19. Can you look at this?
20. Bobby has many good friends.

F **Place periods, exclamation points, and commas where needed.**

1. Jerry, do you like cartoons?
2. We left at 7:00 p.m.
3. There are Pat, Jim, and Frank.
4. Yes, I want more cake.
5. Wow! This is neat!
6. Mr. and Mrs. Dotson arrived.
7. Did you watch the news, Barbara?
8. Steve, Mike, and Don are in the band.
9. Dr. Webb checked my eyes.
10. Cheryl bought shorts, blouses, and shoes.
11. Give me the money, please.
12. Stop! You're hurting my hand!
13. June, take a letter.
14. Is this your cap, Willis?
15. Ouch! I hurt my foot.
16. Would you like to meet Lt. Frye?
17. Ms. Barber is my favorite teacher.
18. Peel the apples, pears, and peaches.
19. I have it, Barry.
20. We get up at 6:00 a.m.
21. I promise, Marilyn, that you can go.
22. Don't! You'll break the eggs.
23. I need to buy pink, yellow, and green ribbons.
24. Angie, go to the board.
25. Danny, will you drive me home?
26. Look out! The spaghetti is burning!
27. Turn around this minute, Rae!
28. Would you invite Pam, Betty, and Rhonda?
29. Andy, Mr Whitney asked about you.
30. You know, Kim, that you're tardy.
31. The ballgame begins at 7:30 p.m.
32. Look, Ray, at this answer.

Write a paragraph about a pet. Unscramble these words and use them in your paragraph. Underline each word when you use it.

etp	yoenj	unf	cwtah	evah
pet	_enjoy_	_fun_	_watch_	_have_

_____
_____
_____
_____
_____
_____
_____
_____

244

The Alphabet — Vowels and Consonants

The alphabet is divided into vowels and consonants.

There are five main vowels. They include "a," "e," "i," "o," and "u." The letters "y" and "w" are sometimes vowels.

a. The word "music" contains the vowels "u" and "i."

b. The word "welcome" contains the vowels "e," "o," and "e."

There are 21 consonants. They include "b," "c," "d," "f," "g," "h," "j," "k," "l," "m," "n," "p," "q," "r," "s," "t," "v," "w," "x," "y," and "z."

a. The word "rule" contains the consonants "r" and "l."

b. The word "cat" contains the consonants "c" and "t."

A Add the missing vowels.

1. l__o__nesome
2. r__A__w
3. v__I__sit
4. __O__ther
5. gh__O__st
6. p__O__ssible
7. tom__A__to
8. __E__normous
9. countr__Y__
10. m__O__dern

11. f__I__nally
12. qu__I__t
13. pr__O__mise
14. nons__E__nse
15. hab__I__t
16. mach__I__ne
17. zer__O__
18. c__A__stle
19. perh__A__ps
20. surpr__I__se

21. bl__A__nket
22. m__I__nute
23. __U__mbrella
24. welc__O__me
25. j__E__wel
26. separ__A__te
27. cr__O__wd
28. wr__I__te
29. t__U__nnel
30. str__A__nger

31. adv__E__nture
32. v__A__luable
33. sk__Y__
34. d__O__zen
35. sm__A__rt
36. bab__Y__
37. abs__E__nt
38. underst__A__nd
39. t__I__cket
40. __O__pinion

B Add the missing consonants.

1. in__f__ormation
2. __C__ontest
3. __M__ovie
4. a__D__ult
5. __J__ourney
6. __Y__ourself
7. __S__oldier
8. pia__N__o
9. mis__T__ake
10. te__L__ephone
11. __R__eason

12. a__W__ard
13. to__G__ether
14. __D__eadline
15. e__X__cuse
16. __C__omedian
17. un__L__ess
18. __T__elevision
19. na__T__ure
20. flowe__R__s
21. __H__ungry
22. __C__ontinue

23. po__T__ato
24. re__M__ember
25. __B__usiness
26. diffi__C__ult
27. __M__agic
28. __Z__ebra
29. high__W__ay
30. __K__ey
31. __S__uddenly
32. in__T__eresting
33. progra__M__

34. he__R__o
35. __H__oliday
36. fore__V__er
37. e__D__ucation
38. __N__obody
39. encyclope__D__ia
40. re__P__ort
41. __Q__uick
42. break__F__ast
43. outli__N__e
44. alpha__B__et

COMPOSITION EXERCISE

Write a word for each letter of the alphabet.

1. _____ 8. _____ 15. _____ 21. _____
2. _____ 9. _____ 16. _____ 22. _____
3. _____ 10. _____ 17. _____ 23. _____
4. _____ 11. _____ 18. _____ 24. _____
5. _____ 12. _____ 19. _____ 25. _____
6. _____ 13. _____ 20. _____ 26. _____
7. _____ 14. _____

Unit 101 cont'd

The Long Vowel Symbol

Some pronunciation symbols in the dictionary are letters with special marks over them. Most often you will find four pronunciation symbols that sound the same as the names of their letters. These symbols are "a," "e," "i," and "o." These are called long "a," long "e," long "i," and long "o."

EXAMPLE: You can hear the long "a" in "age," the long "e" in "sea," the long "i" in "ice," and the long "o" in "go."

A There is a long vowel in the name of each of these pictures. In the blank beside each, write what each picture is and put the long vowel symbol in its proper place.

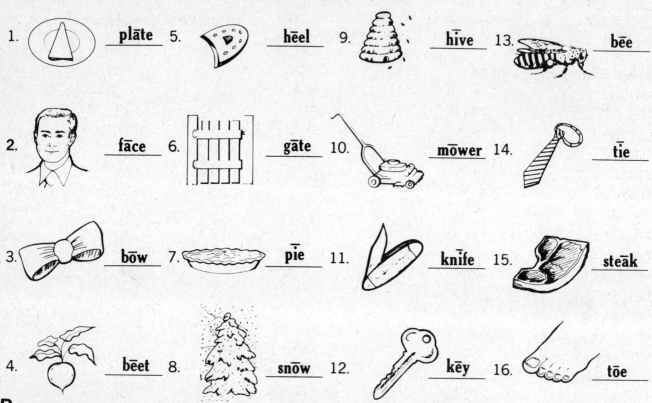

1. plāte 5. hēel 9. hīve 13. bēe

2. fāce 6. gāte 10. mōwer 14. tīe

3. bōw 7. pīe 11. knīfe 15. steāk

4. bēet 8. snōw 12. kēy 16. tōe

B In each sentence is a word in brackets. The pronunciation of the word in brackets is shown at the end of the sentence. Underline the correct pronunciation of each.

1. I see a sailboat on the [**bay**]. (ba, bā)
2. It has beautiful [**white**] sails. (hwĭt, hwīt)
3. What fun it would be to [**sail**] it! (săl, sāl)
4. The boat is [**painted**] red. (pānted, panted)

5. It has a white [**stripe**] down the side. (strīp, strĭp)
6. The water looks emerald [**green**] today. (grēn, grĕn)
7. The boat was fastened to the dock with a [**cable**]. (cāble, kăb-l)
8. A [**chain**] attached the anchor to the boat. (chăn, chāin)

COMPOSITION EXERCISE

Write 5 examples of each long vowel.

ā	ē	ī	ō
1. _____	1. _____	1. _____	1. _____
2. _____	2. _____	2. _____	2. _____
3. _____	3. _____	3. _____	3. _____
4. _____	4. _____	4. _____	4. _____
5. _____	5. _____	5. _____	5. _____

Long Vowels

"A," "e," "i," "o," and "u" are vowels. "Y"
may also be a vowel.

A long vowel sound says its own name.

EXAMPLES:
a	e	i	o	u
ate	me	five	go	use
cake	we	find	old	cute
game	hero	right	home	rule

 What are the sounds of the long vowels in the words?

1. advice $\bar{i}$
2. idea $\bar{I}$ $\bar{E}$
3. bold $\bar{O}$
4. change $\bar{A}$
5. cute $\bar{U}$
6. danger $\bar{A}$
7. deadline $\bar{I}$
8. educate $\bar{A}$
9. became $\bar{E}$ $\bar{A}$
10. escape $\bar{A}$
11. excuse $\bar{U}$
12. favorite $\bar{A}$
13. famous $\bar{A}$
14. finally $\bar{I}$ $\bar{E}$
15. ghost $\bar{O}$
16. grade $\bar{A}$
17. giant $\bar{I}$
18. globe $\bar{O}$
19. joke $\bar{O}$
20. key $\bar{E}$
21. later $\bar{A}$
22. lonely $\bar{O}$ $\bar{E}$
23. mistake $\bar{A}$
24. newspaper $\bar{A}$
25. lake $\bar{A}$

26. night $\bar{I}$
27. nobody $\bar{O}$ $\bar{E}$
28. opinion $\bar{O}$
29. potato $\bar{A}$ $\bar{O}$
30. basement $\bar{A}$
31. quite $\bar{I}$
32. prize $\bar{I}$
33. crude $\bar{U}$
34. safely $\bar{A}$ $\bar{E}$
35. shape $\bar{A}$
36. surprise $\bar{I}$
37. strange $\bar{A}$
38. used $\bar{U}$
39. telephone $\bar{O}$
40. vacation $\bar{A}$ $\bar{A}$
41. vine $\bar{I}$
42. zero $\bar{E}$ $\bar{O}$
43. motto $\bar{O}$
44. confuse $\bar{U}$
45. truth $\bar{U}$
46. ignore $\bar{O}$
47. pace $\bar{A}$
48. zone $\bar{O}$
49. combine $\bar{I}$
50. notice $\bar{O}$

51. postage $\bar{O}$
52. identical $\bar{I}$
53. phase $\bar{A}$
54. hesitate $\bar{A}$
55. parachute $\bar{U}$
56. legal $\bar{E}$
57. hibernate $\bar{I}$ $\bar{A}$
58. quiet $\bar{I}$
59. site $\bar{I}$
60. obligate $\bar{A}$
61. vacant $\bar{A}$
62. kind $\bar{I}$
63. ashamed $\bar{A}$
64. place $\bar{A}$
65. notebook $\bar{O}$
66. stupid $\bar{U}$
67. sign $\bar{I}$
68. silent $\bar{I}$
69. hike $\bar{I}$
70. echo $\bar{O}$
71. state $\bar{A}$
72. wife $\bar{I}$
73. stone $\bar{O}$
74. table $\bar{A}$
75. time $\bar{I}$

76. music $\bar{U}$
77. knife $\bar{I}$
78. cave $\bar{A}$
79. awake $\bar{A}$
80. tomato $\bar{A}$ $\bar{O}$
81. chrome $\bar{O}$
82. company $\bar{E}$
83. hyphen $\bar{I}$
84. item $\bar{I}$
85. jersey $\bar{E}$
86. lotion $\bar{O}$
87. pavement $\bar{A}$
88. nature $\bar{A}$
89. pronoun $\bar{O}$
90. secret $\bar{E}$
91. station $\bar{A}$
92. strike $\bar{I}$
93. sunshine $\bar{I}$
94. total $\bar{O}$
95. student $\bar{U}$
96. style $\bar{I}$
97. ache $\bar{A}$
98. title $\bar{I}$
99. race $\bar{A}$
100. both $\bar{O}$

COMPOSITION EXERCISE

Choose 12 words from today's exercise. Write a sentence with each.

1. _____
2. _____
3. _____
4. _____
5. _____
6. _____
7. _____
8. _____
9. _____
10. _____
11. _____
12. _____

Unit 102 cont'd

The Final Silent "e"

When a one-syllable word ends in a silent "e," the vowel sound of that word is usually long. For example, look at the word "cut." The "u" in "cut" is short. Now add a final silent "e" to "cut." The "u" in the word "cute" is long.

Underline the word in each pair which contains the final silent "e." Then complete each sentence with the correct word.

1. hug huge
   a. The elephant is a ___huge___ animal.
   b. The child gave the dog a big ___hug___ .

2. us use
   a. Learn to ___USE___ your time wisely.
   b. Tell ___US___ about your trip to Italy.

3. hope hop
   a. I ___HOPE___ you can come with us.
   b. ___HOP___ like a frog.

4. pin pine
   a. That is a ___PINE___ tree.
   b. ___PIN___ the tail on the donkey.

5. not note
   a. I am ___NOT___ going to the party.
   b. I will write Mother a ___NOTE___ .

6. here her
   a. Can you be ___HERE___ by noon?
   b. Did anyone tell ___HER___ to come in?

7. ate at
   a. The bell will ring ___AT___ two o'clock.
   b. Sally ___ATE___ all of the cake.

8. rang range
   a. Who ___RANG___ the bell?
   b. The mountain ___RANGE___ lay before us.

9. stare star
   a. Don't ___STARE___ at me.
   b. The ___STAR___ sparkled.

10. quite quit
    a. Gerald has ___QUIT___ his job.
    b. The play was ___QUITE___ a success.

11. pan pane
    a. Fill the ___PAN___ with water.
    b. The window ___PANE___ was cracked.

12. rate rat
    a. Now determine the ___RATE___ of speed.
    b. Charles has a pet ___RAT___ .

13. robe rob
    a. The queen wore a purple ___ROBE___ .
    b. The man tried to ___ROB___ a bank.

14. glob globe
    a. The teacher showed the class a ___GLOBE___ .
    b. A ___GLOB___ of ink fell on the floor.

15. hate hat
    a. Quincy wore a feather in his ___HAT___ .
    b. We ___HATE___ spinach and liver.

16. car care
    a. The ___CAR___ skidded into the truck.
    b. They ___CARE___ about you too.

17. tone ton
    a. A ___TON___ weighs 2000 pounds.
    b. The ___TONE___ of her voice scared me.

18. cap cape
    a. Dracula always wears a black ___CAPE___ .
    b. The wind blew the boy's ___CAP___ .

COMPOSITION EXERCISE

Use each of these words in a sentence.

1. not, note

2. bit, bite

_____

_____

248

Short Vowels

A short vowel does not say its own name. Study the following examples of short vowels.

a	e	i	o	u
cat	jet	fit	rob	hug
lap	red	rip	pop	us
stab	well	fill	shop	bump

✳ Identify the short vowel in each word.

u	1. bug	O	26. adopt	O	51. problem	E	76. twenty
U	2. ugly	U	27. product	I	52. fifty	A	77. alley
I	3. film	A	28. program	U	53. utter	A	78. ankle
E	4. arrest	I	29. finger	U	54. puzzle	A	79. valley
A	5. back	U	30. walnut	I	55. rid	A	80. flashlight
O	6. rotten	E	31. melon	A	56. gallon	U	81. bluff
U	7. buckle	U	32. multiply	U	57. rung	I	82. whistle
A	8. cabin	U	33. humble	A	58. saddle	E	83. wreck
I	9. important	A	34. canyon	E	59. seldom	A	84. flat
I	10. kitchen	I	35. wrist	I	60. fish	E	85. lemon
E	11. cell	I	36. ship	A	61. castle	E	86. net
O	12. lodge	E	37. central	I	62. signal	O	87. flock
A	13. chapter	E	38. mental	I	63. shrink	I	88. drill
I	14. mixture	E	39. chef	I	64. sixty	O	89. chop
E	15. clever	U	40. mumps	E	65. chest	I	90. slippery
O	16. collect	I	41. native	O	66. solve	A	91. candy
I	17. notice	U	42. company	U	67. bulb	A	92. staff
E	18. debt	I	43. orbit	U	68. struggle	E	93. test
E	19. design	A	44. passenger	U	69. summer	E	94. yellow
E	20. direct	U	45. sunlight	A	70. ant	E	95. belt
A	21. piano	E	46. lesson	I	71. swift	A	96. stand
A	22. draft	I	47. picture	O	72. robin	I	97. switch
E	23. echo	A	48. plant	U	73. thunder	A	98. ranch
A	24. fashion	U	49. tunnel	U	74. pump	I	99. timber
I	25. ditch	I	50. prison	I	75. fix	I	100. winter

COMPOSITION EXERCISE

Choose 12 words from today's exercise. Write a sentence with each.

1. _____
2. _____
3. _____
4. _____
5. _____
6. _____
7. _____
8. _____
9. _____
10. _____
11. _____
12. _____

Unit 103 cont'd ➡

"y" and "w" as Vowels

The letters "y" and "w" may function as both vowels and consonants.

The letter "y" has a consonant sound in the word "yellow." The letter "y" has a vowel sound in the word "my."

The letter "w" has a consonant sound in the word "wait." The letter "w" has a vowel sound in the word "how."

A Underline the words in which the "y" has the vowel sound.

1. <u>sky</u>	16. yes	31. <u>twenty</u>	46. <u>type</u>
2. young	17. <u>tryout</u>	32. <u>cycle</u>	47. <u>myth</u>
3. <u>lyric</u>	18. <u>mystery</u>	33. <u>typical</u>	48. <u>bygone</u>
4. you	19. <u>fly</u>	34. <u>rhythm</u>	49. <u>symbol</u>
5. <u>bicycle</u>	20. <u>by</u>	35. year	50. <u>dynamite</u>
6. <u>system</u>	21. yell	36. <u>hymn</u>	51. <u>style</u>
7. <u>pygmy</u>	22. <u>symbol</u>	37. your	52. <u>antonym</u>
8. yacht	23. yawn	38. <u>tyrant</u>	53. <u>syllable</u>
9. <u>hybrid</u>	24. <u>lazy</u>	39. yesterday	54. <u>gym</u>
10. yoke	25. <u>ugly</u>	40. <u>berry</u>	55. <u>funny</u>
11. <u>homonym</u>	26. yolk	41. <u>yourself</u>	56. <u>ready</u>
12. yo-yo	27. <u>synonym</u>	42. <u>sly</u>	57. <u>xylophone</u>
13. <u>plenty</u>	28. yonder	43. yearn	58. <u>gypsy</u>
14. yak	29. <u>county</u>	44. <u>cry</u>	59. <u>yearly</u>
15. yard	30. <u>canary</u>	45. yarn	60. yeast

B Underline the words in which the "w" has a vowel sound.

1. <u>below</u>	11. white	21. crow	31. walrus
2. wish	12. we	22. blow	32. <u>cow</u>
3. <u>bowl</u>	13. how	23. weed	33. wind
4. rows	14. <u>chow</u>	24. <u>allow</u>	34. welcome
5. water	15. wisdom	25. <u>vowel</u>	35. <u>howl</u>
6. flow	16. blower	26. <u>flower</u>	36. throw
7. what	17. <u>owl</u>	27. wild	37. <u>brown</u>
8. war	18. wolf	28. grow	38. work
9. towed	19. <u>town</u>	29. <u>frown</u>	39. with
10. walk	20. worm	30. waste	40. <u>crown</u>

COMPOSITION EXERCISE

Choose 3 words in which "y" has a vowel sound. Then choose 3 words in which "w" has a vowel sound. Write a sentence with each of your choices.

y	w
1. _____	1. _____
2. _____	2. _____
3. _____	3. _____

Vowel Digraphs   Unit 104

A vowel digraph occurs when two letters are used to spell a single vowel sound. Many vowel digraphs spell a long vowel sound. The most common vowel digraphs are "ai," "ea," "ee," and "oa."

A long "a" sound is usually spelled by "ai."
A long "e" sound is usually spelled by "ea."
A long "e" sound is usually spelled by "ee."
A long "o" sound is usually spelled by "oa."

EXAMPLES:

ā	ē	ō
a. fail	a. seam	a. coal
b. rain	b. peak	b. loaf
c. bait	c. seed	c. throat

A Complete each word by adding "ai," "ea," "ee," or "oa."

1. fr __ee__ ze
2. cl __ai__ m
3. b __ee__ tle
4. __ea__ ch
5. sl __ee__ p
6. t __ea__ cher
7. l __oa__ n
8. b __oa__ t
9. sp __ea__ k
10. bl __ea__ ch
11. sm __ea__ red
12. s __ea__ ms
13. pr __ea__ cher
14. tr __ee__
15. s __oa__ p
16. f __ai__ lure
17. sh __ee__ ts
18. g __oa__ ls
19. sp __ea__ ker
20. __ea__ gle

21. tr __ai__ n
22. w __ai__ st
23. t __oa__ d
24. __oa__ k
25. r __ai__ ning
26. c __oa__ l
27. kn __ee__
28. l __ea__ der
29. r __ai__ lroad
30. cl __ea__ ring
31. t __ee__ th
32. ch __ee__ r
33. c __oa__ t
34. fr __ee__ dom
35. k __ee__ p
36. b __ea__ st
37. d __ee__ r
38. r __oa__ m
39. __oa__ tmeal
40. __oa__ th

41. p __ai__ n
42. scr __ee__ n
43. l __es__ ves
44. g __ai__ ning
45. s __ea__ son
46. t __ea__ se
47. ch __ee__ se
48. m __ea__ ning
49. thr __ee__
50. expl __ai__ n
51. pl __ea__ se
52. g __oa__ t
53. __ea__ st
54. w __ee__ ks
55. n __ea__ rby
56. wh __ee__ l
57. f __ee__ ding
58. j __ai__ l
59. l __ea__ king
60. succ __ee__ d

61. gr __ee__ n
62. sn __ai__ l
63. __ea__ sy
64. p __ea__ ce
65. r __ea__ ch
66. cl __ea__ n
67. p __ea__ nut
68. __ea__ ten
69. gr __ee__ dy
70. r __ea__ son
71. h __ea__ ting
72. r __oa__ red
73. m __ee__ ting
74. r __oa__ d
75. w __ea__ ken
76. n __ee__ dless
77. w __ai__ l
78. m __ai__ lbox
79. __ai__ ming
80. r __ea__ ding

B What is the main vowel sound of each word?

1. green __ē__
2. meat __ē__
3. tail __ā__
4. eel __ē__
5. pain __ā__

6. leak __ē__
7. deer __ē__
8. coal __ō__
9. needle __ē__
10. team __ē__

11. oat __ō__
12. sail __ā__
13. seen __ē__
14. rail __ā__
15. oak __ō__

16. peach __ē__
17. neat __ē__
18. nail __ā__
19. peel __ē__
20. see __ē__

COMPOSITION EXERCISE

Choose 12 words from today's exercise. Write a sentence with each.

1. _____
2. _____
3. _____
4. _____
5. _____
6. _____

7. _____
8. _____
9. _____
10. _____
11. _____
12. _____

Unit 104 cont'd

Diphthongs

Two vowel sounds blended together in a single syllable form a diphthong. The most common diphthongs are "ou" and "oi."

EXAMPLES: a. ouch   b. town   c. boy   d. void

A Each of the following sentences contains a word with the diphthong "ou." The diphthong "ou" may be spelled as "ou" or "ow." Complete each word correctly.

1. C_ou_nt the money again.
2. H_OW_ did you do it?
3. The gr_OU_nd was too wet.
4. The _OW_l hooted.
5. Alex pl_OW_ed the garden.
6. "A" is a v_OW_el.
7. Don't sh_OU_t!
8. The cat chased the m_OU_se.
9. He ordered a p_OU_nd of beef.
10. All_OW_ me to introduce myself.
11. I want br_OW_n shoes.
12. Milk comes from c_OW_s.
13. The dog h_OW_led all night.
14. This candy is s_OU_r.
15. _OU_r teacher is Ms. Maddox.
16. The ball rolled d_OW_n the hill.
17. The music is too l_OU_d.
18. Her h_OU_se is next door.
19. It s_OU_nded like an explosion.
20. Where is my t_OW_el?
21. A circle is r_OU_nd.
22. Ginger and I went to t_OW_n.
23. Eric is pr_OU_d of his good trade.
24. The bride wore a long g_OW_n.
25. Smile; don't fr_OW_n.
26. This word is a n_OU_n.
27. Chris cleaned the c_OU_nter.
28. The queen wore a gold cr_OW_n.
29. The actor took an extra b_OW_.
30. I like to fish for tr_OU_t.

B Each of the following sentences contains a word with the diphthong "oi." The diphthong "oi" may be spelled as "oi" or "oy." Complete each word correctly.

1. The child played with the t_oy_.
2. The people rej_OI_ced at the news.
3. Who is that b_OY_?
4. The storm destr_OY_ed the crops.
5. Dad changed the car's _OI_l.
6. Kings and queens are r_OY_alty.
7. Don't touch the p_OI_son.
8. Kent j_OI_ned the Scouts.
9. What was that n_OI_se?
10. He av_OI_ded my question.
11. The v_OY_age lasted six months.
12. The penny is a copper c_OI_n.
13. Christmas is a j_OY_ous holiday.
14. Did you enj_OY_ the show?
15. The man had a deep v_OI_ce.
16. The snake c_OI_led and struck.
17. Peter is l_OY_al and trustworthy.
18. She p_OI_nted at the blue one.
19. The s_OI_l was rich in minerals.
20. You've made a wise ch_OI_ce.

COMPOSITION EXERCISE

Choose 8 words which contain the diphthongs "ou" and "oi." Write a sentence with each.

1. _____
2. _____
3. _____
4. _____
5. _____
6. _____
7. _____
8. _____

Vowels Before "r"

It is very difficult to hear the sound of a vowel before "r." There are no rules to help you spell a word which contains a vowel plus "r." You must learn how such words are spelled.

EXAMPLES: a. sorrow   c. fir   e. berry   g. sparrow
b. secure   d. luxury   f. effort   h. solitary

 Add the missing vowels.

1. advent_**u**_re
2. airp_**O**_rt
3. c_**A**_reful
4. dess_**E**_rt
5. en_**O**_rmous
6. fav_**O**_rite
7. f_**O**_rever
8. forw_**A**_rd
9. gen_**E**_ral
10. hist_**O**_ry
11. h_**U**_rry
12. imp_**O**_rtant
13. inf_**O**_rmation
14. int_**E**_resting
15. m_**A**_rket
16. s_**E**_rve
17. _**O**_rder
18. ret_**U**_rn
19. sep_**A**_rate
20. tow_**A**_rd
21. t_**E**_rrible
22. av_**E**_rage
23. f_**U**_rious
24. b_**A**_rber
25. g_**A**_rden

26. b_**A**_rrel
27. b_**O**_rder
28. b_**U**_rden
29. c_**A**_rbon
30. c_**A**_rpenter
31. c_**A**_rrot
32. ch_**A**_rm
33. ch_**O**_re
34. c_**A**_rtoon
35. cl_**E**_rk
36. coll_**A**_r
37. conf_**O**_rm
38. c_**U**_rtain
39. dep_**A**_rt
40. dist_**O**_rt
41. mod_**E**_rn
42. en_**E**_rgy
43. expl_**O**_re
44. f_**O**_rmal
45. g_**A**_rbage
46. fut_**U**_re
47. f_**I**_replace
48. et_**E**_rnal
49. aw_**A**_re
50. h_**O**_rrible

51. g_**A**_rment
52. j_**E**_rsey
53. h_**A**_rbor
54. h_**A**_rdware
55. h_**E**_rd
56. h_**O**_rse
57. ins_**U**_re
58. p_**E**_rfume
59. platf_**O**_rm
60. f_**U**_rnace
61. p_**U**_rse
62. reg_**A**_rd
63. sc_**A**_rf
64. sc_**O**_rn
65. sh_**A**_rk
66. sh_**O**_rtage
67. st_**A**_rch
68. w_**A**_rehouse
69. p_**A**_rachute
70. w_**O**_rse
71. w_**O**_rkable
72. f_**A**_rmer
73. f_**O**_reign
74. ch_**A**_rge
75. w_**E**_re

76. m_**A**_rble
77. m_**E**_rcy
78. n_**E**_rve
79. n_**O**_rth
80. _**O**_rbit
81. n_**O**_rmal
82. p_**A**_rtner
83. p_**E**_rform
84. rem_**A**_rk
85. _**O**_rchard
86. res_**O**_rt
87. ret_**I**_re
88. sc_**A**_rlet
89. s_**E**_rvice
90. s_**U**_rprise
91. t_**A**_rdy
92. th_**O**_rn
93. v_**E**_rb
94. s_**U**_rrender
95. evap_**O**_rate
96. w_**O**_rry
97. t_**A**_rget
98. ign_**O**_re
99. p_**U**_rpose
100. sh_**A**_re

COMPOSITION EXERCISE

Choose 6 words which contain vowels before "r." Write a sentence with each.

1. _____   4. _____

2. _____   5. _____

3. _____   6. _____

Unit 105 cont'd

Matching Vowel Sounds

"A," "e," "i," "o," and "u" are vowels.

A long vowel sound says its own name.
EXAMPLE: ā take   ē me   ī right
ō fold   ū ruler

A short vowel sound does not say its own name.
EXAMPLE: ă at   ĕ let   ĭ it
ŏ pot   ŭ cut

 In each row underline the words which contain the same vowel sound as the first word.

1. rug	<u>hut</u>	rule	<u>dumb</u>	<u>tub</u>	huge	<u>funnel</u>
2. so	<u>nobody</u>	<u>bold</u>	none	<u>owner</u>	on	<u>pole</u>
3. list.	tide	<u>quit</u>	<u>missed</u>	wider	<u>visit</u>	<u>with</u>
4. cute.	<u>suit</u>	<u>cube</u>	sudden	up	<u>tube</u>	<u>rude</u>
5. leaf	<u>eagle</u>	center	<u>east</u>	<u>key</u>	<u>neat</u>	help
6. late	<u>rain</u>	have	<u>straight</u>	<u>shape</u>	sofa	<u>maid</u>
7. hot	hold	<u>job</u>	<u>solve</u>	<u>top</u>	note	<u>not</u>
8. ice.	<u>mile</u>	kitten	<u>side</u>	<u>license</u>	<u>night</u>	written
9. rat	male	<u>cabin</u>	<u>match</u>	cave	blank	<u>ask</u>
10. let	<u>led</u>	<u>seldom</u>	<u>spend</u>	<u>better</u>	even	<u>test</u>
11. ghost. . . .	<u>lonely</u>	<u>locate</u>	<u>open</u>	drop	<u>joke</u>	cot
12. shut	<u>rush</u>	<u>adult</u>	bugle	<u>hunger</u>	using	<u>lucky</u>
13. ticket. . . .	<u>thick</u>	<u>rich</u>	<u>skip</u>	tile	while	<u>hit</u>
14. speak . . .	<u>sleep</u>	get	<u>reason</u>	bed	<u>beast</u>	<u>seed</u>
15. vine.	<u>prize</u>	<u>quiet</u>	sit	<u>pride</u>	riddle	<u>idea</u>
16. came. . . .	bat	<u>safe</u>	<u>potato</u>	<u>escape</u>	<u>famous</u>	ran
17. under . . .	<u>unless</u>	<u>tunnel</u>	<u>uncle</u>	<u>umbrella</u>	usually	fuse
18. lip	<u>sing</u>	tie	<u>fit</u>	<u>magic</u>	<u>hilly</u>	white
19. sea	met	<u>greed</u>	<u>me</u>	<u>easy</u>	<u>bee</u>	fed
20. use	<u>usual</u>	<u>you</u>	cup	<u>tune</u>	<u>used</u>	stuff
21. wet	<u>nest</u>	<u>fence</u>	feet	<u>melt</u>	<u>spell</u>	real
22. lake.	<u>train</u>	<u>cable</u>	pattern	cab	<u>frame</u>	<u>game</u>
23. ride	<u>tried</u>	trick	<u>island</u>	<u>bride</u>	is	<u>light</u>
24. kid	kite	<u>didn't</u>	<u>chicken</u>	isle	<u>sip</u>	<u>mitt</u>
25. old.	<u>piano</u>	word	<u>tomato</u>	<u>vote</u>	<u>boat</u>	dot
26. at	fate	<u>sad</u>	<u>ample</u>	<u>map</u>	<u>fat</u>	stay
27. us	<u>bus</u>	glue	<u>hunt</u>	<u>but</u>	mule	<u>mud</u>
28. stop.	load	<u>lot</u>	<u>robber</u>	rope	<u>mop</u>	<u>knot</u>
29. acre.	<u>grade</u>	<u>remain</u>	cats	<u>pane</u>	<u>day</u>	sat
30. time.	rip	<u>ripe</u>	<u>high</u>	suffix	<u>find</u>	<u>die</u>

Comprehension Check

(A) What is the long vowel sound in each word?

1. spoke	*long o*	11. phrase	*long a*	21. nose	*long o*
2. mice	*long i*	12. home	*long o*	22. peace	*long e*
3. freeze	*long e*	13. favor	*long a*	23. queen	*long e*
4. season	*long e*	14. ninety	*long i*	24. silent	*long i*
5. coast	*long o*	15. game	*long a*	25. parade	*long a*
6. sail	*long a*	16. quote	*long o*	26. local	*long o*
7. cream	*long e*	17. rail	*long a*	27. relate	*long a*
8. photo	*long o*	18. divide	*long i*	28. ocean	*long o*
9. light	*long i*	19. feeble	*long e*	29. safe	*long a*
10. bonus	*long o*	20. paint	*long a*	30. notice	*long o*

(B) What is the short vowel sound in each word?

1. with	*short i*	11. tunnel	*short u*	21. memo	*short e*
2. rust	*short u*	12. brick	*short i*	22. level	*short e*
3. tent	*short e*	13. hunter	*short u*	23. step	*short e*
4. chick	*short i*	14. flap	*short a*	24. match	*short a*
5. brand	*short a*	15. pulp	*short u*	25. number	*short u*
6. tax	*short a*	16. glimpse	*short i*	26. stand	*short a*
7. bitter	*short i*	17. pinch	*short i*	27. plumber	*short u*
8. fender	*short e*	18. mud	*short u*	28. swamp	*short a*
9. bunch	*short u*	19. refund	*short u*	29. whistle	*short i*
10. chunk	*short u*	20. snap	*short a*	30. summer	*short u*

(C) Underline the words in each row which contain the same vowel sounds.

1. slice	fine	sit	hive					
2. west	egg	easy	melon					
3. cut	up	under	mule					
4. friend	meal	seen	reason					
5. trick	limp	slide	if	13. eat	wet	bend	rest
6. trap	cave	main	frame	14. row	toe	no	not
7. most	cop	old	over	15. ivory	ice	it	island
8. reach	cell	team	the	16. fun	uncle	ump	rule
9. by	rib	little	ship	17. so	knob	blow	oak
10. whip	wipe	like	drive	18. fight	itch	pick	fit
11. tub	hum	cube	fund	19. three	east	neat	net
12. ant	lake	ape	same	20. reads	plea	me	sell

255

Test 21 cont'd

Comprehension Check (continued)

Ⓓ Add the missing vowels.

1. p _e_ st
2. st _a_ te
3. h _i_ ppo
4. p _a_ th
5. m _u_ sic
6. l _e_ tters
7. br _i_ dge
8. d _i_ nner
9. tr _u_ th
10. comm _a_

11. r _e_ ward
12. h _o_ me
13. b _a_ seb _a_ ll
14. n _e_ ws
15. t _e_ sts
16. v _a_ n
17. _e_ ssay
18. m _o_ ney
19. c _a_ mping
20. r _i_ ver

21. bl _i_ mp
22. d _o_ llar
23. sk _y_
24. fl _a_ vor
25. cl _o_ thes
26. l _u_ nch
27. m _a_ rbles
28. r _a_ dio
29. q _u_ iet
30. r _a_ nger

31. r _e_ cords
32. t _e_ nnis
33. g _y_ m
34. extr _a_
35. r _o_ bot
36. v _o_ ice
37. sc _i_ ssors
38. waln _u_ t
39. z _e_ bra
40. s _u_ bway

Ⓔ Complete each sentence with a word that follows the pattern in the parentheses.

(short a sound) 1. The ___cab___ took us from the hotel to the airport.

(long o sound) 2. I love to watch ships on the ___ocean___.

(short i sound) 3. Don't ___sit___ on the bench marked "Wet Paint."

(short u sound) 4. I love to eat hot ___fudge___ sundaes.

(long a sound) 5. My feet ___ache___ from all that walking.

(long e sound) 6. I thought the history test was ___easy___.

(short e sound) 7. A ___dentist___ examines teeth for cavities.

(short o sound) 8. Dennis and I went ___off___ our diets again.

(long a sound) 9. The ___sale___ on coats ends Thursday.

(long a sound) 10. Let's enter the bicycle ___race___ next Saturday.

(short a sound) 11. She wore a pink shirt, yellow pants, and a blue ___hat___.

(long e sound) 12. The campgrounds are ___east___ of Willow Lake.

(long i sound) 13. Park your car in the ___driveway___.

(long o sound) 14. You must ___focus___ the camera first.

(short i sound) 15. Terry ___kicked___ the ball out of bounds.

Write a paragraph about your favorite teacher. Then underline all the words that did not have a vowel sound. How many words did you underline?

_____
_____
_____
_____
_____
_____
_____
_____

Consonant Sounds

Most consonants make their own sounds. Some, however, spell their sounds in many different ways. The "k" sound may be spelled as "k," "c," "ck," or "ch." The "f" sound may be spelled as "f," "ph," or "gh." The "s" sound may be spelled as "s" or "c." The "z" sound may be spelled as "z" or "s." The "j" sound may be spelled as "j" or "g." The "ks" sound is often spelled with an "x." The "q" is usually followed by a "u"; "qu" spells the "kw" sound.

A What is the beginning sound of each word?

b	1. battle	l	13. luxury	t	25. tone	g	37. ghast
kw	2. quit	z	14. zebra	kw	26. quack	s	38. cedar
d	3. daughter	s	15. center	j	27. jacks	f	39. phony
s	4. circus	j	16. giant	s	28. sudsy	ch	40. check
d	5. decision	s	17. sorrow	m	29. mud	s	41. sink
f	6. favorite	m	18. multiply	b	30. bubble	f	42. fill
h	7. hardware	f	19. phony	d	31. deer	g	43. gas
f	8. fireplace	t	20. tooth	h	32. high	g	44. quest
g	9. ghost	k	21. chorus	l	33. luck	d	45. dawn
r	10. reward	j	22. gentle	m	34. monkey	n	46. nix
k	11. cabin	n	23. nothing	z	35. zeal	j	47. jester
f	12. phase	p	24. push	k	36. kangaroo	m	48. marry

B Answer each question.

1. What is the sound of the "g" in "general"? __j__
2. What is the sound of the "ph" in "elephant"? __f__
3. What is the sound of the "qu" in "quite"? __kw__
4. What is the sound of the first "c" in "collection"? __k__
5. What is the sound of the "p" in "important"? __p__
6. What is the sound of the "z" in "zookeeper"? __z__
7. What is the sound of the "j" in "juice"? __j__
8. What is the sound of the "s" in "usually"? __z__
9. What is the sound of the "g" in "target"? __g__
10. What is the sound of the "gh" in "enough"? __f__
11. What is the sound of the first "n" in "information"? __n__

12. What is the sound of the "s" in "suddenly"? __s__
13. What is the sound of the "x" in "taxable"? __ks__
14. What is the sound of the "ch" in "choir"? __k__
15. What is the sound of the "b" in "handbook"? __b__
16. What is the sound of the "l" in "lonesome"? __l__
17. What is the sound of the "s" in "newspaper"? __z__
18. What is the sound of the "qu" in "question"? __kw__
19. What is the sound of the first "t" in "together"? __t__
20. What is the sound of the "j" in "journey"? __j__
21. What is the sound of the "c" in "century"? __s__
22. What is the sound of the second "s" in "surprise"? __z__

Unit 106 cont'd

Matching Consonant Sounds

A consonant sound may be made by a single consonant, or it may be made by a combination of two or more consonants.

EXAMPLES: *a. The words "break," "breeze," and "bruise" begin with the consonant sound of "br."*
          b. The words "goal," "game," and "good" begin with the consonant sound of "g."
          c. The words "peach," "church," and "hunch" end with the consonant sound of "ch."

A In each row underline the words which begin with the same consonant sound as the first word.

1.	history......honest	<u>habit</u>	heir	<u>hunger</u>	honor	<u>house</u>
2.	confident....<u>career</u>	cleanser	change	<u>capital</u>	center	<u>kitten</u>
3.	breakfast....<u>brush</u>	blouse	bug	<u>brother</u>	biggest	<u>bread</u>
4.	knock......<u>key</u>	<u>knee</u>	<u>know</u>	<u>needle</u>	<u>new</u>	crazy
5.	flood.......favor	<u>flea</u>	<u>flame</u>	frozen	<u>flower</u>	<u>flexible</u>
6.	wise.......<u>work</u>	whistle	<u>wait</u>	<u>wrong</u>	<u>while</u>	<u>wonderful</u>
7.	piano.......<u>pencil</u>	<u>protect</u>	<u>press</u>	<u>perhaps</u>	<u>pleasant</u>	<u>pal</u>
8.	thick.......<u>thin</u>	<u>thought</u>	<u>terrible</u>	<u>thousand</u>	truth	<u>thimble</u>
9.	circus......<u>circle</u>	chew	<u>sudden</u>	<u>season</u>	<u>suds</u>	strange
10.	slice.......separate	<u>sleeve</u>	<u>slow</u>	straight	<u>sled</u>	<u>small</u>
11.	proof.......person	<u>praise</u>	<u>poison</u>	<u>play</u>	<u>prize</u>	<u>pout</u>
12.	shy.......<u>shout</u>	sleep	<u>shade</u>	secret	<u>shine</u>	<u>shoulder</u>
13.	freedom.....forever	frame	<u>frighten</u>	future	<u>fragile</u>	<u>frost</u>
14.	dream......<u>dread</u>	<u>dry</u>	discover	<u>drink</u>	dozen	<u>drown</u>
15.	challenge...<u>chance</u>	country	<u>cheap</u>	castle	<u>chilly</u>	<u>choose</u>
16.	black.......brown	<u>blend</u>	<u>bless</u>	business	<u>blond</u>	battle
17.	machine....<u>music</u>	<u>magic</u>	night	nonsense	<u>mistake</u>	<u>middle</u>
18.	street......<u>strong</u>	<u>stand</u>	<u>student</u>	<u>stretch</u>	<u>struggle</u>	scale
19.	tremble.....<u>trust</u>	towel	<u>treatment</u>	thank	<u>trouble</u>	tell
20.	please......<u>play</u>	prowler	<u>plane</u>	powder	<u>plum</u>	position

B In each row underline the words which end with the same consonant sound as the first word.

1.	exercise.....<u>is</u>	nonsense	<u>cause</u>	<u>prize</u>	famous	<u>was</u>
2.	advice.......<u>business</u>	was	<u>enormous</u>	surprise	<u>license</u>	size
3.	absent.......added	<u>habit</u>	<u>helped</u>	<u>cut</u>	<u>minute</u>	<u>caught</u>
4.	against......<u>honest</u>	guess	<u>breakfast</u>	honesty	<u>guest</u>	house
5.	enough.....<u>if</u>	<u>roof</u>	through	<u>laugh</u>	<u>stuff</u>	of
6.	cabin........some	<u>explain</u>	<u>none</u>	<u>lining</u>	<u>in</u>	find
7.	bridge.......<u>edge</u>	hug	<u>huge</u>	log	<u>large</u>	<u>fudge</u>
8.	escape......<u>up</u>	hoped	<u>help</u>	<u>rip</u>	mapped	<u>stop</u>

Consonant Blends

A consonant blend occurs when two consonant letters spell one sound.

Common Consonant Blends

bl	ch	pl	th	pr	fl	br	cr	sh
sp	fr	sc	gl	gr	st	sn	sk	wh
	sw	str	thr	tch	dr			

EXAMPLES:
- **a. gr** — gravity
- **b. thr** — threat
- **c. sp** — spoon
- **d. th** — with
- **e. sk** — skunk
- **f. tch** — match
- **g. bl** — blast
- **h. str** — string

 Supply the consonant blends.

1. **bl** anket
2. um **BR** ella
3. **CH** eat
4. **ST** ampede
5. under **ST** and
6. lu **BR** icate
7. toge **TH** er
8. ma **CH** ine
9. **CH** eese
10. **SC** atter
11. **GR** eater
12. **TH** ought
13. in **TR** oduce
14. **SH** ip
15. **FL** ashlight
16. un **PL** easant
17. runni **NG**
18. Engli **SH**
19. any **WH** ere
20. ru **SH** ing
21. everythi **NG**
22. in **STR** ument
23. **FR** ontier
24. sub **ST** itute
25. accom **PL** ish

26. **STR** ange
27. breakfa **ST**
28. **BR** ead
29. an **TH** em
30. ki **TCH** en
31. **ST** agecoach
32. **PR** essure
33. **CH** imney
34. **CH** alkboard
35. **BR** eeze
36. ri **CH**
37. far **TH** er
38. **TR** emble
39. **SC** ore
40. ex **PL** ore
41. some **WH** at
42. **TR** ustworthy
43. belo **NG**
44. dia **GR** am
45. **TH** ief
46. **FR** iendship
47. **CH** ampion
48. again **ST**
49. **SH** adow
50. **FR** ighten

51. **SK** unk
52. **GL** ance
53. ari **TH** metic
54. **THR** ough
55. **WH** enever
56. **BL** ind
57. **SH** ould
58. **PR** omise
59. **PR** otection
60. **TR** ouble
61. ano **TH** er
62. **WH** ere
63. **BR** oom
64. **FR** action
65. **SN** owball
66. fooli **SH**
67. con **TR** ol
68. **BR** own
69. **GL** oomy
70. nor **TH**
71. **BR** eathe
72. com **PL** ete
73. **SP** ecial
74. waiti **NG**
75. **SP** ider

76. lea **SH**
77. **FR** eedom
78. **PR** omise
79. ex **PL** ain
80. **GR** eedy
81. **PR** actice
82. sur **PR** ise
83. a **SL** eep
84. **STR** aight
85. **TR** ee
86. **TR** ousers
87. **SP** elling
88. por **CH**
89. **DR** iveway
90. heal **TH**
91. **ST** ation
92. dis **CH** arge
93. bewi **TCH**
94. **ST** upid
95. **TH** orough
96. ex **PR** essed
97. **TH** under
98. **FR** equently
99. sou **TH** ern
100. **THR** illing

Unit 107 cont'd

Beginning and Ending Sounds

Vowel sounds may be either long or short.
Sometimes it takes two vowels to make
one sound.

Most consonants make their own sounds. However,
some consonants may have more than one sound.
Sometimes two consonants work together to make
one sound.

EXAMPLES: a. The word "blanket" begins with "bl" and ends with "t."
b. The word "dozen" begins with "d" and ends with "en."
c. The word "key" begins with "k" and ends with long "e."
d. The word "cause" begins with "k" and ends with "z."

  Write the beginning and ending sounds of each word.

#	Word	Begin	End	#	Word	Begin	End	#	Word	Begin	End	#	Word	Begin	End
1.	laugh	l	f	26.	none	n	n	51.	speak	sp	k	76.	voice	v	s
2.	smart	sm	t	27.	check	ch	k	52.	thought	th	t	77.	tomato	t	ō
3.	catch	k	ch	28.	vine	v	n	53.	zero	z	ō	78.	eagle	ē	əl
4.	giant	j	t	29.	cute	k	t	54.	habit	h	t	79.	break	br	k
5.	sound	s	d	30.	number	n	ər	55.	nurse	n	s	80.	health	h	th
6.	heart	h	t	31.	green	gr	n	56.	drink	dr	k	81.	wheel	wh	l
7.	climb	kl	m	32.	find	f	d	57.	match	m	ch	82.	glove	gl	v
8.	church	ch	ch	33.	differ	d	ər	58.	funny	f	ē	83.	think	th	k
9.	mouse	m	s	34.	write	r	t	59.	because	b	z	84.	rude	r	d
10.	trip	tr	p	35.	value	v	ū	60.	polite	p	t	85.	foolish	f	sh
11.	garden	g	n	36.	dress	dr	s	61.	spoon	sp	n	86.	cartoon	k	n
12.	locate	l	t	37.	quit	kw	t	62.	flag	fl	g	87.	stop	st	p
13.	light	l	t	38.	wash	w	sh	63.	three	thr	ē	88.	large	l	j
14.	gave	g	v	39.	coat	k	t	64.	then	th	n	89.	would	w	d
15.	does	d	z	40.	train	tr	n	65.	horse	h	s	90.	work	w	k
16.	start	st	t	41.	talent	t	t	66.	branch	br	ch	91.	breeze	br	z
17.	perfect	p	t	42.	stupid	st	d	67.	silent	s	t	92.	village	v	j
18.	birth	b	th	43.	teeth	t	th	68.	please	pl	z	93.	strong	str	ng
19.	friend	fr	d	44.	magnet	m	t	69.	unit	ū	t	94.	confess	k	s
20.	state	st	t	45.	equip	ē	p	70.	delay	d	ā	95.	motto	m	ō
21.	gain	g	n	46.	fierce	f	s	71.	lose	l	z	96.	ghost	g	t
22.	borrow	b	ō	47.	safe	s	f	72.	change	ch	j	97.	grape	gr	p
23.	phone	f	n	48.	honest	ŏ	st	73.	prefix	pr	ks	98.	count	k	t
24.	greed	gr	d	49.	free	fr	ē	74.	job	j	b	99.	later	l	ər
25.	magic	m	k	50.	prize	pr	z	75.	visit	v	t	100.	potato	p	ō

Alphabetical Order

Words are arranged in alphabetical order according to their first letters. If two words begin with the same letter, then the second letter is used to determine order.

EXAMPLES: a. "Orange" comes before "peach" because "o" comes before "p."
b. "Wall" comes before "window" because "a" comes before "i."

✳ Arrange the words in alphabetical order.

A.
1. nose — *ear*
2. eye — *eye*
3. ear — *nose*
4. toe — *toe*

B.
1. trip — HIKE
2. hike — RACE
3. stroll — STROLL
4. race — TRIP

C.
1. vegetable — BREAD
2. meat — MEAT
3. bread — POULTRY
4. poultry — VEGETABLE

D.
1. car — AUTO
2. auto — BIKE
3. train — CAR
4. plane — PLANE
5. bike — SHIP
6. ship — TRAIN

E.
1. sea — FOREST
2. plain — HILL
3. hill — LAKE
4. forest — OCEAN
5. ocean — PLAIN
6. lake — SEA

F.
1. happy — BASHFUL
2. sad — BOLD
3. bashful — FEARLESS
4. shy — HAPPY
5. bold — SAD
6. fearless — SHY

G.
1. snake — BEAR
2. sheep — BIRD
3. cow — CAMEL
4. zebra — CAT
5. camel — COW
6. lion — DOG
7. cat — HIPPO
8. dog — LION
9. bird — SHEEP
10. bear — SNAKE
11. hippo — WOLF
12. wolf — ZEBRA

H.
1. man — AUNT
2. she — BABY
3. lady — BOY
4. aunt — CHILD
5. girl — DAD
6. boy — GIRL
7. baby — HE
8. child — LADY
9. mom — MAN
10. dad — MOM
11. he — SHE
12. they — THEY

I.
1. teacher — ACTOR
2. mailman — ACTRESS
3. policeman — BANKER
4. lawyer — DOCTOR
5. nurse — LAWYER
6. doctor — MAILMAN
7. writer — MUSICIAN
8. banker — NURSE
9. musician — POLICEMAN
10. singer — SINGER
11. actor — TEACHER
12. actress — WRITER

COMPOSITION EXERCISE

List 20 items in your classroom. Arrange the list in alphabetical order.

1. _____   6. _____   11. _____   16. _____
2. _____   7. _____   12. _____   17. _____
3. _____   8. _____   13. _____   18. _____
4. _____   9. _____   14. _____   19. _____
5. _____   10. _____   15. _____   20. _____

Unit 108 cont'd ➡

Putting Words in Alphabetical Order

Words arranged according to the letters of the alphabet are in alphabetical order. If two words begin with the same letter, the second letter determines order. If two words begin with the same two letters, the third letter determines order.

EXAMPLES:
a. "Field" comes before "soldier" because "f" comes before "s."
b. "Zebra" comes before "zoo" because "e" comes before "o."
c. "Glass" comes before "glove" because "a" comes before "o."

 Arrange each list of words in alphabetical order.

Box One

1. press	advice
2. bleach	BATTLE
3. luxury	BLEACH
4. advice	CLOTHES
5. phase	DANGER
6. skeleton	EXILE
7. battle	FANTASTIC
8. guest	GOSSIP
9. ideal	GUEST
10. exile	HABIT
11. normal	IDEAL
12. secure	JOY
13. gossip	LUXURY
14. modern	MODERN
15. occupy	NORMAL
16. zone	OCCUPY
17. remedy	PHASE
18. threat	PRESS
19. fantastic	REMEDY
20. wink	SECURE
21. habit	SKELETON
22. clothes	THREAT
23. danger	WINK
24. joy	ZONE

Box Two

25. thorn	tablet
26. threat	TALE
27. tornado	TALENT
28. thunder	TEA
29. talent	TEAR
30. tea	TEETH
31. tablet	TENT
32. train	TEST
33. thief	THIEF
34. test	THING
35. thus	THORN
36. two	THREAT
37. tale	THUMB
38. time	THUNDER
39. trust	THUS
40. tunnel	TIME
41. trip	TONE
42. tear	TORNADO
43. tone	TRAIN
44. teeth	TRIP
45. thumb	TRUST
46. turtle	TUNNEL
47. tent	TURTLE
48. thing	TWO

Box Three

49. candle	cake
50. car	CANDLE
51. cane	CANE
52. coffee	CAPTIVITY
53. cookie	CAR
54. cake	CAREER
55. country	CAREFREE
56. cook	CARTOON
57. confuse	CAVITY
58. clatter	CHILL
59. career	CHURCH
60. combine	CLATTER
61. cruel	COFFEE
62. carefree	COMBINE
63. conquer	CONFESS
64. captivity	CONFUSE
65. cure	CONQUER
66. cavity	COOK
67. cartoon	COOKIE
68. confess	COUNTRY
69. church	COZY
70. crown	CROWN
71. chill	CRUEL
72. cozy	CURE

COMPOSITION EXERCISE

List 20 words that begin with the letter "s." Arrange the words in alphabetical order.

1. _____ 6. _____ 11. _____ 16. _____

2. _____ 7. _____ 12. _____ 17. _____

3. _____ 8. _____ 13. _____ 18. _____

4. _____ 9. _____ 14. _____ 19. _____

5. _____ 10. _____ 15. _____ 20. _____

Arranging Words Alphabetically

Words arranged according to the letters of the alphabet are in alphabetical order. If two words begin with the same letter, the second letter determines the order. If two words begin with the same two letters, the third letter determines the order.

EXAMPLES:
a. "Yes" comes before "you" because "e" comes before "o."
b. "Evening" comes before "every" because "n" comes before "r."
c. "Lake" comes before "lazy" because "k" comes before "z."

 Arrange each list of words in alphabetical order.

1. adopt	adopt	31. campus	CABBAGE	61. loose	LANGUAGE
2. arrive	AGAINST	32. common	CALM	62. lemon	LAWYER
3. against	AGREE	33. carpenter	CAMPUS	63. luggage	LEMON
4. alley	ALLEY	34. carrot	CANYON	64. lawyer	LIMIT
5. attend	ANGER	35. cabbage	CARPENTER	65. lose	LOAF
6. ankle	ANKLE	36. canyon	CARROT	66. locate	LOCATE
7. anger	APPLY	37. calm	CHANCE	67. loaf	LOOSE
8. agree	ARRIVE	38. chance	CLERK	68. language	LOSE
9. apply	ATTEND	39. clerk	COMMON	69. limit	LUGGAGE
10. average	AVERAGE	40. complete	COMPLETE	70. lump	LUMP

11. sausage	SAFE	41. differ	DAMAGE	71. breeze	BACON
12. scream	SAUSAGE	42. decide	DAWN	72. barber	BAKER
13. spy	SCATTER	43. damage	DECIDE	73. blur	BARBER
14. safe	SCREAM	44. district	DEFEAT	74. baker	BLANKET
15. secret	SECRET	45. doubt	DIFFER	75. border	BLUR
16. signal	SELDOM	46. double	DISTRICT	76. bushel	BORDER
17. shelter	SERVICE	47. dawn	DODGE	77. borrow	BORROW
18. service	SHELTER	48. dye	DOUBLE	78. blanket	BREEZE
19. scatter	SIGNAL	49. dodge	DOUBT	79. bacon	BURDEN
20. seldom	SPY	50. defeat	DYE	80. burden	BUSHEL

21. gentle	GENTLE	51. water	WATER	81. frown	FALSE
22. guard	GIANT	52. worth	WHISTLE	82. folder	FAULT
23. grass	GOLDEN	53. whistle	WHOSE	83. film	FIGURE
24. golf	GOLF	54. wrong	WORKABLE	84. fault	FILM
25. giant	GRASS	55. workable	WORLD	85. finger	FINGER
26. growth	GROWTH	56. whose	WORRY	86. figure	FOLDER
27. guilty	GUARD	57. worse	WORSE	87. future	FOLK
28. guide	GUARDIAN	58. wreck	WORTH	88. folk	FROWN
29. golden	GUIDE	59. worry	WRECK	89. false	FROZEN
30. guardian	GUILTY	60. world	WRONG	90. frozen	FUTURE

Unit 109 cont'd

Determining Alphabetical Order

Words arranged according to the letters of the alphabet are in alphabetical order. If two words begin with the same letter, the second letter determines the order. If two words begin with the same two letters, the third letter determines the order.

EXAMPLES: a. "Silly" comes before "taste."

b. "Pet" comes before "zoo."

c. "Banana" comes before "buggy."

d. "Melody" comes before "mystery."

 Using the lists of words in the boxes, write either true (t) or false (f) in the blanks. Remember that the questions refer to the words directly before or after the given words.

Word List		
1. pace	_t_	1. The word "pleasant" would come before "please."
2. peace	F	2. The word "plant" would follow "prize."
3. piano	F	3. The word "palm" would come before "poet."
4. please	T	4. The word "public" would follow "promise."
5. plum	T	5. The word "perfume" would come before "piano."
6. poet	F	6. The word "provide" would come before "potato."
7. potato	F	7. The word "perhaps" would follow "pace."
8. prize	T	8. The word "prison" would come before "prize."
9. promise	F	9. The word "practice" would come before "promise."
10. put	T	10. The word "piece" would follow "piano."

Word List		
11. eagle	T	1. The word "enemy" would follow "end."
12. easy	T	2. The word "explore" would follow "event."
13. echo	F	3. The word "east" would come before "eagle."
14. either	F	4. The word "entire" would follow "error."
15. elder	T	5. The word "education" would come before "either."
16. end	T	6. The word "elephant" would follow "elder."
17. error	F	7. The word "elbow" would come before "echo."
18. escape	F	8. The word "enormous" would follow "easy."
19. event	•T	9. The word "entire" would come before "error."
20. express	F	10. The word "eight" would come before "express."

Word List		
21. talk	F	1. The word "television" would follow "through."
22. telephone	T	2. The word "text" would come before "thought."
23. terrible	F	3. The word "tennis" would follow "time."
24. thought	F	4. The word "thunder" would follow "together."
25. through	F	5. The word "target" would come before "trouble."
26. ticket	T	6. The word "tickle" would come before "time."
27. time	F	7. The word "treasure" would come before "telephone."
28. together	F	8. The word "tumble" would follow "tunnel."
29. trouble	T	9. The word "total" would follow "together."
30. tunnel	F	10. The word "though" would follow "thought."

Arranging Proper Names in Alphabetical Order

EXAMPLES: a. *"Mike Cook" comes before "Lynn Fisher" because "c" comes before "f."*
b. *"Chris Allen" comes before "Roger Allen" because "c" comes before "r."*

 Arrange each group of words in alphabetical order.

1. Paul Mason
2. Carrie Jones
3. Susan Dane

Dane, Susan
Jones, Carrie
Mason, Paul

4. Linda Mint
5. Karen Shark
6. Wanda Field

FIELD, WANDA
MINT, LINDA
SHARK, KAREN

7. Diane Peters
8. Kay West
9. Dave Brown

BROWN, DAVE
PETERS, DIANE
WEST, KAY

10. Sam Collins
11. James Green
12. Don Palace

COLLINS, SAM
GREEN, JAMES
PALACE, DON

13. Al Smith
14. Tom Smith
15. Laura Smith

SMITH, AL
SMITH, LAURA
SMITH, TOM

16. Lou Jones
17. Barry Jones
18. Andy Jones

JONES, ANDY
JONES, BARRY
JONES, LOU

19. Alex Carter
20. Mike Paxton
21. Sara House
22. Sandy Moore

CARTER, ALEX
HOUSE, SARA
MOORE, SANDY
PAXTON, MIKE

23. Nancy Dans
24. Nora Bloom
25. Neva Baker
26. Norma Kent

BAKER, NEVA
BLOOM, NORA
DANS, NANCY
KENT, NORMA

27. Leo Madison
28. Jeff Madison
29. Walt Madison
30. Gus Madison
31. Bo Madison
32. Steve Madison

MADISON, BO
MADISON, GUS
MADISON, JEFF
MADISON, LEO
MADISON, STEVE
MADISON, WALT

33. Jill Francis
34. Deb Francis
35. Rona Francis
36. Anne Francis
37. Barb Francis
38. Chris Francis

FRANCIS, ANNE
FRANCIS, BARB
FRANCIS, CHRIS
FRANCIS, DEB
FRANCIS, JILL
FRANCIS, RONA

COMPOSITION EXERCISE

List 10 names of your classmates. Arrange these names in alphabetical order.

1. _____
2. _____
3. _____
4. _____
5. _____

6. _____
7. _____
8. _____
9. _____
10. _____

Unit 110 cont'd

Arranging Titles Alphabetically

Titles are arranged alphabetically according to
the first word of the title. However, if the words
"a," "an," or "the" begin the title, go to the
second word to determine the order.

EXAMPLES:

out of order	alphabetical order
a. Snare of the Hunter	a. Flowers in the Attic
b. Flowers in the Attic	b. Life Among the Savages
c. Life Among the Savages	c. The Prince and the Pauper
d. The Prince and the Pauper	d. Snare of the Hunter

❋ Arrange each list of titles in alphabetical order by
numbering them 1-4.

__4__ 1. Portrait of Ivan
__3__ 2. Little Women
__2__ 3. I Am Third
__1__ 4. Huckleberry Finn

__3__ 5. Catch-22
__1__ 6. And Then There Were None
__4__ 7. The Shining
__2__ 8. Animal Farm

__1__ 9. The Bell Jar
__2__ 10. Jane Eyre
__4__ 11. Robinson Crusoe
__3__ 12. The Learning Tree

__2__ 13. Brian's Song
__1__ 14. Arrow to the Sun
__3__ 15. First on the Moon
__4__ 16. The Road West

__3__ 17. The Iron Cross
__2__ 18. Centennial
__4__ 19. The White Buffalo
__1__ 20. The Cathedral

__1__ 21. An American Dream
__2__ 22. To Catch a Thief
__3__ 23. Watership Down
__4__ 24. Winter of our Discontent

__2__ 25. Midnight Sun
__1__ 26. Land of the Giants
__4__ 27. The Scarlet Letter
__3__ 28. Music Man

__3__ 29. The Robe
__2__ 30. The Deep
__4__ 31. The Silver Chalice
__1__ 32. The Brain

__2__ 33. Echoes from the Past
__1__ 34. Ashanti to Zulu
__4__ 35. Raisin in the Sun
__3__ 36. Fiddler on the Roof

__1__ 37. Call to Glory
__3__ 38. I Am Third
__2__ 39. Gone with the Wind
__4__ 40. On the Beach

COMPOSITION EXERCISE

List 5 of your favorite books. Then arrange their titles alphabetically.

1. _____   _____
2. _____   _____
3. _____   _____
4. _____   _____
5. _____   _____

Comprehension Check

A Answer these questions.

1. What are two ways to spell the "k" sound?   _____ **k, c, ck, ch**
2. What sound does "ph" spell?   _____ **f sound**
3. How do you spell the "l" sound?   _____ **l or ll**
4. What are three ways to spell the "s" sound?   _____ **s, ss, c**
5. What sound does "z" and "s" spell?   _____ **z sound**
6. What sound does "wh" spell?   _____ **hw sound**
7. How do you spell the "j" sound?   _____ **j or g**
8. What sound does "qu" spell?   _____ **kw sound**
9. What sound does "ch" spell?   _____ **k sound**
10. What are three ways to spell the "f" sound?   _____ **f, ff, gh, ph**

B Identify the beginning sound of each word.

s	1. circle	**k**	11. carpet
j	2. giant	**r**	12. reason
s	3. sun	**j**	13. jeep
b	4. bonnet	**v**	14. violin
z	5. zebra	**n**	15. noon
m	6. maze	**h**	16. horror
d	7. dial	**y**	17. yes
f	8. photo	**p**	18. push
t	9. time	**k**	19. coward
l	10. listen	**hw**	20. when

C Identify the ending sound of each word.

n	1. in	**f**	11. rough
k	2. music	**p**	12. up
s	3. prince	**t**	13. sat
b	4. hub	**m**	14. home
f	5. stuff	**v**	15. love
l	6. thrill	**s**	16. gas
j	7. age	**k**	17. rock
n	8. can	**z**	18. jazz
ks	9. ax	**r**	19. car
g	10. rag	**d**	20. divide

D Identify the consonant blends.

th	1. thunder	**st**	6. toast	**cr**	11. cross
sh	2. rush	**ch**	7. chant	**br**	12. brace
th	3. forth	**sp**	8. spit	**tch**	13. witch
str	4. stroll	**pr**	9. prize	**bl**	14. blood
pl	5. explain	**gr**	10. grown	**fr**	15. freeze

E Add the consonants.

1. **r** ule
2. **gr** ade
3. **f** orest
4. hu **g**
5. **r** ight
6. **n** othing
7. tu **b**
8. **q** uiet
9. **j** elly
10. **w** aste
11. e **x** tra
12. **d** umb
13. **s** ix
14. **c** atch
15. **st** op
16. **y** ellow
17. **ch** ildren
18. **h** igher
19. bree **z** e
20. **s** andy
21. **p** iano
22. co **v** er
23. **m** aster
24. a **d** ult
25. **l** unch

Test 22 cont'd

Comprehension Check (continued)

F Underline the word in each list which would come first in alphabetical order.

1. dancer, hand, person, <u>brain</u>, poster, sound, flood
2. Mark, Larry, Ron, Charles, Roger, Jim, <u>Adam</u>
3. ghost, scene, news, valley, film, <u>cloud</u>, water
4. clinic, <u>canyon</u>, clock, chili, carrot, collect, curve
5. write, <u>country</u>, travel, money, ship, jet, train
6. <u>air</u>, land, sky, space, beauty, ocean, cloud
7. wax, <u>wagon</u>, way, wash, wake, wall, want
8. Whitney, Dyan, Nancy, <u>Candace</u>, Heather, Ryan
9. leaf, library, lion, lunch, lying, <u>label</u>, look
10. need, present, wonder, stereo, <u>diary</u>, radio

G Arrange each set of words in alphabetical order.

1. family — *brother*
2. brother — *buddy*
3. friend — *driver*
4. sister — *family*
5. driver — *friend*
6. buddy — *neighbor*
7. teacher — *parents*
8. parents — *sister*
9. student — *student*
10. neighbor — *teacher*

1. Randy Smith — *Akers, Sandra*
2. Kate Lawson — *Fisher, Dave*
3. Mark Preston — *Hawkins, Joel*
4. Pam Overton — *Imas, Ted*
5. Alex Martin — *Knight, Eric*
6. Eric Knight — *Lawson, Kate*
7. Dave Fisher — *Martin, Alex*
8. Joel Hawkins — *Overton, Pam*
9. Sandra Akers — *Preston, Mark*
10. Ted Imas — *Smith, Randy*

Write a paragraph about what subjects you would like to see taught in school. Tell why you choose these subjects. Underline all words you use that begin with consonant sounds.

_____

_____

_____

_____

_____

_____

_____

_____

_____

_____

Forming Compound Words

A compound word is formed by joining two words together as one word.

EXAMPLES: a. door + bell = doorbell   c. ball + game = ballgame
b. wish + bone = wishbone   d. cow + boy = cowboy

 Join the two words to form a compound word.

1. fire + place = *fireplace*
2. black + smith = **BLACKSMITH**
3. story + book = **STORYBOOK**
4. night + gown = **NIGHTGOWN**
5. out + side = **OUTSIDE**
6. yard + stick = **YARDSTICK**
7. door + knob = **DOORKNOB**
8. butter + milk = **BUTTERMILK**
9. your + self = **YOURSELF**
10. like + wise = **LIKEWISE**
11. bitter + sweet = **BITTERSWEET**
12. pass + word = **PASSWORD**
13. tooth + pick = **TOOTHPICK**
14. horse + shoe = **HORSESHOE**
15. house + boat = **HOUSEBOAT**
16. gate + house = **GATEHOUSE**
17. ink + well = **INKWELL**
18. with + hold = **WITHHOLD**
19. short + stop = **SHORTSTOP**
20. wood + land = **WOODLAND**
21. eye + ball = **EYEBALL**
22. base + ball = **BASEBALL**
23. day + light = **DAYLIGHT**
24. gentle + man = **GENTLEMAN**
25. god + father = **GODFATHER**

26. house + wife = **HOUSEWIFE**
27. land + scape = **LANDSCAPE**
28. cross + word = **CROSSWORD**
29. never + more = **NEVERMORE**
30. up + stairs = **UPSTAIRS**
31. grape + vine = **GRAPEVINE**
32. flag + ship = **FLAGSHIP**
33. sand + man = **SANDMAN**
34. side + walk = **SIDEWALK**
35. broom + stick = **BROOMSTICK**
36. class + room = **CLASSROOM**
37. foot + ball = **FOOTBALL**
38. play + ground = **PLAYGROUND**
39. home + sick = **HOMESICK**
40. girl + friend = **GIRLFRIEND**
41. in + doors = **INDOORS**
42. fish + net = **FISHNET**
43. work + man = **WORKMAN**
44. hair + brush = **HAIRBRUSH**
45. dark + room = **DARKROOM**
46. gold + fish = **GOLDFISH**
47. hand + cuff = **HANDCUFF**
48. land + slide = **LANDSLIDE**
49. milk + man = **MILKMAN**
50. chalk + board = **CHALKBOARD**

COMPOSITION EXERCISE

List 15 compound words not used in today's exercise.

1. _____   6. _____   11. _____
2. _____   7. _____   12. _____
3. _____   8. _____   13. _____
4. _____   9. _____   14. _____
5. _____   10. _____   15. _____

Unit 111 cont'd

Using Compound Words

A compound word is two words combined to make one word.

EXAMPLES: a. **in** + **to** = **into**
                The dog ran into the house.
          b. **my** + **self** = **myself**
                I did it myself.
          c. **fire** + **place** = **fireplace**
                Sit beside the fireplace.

 In each row combine two words to make a compound word that will complete the sentence.

1. (a) light (b) dark (c) flash (d) stop — Hand me the ___*flashlight*___.
2. (a) side (b) over (c) walk (d) run — She's sweeping the ___*sidewalk*___.
3. (a) draw (b) out (c) paint (d) with — I ___*withdraw*___ my objection.
4. (a) pop (b) core (c) corn (d) hop — We ate ___*popcorn*___ and candy.
5. (a) what (b) some (c) why (d) where — Are you going ___*somewhere*___?
6. (a) over (b) stand (c) under (d) sit — He didn't ___*understand*___ the question.
7. (a) in (b) line (c) out (d) circle — ___*Outline*___ the next chapter.
8. (a) wall (b) door (c) knob (d) bell — Ring the ___*doorbell*___ again.
9. (a) word (b) phrase (c) cross (d) letter — Dale likes to work ___*crossword*___ puzzles.
10. (a) up (b) stairs (c) steps (d) over — Your room is ___*upstairs*___.
11. (a) night (b) star (c) day (d) light — We still have two hours of ___*daylight*___.
12. (a) teeth (b) tooth (c) brush (d) cloth — I can't find my ___*toothbrush*___.
13. (a) yellow (b) gold (c) bronze (d) fish — My cat ate my ___*goldfish*___.
14. (a) rail (b) street (c) road (d) path — We should stop at ___*railroad*___ crossings.
15. (a) skillet (b) pan (c) pot (d) cakes — Jill likes ___*pancakes*___ for breakfast.
16. (a) novel (b) store (c) shop (d) book — Sam works at the ___*bookstore*___.
17. (a) pass (b) past (c) word (d) passed — Do you know the ___*password*___?
18. (a) snow (b) coat (c) rain (d) sun — Don't forget your ___*raincoat*___.
19. (a) die (b) died (c) dead (d) line — The ___*deadline*___ is Wednesday.
20. (a) him (b) self (c) selves (d) he — James ___*himself*___ said so.
21. (a) board (b) drive (c) plank (d) way — The truck blocked the ___*driveway*___.
22. (a) eraser (b) board (c) chalk (d) blue — Write the answer on the ___*chalkboard*___.
23. (a) short (b) stop (c) long (d) go — Dianne will play ___*shortstop*___.
24. (a) side (b) below (c) inner (d) in — Please come ___*inside*___.
25. (a) butter (b) cheese (c) milk (d) sour — Do you like ___*buttermilk*___?
26. (a) sky (b) plane (c) air (d) cloud — I have never ridden an ___*airplane*___.
27. (a) ball (b) base (c) bat (d) glove — Let's play ___*baseball*___.
28. (a) class (b) desk (c) room (d) book — The ___*classroom*___ was locked.
29. (a) rain (b) flower (c) sun (d) heat — I brought you a ___*sunflower*___.
30. (a) ill (b) sick (c) house (d) home — Pete is ___*homesick*___ for Texas.
31. (a) born (b) birth (c) week (d) day — Joe's ___*birthday*___ is June 23.
32. (a) high (b) low (c) lane (d) way — The dog ran across the ___*highway*___.
33. (a) throat (b) tie (c) neck (d) arm — I bought Dad a ___*necktie*___.
34. (a) cup (b) cake (c) cookie (d) loaf — Have another ___*cupcake*___.
35. (a) place (b) stick (c) fire (d) match — All of us sat around the ___*fireplace*___.

Compound Words

A compound word is made up of two smaller words.

EXAMPLES:
a. sidewalk
b. background
c. flashlight
d. fireproof
e. warehouse
f. watermelon

A Draw a line between the two separate words that make up each compound word.

1. Sun/flowers
2. PLAY/MATE
3. UNDER/STAND
4. WIND/MILL
5. OTHER/WISE
6. FINGER/PRINT
7. SEA/SHELL
8. CLASS/ROOM
9. SHORT/STOP
10. PASS/WORD
11. FOOT/BALL
12. HALL/WAY
13. RAIN/COAT
14. BROOM/STICK
15. SONG/BIRD
16. SOME/WHERE
17. IN/DOORS
18. BED/ROOM
19. WHEN/EVER
20. EVERY/BODY
21. BOOK/WORM
22. TOOTH/PASTE
23. TIP/TOE
24. NIGHT/GOWN
25. DAY/LIGHT

26. HEAD/QUARTERS
27. GRASS/HOPPER
28. NEWS/PAPERS
29. WHEEL/CHAIR
30. UP/STAIRS
31. DISH/WASHER
32. YARD/STICK
33. CHALK/BOARD
34. BUTTER/MILK
35. HOME/SICK
36. TOOTH/BRUSH
37. PLAY/GROUND
38. RAIL/ROAD
39. BATTLE/SHIP
40. CAT/NAP
41. POP/CORN
42. OVER/DUE
43. RAIN/BOW
44. NO/BODY
45. AIR/PORT
46. LUNCH/ROOM
47. UNDER/LINE
48. GINGER/BREAD
49. BOOK/STORE
50. NEVER/MORE

51. CARD/BOARD
52. DEAD/LINE
53. IN/SIDE
54. BIRTH/DAY
55. STRAW/BERRY
56. EARTH/QUAKE
57. CROSS/WORD
58. GOLD/FISH
59. WISH/BONE
60. HOUSE/BOAT
61. PAN/CAKE
62. HIGH/WAY
63. SUN/SET
64. SPACE/SHIP
65. OUT/LINE
66. IT/SELF
67. RAIN/FALL
68. YOUR/SELF
69. HENCE/FORTH
70. BASKET/BALL
71. AN/OTHER
72. SAFE/GUARD
73. COUNTRY/SIDE
74. SUN/SHINE
75. HAND/CUFF

76. OUT/SIDE
77. FOR/EVER
78. TOUCH/DOWN
79. HITCH/HIKER
80. BEES/WAX
81. WHO/EVER
82. GRAPE/VINE
83. BASE/BALL
84. DOOR/BELL
85. BITTER/SWEET
86. BATH/ROOM
87. FIRE/FLY
88. NECK/TIE
89. CUP/CAKES
90. SCHOOL/HOUSE
91. BOOK/KEEPER
92. SNOW/FLAKE
93. DRIVE/WAY
94. OUT/DOORS
95. SOUTH/WEST
96. WITH/OUT
97. OVER/SIGHT
98. FOOT/PRINT
99. FISH/NET
100. EYE/BALL

B Match each word in "Box A" with a word from "Box B" to write ten compound words.

BOX A

1. hair
2. tooth
3. down
4. bunk
5. sun
6. him
7. home
8. ant
9. cat
10. mail

BOX B

1. work
2. hill
3. town
4. box
5. burn
6. ache
7. fish
8. bed
9. brush
10. self

1. toothache
2. hairbrush
3. downtown
4. bunkbed
5. sunburn
6. himself
7. homework
8. anthill
9. catfish
10. mailbox

Unit 112 cont'd

Adding Compound Words

A Use compound words to fill in the blanks.

1. My ___shoestring___ on my tennis shoe broke this ___afternoon___ while I was playing ___basketball___ .

2. I learned to bake ___oatmeal___ cookies from my Betty Crocker ___cookbook___ .

3. My favorite sport in the fall is ___football___ , but in the summer I like ___baseball___ .

4. I check the ___mailbox___ every day to see if the ___postman___ brought me a letter.

5. I will be eleven years old on my next ___birthday___ , in the month of June.

6. On nice days at recess time, we play on the ___playground___ ; but on bad days we usually play games ___inside___ the room.

7. When it is cold outside, we wear our ___overcoats___ .

8. We park our cars in the ___driveway___ and drive them on the ___highway___ .

9. Our ___doorbell___ is broken, so people must knock on the door to let us know they are there.

10. For breakfast I like to eat ___pancakes___ with a lot of syrup and butter.

B Make compound words from these words.

1. ___strawberry___   6. ___drugstore___   11. ___peanut___

2. ___fireplace___   7. ___floodway___   12. ___seashell___

3. ___haystack___   8. ___eggshell___   13. ___scarecrow___

4. ___jawbone___   9. ___seaweed___   14. ___corncob___

5. ___blueberry___   10. ___hallway___   15. ___floodlight___

Dividing Compound Words

A compound word is made up of two words.

EXAMPLES:
  a. in + side = *inside*
  b. foot + ball = *football*
  c. bath + room = *bathroom*
  d. news + paper = *newspaper*
  e. rain + coat = *raincoat*
  f. wish + bone = *wishbone*

A Write the small words which are contained in each compound word.

1. railroad	*rail*	*road*
2. grasshopper	**grass**	**hopper**
3. horseback	**horse**	**back**
4. underground	**under**	**ground**
5. shoestring	**shoe**	**string**
6. baseball	**base**	**ball**
7. footstool	**foot**	**stool**
8. driveway	**drive**	**way**

9. highway	**high**	**way**
10. cowboy	**cow**	**boy**
11. snowball	**snow**	**ball**
12. eggshell	**egg**	**shell**
13. playground	**play**	**ground**
14. afternoon	**after**	**noon**
15. football	**foot**	**ball**
16. overcoat	**over**	**coat**

B Put the following words together to make 20 compounds.

birth	after	day	rain	on	rail
milk	man	side	office	grand	step
over	butter	green	wear	base	shine
under	ground	body	out	snow	plane
some	day	post	every	thing	father
foot	where	air	up	in	way
sun	ball	noon	bow	mother	road

1. *birthday*	6. *underground*	11. *someday*	16. *football*
2. *sunshine*	7. *rainbow*	12. *airplane*	17. *stepmother*
3. *postman*	8. *railroad*	13. *afternoon*	18. *grandmother*
4. *upon*	9. *inside*	14. *everything*	19. *noonday*
5. *outside*	10. *buttermilk*	15. *snowball*	20. *milkman*

Unit 113 cont'd ⟹

More Compound Words

A compound word is the joining of two words to make one.

EXAMPLES: a. foot + ball = football   c. birth + day = birthday
              b. sun + set = sunset   d. home + sick = homesick

 Join the words, and write the new compound words in the blanks.

1. home + work =	*homework*	26. sun + shine =	**SUNSHINE**
2. sun + light =	**SUN LIGHT**	27. bed + room =	**BEDROOM**
3. in + come =	**INCOME**	28. fire + man =	**FIREMAN**
4. side + walk =	**SIDEWALK**	29. with + out =	**WITHOUT**
5. cat + fish =	**CATFISH**	30. chalk + board =	**CHALKBOARD**
6. gentle + man =	**GENTLEMAN**	31. space + ship =	**SPACESHIP**
7. foot + print =	**FOOTPRINT**	32. him + self =	**HIMSELF**
8. black + bird =	**BLACKBIRD**	33. base + ball =	**BASEBALL**
9. door + knob =	**DOORKNOB**	34. ant + hill =	**ANTHILL**
10. cook + book =	**COOKBOOK**	35. in + to =	**INTO**
11. space + man =	**SPACEMAN**	36. water + melon =	**WATERMELON**
12. down + town =	**DOWNTOWN**	37. rain + coat =	**RAINCOAT**
13. steam + ship =	**STEAMSHIP**	38. air + plane =	**AIRPLANE**
14. drive + way =	**DRIVEWAY**	39. bath + room =	**BATHROOM**
15. quick + sand =	**QUICKSAND**	40. drum + beat =	**DRUMBEAT**
16. tooth + ache =	**TOOTHACHE**	41. butter + milk =	**BUTTERMILK**
17. store + room =	**STOREROOM**	42. police + man =	**POLICEMAN**
18. under + stand =	**UNDERSTAND**	43. full + back =	**FULLBACK**
19. neck + tie =	**NECKTIE**	44. class + room =	**CLASSROOM**
20. to + night =	**TONIGHT**	45. out + door =	**OUTDOOR**
21. mail + man =	**MAILMAN**	46. play + ground =	**PLAYGROUND**
22. house + hold =	**HOUSEHOLD**	47. hall + way =	**HALLWAY**
23. friend + ship =	**FRIENDSHIP**	48. sun + flower =	**SUNFLOWER**
24. sun + burn =	**SUNBURN**	49. child + hood =	**CHILDHOOD**
25. under + line =	**UNDERLINE**	50. news + paper =	**NEWSPAPER**

COMPOSITION EXERCISE

List three compound words using each of these words.

1. room

_____
_____
_____

2. ball

_____
_____
_____

3. in

_____
_____
_____

4. sun

_____
_____
_____

5. man

_____
_____
_____

6. door

_____
_____
_____

Changing Compounds to Plurals

When a compound noun is changed to plural, only the last part of the word undergoes the change.

EXAMPLES:
a. football   footballs
b. yourself   yourselves
c. mailman   mailmen
d. ballgown   ballgowns

✳ Write the plural of each word.

#	Word	Plural	#	Word	Plural
1.	cowboy	*cowboys*	26.	sandman	SANDMEN
2.	railroad	RAILROADS	27.	sidewalk	SIDEWALKS
3.	cornstalk	CORNSTALKS	28.	broomstick	BROOMSTICKS
4.	nightgown	NIGHTGOWNS	29.	toothbrush	TOOTHBRUSHES
5.	crossword	CROSSWORDS	30.	password	PASSWORDS
6.	storybook	STORYBOOKS	31.	classroom	CLASSROOMS
7.	grapevine	GRAPEVINES	32.	deadline	DEADLINES
8.	yardstick	YARDSTICKS	33.	toothpick	TOOTHPICKS
9.	flagship	FLAGSHIPS	34.	playground	PLAYGROUNDS
10.	raincoat	RAINCOATS	35.	pancake	PANCAKES
11.	doorknob	DOORKNOBS	36.	housecoat	HOUSECOATS
12.	birthday	BIRTHDAYS	37.	policeman	POLICEMEN
13.	bathroom	BATHROOMS	38.	spaceship	SPACESHIPS
14.	milkmaid	MILKMAIDS	39.	baseball	BASEBALLS
15.	hallway	HALLWAYS	40.	blackbird	BLACKBIRDS
16.	gentleman	GENTLEMEN	41.	highway	HIGHWAYS
17.	footprint	FOOTPRINTS	42.	steamship	STEAMSHIPS
18.	necktie	NECKTIES	43.	cupcake	CUPCAKES
19.	postman	POSTMEN	44.	bookstore	BOOKSTORES
20.	sunset	SUNSETS	45.	girlfriend	GIRLFRIENDS
21.	driveway	DRIVEWAYS	46.	battleship	BATTLESHIPS
22.	spaceman	SPACEMEN	47.	busboy	BUSBOYS
23.	wishbone	WISHBONES	48.	calfskin	CALFSKINS
24.	housecoat	HOUSECOATS	49.	songbird	SONGBIRDS
25.	chalkboard	CHALKBOARDS	50.	firefly	FIREFLIES

COMPOSITION EXERCISE

List 20 plural compound words not used in today's exercise.

1. _____
2. _____
3. _____
4. _____
5. _____
6. _____
7. _____
8. _____
9. _____
10. _____
11. _____
12. _____
13. _____
14. _____
15. _____
16. _____
17. _____
18. _____
19. _____
20. _____

Unit 114 cont'd →

Contractions

A contraction is a shortened word made from two words written together.

An apostrophe shows where one or more letters have been omitted to make a contraction.

EXAMPLES: a. can + not = can't   c. you + are = you're
          b. I + will = I'll   d. was + not = wasn't

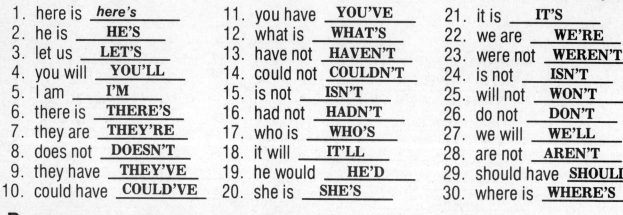

A Write the contraction for each set of words.

1. here is _here's_
2. he is _HE'S_
3. let us _LET'S_
4. you will _YOU'LL_
5. I am _I'M_
6. there is _THERE'S_
7. they are _THEY'RE_
8. does not _DOESN'T_
9. they have _THEY'VE_
10. could have _COULD'VE_

11. you have _YOU'VE_
12. what is _WHAT'S_
13. have not _HAVEN'T_
14. could not _COULDN'T_
15. is not _ISN'T_
16. had not _HADN'T_
17. who is _WHO'S_
18. it will _IT'LL_
19. he would _HE'D_
20. she is _SHE'S_

21. it is _IT'S_
22. we are _WE'RE_
23. were not _WEREN'T_
24. is not _ISN'T_
25. will not _WON'T_
26. do not _DON'T_
27. we will _WE'LL_
28. are not _AREN'T_
29. should have _SHOULD'VE_
30. where is _WHERE'S_

B Complete each sentence by adding a contraction.

1. _Let's_ visit my Aunt Martha.
2. Katherine _HASN'T_ arrived yet.
3. _WON'T_ someone help me?
4. _WE'VE_ already chosen our leader.
5. I _COULD'VE_ told you that.
6. The teacher _WASN'T_ surprised.
7. _WHERE'S_ my coat?
8. _SHE'S_ the owner of the blue car.
9. _DON'T_ you remember who he is?
10. _WHAT'S_ going on here!
11. We _WEREN'T_ allowed to go outside.
12. _THERE'S_ someone in the house!
13. Gilbert _ISN'T_ finished yet.
14. Why _DIDN'T_ you call me?
15. Surely you _DON'T_ believe that!

16. _I'M_ too tired to do anything.
17. They _HADN'T_ heard the news.
18. _WHO'S_ that man in the gray suit?
19. Lynn _ISN'T_ coming to the party.
20. It _WASN'T_ anyone's fault.
21. _LET'S_ discuss the matter further.
22. I _CAN'T_ understand the assignment.
23. Mr. Johns _DOESN'T_ like sports.
24. _SHOULDN'T_ you give him the message?
25. _IT'S_ too late to stop her.
26. _HERE'S_ a letter for you, Mark.
27. It _WON'T_ hurt you.
28. You _SHOULD'VE_ been here at noon.
29. _THEY'RE_ waiting in the hallway.
30. _HE'S_ predicted snow for tomorrow.

COMPOSITION EXERCISE

List 20 contractions.

1. _____
2. _____
3. _____
4. _____
5. _____

6. _____
7. _____
8. _____
9. _____
10. _____

11. _____
12. _____
13. _____
14. _____
15. _____

16. _____
17. _____
18. _____
19. _____
20. _____

Base Words

*The base word is the word to which prefixes
and suffixes are added. Every word contains
a base word.*

EXAMPLES: a. The base word of "freedom" is "free."
b. The base word of "keys" is "key."
c. The base word of "musical" is "music."
d. The base word of "bicycle" is "cycle."

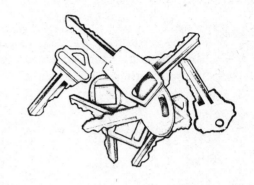

A Write the base word of each word.

1. lonesome	*lone*	26. misspell	SPELL	51. useful	USE
2. voices	VOICE	27. easily	EASY	52. owner	OWN
3. careful	CARE	28. knocking	KNOCK	53. written	WRITE
4. asked	ASK	29. rework	WORK	54. undivided	DIVIDE
5. exchange	CHANGE	30. biting	BITE	55. truthful	TRUTH
6. recount	COUNT	31. talked	TALK	56. courts	COURT
7. unable	ABLE	32. ponies	PONY	57. suggestion	SUGGEST
8. equipment	EQUIP	33. carried	CARRY	58. building	BUILD
9. laughing	LAUGH	34. tricycle	CYCLE	59. distrust	TRUST
10. asleep	SLEEP	35. farmer	FARM	60. ashamed	SHAME
11. incorrect	CORRECT	36. valuable	VALUE	61. statement	STATE
12. different	DIFFER	37. seventy	SEVEN	62. uninvited	INVITE
13. confession	CONFESS	38. healthy	HEALTH	63. prosperous	PROSPER
14. misplace	PLACE	39. unkind	KIND	64. helpless	HELP
15. clothes	CLOTH	40. battles	BATTLE	65. clearing	CLEAR
16. boldness	BOLD	41. hidden	HIDE	66. honest	HONEST
17. accidentally	ACCIDENT	42. countries	COUNTRY	67. backward	BACK
18. jewelry	JEWEL	43. graded	GRADE	68. following	FOLLOW
19. artist	ART	44. lucky	LUCK	69. secretly	SECRET
20. suddenly	SUDDEN	45. visitor	VISIT	70. nonsense	SENSE
21. latest	LATE	46. inches	INCH	71. magical	MAGIC
22. reordered	ORDER	47. modernize	MODERN	72. straighten	STRAIGHT
23. weight	WEIGH	48. selfish	SELF	73. whom	WHO
24. teacher	TEACH	49. shortage	SHORT	74. obedience	OBEY
25. reheat	HEAT	50. fifteen	FIVE	75. lower	LOW

B Which of the words are base words? Underline them.

1. words   wordy   <u>word</u>   wordless
2. <u>tell</u>   untold   told   telling
3. opening   <u>open</u>   reopen   opened
4. used   unused   reuse   <u>use</u>
5. homes   homely   <u>home</u>   homeward

6. <u>small</u>   smaller   smallest   smallness
7. farmer   farms   <u>farm</u>   farmland
8. renew   newer   newly   <u>new</u>
9. doing   <u>do</u>   done   does
10. <u>take</u>   mistake   taken   taking

Unit 115 cont'd

Derived Words

A derived word is a base word plus a prefix and/or a suffix.

EXAMPLES: *a. The base word "be" helps to make "being" and "been."*

b. The base word "work" helps to make "worker," "works," "worked," and "rework."

 At the beginning of each row is a base word.
Underline the derived words which have been
formed from that base word.

1. do (a) <u>doing</u> (b) <u>done</u> (c) doom (d) <u>does</u> (e) <u>did</u>
2. sit (a) <u>sat</u> (b) see (c) <u>sitting</u> (d) shall (e) <u>sits</u>
3. hurry (a) hurt (b) <u>hurried</u> (c) <u>hurriedly</u> (d) <u>hurries</u> (e) heart
4. leave (a) <u>left</u> (b) lease (c) leaf (d) <u>leaving</u> (e) <u>leaves</u>
5. safe (a) <u>unsafe</u> (b) <u>safer</u> (c) salve (d) <u>safely</u> (e) <u>safest</u>
6. night (a) knight (b) <u>nights</u> (c) <u>tonight</u> (d) <u>nightly</u> (e) not
7. please (a) peace (b) <u>pleasant</u> (c) <u>pleases</u> (d) plus (e) <u>pleased</u>
8. use (a) <u>reuse</u> (b) us (c) <u>useless</u> (d) unless (e) <u>uses</u>
9. own (a) on (b) <u>owner</u> (c) <u>owned</u> (d) <u>owns</u> (e) only
10. turn (a) <u>return</u> (b) <u>turning</u> (c) tune (d) <u>turned</u> (e) ton
11. wise (a) was (b) <u>wisdom</u> (c) <u>wisely</u> (d) wish (e) <u>wiser</u>
12. you (a) young (b) <u>your</u> (c) <u>yourself</u> (d) youth (e) <u>yours</u>
13. change (a) chance (b) chase (c) <u>changes</u> (d) exchange (e) <u>changing</u>
14. care (a) <u>careful</u> (b) <u>caring</u> (c) card (d) <u>uncaring</u> (e) car
15. gain (a) <u>regain</u> (b) <u>gained</u> (c) <u>gaining</u> (d) giant (e) general
16. collect (a) <u>recollect</u> (b) correct (c) collar (d) <u>collected</u> (e) <u>collects</u>
17. honest (a) <u>honestly</u> (b) honey (c) <u>dishonest</u> (d) home (e) hunt
18. spend (a) <u>spent</u> (b) <u>spending</u> (c) spin (d) <u>spends</u> (e) spun
19. visit (a) advise (b) <u>visitor</u> (c) <u>visited</u> (d) vice (e) <u>visits</u>
20. magic (a) <u>magical</u> (b) <u>magician</u> (c) made (d) make (e) <u>magically</u>
21. rain (a) <u>raining</u> (b) <u>rained</u> (c) reign (d) <u>rains</u> (e) rein
22. sleep (a) sheep (b) <u>asleep</u> (c) <u>sleeps</u> (d) sheet (e) <u>sleeping</u>
23. worth (a) <u>worthy</u> (b) word (c) <u>unworthy</u> (d) <u>worthless</u> (e) work
24. kind (a) kite (b) <u>unkind</u> (c) <u>kindly</u> (d) <u>kinder</u> (e) kin
25. pay (a) <u>repay</u> (b) <u>paid</u> (c) pale (d) <u>paying</u> (e) paper
26. build (a) <u>building</u> (b) big (c) <u>rebuild</u> (d) <u>builds</u> (e) <u>built</u>
27. act (a) <u>actor</u> (b) ask (c) apt (d) <u>acting</u> (e) <u>react</u>
28. friend (a) <u>friendly</u> (b) <u>unfriendly</u> (c) afraid (d) <u>friends</u> (e) free
29. write (a) right (b) <u>rewrite</u> (c) <u>written</u> (d) wrong (e) <u>writes</u>
30. long (a) <u>longer</u> (b) log (c) <u>longest</u> (d) lone (e) <u>longwise</u>

COMPOSITION EXERCISE

List three words made from each of these base words.

1. laugh   2. slow   3. read   4. move

_____   _____   _____   _____

_____   _____   _____   _____

_____   _____   _____   _____

Comprehension Check

Ⓐ Underline the compound words.

1. birthday
2. football
3. compound
4. sunburn
5. rosebush
6. alphabet
7. number
8. horsefly
9. necktie
10. contraction

11. toothbrush
12. suddenly
13. baseball
14. raincoat
15. sentence
16. anthill
17. bicycle
18. window
19. bloodhound
20. paragraph

21. deadline
22. bedroom
23. favorite
24. camera
25. following
26. bookworm
27. picture
28. shortstop
29. express
30. playground

Ⓑ Connect the words which could join together to make a compound word. Write the compound word.

1. rail — shine   *railroad*
2. sun — road   *sunshine*
3. hall — room   *hallway*
4. class — ache   *classroom*
5. tooth — way   *toothache*
6. cow — bell   *cowboy*
7. out — boy   *outfit*
8. door — fit   *doorbell*
9. over — ship   *overcoat*
10. steam — coat   *steamship*

11. finger — print   *fingerprint*
12. cat — sand   *catfish*
13. butter — fish   *buttermilk*
14. quick — milk   *quicksand*
15. bunk — ball   *bunkbed*
16. home — sick   *homesick*
17. soft — bed   *softball*
18. down — cake   *downtown*
19. blue — berry   *blueberry*
20. cup — town   *cupcake*

Ⓒ Complete each sentence with a plural form of the compound words in the box.

a. strawberry
b. driveway
c. sunflower
d. cookbook
e. watermelon
f. pancake
g. newspaper
h. sidewalk
i. footprint
j. wastebasket
k. mailbox
l. doorknob

1. We planted _____*sunflowers*_____ at the edge of the garden.
2. Cars blocked both _____*driveways*_____ .
3. I followed the _____*footprints*_____ in the sand.
4. How do you know when _____*watermelons*_____ are ripe?
5. Sylvia picked the _____*strawberries*_____ and I ate them.
6. Empty the _____*wastebaskets*_____ before you leave.
7. Delories collects _____*cookbooks*_____ from all over the world.
8. The _____*sidewalks*_____ were lined with toys.
9. Stephen delivers _____*newspapers*_____ after school.
10. Brass _____*doorknobs*_____ are pretty.
11. We had blueberry _____*pancakes*_____ for breakfast.
12. Someone had painted all the _____*mailboxes*_____ orange.

Test 23 cont'd

Comprehension Check (continued)

D **Write the contractions.**

1. I am   *I'm*
2. are not   *aren't*
3. he is   *he's*
4. is not   *isn't*
5. what is   *what's*

6. you are   *you're*
7. I have   *I've*
8. will not   *won't*
9. we will   *we'll*
10. did not   *didn't*

11. of the clock   *o'clock*
12. where is   *where's*
13. they are   *they're*
14. she had   *she'd*
15. we were   *we're*

E **Identify the base words.**

1. working   *work*
2. redo   *do*
3. enable   *able*
4. speaks   *speak*
5. untie   *tie*
6. rolled   *roll*
7. your   *you*
8. ending   *end*
9. quickly   *quick*
10. subway   *way*

11. careless   *care*
12. writes   *write*
13. lighten   *light*
14. watches   *watch*
15. hopeful   *hope*
16. teacher   *teach*
17. suddenly   *sudden*
18. interstate   *state*
19. outer   *out*
20. musical   *music*

21. sweetly   *sweet*
22. relive   *live*
23. nearest   *near*
24. non-smoker   *smoke*
25. incorrect   *correct*

F **Write a derived word for each base word listed below.**

1. word   *words*
2. friend   *friendly*
3. house   *housing*
4. ever   *never*
5. side   *sides*

6. read   *reading*
7. able   *unable*
8. tree   *trees*
9. do   *doer*
10. lift   *lifted*

11. look   *looks*
12. room   *roomy*
13. count   *counted*
14. add   *adding*
15. eat   *eaten*

Write a paragraph about your favorite place to live. Use at least two compound words.

_____
_____
_____
_____
_____
_____
_____
_____
_____
_____

Prefixes

Prefixes are letters added to the beginnings
of words. They have definite meanings and
change the meanings of the words they are
added to.

EXAMPLES: a. re — means again
"Regain" means "gain again."
b. mis — means wrong
"Mistake" means "to take wrong."

A Underline each correct meaning. Use your dictionary if necessary.

1. bi- (a. one b. two c. three)
2. ex- (a. out b. in c. between)
3. fore- (a. front b. back c. middle)
4. mis- (a. try b. right c. wrong)
5. non- (a. for b. not c. in)
6. ob- (a. for b. against c. with)
7. re- (a. once b. again c. now)
8. sub- (a. under b. over c. again)
9. trans- (a. up b. down c. across)
10. un- (a. for b. with c. not)
11. up- (a. up b. in c. down)
12. ab- (a. here b. away c. there)
13. circum- (a. up b. out c. around)
14. dia- (a. across b. in c. down)
15. en- (a. out b. with c. in)
16. in- (a. between b. in c. out)
17. inter- (a. between b. out c. with)
18. intra- (a. within b. out c. across)
19. para- (a. two b. in c. beside)
20. post- (a. now b. before c. after)
21. pre- (a. after b. before c. for)
22. tri- (a. one b. three c. six)
23. mono- (a. three b. two c. one)
24. pro- (a. forward b. back c. with)
25. super- (a. under b. over c. against)

B Add the prefix and write the new word.

1. bi + cycle =
2. ex + change =
3. fore + head =
4. mis + lead =
5. non + sense =
6. ob + long =
7. re + work =
8. sub + marine =
9. trans + port =
10. un + done =
11. up + grade =
12. ab + sent =
13. circum + stance =
14. dia + graph =
15. en + rich =
16. in + side =
17. inter + state =
18. intra + state =
19. para + mount =
20. post + pone =
21. pre + test =
22. tri + cycle =
23. mono + gram =
24. pro + file =
25. super + star =

bicycle
EXCHANGE
FOREHEAD
MISLEAD
NONSENSE
OBLONG
REWORK
SUBMARINE
TRANSPORT
UNDONE
UPGRADE
ABSENT
CIRCUMSTANCE
DIAGRAPH
ENRICH
INSIDE
INTERSTATE
INTRASTATE
PARAMOUNT
POSTPONE
PRETEST
TRICYCLE
MONOGRAM
PROFILE
SUPERSTAR

COMPOSITION EXERCISE

Write a word which begins with each prefix in part A.

1. _____   6. _____   11. _____   16. _____   21. _____
2. _____   7. _____   12. _____   17. _____   22. _____
3. _____   8. _____   13. _____   18. _____   23. _____
4. _____   9. _____   14. _____   19. _____   24. _____
5. _____   10. _____   15. _____   20. _____   25. _____

Unit 116 cont'd

Adding a Prefix

Prefixes are letters added to the beginnings of words. They have definite meanings and change the meanings of the words to which they are added.

EXAMPLES: a. non — → nonprofit   c. bi — → biweekly
              b. pro — → proceed   d. ex — → exit

A Match each prefix with its meaning.

_k_	1. re-	a.	well
L	2. con-	b.	within
M	3. ex-	c.	wrong
R	4. fore-	d.	inside
G	5. ab-	e.	two
T	6. pre-	f.	above
U	7. circum-	g.	away
E	8. bi-	h.	under
J	9. in-	i.	through
P	10. up-	j.	in
X	11. semi-	k.	again
D	12. intro-	l.	with
C	13. mis-	m.	out of
A	14. bene-	n.	opposite
W	15. trans-	o.	against
Q	16. en-	p.	up
V	17. inter-	q.	into
B	18. intra-	r.	front
N	19. dis-	s.	beside
O	20. ob-	t.	before
H	21. sub-	u.	around
I	22. dia-	v.	between
F	23. super-	w.	across
S	24. para-	x.	half

B The prefix is given for you. Complete each word.

1. She can re___*view*___ my work.
2. We formed a semi**CIRCLE**_____.
3. The show bene**FITS**_____ needy children.
4. I rode my bi**CYCLE**_____ to school.
5. Go out the ex**IT**_____ door.
6. Wes trans**FERRED**_____ to another school.
7. Joey and Chris are ab**SENT**_____.
8. Come in**SIDE**_____ and talk to me.
9. Draw a dia**GONAL**_____ line.
10. I ob**JECT**_____ to your plan.
11. A pre**FIX**_____ comes at the beginning.
12. The ship is a sub**MARINE**_____.
13. That would dis**COURAGE**_____ her.
14. Won't you intro**DUCE**_____ us?
15. What is the circum**FERENCE**_____?
16. The en**TRANCE**_____ is closed.
17. He is up**STAIRS**_____ in his room.
18. The cars are parked para**LLEL**_____.
19. Between states is inter**STATE**_____.
20. Within states is intra**STATE**_____.
21. He must be super**MAN**_____.
22. Read the con**CLUSION**_____ again.
23. The bill is a mis**TAKE**_____.
24. Dad rubbed his fore**HEAD**_____.

COMPOSITION EXERCISE

Write two words beginning with each of these prefixes.

1. re-

_____

2. non-

_____

3. bi-

_____

4. up-

_____

5. sub-

_____

6. super-

_____

7. pre-

_____

8. in-

_____

Adding Prefixes

Prefixes are letters added to the beginnings
of words. They have definite meanings and
change the meanings of the words to which
they are added.

EXAMPLES:
  a. to do again ⟶ redo
  b. above man ⟶ superman
  c. to take wrong ⟶ mistake
  d. three wheels ⟶ tricycle

  e. not conforming ⟶ nonconforming
  f. front of arm ⟶ forearm
  g. to be away ⟶ absent
  h. many people ⟶ multitude

 Study the following list of prefixes and their meanings.

a.	inter-	between	h.	fore-	front	o.	mis-	wrong
b.	re-	again	i.	trans-	across	p.	post-	after
c.	sub-	under	j.	pre-	before	q.	non-	not
d.	bi-	two	k.	super-	above	r.	com-	with
e.	semi-	half	l.	dis-	opposite	s.	tri-	three
f.	intra-	within	m.	anti-	against	t.	ex-	out of
g.	ab-	way	n.	multi-	many	u.	auto-	self

 Using the list of prefixes, write the word described by each definition.

1. half a circle — **semicircle**
2. front of head — **FOREHEAD**
3. within states — **INTRASTATE**
4. to work again — **REWORK**
5. opposite of agree — **DISAGREE**
6. across the Atlantic — **TRANSATLANTIC**
7. to come between — **INTERRUPT**
8. against rust — **ANTIRUST**
9. to contend with another — **COMPETE**
10. soil under the surface soil — **SUBSOIL**
11. many syllables — **MULTISYLLABLE**
12. not poisonous — **NONPOISONOUS**
13. three feet — **TRIPOD**
14. before school — **PRESCHOOL**
15. opposite of believer — **DISBELIEVER**
16. to pay before due — **PREPAY**
17. to mix with another — **COMBINE**
18. front of the deck — **FOREDECK**
19. against slavery — **ANTISLAVERY**
20. to build again — **REBUILD**

21. two wheels — **BICYCLE**
22. between states — **INTERSTATE**
23. underwater — **SUBMARINE**
24. before the war — **PREWAR**
25. against communism — **ANTICOMMUNISM**
26. to carry away wrongfully — **ABDUCT**
27. once in two months — **BIMONTHLY**
28. opposite of honor — **DISHONOR**
29. door leading out — **EXIT**
30. hero above all others — **SUPERHERO**
31. story about oneself — **AUTOBIOGRAPHY**
32. not having a profit — **NONPROFIT**
33. to lead wrong — **MISLEAD**
34. train under the ground — **SUBWAY**
35. three times a week — **TRIWEEKLY**
36. to spell wrong — **MISSPELL**
37. opposite of approve — **DISAPPROVE**
38. across the border — **TRANSBORDER**
39. to breathe out — **EXHALE**
40. half finished — **SEMIFINISHED**

Unit 117 cont'd

Verb Prefixes

Prefixes are letters added to the beginnings of words. Each prefix has a definite meaning and changes the meaning of the word to which it is added.

EXAMPLES: a. The teacher <u>dismissed</u> the class. c. You <u>delivered</u> the wrong package.
  b. John <u>confirmed</u> my suspicions. d. I must <u>return</u> the call immediately.

Many verbs begin with prefixes. The most common verb prefixes include "re," "dis," "con," "ex," and "de." Notice the meaning of each prefix.

re-	repeat, again	con-	with
dis-	away from	ex-	out of, formerly
de-	away, down		

✱ Complete each sentence by adding a prefix to the verb. Choose from those prefixes listed in the box.

1. You must _con_ trol your temper.
2. Janet _DE_ clined the invitation.
3. No one was _EX_ cused to go home.
4. Alex _DE_ voted his time to studying.
5. Dad finally _CON_ sented to let me go.
6. We _DIS_ cussed plans for the picnic.
7. The lawyer _DE_ fended his client.
8. Jason was _EX_ pelled from school.
9. Henry and I _EX_ changed gifts.
10. He is an _EX_ -president.
11. The country _EX_ ports rice and wheat.
12. The ghost _DIS_ appeared.
13. We were _DE_ layed at the airport.
14. The jewels were never _RE_ covered.
15. Why did you _DE_ ceive me?
16. She _DIS_ approves of my friends.
17. _RE_ count the money.
18. You'll _DIS_ turb the next class.
19. Would you _RE_ peat the statement?
20. The building was _CON_ demned.

21. The army was _DE_ feated.
22. _CON_ nect wire "A" with wire "B."
23. The acid _DIS_ solved the tablet.
24. _RE_ main calm in an emergency.
25. Pam _EX_ plained the problem.
26. Columbus _DIS_ covered America.
27. _CON_ sult a dictionary.
28. Adam _RE_ hearsed his part in the play.
29. I _DIS_ agree with you.
30. The train will _DE_ part at noon.
31. Allen _RE_ assured us.
32. The building was _DE_ molished.
33. Did you _RE_ place the light bulb?
34. The bomb _EX_ ploded.
35. The man was _CON_ fronted by reporters.
36. Did you _RE_ examine the contents?
37. I couldn't _RE_ member his name.
38. _CON_ tinue working on your assignment.
39. He _RE_ considered his opinion.
40. _RE_ write the sentence correctly.

COMPOSITION EXERCISE

Write four examples of verbs that use each of these prefixes.

1. re- _____ _____ _____
2. dis- _____ _____ _____
3. de- _____ _____ _____
4. con- _____ _____ _____
5. ex- _____ _____ _____

Suffixes

Suffixes are letters added to the ends of words. They have definite meanings and change the meanings of the words they are added to.

EXAMPLES: a. *-let means small*
  A "booklet" is a small book.
  b. *-ish means like*
  "Childish" means "like a child."

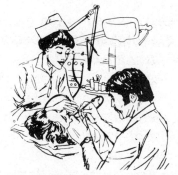

A Underline each correct meaning and put its letter in the blank. Use the dictionary if necessary.

_b_	1. -ful	(a. out of	b. full of	c. because of)
_A_	2. -hood	(a. state of being	b. without	c. period of time)
_C_	3. -yer	(a. because of	b. the middle of	c. person concerned with)
_A_	4. -ish	(a. like	b. to do without	c. to go beyond)
_C_	5. -ist	(a. state of being	b. against	c. person who)
_B_	6. -itis	(a. person	b. inflammation of	c. seek help)
_A_	7. -less	(a. without	b. along with	c. reason for)
_B_	8. -let	(a. large size	b. little	c. to allow)
_B_	9. -ness	(a. to build	b. state of being	c. person who)
_C_	10. -ous	(a. to do without	b. to include	c. full of)
_A_	11. -sect	(a. to cut	b. to divide in half	c. to make again)
_C_	12. -tion	(a. to go away	b. to understand	c. the act)
_B_	13. -cule	(a. part of	b. small	c. to separate equally)
_A_	14. -ward	(a. leading to	b. against	c. in front of)

B Add each prefix and write each new word.

1. play + ful =   *playful*
2. child + hood =   **CHILDHOOD**
3. law + yer =   **LAWYER**
4. green + ish =   **GREENISH**
5. appendix + itis =   **APPENDICITIS**
6. time + less =   **TIMELESS**
7. book + let =   **BOOKLET**
8. dark + ness =   **DARKNESS**
9. joy + ous =   **JOYOUS**
10. care + less =   **CARELESS**

11. act + tion =   **ACTION**
12. dread + ful =   **DREADFUL**
13. home + ward =   **HOMEWARD**
14. dent + ist =   **DENTIST**
15. sad + ness =   **SADNESS**
16. soft + er =   **SOFTER**
17. care + ful =   **CAREFUL**
18. busy + ness =   **BUSINESS**
19. adult + hood =   **ADULTHOOD**
20. price + less =   **PRICELESS**

COMPOSITION EXERCISE

Write two words using each suffix in part A.

1. _____ _____
2. _____ _____
3. _____ _____
4. _____ _____
5. _____ _____

6. _____ _____
7. _____ _____
8. _____ _____
9. _____ _____
10. _____ _____

11. _____ _____
12. _____ _____
13. _____ _____
14. _____ _____

Unit 118 cont'd

Adding Suffixes

Suffixes are letters added to the ends of words. They have definite meanings and change the meanings of the words to which they are added.

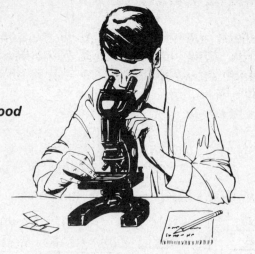

EXAMPLES:
a. *the condition of being a child* → *childhood*
b. *the state of being happy* → *happiness*
c. *act of doing work* → *working*
d. *full of joy* → *joyful*

 Study the following list of suffixes and their meanings.

a.	-hood	the condition of	h.	-ish	like	o.	-dom	the state of
b.	-cule	very small	i.	-ful	full of	p.	-er	more
c.	-ward	leading to	j.	-ness	state of being	q.	-ship	condition of
d.	-logy	study	k.	-yer	person who	r.	-est	most
e.	-scope	to see	l.	-itis	inflammation of	s.	-ic	resembling
f.	-gram	written	m.	-ous	full of	t.	-ing	act of doing
g.	-less	without	n.	-tion	the act of	u.	-ly	characteristic of

 Using the list of suffixes, write the word described by each definition.

1. the condition of being friends _friendship_
2. resembling an angel __ANGELIC__
3. without help __HELPLESS__
4. person who deals with the law __LAWYER__
5. used to see very small things __MICROSCOPE__
6. inflammation of tonsils __TONSILLITIS__
7. most green __GREENEST__
8. characteristic of a man __MANLY__
9. like a child __CHILDISH__
10. the act of acting __ACTION__
11. the condition of being adult __ADULTHOOD__
12. resembling a volcano __VOLCANIC__
13. more soft __SOFTER__
14. state of being sad __SADNESS__
15. leading to home __HOMEWARD__
16. very small animal __ANIMALCULE__
17. study of life __BIOLOGY__
18. state of being kind __KINDNESS__
19. more easy __EASIER__
20. without care __CARELESS__

21. leading back __BACKWARD__
22. characteristic of coward __COWARDLY__
23. used to see the stars __TELESCOPE__
24. message sent by telegraph __TELEGRAM__
25. inflammation of appendix __APPENDICITIS__
26. full of help __HELPFUL__
27. full of glory __GLORIOUS__
28. without fear __FEARLESS__
29. the state of being free __FREEDOM__
30. leading out __OUTWARD__
31. most sweet __SWEETEST__
32. characteristic of brave __BRAVELY__
33. without a penny __PENNILESS__
34. the state of being dark __DARKNESS__
35. full of glamor __GLAMOROUS__
36. like yellow __YELLOWISH__
37. characteristic of a ghost __GHOSTLY__
38. act of doing exercise __EXERCISING__
39. more late __LATER__
40. the act of protecting __PROTECTION__

Using Suffixes

Suffixes are letters added to the ends of words. They have definite meanings and change the meanings of the words to which they are added.

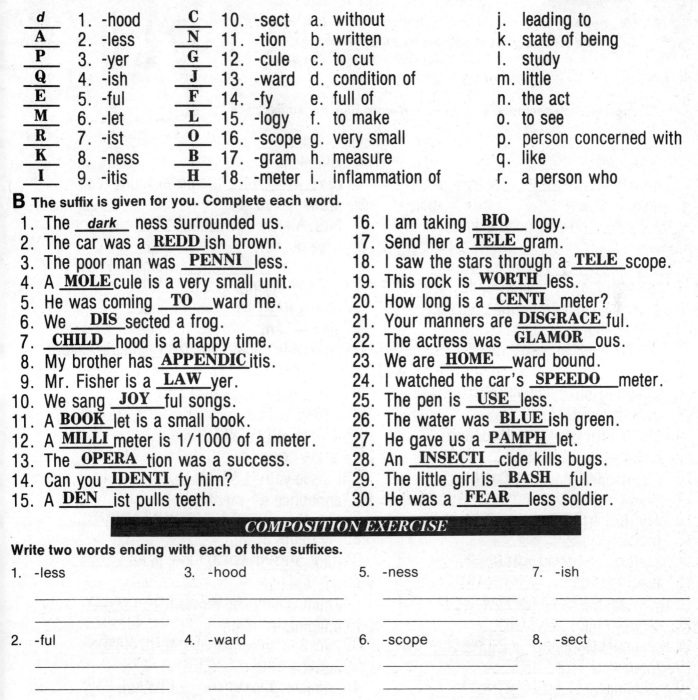

EXAMPLES: a. -ous   joyous   c. -less   hopeless
              b. -cide   homicide   d. -ness   greatness

A Match each suffix with its meaning.

_d_	1. -hood	_C_	10. -sect	a. without	j. leading to
_A_	2. -less	_N_	11. -tion	b. written	k. state of being
_P_	3. -yer	_G_	12. -cule	c. to cut	l. study
_Q_	4. -ish	_J_	13. -ward	d. condition of	m. little
_E_	5. -ful	_F_	14. -fy	e. full of	n. the act
_M_	6. -let	_L_	15. -logy	f. to make	o. to see
_R_	7. -ist	_O_	16. -scope	g. very small	p. person concerned with
_K_	8. -ness	_B_	17. -gram	h. measure	q. like
_I_	9. -itis	_H_	18. -meter	i. inflammation of	r. a person who

B The suffix is given for you. Complete each word.

1. The __dark__ ness surrounded us.
2. The car was a **REDD** ish brown.
3. The poor man was **PENNI** less.
4. A **MOLE** cule is a very small unit.
5. He was coming __TO__ ward me.
6. We __DIS__ sected a frog.
7. **CHILD** hood is a happy time.
8. My brother has **APPENDIC** itis.
9. Mr. Fisher is a **LAW** yer.
10. We sang **JOY** ful songs.
11. A **BOOK** let is a small book.
12. A **MILLI** meter is 1/1000 of a meter.
13. The **OPERA** tion was a success.
14. Can you **IDENTI** fy him?
15. A **DEN** ist pulls teeth.
16. I am taking **BIO** logy.
17. Send her a **TELE** gram.
18. I saw the stars through a **TELE** scope.
19. This rock is **WORTH** less.
20. How long is a **CENTI** meter?
21. Your manners are **DISGRACE** ful.
22. The actress was **GLAMOR** ous.
23. We are **HOME** ward bound.
24. I watched the car's **SPEEDO** meter.
25. The pen is **USE** less.
26. The water was **BLUE** ish green.
27. He gave us a **PAMPH** let.
28. An **INSECTI** cide kills bugs.
29. The little girl is **BASH** ful.
30. He was a **FEAR** less soldier.

COMPOSITION EXERCISE

Write two words ending with each of these suffixes.

1. -less

3. -hood

5. -ness

7. -ish

2. -ful

4. -ward

6. -scope

8. -sect

Unit 119 cont'd

Suffixes and the Final Silent "e"

*A suffix is added to the end of a word.
When a word ends in a silent "e," drop the "e" before adding a suffix that begins with a vowel.
When a word ends in a silent "e," keep the "e" before adding a suffix that begins with a consonant.*

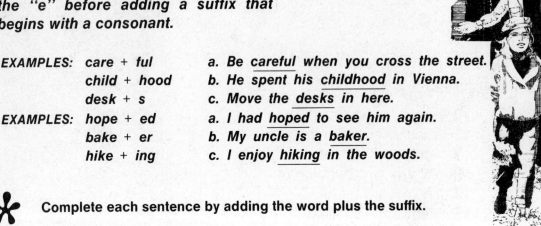

EXAMPLES: care + ful   a. Be <u>careful</u> when you cross the street.
          child + hood   b. He spent his <u>childhood</u> in Vienna.
          desk + s   c. Move the <u>desks</u> in here.

EXAMPLES: hope + ed   a. I had <u>hoped</u> to see him again.
          bake + er   b. My uncle is a <u>baker</u>.
          hike + ing   c. I enjoy <u>hiking</u> in the woods.

 Complete each sentence by adding the word plus the suffix.

1. use + less
   It would be _____ **useless** _____ to try again.
2. dance + ing
   DANCING _____ is very good exercise.
3. invite + ed
   Everyone is _____ **INVITED** _____ to attend.
4. write + er
   Hemingway is my favorite _____ **WRITER** _____ .
5. argue + ment
   Let's not have an **ARGUMENT** .
6. love + ly
   Everything looks _____ **LOVELY** _____ .
7. home + ward
   This plane is **HOMEWARD** bound.
8. escape + ed
   Two prisoners have _____ **ESCAPED** _____ .
9. office + s
   All of the _____ **OFFICES** _____ are locked.
10. value + able
    Diamonds are _____ **VALUABLE** _____ .
11. safe + ly
    The plane landed _____ **SAFELY** _____ .
12. peace + ful
    The winds were calm and _____ **PEACEFUL** _____ .
13. minute + s
    It will take only a few _____ **MINUTES** _____ .

14. joke + s
    His _____ **JOKES** _____ are never funny.
15. grade + ed
    Mrs. Morris has _____ **GRADED** _____ our papers.
16. wise + est
    She is the _____ **WISEST** _____ woman I know.
17. change + ing
    Stop **CHANGING** your mind.
18. hide + en
    The money was _____ **HIDDEN** _____ in the cave.
19. dive + er
    The _____ **DIVER** _____ hurt his hand.
20. believe + ed
    No one **BELIEVED** her.
21. late + er
    I'll see you _____ **LATER** _____ .
22. announce + ment
    Mr. Aldon has an **ANNOUNCEMENT** _____ .
23. persuade + ed
    Rick **PERSUADED** Ken to go.
24. polite + ly
    Thomas excused himself **POLITELY** .
25. imagine + ation
    Paul has an excellent **IMAGINATION** .
26. leave + ing
    Diane is **LEAVING** for Boston.

Suffixes and the Final "y"

A suffix is added to the end of a word.

When a word ends in a consonant plus "y," change the "y" to "i" before adding a suffix unless the suffix begins with "i."

EXAMPLES: a. *lazy + ly = lazily*   c. *busy + est = busiest*
 b. *identify + ed = identified*   d. *fry + ing = frying*

When a word ends in a vowel plus "y," keep the "y" and add the suffix.

EXAMPLES: a. *stay + ed = stayed*   c. *enjoy + ing = enjoying*
 b. *highway + s = highways*   d. *essay + s = essays*

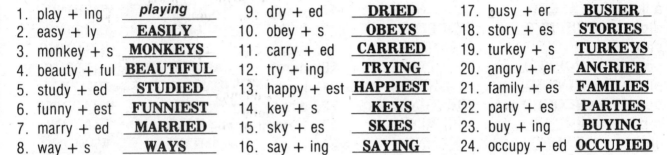

A Add each word and the suffix, and write the new word.

1. play + ing ___playing___
2. easy + ly ___EASILY___
3. monkey + s ___MONKEYS___
4. beauty + ful ___BEAUTIFUL___
5. study + ed ___STUDIED___
6. funny + est ___FUNNIEST___
7. marry + ed ___MARRIED___
8. way + s ___WAYS___

9. dry + ed ___DRIED___
10. obey + s ___OBEYS___
11. carry + ed ___CARRIED___
12. try + ing ___TRYING___
13. happy + est ___HAPPIEST___
14. key + s ___KEYS___
15. sky + es ___SKIES___
16. say + ing ___SAYING___

17. busy + er ___BUSIER___
18. story + es ___STORIES___
19. turkey + s ___TURKEYS___
20. angry + er ___ANGRIER___
21. family + es ___FAMILIES___
22. party + es ___PARTIES___
23. buy + ing ___BUYING___
24. occupy + ed ___OCCUPIED___

B Complete each sentence by adding the word plus the suffix in the parentheses.

1. (disobey + ed)
You have ___disobeyed___ my orders.
2. (dry + ing)
Brad is ___DRYING___ the dishes.
3. (study + ing)
We are ___STUDYING___ for our math test.
4. (lovely + er)
Today was ___LOVELIER___ than yesterday.
5. (delay + ed)
The train was ___DELAYED___ for two hours.
6. (hurry + ed)
Everyone ___HURRIED___ to see the ship.
7. (fry + ed)
Nick ordered ___FRIED___ fish.
8. (lazy + est)
Luther is the ___LAZIEST___ dog of all.

9. (silly + est)
That's the ___SILLIEST___ story I've ever heard.
10. (try + ed)
We ___TRIED___ to warn you.
11. (marry + ed)
My sister ___MARRIED___ an actor.
12. (cry + ing)
Why are you ___CRYING___?
13. (play + s)
Quincy ___PLAYS___ the piano.
14. (happy + er)
Steve has never looked ___HAPPIER___.
15. (penny + es)
I counted thirty-six ___PENNIES___.
16. (pretty + er)
Kelly is ___PRETTIER___ than Karen.

COMPOSITION EXERCISE

Write a sentence with each of these words.

(stopped) 1. _____
(sitting) 2. _____
(robbed) 3. _____
(jumped) 4. _____
(wished) 5. _____

(planned) 6. _____
(filling) 7. _____
(walked) 8. _____
(beginning) 9. _____
(watched) 10. _____

Unit 120 cont'd

Doubling Final Consonants

A suffix is added to the end of a word.

To add a suffix to a one-syllable word that ends in a single consonant after a single vowel, double the final consonant before adding a suffix that begins with a vowel.

EXAMPLES: a. *stop* + *ed* = *stopped*   d. *lock* + *ed* = *locked*

                b. *pick* + *ing* = *picking*   e. *shop* + *s* = *shops*

                c. *run* + *ing* = *running*   f. *hit* + *ing* = *hitting*

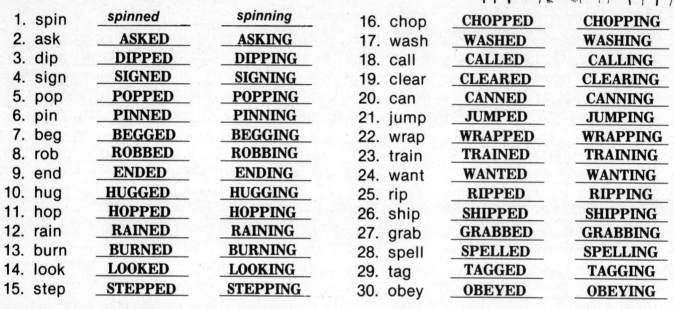

A Add "ed" and "ing" to each word.

1. spin	*spinned*	*spinning*	16. chop	CHOPPED	CHOPPING
2. ask	ASKED	ASKING	17. wash	WASHED	WASHING
3. dip	DIPPED	DIPPING	18. call	CALLED	CALLING
4. sign	SIGNED	SIGNING	19. clear	CLEARED	CLEARING
5. pop	POPPED	POPPING	20. can	CANNED	CANNING
6. pin	PINNED	PINNING	21. jump	JUMPED	JUMPING
7. beg	BEGGED	BEGGING	22. wrap	WRAPPED	WRAPPING
8. rob	ROBBED	ROBBING	23. train	TRAINED	TRAINING
9. end	ENDED	ENDING	24. want	WANTED	WANTING
10. hug	HUGGED	HUGGING	25. rip	RIPPED	RIPPING
11. hop	HOPPED	HOPPING	26. ship	SHIPPED	SHIPPING
12. rain	RAINED	RAINING	27. grab	GRABBED	GRABBING
13. burn	BURNED	BURNING	28. spell	SPELLED	SPELLING
14. look	LOOKED	LOOKING	29. tag	TAGGED	TAGGING
15. step	STEPPED	STEPPING	30. obey	OBEYED	OBEYING

B Complete each sentence by adding either "ed" or "ing" to the word in the parentheses.

(let) 1. You're *letting* him get away.

(trip) 2. I **TRIPPED** on the rug.

(begin) 3. It is **BEGINNING** to snow.

(work) 4. Ellen is **WORKING** on her paper.

(swim) 5. Fran is **SWIMMING** across the lake.

(wish) 6. Everyone **WISHED** them luck.

(map) 7. We **MAPPED** our course carefully.

(chip) 8. All the dishes were **CHIPPED**.

(learn) 9. I'm **LEARNING** French.

(push) 10. Who **PUSHED** the button?

(plan) 11. The class **PLANNED** the picnic.

(put) 12. He is **PUTTING** it in the garage.

(watch) 13. No one is **WATCHING** the game.

(rip) 14. You **RIPPED** my paper.

(eat) 15. I am **EATING** my lunch.

(flip) 16. We **FLIPPED** a coin.

(bet) 17. Ben is **BETTING** that we'll lose.

(regret) 18. He **REGRETTED** his decision.

(hum) 19. Carl was **HUMMING** a sad song.

(rub) 20. Ann was **RUBBING** her arm.

COMPOSITION EXERCISE

Write a sentence with each of these words.

(turkeys)   1. _____

(easily)   2. _____

(flies)   3. _____

(buying)   4. _____

(funnier)   5. _____

(obeyed)   6. _____

(busier)   7. _____

(prettiest)   8. _____

(days)   9. _____

(carried)   10. _____

Comprehension Check

(A) Underline the words that begin with prefixes. Identify the prefixes.

1. tricycle — _tri-_
2. walking — ____
3. upset — _up-_
4. biweekly — _bi-_
5. uses — ____
6. distrust — _dis-_
7. listens — ____
8. review — _re-_
9. foreclose — _fore-_
10. submarine — _sub-_
11. mislead — _mis-_
12. wishful — ____
13. absent — _ab-_
14. transfer — _trans-_
15. smoker — ____
16. co-worker — _co-_
17. counted — ____
18. enable — _en-_
19. wisest — ____
20. unlock — _un-_

(B) Underline the words that end with suffixes. Identify the suffixes.

1. looked — _-ed_
2. talking — _-ing_
3. exit — ____
4. childhood — _-hood_
5. untie — ____
6. highest — _-est_
7. homeward — _-ward_
8. reporter — _-er_
9. postwar — ____
10. joyful — _-ful_
11. careless — _-less_
12. superman — ____
13. booklet — _-let_
14. weekly — _-ly_
15. enclose — ____
16. dentist — _-ist_
17. recall — ____
18. closer — _-er_
19. student — _-ent_
20. weakness — _-ness_

(C) Add the prefix or suffix to the word and write the new word.

1. friend + -ship — _friendship_
2. trust + -ing — _trusting_
3. need + -y — _needy_
4. state + intra- — _intrastate_
5. day + -ly — _daily_
6. part + de- — _depart_
7. home + -less — _homeless_
8. smart + -er — _smarter_
9. heat + re- — _reheat_
10. rich + -est — _richest_
11. govern + -ment — _government_
12. war + anti- — _antiwar_
13. shy + -ly — _shyly_
14. needle + -s — _needles_
15. reason + -able — _reasonable_
16. close + en- — _enclose_
17. to + -ward — _toward_
18. grade + up- — _upgrade_
19. perfect + -ion — _perfection_
20. act + -ive — _active_

(D) Complete each sentence with a word that contains the prefix or suffix in the parentheses.

(-ish) 1. George acted very _childish_ .
(-less) 2. There are _countless_ stars in the sky.
(-ly) 3. Everyone was very _friendly_ .
(re-) 4. Let me _review_ the problem.
(-ing) 5. My brother is _playing_ golf.
(un-) 6. I _unfolded_ the letter carefully.
(-let) 7. Read this _pamphlet_ on drugs.
(ante-) 8. We are studying _antewar_ Europe.
(-ness) 9. _Darkness_ covered the land.
(-s) 10. All the _stores_ open at noon.

(mis-) 11. You made only one _mistake_ .
(bi-) 12. The magazine is published _bimonthly_ .
(-ed) 13. She _cooked_ homemade spaghetti.
(-es) 14. I packed seven _boxes_ of books.
(super-) 15. The monster had _superhuman_ strength.
(non-) 16. My parents are _non-smokers_ .
(up-) 17. Kim _updated_ his report.
(dis-) 18. He _disapproves_ of my plan.
(-er) 19. Twain was a famous _writer_ .
(-ward) 20. We headed _homeward_ .

Test 24 cont'd

Comprehension Check (continued)

E Match the prefix or suffix with its definition.

_g_ 1. bi-   _f_ 11. -er   f. suffix meaning "more" or "a person"
_j_ 2. un-   _k_ 12. -ish   g. prefix meaning "two"
_o_ 3. re-   _d_ 13. -est   h. suffix meaning "cause to be"
_c_ 4. pre-   _n_ 14. -hood   i. prefix meaning "not"
_h_ 5. -en   _a_ 15. fore-   j. prefix meaning "opposite of"
_m_ 6. sub-   k. suffix meaning "like"
_b_ 7. -less   a. prefix meaning "front"   l. prefix meaning "half"
_l_ 8. semi-   b. suffix meaning "without"   m. prefix meaning "under"
_i_ 9. dis-   c. prefix meaning "before"   n. suffix meaning "state of being"
_e_ 10. -ful   d. suffix meaning "most"   o. prefix meaning "again"
                 e. suffix meaning "full of"

F How does the prefix or suffix affect the meaning of each word?

1. penniless   *"-less" means "without" "Penniless" means "without a penny."*
2. lighten   *"-en" means "cause to be" "Lighten" means "cause to be light."*
3. rewrite   *"re-" means "again" "Rewrite" means "to write again."*
4. teacher   *"-er" means "a person" "Teacher" means "a person who teaches."*
5. semicircle   *"semi-" means "half" "Semicircle" means "half a circle."*
6. uncover   *"un-" means "opposite of" "Uncover" means "opposite of cover."*
7. sweetest   *"-est" means "most" "Sweetest" means "most sweet."*
8. subway   *"sub-" means "under" "Subway" means "way under ground."*
9. adulthood   *"-hood" means "state of being" "Adulthood" means "state of being an adult."*
10. bicycle   *"bi-" means "two" "Bicycle" means "cycle with two wheels."*
11. forehead   *"fore-" means "front" "Forehead" means "front of the head."*
12. helpful   *"-ful" means "full of" "Helpful" means "full of help."*
13. preview   *"pre-" means "before" "Preview" means "to view before."*
14. dislike   *"dis-" means "not" "Dislike" means "to not like."*
15. childish   *"-ish" means "like" "Childish" means "like a child."*

Write a paragraph about the importance or unimportance of school. Underline all words which contain prefixes or suffixes.

_____
_____
_____
_____
_____
_____
_____

Guide Words

At the top of each page in a dictionary are the guide words.
The guide words name the first and last entry words found
on that particular page of the dictionary.

Read the following sets of guide words. Then write the page
number on which each of the following words would be found.

bird	15	blame

blank	16	block

blond	17	board

boast	18	booth

border	19	boundary

bow	20	breed

breeze	21	broil

brown	22	brute

15	1. birth	18	26. boat	15	51. birthday
17	2. blush	16	27. blemish	21	52. brick
22	3. brutal	15	28. blame	20	53. bread
18	4. boil	16	29. blister	17	54. blow
16	5. blaze	20	30. brain	21	55. brim
20	6. branch	15	31. black	17	56. blot
16	7. blend	19	32. bounce	20	57. box
21	8. bridge	16	33. bleed	15	58. bit
16	9. blink	16	34. blest	21	59. bring
19	10. borrow	15	35. bitter	18	60. body
19	11. bough	15	36. bishop	19	61. bore
17	12. blue	16	37. bless	21	62. bride
15	13. bison	16	38. blank	18	63. bolt
18	14. boot	18	39. bone	17	64. blouse
21	15. brief	15	40. bird	17	65. board
20	16. brass	16	41. bleak	21	66. brew
15	17. bite	16	42. blast	15	67. blade
18	18. bonnet	20	43. break	16	68. block
22	19. brute	17	44. blond	17	69. blur
19	20. born	19	45. boundary	20	70. bowl
16	21. blanket	16	46. blind	19	71. bound
17	22. bloom	20	47. bow	17	72. blunt
21	23. bright	20	48. breed	18	73. boast
21	24. breeze	19	49. bother	19	74. bossy
20	25. breath	18	50. booklet	18	75. boost

18	76. book
19	77. bottom
22	78. brush
19	79. both
22	80. brown
16	81. bleach
21	82. broad
20	83. brake
18	84. booth
20	85. boy
18	86. bomb
22	87. bruise
21	88. broil
19	89. boss
19	90. border
20	91. brand
17	92. bluff
17	93. blood
19	94. bottle
20	95. brave
18	96. bold
18	97. boom
17	98. blunder
18	99. bond
17	100. boar

Unit 121 cont'd

Respellings

In a dictionary the respelling shows how
to pronounce a word.

EXAMPLES:
 a. chēz   cheese
 b. hid ′ ən   hidden
 c. chānj   change

 Write the word for each respelling.

1. pub′lik   *public*
2. kwī′ət   QUIET
3. kroud   CROWD
4. en′i   ANY
5. puz′əl   PUZZLE
6. yung   YOUNG
7. pē an′ō   PIANO
8. sāf   SAFE
9. ī′lənd   ISLAND
10. nē′dəl   NEEDLE
11. di sīd′   DECIDE
12. kwēn   QUEEN
13. lim′it   LIMIT
14. rông   WRONG
15. koun′tē   COUNTY
16. sē′krit   SECRET
17. kich′ən   KITCHEN
18. mach   MATCH
19. ī′təm   ITEM
20. plā   PLAY
21. ə grē′   AGREE
22. kuz′ən   COUSIN
23. fā′vər   FAVOR
24. noun   NOUN
25. pō′it   POET
26. gras   GRASS
27. lōf   LOAF
28. myül   MULE
29. tun′əl   TUNNEL
30. sum′ər   SUMMER
31. welth   WEALTH
32. yü′nit   UNIT
33. wėrld   WORLD

34. un′yən   ONION
35. prə tekt′   PROTECT
36. skärf   SCARF
37. flou′ər   FLOWER
38. tou′əl   TOWEL
39. ug′lē   UGLY
40. wô′tər   WATER
41. pō′əm   POEM
42. ə lou′   ALLOW
43. bā′ker   BAKER
44. kloz′it   CLOSET
45. en′ə mē   ENEMY
46. froun   FROWN
47. hir′ō   HERO
48. jü′əl   JEWEL
49. gärd   GUARD
50. jī′ənt   GIANT
51. grō   GROW
52. in vent ′   INVENT
53. man′ər   MANNER
54. ə līv′   ALIVE
55. kab′ən   CABIN
56. dif′ər   DIFFER
57. jen′təl   GENTLE
58. pub′lish   PUBLISH
59. līt   LIGHT
60. fing′gər   FINGER
61. jump   JUMP
62. nā′tiv   NATIVE
63. prob′ləm   PROBLEM
64. ri zult′   RESULT
65. sīn   SIGN
66. tėrn   TURN

67. in vīt′   INVITE
68. mes′ij   MESSAGE
69. lō′kāt   LOCATE
70. mer′ē   MERRY
71. pärt′nər   PARTNER
72. ôr′chərd   ORCHARD
73. nā′chər   NATURE
74. prīz   PRIZE
75. risk   RISK
76. tik′əl   TICKLE
77. hwis′əl   WHISTLE
78. wiz′dəm   WISDOM
79. dich   DITCH
80. ē′gər   EAGER
81. fif′tē   FIFTY
82. gōl′dən   GOLDEN
83. hel′mit   HELMET
84. lā′bər   LABOR
85. kou′boi   COWBOY
86. chüz   CHOOSE
87. kan′yən   CANYON
88. ek′ō   ECHO
89. frō′zən   FROZEN
90. hun′drəd   HUNDRED
91. nīt   NIGHT
92. juj   JUDGE
93. prom′is   PROMISE
94. rī′fəl   RIFLE
95. on′ər   HONOR
96. man′ij   MANAGE
97. plan′it   PLANET
98. snēk   SNEAK
99. sē′zən   SEASON
100. wôl′nut   WALNUT

The Schwa Sound

The schwa (ə) is used to mark a soft vowel sound. The schwa sound occurs in an unstressed syllable.

EXAMPLES: a. mezh′ ər   measure   c. ā′ bəl   able
          b. par′ ə graf   paragraph   d. ə frād′   afraid

 Each respelling contains a schwa sound. Rewrite the word described by the respelling.

1.	sėr′tən li	_certainly_	31.	lem′ən	LEMON	61.	kə när′i	CANARY
2.	ə kount′	ACCOUNT	32.	mə shēn	MACHINE	62.	en′ər jē	ENERGY
3.	pas′ən jər	PASSENGER	33.	ə dapt′	ADAPT	63.	kol′ə ni	COLONY
4.	kwī′et	QUIET	34.	un′yən	ONION	64.	ə dorn′	ADORN
5.	jī′ent	GIANT	35.	sə plī′	SUPPLY	65.	pə rād′	PARADE
6.	en′jən	ENGINE	36.	pāv′mənt	PAVEMENT	66.	sī′ləns	SILENCE
7.	his′tə ri	HISTORY	37.	ə genst′	AGAINST	67.	priz′ən	PRISON
8.	kəm plēt′	COMPLETE	38.	uv′ən	OVEN	68.	sə pōz′	SUPPOSE
9.	ə buv′	ABOVE	39.	pe tā′tō	POTATO	69.	wel′kəm	WELCOME
10.	al′fə bet	ALPHABET	40.	də rekt′	DIRECT	70.	sē′zən	SEASON
11.	tel′ə fōn	TELEPHONE	41.	el′ə fənt	ELEPHANT	71.	kum′pə nē	COMPANY
12.	hol′ə dā	HOLIDAY	42.	fash′ən	FASHION	72.	an′sər	ANSWER
13.	ə grē	AGREE	43.	prod′əkt	PRODUCT	73.	prob′lem	PROBLEM
14.	frīt′ən	FRIGHTEN	44.	ə līv′	ALIVE	74.	strān′jər	STRANGER
15.	lōn′səm	LONESOME	45.	thou′zənd	THOUSAND	75.	sər prīz′	SURPRISE
16.	dis′tənt	DISTANT	46.	kab′ən	CABIN	76.	bot′əm	BOTTOM
17.	pō′əm	POEM	47.	rot′ən	ROTTEN	77.	ə lou′	ALLOW
18.	sel′dəm	SELDOM	48.	lis′ən	LISTEN	78.	frō′zən	FROZEN
19.	pər haps′	PERHAPS	49.	ī′lənd	ISLAND	79.	prə vīd′	PROVIDE
20.	hī′fən	HYPHEN	50.	bās′mənt	BASEMENT	80.	sud′ən	SUDDEN
21.	bā′kən	BACON	51.	kə lekt′	COLLECT	81.	sen′təns	SENTENCE
22.	dol′ər	DOLLAR	52.	gōl′dən	GOLDEN	82.	yü′nyən	UNION
23.	ā′prən	APRON	53.	sil′vər	SILVER	83.	tə môr′ō	TOMORROW
24.	lī′ən	LION	54.	sit′ə zən	CITIZEN	84.	rē′əl	REAL
25.	trav′əl	TRAVEL	55.	ə rīv′	ARRIVE	85.	moun′tən	MOUNTAIN
26.	bil′yən	BILLION	56.	kich′ən	KITCHEN	86.	ter′ə bəl	TERRIBLE
27.	ō′shən	OCEAN	57.	wiz′dəm	WISDOM	87.	ə rith′mə tik	ARITHMETIC
28.	sig′nəl	SIGNAL	58.	kot′ən	COTTON	88.	ə hwīl′	AWHILE
29.	ə krôs′	ACROSS	59.	mul′tə plī	MULTIPLY	89.	vā kā′shən	VACATION
30.	jung′gəl	JUNGLE	60.	sev′ən tē	SEVENTY	90.	wėr′kə bəl	WORKABLE

Unit 122 cont'd →

The "əl" Sound

Look at the words "turtle," "camel," and "total." All three words end with the "əl" sound, but the end of each word is spelled differently. There is no rule to help you spell words with the "əl" sound. You must remember how each word is spelled.

EXAMPLES:
a. candle   c. metal   e. final
b. tickle   d. bushel   f. pickle

 Complete the spelling of each word by adding "le," "el," or "al." Each word ends with the "əl" sound.

1. troub **le**
2. gener **AL**
3. simp **LE**
4. hospit **AL**
5. magic **AL**
6. flexib **LE**
7. cab **LE**
8. batt **LE**
9. freck **LE**
10. speci **AL**
11. bott **LE**
12. ridd **LE**
13. funn **EL**
14. need **LE**
15. sprink **LE**
16. loc **AL**
17. ratt **LE**
18. fab **LE**
19. purp **LE**
20. grav **EL**
21. capit **AL**
22. horrib **LE**
23. squirr **EL**
24. peop **LE**
25. equ **AL**

26. post **AL**
27. eag **LE**
28. kett **LE**
29. jew **EL**
30. norm **AL**
31. enjoyab **LE**
32. obstac **LE**
33. anim **AL**
34. ang **EL**
35. samp **LE**
36. sing **LE**
37. sadd **LE**
38. vess **EL**
39. loy **AL**
40. ment **AL**
41. kenn **EL**
42. stab **LE**
43. babb **LE**
44. mort **AL**
45. centr **AL**
46. princip **AL**
47. plur **AL**
48. musc **LE**
49. coup **LE**
50. shov **EL**

51. humb **LE**
52. tab **LE**
53. vow **EL**
54. possib **LE**
55. med **AL**
56. brut **AL**
57. interv **AL**
58. app **LE**
59. nov **EL**
60. tremb **LE**
61. mod **EL**
62. puzz **LE**
63. ank **LE**
64. barr **EL**
65. chann **EL**
66. music **AL**
67. smugg **LE**
68. map **LE**
69. wrigg **LE**
70. trav **EL**
71. carniv **AL**
72. fragi **LE**
73. beag **LE**
74. movab **LE**
75. pan **EL**

76. tunn **EL**
77. festiv **AL**
78. examp **LE**
79. doub **LE**
80. ped **AL**
81. cru **EL**
82. catt **LE**
83. pudd **LE**
84. hand **LE**
85. jung **LE**
86. rif **LE**
87. strugg **LE**
88. gent **LE**
89. crumb **LE**
90. cobb **LE**
91. amp **LE**
92. gridd **LE**
93. marb **LE**
94. punctu **AL**
95. sand **AL**
96. numer **AL**
97. rur **AL**
98. usu **AL**
99. grumb **LE**
100. tow **EL**

The "ər" Sound

Look at the words "offer," "doctor," and "burglar." All three words end with the "ər" sound, but the end of each word is spelled differently. There is no rule to help you spell words with the "ər" sound. You must remember how each word is spelled.

EXAMPLES: a. labor c. forever e. grammar
b. error d. differ f. father

* Complete the spelling of each word by adding "er," "or," or "ar." Each word ends with the "ər" sound.

1. deliv_er_
2. dang_ER_
3. cov_ER_
4. riv_ER_
5. rememb_ER_
6. moth_ER_
7. transf_ER_
8. mirr_OR_
9. fav_OR_
10. thund_ER_
11. bett_ER_
12. weath_ER_
13. maj_OR_
14. sweat_ER_
15. und_ER_
16. lumb_ER_
17. murd_ER_
18. spons_OR_
19. radiat_OR_
20. messeng_ER_
21. irregul_AR_
22. easi_ER_
23. wat_ER_
24. pol_AR_
25. rad_AR_

26. hum_OR_
27. daught_ER_
28. eith_ER_
29. barb_ER_
30. nect_AR_
31. numb_ER_
32. laught_ER_
33. own_ER_
34. slend_ER_
35. rum_OR_
36. timb_ER_
37. whisp_ER_
38. col_OR_
39. lawy_ER_
40. neith_ER_
41. silv_ER_
42. debt_OR_
43. sculpt_OR_
44. emper_OR_
45. ancest_OR_
46. caterpill_AR_
47. lett_ER_
48. prosp_ER_
49. charact_ER_
50. count_ER_

51. cent_ER_
52. cell_AR_
53. broth_ER_
54. newspap_ER_
55. aft_ER_
56. flav_OR_
57. should_ER_
58. flow_ER_
59. copp_ER_
60. disast_ER_
61. act_OR_
62. schol_AR_
63. neighb_OR_
64. fing_ER_
65. oth_ER_
66. butch_ER_
67. answ_ER_
68. plund_ER_
69. cucumb_ER_
70. edit_OR_
71. togeth_ER_
72. sist_ER_
73. wint_ER_
74. ref_ER_
75. reconsid_ER_

76. regul_AR_
77. mot_OR_
78. coll_AR_
79. ord_ER_
80. ang_ER_
81. terr_OR_
82. liv_ER_
83. bewild_ER_
84. passeng_ER_
85. prop_ER_
86. paint_ER_
87. od_OR_
88. min_ER_
89. surrend_ER_
90. sug_AR_
91. val_OR_
92. ov_ER_
93. clatt_ER_
94. calend_AR_
95. wherev_ER_
96. singul_AR_
97. teach_ER_
98. summ_ER_
99. burg_ER_
100. vap_OR_

Unit 123 cont'd

Counting Syllables

Each sound in a word is called a syllable.

EXAMPLES:

one syllable	two syllables	three or more syllables
a. juice	a. pencil	a. exercise
b. bowl	b. honest	b. deliver
c. friend	c. baseball	c. bicycle
d. class	d. homework	d. information

A Count the number of syllables in each word. Write the number in the blank.

2	1. practice	2	26. machine	2	51. vacant	1	76. quit
3	2. understand	3	27. opinion	3	52. possible	2	77. modern
1	3. wrong	3	28. forever	2	53. breakfast	2	78. although
2	4. advice	3	29. idea	2	54. battle	4	79. education
1	5. rush	3	30. protection	1	55. smart	2	80. visit
3	6. suddenly	3	31. submarine	1	56. thought	3	81. terrible
2	7. himself	1	32. straight	2	57. attempt	2	82. city
3	8. piano	2	33. magic	4	58. community	1	83. sky
2	9. fortune	2	34. circle	2	59. perhaps	2	84. science
2	10. complete	3	35. adventure	4	60. dictionary	3	85. capital
2	11. visit	2	36. somewhere	1	61. prize	2	86. rather
1	12. change	2	37. dessert	3	62. holiday	1	87. joke
3	13. finally	2	38. giant	2	63. postpone	3	88. ambition
3	14. discourage	1	39. zone	2	64. forbid	2	89. prosper
3	15. difficult	1	40. phase	2	65. anxious	1	90. grief
3	16. accomplish	2	41. carefree	3	66. bewilder	3	91. ignorance
2	17. fragile	3	42. estimate	2	67. distinct	3	92. parachute
3	18. obstacle	3	43. occupy	2	68. suggest	1	93. globe
1	19. grade	2	44. equip	2	69. combine	1	94. sun
3	20. hesitate	3	45. skeleton	2	70. balance	1	95. truth
3	21. radio	2	46. foreign	2	71. precise	3	96. surrender
2	22. effort	3	47. almanac	2	72. budget	3	97. furious
1	23. bleach	1	48. safe	2	73. seven	2	98. enjoy
2	24. confuse	2	49. notice	2	74. dozen	2	99. center
2	25. although	2	50. without	1	75. weigh	3	100. together

B Underline the one-syllable words.

1. folks
2. cabin
3. guest
4. among
5. cause
6. escape
7. through
8. lawn
9. quiet
10. shape
11. trouble
12. night
13. voice
14. melted
15. young
16. secret
17. match
18. snow
19. piano
20. dream
21. peace
22. none
23. strange
24. causes

Dividing Words into Syllables

Each sound within a word is called a syllable.

EXAMPLES: a. *captain*   **cap tain**   c. *journey*   **jour ney**
                  b. *deadline*   **dead line**   d. *hospital*   **hos pi tal**

A Divide each word into syllables.

1. hungry — *hun gry*	21. itself — **IT SELF**	41. forward — **FOR WARD**
2. excuse — **EX CUSE**	22. greedy — **GREED Y**	42. collect — **COL LECT**
3. became — **BE CAME**	23. newspaper — **NEWS PA PER**	43. tomato — **TO MA TO**
4. tunnel — **TUN NEL**	24. pleasant — **PLEAS ANT**	44. useful — **USE FUL**
5. vacation — **VA CA TION**	25. protection — **PRO TEC TION**	45. mistake — **MIS TAKE**
6. straight — **STRAIGHT**	26. market — **MAR KET**	46. outline — **OUT LINE**
7. nonsense — **NON SENSE**	27. seldom — **SEL DOM**	47. question — **QUES TION**
8. telephone — **TE LE PHONE**	28. remember — **RE MEM BER**	48. laugh — **LAUGH**
9. wisdom — **WIS DOM**	29. zoo — **ZOO**	49. practice — **PRAC TICE**
10. guide — **GUIDE**	30. sorrow — **SOR ROW**	50. wonderful — **WON DER FUL**
11. promise — **PRO MISE**	31. umbrella — **UM BREL LA**	51. normal — **NOR MAL**
12. separate — **SEP A RATE**	32. difficult — **DIF FI CULT**	52. change — **CHANGE**
13. angry — **AN GRY**	33. enormous — **E NOR MOUS**	53. key — **KEY**
14. freedom — **FREE DOM**	34. idea — **I DE A**	54. easy — **EAS Y**
15. adventure — **AD VEN TURE**	35. daughter — **DAUGH TER**	55. habit — **HAB IT**
16. crowd — **CROWD**	36. welcome — **WEL COME**	56. surprise — **SUR PRISE**
17. return — **RE TURN**	37. opinion — **O PIN ION**	57. reason — **REA SON**
18. important — **IM POR TANT**	38. accident — **AC CI DENT**	58. island — **IS LAND**
19. forget — **FOR GET**	39. decide — **DE CIDE**	59. hurry — **HUR RY**
20. ghost — **GHOST**	40. signature — **SIG NA TURE**	60. ocean — **O CEAN**

An open syllable is one ending in a vowel.

A closed syllable is one ending in a consonant.

EXAMPLES: open   closed
                   a. si lent   a. es cape
                   b. fa mous   b. lead ing
                   c. ru in   c. hap py
                   d. su per   d. in side

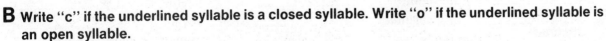

B Write "c" if the underlined syllable is a closed syllable. Write "o" if the underlined syllable is an open syllable.

c 1. o <u>pen</u>	C 7. <u>fun</u> nel	C 13. <u>of</u> fice	O 19. <u>he</u> ro
O 2. <u>dai</u> ly	O 8. <u>pro</u> tect	C 14. <u>list</u>	C 20. sud <u>den</u>
C 3. air <u>port</u>	O 9. <u>no</u> where	C 15. <u>ab</u> sent	C 21. ex <u>plain</u>
C 4. <u>own</u> er	C 10. <u>test</u>	C 16. <u>con</u> test	O 22. i <u>de</u> a
O 5. <u>re</u> main	C 11. <u>plen</u> ty	O 17. <u>a</u> part	O 23. <u>mu</u> sic
O 6. <u>rea</u> son	C 12. <u>sun</u> shine	C 18. <u>ham</u> mer	C 24. <u>grab</u>

Unit 124 cont'd

The Accented Syllable

A word that has two or more syllables usually has one syllable which is said harder than the other(s). To show which syllable is said hardest, write an accent mark (′).

EXAMPLES:
   a. person   per ′ son   d. famous   fa ′ mous
   b. became   be ′ came   e. adventure ad ven ′ ture
   c. journey   jour ′ ney   f. vacation   va ca ′ tion

 Divide each word into syllables. Then place an accent mark over the syllable that is said harder than the other(s).

#	Word	Answer		#	Word	Answer		#	Word	Answer
1.	return	re turn′		34.	office	of′fice		67.	understand	un der stand′
2.	question	ques′tion		35.	useful	use′ful		68.	reason	rea′son
3.	lonely	lone′ly		36.	practice	prac′tice		69.	vacant	va′cant
4.	machine	ma chine′		37.	hurry	hur′ry		70.	forever	for ev′er
5.	freedom	free′dom		38.	itself	it self′		71.	angry	an′gry
6.	follow	fol′low		39.	welcome	wel′come		72.	nobody	no′bod y
7.	wisdom	wis′dom		40.	surprise	sur prise′		73.	tomato	to ma′to
8.	opinion	o pin′ion		41.	mistake	mis take′		74.	hungry	hun′gry
9.	excuse	ex cuse′		42.	defend	de fend′		75.	valley	val′ley
10.	blanket	blan′ket		43.	absent	ab′sent		76.	center	cen′ter
11.	daughter	daugh′ter		44.	remember	re mem′ber		77.	ticket	tic′ket
12.	perhaps	per haps′		45.	outline	out′line		78.	umbrella	um brel′la
13.	license	li′cense		46.	minute	min′ute		79.	nonsense	non′sense
14.	selfish	self′ish		47.	number	num′ber		80.	zero	ze′ro
15.	plastic	plas′tic		48.	notebook	note′book		81.	although	al though′
16.	history	his′to ry		49.	final	fi′nal		82.	deliver	de liv′er
17.	difficult	dif′fi cult		50.	captain	cap′tain		83.	inform	in form′
18.	danger	dan′ger		51.	ambition	am bi′tion		84.	adult	a dult′
19.	rejoice	re joice′		52.	budget	bud′get		85.	signal	sig′nal
20.	ignore	ig nore′		53.	transfer	trans′fer		86.	nectar	nec′tar
21.	deadline	dead′line		54.	simple	sim′ple		87.	ruthless	ruth′less
22.	balance	bal′ance		55.	delay	de lay′		88.	suggest	sug gest′
23.	almanac	al′ma nac		56.	bashful	bash′ful		89.	bicycle	bi′cy cle
24.	missing	miss′ing		57.	enormous	e nor′mous		90.	stupid	stu′pid
25.	correct	cor rect′		58.	intern	in′tern		91.	talent	ta′lent
26.	approve	ap prove′		59.	splendid	splen′did		92.	voyage	voy′age
27.	pretend	pre tend′		60.	awkward	awk′ward		93.	dungeon	dun′geon
28.	pencil	pen′cil		61.	measure	mea′sure		94.	ashamed	a shamed′
29.	important	im por′tant		62.	mermaid	mer′maid		95.	nightmare	night′mare
30.	sentence	sen′tence		63.	disgraceful	dis grace′ful		96.	obey	o bey′
31.	liberty	lib′er ty		64.	because	be cause′		97.	rumble	rum′ble
32.	garden	gar′den		65.	statement	state′ment		98.	suffer	suf′fer
33.	alphabet	al′pha bet		66.	better	bet′ter		99.	surround	sur round′

Silent Letters

*Silent letters are written but not spoken. The following rules
frequently apply to words which contain silent letters.*

1. **The "b" is silent after "m."**
   comb   lamb

2. **The "k" is silent before "n."**
   know   knight

3. **The "t" is silent in words like "rustle."**
   bustle   castle

4. **The "n" is silent in words ending in "mn."**
   condemn   autumn

5. **The "d" is silent in words like "edge."**
   ledge   bridge

6. **The "t" is silent in words like "ditch."**
   match   itch

7. **The "w" is silent before "r."**
   write   wrong

8. **The "l" is silent in words like "talk."**
   stalk   walk

9. **The "gh" is silent in words like "light."**
   night   bright

*Remember that there are other words which contain silent
letters for which there are no rules.*

 Add the silent letters.

1. dau **gh** ter
2. fo **L** ks
3. si **G** n
4. **K** nee
5. glob **E**
6. dou **B** t
7. g **U** est
8. cas **T** le
9. **H** onest
10. sta **L** k
11. sof **T** en
12. bri **D** ge
13. **W** reck
14. assi **G** n
15. **W** rong
16. **K** night
17. pa **L** m
18. **H** onor
19. ta **L** king
20. i **T** ch
21. escap **E**
22. **G** nat
23. ca **T** cher
24. strang **E**
25. **W** ritten

26. **K** nob
27. i **S** land
28. ans **W** er
29. **H** onesty
30. hi **GH**
31. desi **G** n
32. of **T** en
33. **K** now
34. ple **D** ge
35. hym **N**
36. thi **GH**
37. ti **GH** t
38. **H** our
39. deli **GH** t
40. **W** riter
41. cas **T** le
42. nau **GH** ty
43. ya **CH** t
44. shou **L** d
45. wa **L** ked
46. bris **T** le
47. **H** eir
48. **G** nu
49. ta **L** ker
50. **K** nitted

51. de **B** t
52. g **H** ost
53. s **W** ord
54. ha **L** f
55. cou **L** d
56. thum **B**
57. **W** rote
58. priz **E**
59. ca **L** m
60. **K** new
61. **W** rap
62. cha **L** k
63. dis **H** onest
64. **K** nown
65. **H** onorable
66. condem **N**
67. fas **T** en
68. lov **E**
69. clim **B**
70. unfas **T** en
71. **K** nowledge
72. hors **E**
73. sunli **GH** t
74. ai **S** le
75. practic **E**

76. trib **E**
77. lis **T** en
78. strai **GH** t
79. dis **H** onor
80. **K** nock
81. bri **D** ge
82. fli **GH** t
83. wei **GH**
84. autum **N**
85. midni **GH** t
86. whis **T** le
87. ca **L** f
88. wou **L** d
89. glis **T** en
90. cut **E**
91. rei **G** n
92. **W** ring
93. ali **G** n
94. pi **T** ch
95. chang **E**
96. ju **D** gment
97. g **H** etto
98. refus **E**
99. **G** nome
100. throu **GH**

Unit 125 cont'd

Looking Up Definitions

bill (bil) *n.* **1** a list of things for which money is owed **2** a piece of paper money **3** a law proposed to a body of lawmakers *v.* to send a list of charges to: I will bill you every week.

clear (klēr) *adj.* **1** easy to see through **2** bright; a clear day **3** easy to see **4** easy to understand *v.* **1** to free; clear of any guilt **2** to become clear

date (dāt) *n.* **1** the time when something happens such as March 12, 1985 **2** a period of time to which something belongs like a date in history **3** an appointment like a date to go to the show *v.* **1** to mark with a date **2** to belong to a certain period in time

nurse (nėrse) *n.* **1** a woman or man hired to take care of someone who is ill **2** a woman hired to care for someone's child *v.* to tend the sick

pock et (pok′it) *n.* **1** a small bag sewn into clothing **2** a condition in the atmosphere: The airplane hit an air pocket. *adj.* that which will fit in a pocket like a pocket calculator *v.* to put in a pocket

qui et (kwī′ət) *adj.* **1** silent **2** without motion like a quiet sea **3** peaceful **4** gentle: a gentle voice *n.* **1** silence **2** peacefulness *v.* to make or become silent or still

re ward (ri wôrd′) *n.* **1** something given in return for something else **2** money given or offered *v.* to give a reward to

trail (trāl) *v.* **1** to pull along behind **2** to follow behind **3** to follow the tracks of *n.* a track or scent

voice (vois) *n.* **1** the sound made by a person speaking, singing, etc. **2** the ability to make sounds through the mouth **3** an expressed opinion *v.* to express: Henry voices his opinion on everything.

For each entry word in the dictionary, you will find listed the part of speech. Some words may be more than one part of speech.

A noun names a person, place, or thing. The abbreviation "n." stands for "noun."

A verb shows action. The abbreviation "v." stands for "verb."

An adjective tells how many, which one, or what kind; it describes a noun. The abbreviation "adj." stands for "adjective."

 Answer each question by using the list of entry words on this page.

1. What is the verb definition of the word "nurse"? **to tend the sick**

2. What are the noun definitions of the word "quiet"? **1. SILENCE 2. PEACEFULNESS**

3. How many adjective definitions are given for the word "clear"? **4**

4. What parts of speech are given for the word "pocket"? **N. ADJ. V.**

5. What is the verb definition for the word "reward"? **TO GIVE A REWARD TO**

6. What is the noun definition for the word "trail"? **A TRACK OR SCENT**

7. What is the verb definition of the word "voice"? **TO EXPRESS**

8. What is the adjective definition of the word "pocket"? **THAT WHICH WILL FIT IN A POCKET**

9. How many noun definitions are given for the word "bill"? **3**

10. Are any definitions given for "date" as an adjective? **NO**

11. What is the verb definition of the word "bill"? **TO SEND A LIST OF CHARGES TO**

12. What are the verb definitions of the word "clear"? **1. TO FREE 2. TO BECOME CLEAR**

Comprehension Check

Ⓐ Write the word for each respelling.

1. fer′ē — **ferry**
2. goun — **gown**
3. hōm — **home**
4. pāst — **paste**
5. ri tŭrn′ — **return**
6. in vĕst′ — **invest**
7. pär′tē — **party**
8. kuf — **cuff**
9. ə lärm′ — **alarm**
10. drŭm — **drum**

11. hōld — **hold**
12. nĕkst — **next**
13. ō kā′ — **okay**
14. ô′fis — **office**
15. plās — **place**
16. prŏp′ər — **proper**
17. răb′it — **rabbit**
18. pāv — **pave**
19. yōozd — **used**
20. wôl — **wall**

21. ăk′shən — **action**
22. bīnd — **bind**
23. nēdz — **needs**
24. dēp — **deep**
25. kwôr′tər — **quarter**
26. thēf — **thief**
27. ăk′tiv — **active**
28. sins — **sense**
29. blōo — **blue**
30. hwēl — **wheel**

Ⓑ Put a check (✓) beside each respelling which contains a schwa sound.

1. ✓ piv′ət
2. ✓ rē′əl
3. pās′trē
4. spel
5. mŭn′ē
6. ✓ kôt′ən
7. ✓ mŭs′əl
8. ✓ sev′ən tē
9. them
10. ✓ pā′trən

11. spēch
12. ŏd
13. ✓ pash′ən
14. ✓ sŭl′ən
15. pīp
16. sŭn
17. tekst
18. pich
19. ✓ pə trōl′
20. ✓ en′jən

Ⓒ Add the silent letters.

1. refus **e**
2. thum **b**
3. fas **t** en
4. sunli **gh** t
5. **k** nitted
6. throu **gh**
7. ju **d** gment
8. ha **l** f
9. pi **t** ch
10. g **h** etto
11. **h** onor

12. i **t** ch
13. ca **t** cher
14. assi **g** n
15. rei **g** n
16. trib **e**
17. de **b** t
18. g **h** ost
19. cou **l** d
20. cas **t** le
21. bri **d** ge
22. **w** rong

Ⓓ Complete the spelling of each "ər" word by adding "er," "or," or "ar."

1. fing **er**
2. vap **or**
3. ord **er**
4. regul **ar**
5. teach **er**
6. neighb **or**
7. pol **ar**
8. hum **or**
9. lett **er**
10. maj **or**
11. burg **er**
12. calend **ar**
13. rad **ar**
14. wat **er**

15. flav **or**
16. ang **er**
17. spons **or**
18. mot **or**
19. barb **er**
20. terr **or**
21. liv **er**
22. fav **or**
23. lumb **er**
24. ov **er**
25. moth **er**
26. cell **ar**
27. mirr **or**
28. od **or**

Ⓔ Complete the spelling of each "əl" word by adding "al," "el," or "le."

1. strugg **le**
2. sand **al**
3. rur **al**
4. grumb **le**
5. mod **el**
6. map **le**
7. sadd **le**
8. kenn **el**
9. tunn **el**
10. post **al**
11. magic **al**
12. loc **al**
13. grav **el**
14. horrib **le**

15. peop **le**
16. equ **al**
17. shov **el**
18. trav **el**
19. nov **el**
20. med **al**
21. vow **el**
22. tab **le**
23. eag **le**
24. norm **al**
25. simp **le**
26. gener **al**
27. ridd **le**
28. speci **al**

Test 25 cont'd

Comprehension Check (continued)

(F) Count the number of syllables in each word. Write the number in the blank.

_2_	1. although	_3_	11. proposal
_3_	2. estimate	_2_	12. really
_2_	3. science	_2_	13. running
_3_	4. occupy	_2_	14. above
_3_	5. possible	_4_	15. education
_3_	6. suddenly	_4_	16. dictionary
_3_	7. skeleton	_3_	17. together
_1_	8. zone	_2_	18. methods
_2_	9. service	_3_	19. remember
_2_	10. questions	_1_	20. purse

(G) Place an accent mark (/) over the syllable which is said harder than the others.

1. hom ′ er	11. piz ′ za
2. i ′ tem ize	12. pot ′ hold er
3. la ′ ser	13. pro pel ′ ler
4. pas tel ′	14. rein ′ deer
5. mag nif ′ i cent	15. in fla ′ tion
6. ox ′ y gen	16. e con ′ o my
7. mile ′ age	17. grad ′ u ate
8. nom ′ i nate	18. reg u la ′ tion
9. gob ′ ble	19. tes ′ ti mo ny
10. po si ′ tion	20. con ser ′ va tive

(H) Read the following sets of guide words. Then write the page number on which each of the following words would be found.

pimento 1 pint	pinto 2 pitch	pitcher 3 placement	placer 4 plasma

_4_	1. planter	_2_	6. pirate	_3_	11. pitiful	_2_	16. pipe
_4_	2. plain	_3_	7. pizza	_3_	12. pitcher	_2_	17. piston
_1_	3. pinpoint	_2_	8. pioneer	_2_	13. pistol	_1_	18. pinch
_3_	4. place	_1_	9. pink	_4_	14. plaid	_4_	19. plasma
_2_	5. pit	_1_	10. pint	_2_	15. pinto	_4_	20. planet

(I) Read the entry word information; answer the question beside it.

pock et (pok ′ ĭt) *n.* **1** a small bag sewn into clothing **2** a condition in the atmosphere: The airplane hit an air pocket. *adj.* that which will fit in a pocket like a pocket calculator *v.* to put in a pocket

1. What parts of speech are given for "pocket"?
   a. _noun_
   b. _adjective_
   c. _verb_
2. Write the respelling for "pocket." _pok ′ ĭt_

3. Write the verb definition of "pocket."
   to put in a pocket

Write a paragraph about your dream vacation. Use at least two words with three syllables. Underline the three-syllable words.

_____

_____

_____

_____

_____

_____

_____

Spelling in the Dictionary

The very first item in a dictionary entry is the entry word itself, printed in heavy black type. From this entry word you can get the correct spelling without looking any further.

Suppose you don't know for sure what letter begins a particular word. Then you may have to look in more than one place to find your word.

EXAMPLE: Some words sound like they begin with "f" but actually begin with "ph," such as "phone" and "photo." Some begin with "c" or "ch" but sound as if they begin with "k," such as "chorus" and "clam."

A Use a dictionary to find if the words below begin with "f" or "ph" and fill in the blanks correctly.

1. _f_ og
2. _ph_ ase
3. _f_ ancy
4. _f_ ine
5. _ph_ one

6. _f_ ire
7. _ph_ onograph
8. _f_ ilth
9. _ph_ easant
10. _f_ inance

11. _f_ ilm
12. _ph_ ony
13. _f_ uture
14. _ph_ rase
15. _f_ irst

16. _ph_ lox
17. _ph_ ysical
18. _f_ eather
19. _ph_ otograph
20. _f_ air

21. _f_ ree
22. _ph_ antom
23. _f_ ever
24. _ph_ armacy
25. _f_ ront

B There are twelve words below. Use your dictionary and make the words correct by placing "ch," "c," or "k" in each blank.

1. _k_ ennel
2. _c_ attle
3. _k_ itchen
4. _ch_ aos
5. _ch_ oral

6. _k_ angaroo
7. _ch_ aracter
8. _c_ aught
9. _c_ ave
10. _Ch_ ristian

11. _k_ itten
12. _ch_ rome
13. _k_ ing
14. _c_ oward
15. _ch_ oir

16. _c_ alcium
17. _k_ ite
18. _ch_ ord
19. _c_ olor
20. _k_ indergarten

21. _c_ ave
22. _ch_ emical
23. _c_ avity
24. _k_ idney
25. _c_ aution

C Fill in each blank with the correct letter. Be sure to use a dictionary when in doubt.

g or j

1. _j_ elly
2. _g_ entle
3. _j_ ail
4. _g_ eneral
5. _j_ unk
6. _j_ acket

7. _g_ em
8. _j_ oke
9. _g_ ym
10. _j_ ewel
11. _g_ erm
12. _j_ uice

c or s

1. _c_ edar
2. _s_ een
3. _c_ ellar
4. _s_ eed
5. _s_ ecret
6. _s_ eize

7. _s_ cene
8. _c_ ents
9. _s_ imple
10. _s_ oon
11. _s_ illy
12. _c_ enter

Unit 126 cont'd →

Spelling the "sh" and "ch" Sounds

Look at the words "shake," "chef," "lotion," and "sure." All four words contain the "sh" sound, but the "sh" sound is spelled differently in each word. There is no rule to help you spell words with the "sh" sound. You must remember how such words are spelled.

EXAMPLES:
a. bushel
b. notion
c. machine
d. surely

A Complete each word by adding "sh," "ch," "ti," or "s."

1. publi_sh_
2. fa_SH_ion
3. cru_SH_
4. ac_TI_on
5. battle_SH_ip
6. para_CH_ute
7. ambi_TI_on
8. _SH_ould
9. fi_SH_
10. inven_TI_on

11. vaca_TI_on
12. _CH_ute
13. selfi_SH_
14. sun_SH_ine
15. protec_TI_on
16. _S_ugar
17. sugges_TI_on
18. subtrac_TI_on
19. _SH_oulder
20. mo_TI_on

21. in_S_ure
22. _SH_ine
23. _CH_evrolet
24. _SH_adow
25. collec_TI_on
26. _SH_aring
27. _SH_ortage
28. in_S_urance
29. cu_SH_ion
30. pu_SH_

31. _SH_out
32. sta_TI_on
33. _SH_ower
34. sea_SH_ell
35. _SH_ingle
36. vani_SH_
37. distinc_TI_on
38. greeni_SH_
39. _SH_arp
40. contrac_TI_on

Look at the words "punch," "kitchen," and "future." All three words contain the "ch" sound, but the "ch" sound is spelled differently in each word. There is no rule to help you spell words with the "ch" sound. You must remember how such words are spelled.

EXAMPLES:
a. catch
b. speech
c. future
d. chapter

B Complete each word by adding "ch," "tch," or "t."

1. _ch_oose
2. pi_TCH_er
3. _CH_estnut
4. _CH_oice
5. _CH_alkboard
6. for_T_une
7. signa_T_ure
8. _CH_erish
9. mu_CH_
10. _CH_arging

11. na_T_ural
12. _CH_ance
13. pic_T_ure
14. bu_TCH_er
15. tea_CH_er
16. bran_CH_es
17. ma_T_ure
18. ran_CH_er
19. tou_CH_
20. _CH_eek

21. mix_T_ure
22. pea_CH_es
23. ex_CH_ange
24. bun_CH_
25. _CH_ildren
26. _CH_arcoal
27. _CH_allenge
28. por_CH_
29. wi_TCH_es
30. ca_TCH_er

31. ea_CH_
32. na_T_ure
33. di_TCH_
34. _CH_eese
35. rea_CH_
36. fix_T_ure
37. wren_CH_
38. _CH_eckers
39. ri_CH_
40. na_T_urally

Recognizing Misspelled Words

 In each row underline the word that is spelled correctly. Then write it in the sentence.

EXAMPLES: (a) feer   (b) <u>fear</u>   (c) feir   There is nothing to ___*fear*___ .

(a) <u>wise</u>   (b) wize   (c) wiyse   Mr. Olson is a ___*wise*___ old man.

(a) eaven   (b) evin   (c) <u>even</u>   Two is an ___*even*___ number.

1. (a) <u>career</u>   (b) carear   (c) kareer   Sam wants a ___**career**___ in medicine.
2. (a) kei   (b) <u>key</u>   (c) kee   Here is the ___**KEY**___ .
3. (a) <u>night</u>   (b) nit   (c) niht   The opposite of morning is ___**NIGHT**___ .
4. (a) reeturn   (b) retirn   (c) <u>return</u>   Did you **RETURN** the call?
5. (a) uther   (b) <u>other</u>   (c) othur   You can have the ___**OTHER**___ one.
6. (a) <u>lonely</u>   (b) lonley   (c) lonlee   The puppy looked cold and ___**LONELY**___ .
7. (a) hospitel   (b) <u>hospital</u>   (c) hospetal   My aunt works in the ___**HOSPITAL**___ .
8. (a) <u>danger</u>   (b) dangur   (c) danjer   We will not be in any ___**DANGER**___ here.
9. (a) accidint   (b) <u>accident</u>   (c) acident   Did anyone see the ___**ACCIDENT**___ ?
10. (a) widd   (b) wyde   (c) <u>wide</u>   The bridge is not ___**WIDE**___ enough.
11. (a) <u>holiday</u>   (b) holliday   (c) holaday   Thanksgiving is a ___**HOLIDAY**___ .
12. (a) cussin   (b) <u>cousin</u>   (c) cousen   Matthew is my ___**COUSIN**___ .
13. (a) everbody   (b) <u>everybody</u>   (c) everbode   **EVERYBODY** is invited to come.
14. (a) arrport   (b) airpurt   (c) <u>airport</u>   We took my uncle to the ___**AIRPORT**___ .
15. (a) <u>town</u>   (b) toun   (c) towen   I grew up in a small ___**TOWN**___ .
16. (a) funnee   (b) <u>funny</u>   (c) funy   That was a ___**FUNNY**___ joke.
17. (a) ouner   (b) <u>owner</u>   (c) ownir   The ___**OWNER**___ is Ms. Arnold.
18. (a) <u>magic</u>   (b) magik   (c) majic   I don't believe in ___**MAGIC**___ .
19. (a) <u>exciting</u>   (b) exsiting   (c) excitin   The game was very ___**EXCITING**___ .
20. (a) kompany   (b) <u>company</u>   (c) compeny   They have ___**COMPANY**___ for dinner.
21. (a) inturest   (b) interrest   (c) <u>interest</u>   She has no ___**INTEREST**___ in sports.
22. (a) <u>banana</u>   (b) bannana   (c) bananna   May I have a ___**BANANA**___ ?
23. (a) <u>usually</u>   (b) usualy   (c) ussually   We **USUALLY** have a test on Friday.
24. (a) chanse   (b) <u>chance</u>   (c) chence   Let's give him another ___**CHANCE**___ .
25. (a) famus   (b) fammous   (c) <u>famous</u>   Twain is a ___**FAMOUS**___ writer.
26. (a) <u>together</u>   (b) togither   (c) tugether   You and I can work **TOGETHER** .
27. (a) accross   (b) <u>across</u>   (c) akross   Walk slowly ___**ACROSS**___ the room.
28. (a) chaced   (b) <u>chased</u>   (c) chassed   The lion ___**CHASED**___ the deer.
29. (a) ennemy   (b) enamy   (c) <u>enemy</u>   We must outwit the ___**ENEMY**___ .
30. (a) middel   (b) <u>middle</u>   (c) midle   He stood in the **MIDDLE** of the circle.
31. (a) <u>outlaw</u>   (b) owtlaw   (c) outlow   Jesse James was an ___**OUTLAW**___ .
32. (a) <u>language</u>   (b) langauge   (c) langage   Can you speak a foreign **LANGUAGE** ?
33. (a) evining   (b) evenen   (c) <u>evening</u>   The meeting is this ___**EVENING**___ .
34. (a) titel   (b) <u>title</u>   (c) titil   What is the ___**TITLE**___ of the book?
35. (a) <u>finish</u>   (b) finnish   (c) finesh   Did you **FINISH** your work?

Unit 127 cont'd ➡

Really Tough Ones

 Underline the correctly spelled words. Then write them in the blanks.

1. (a) alluminum   (b) <u>aluminum</u>   (c) alumminum   (d) *aluminum*
2. (a) <u>suspicion</u>   (b) susspicion   (c) suspishion   (d) **SUSPICION**
3. (a) invintory   (b) invantory   (c) <u>inventory</u>   (d) **INVENTORY**
4. (a) coridor   (b) <u>corridor</u>   (c) corrider   (d) **CORRIDOR**
5. (a) mollecules   (b) molekules   (c) <u>molecules</u>   (d) **MOLECULES**
6. (a) <u>pennant</u>   (b) pennent   (c) penant   (d) **PENNANT**
7. (a) himisphere   (b) <u>hemisphere</u>   (c) hemusphere   (d) **HEMISPHERE**
8. (a) subteranean   (b) subterraneon   (c) <u>subterranean</u>   (d) **SUBTERRANEAN**
9. (a) <u>metropolitan</u>   (b) metropollitan   (c) metropoleton   (d) **METROPOLITAN**
10. (a) <u>chlorine</u>   (b) chlorin   (c) klorine   (d) **CHLORINE**
11. (a) mallaria   (b) malarea   (c) <u>malaria</u>   (d) **MALARIA**
12. (a) astronout   (b) <u>astronaut</u>   (c) astronot   (d) **ASTRONAUT**
13. (a) mocasins   (b) <u>moccasins</u>   (c) moccasons   (d) **MOCCASINS**
14. (a) attendunce   (b) attendence   (c) <u>attendance</u>   (d) **ATTENDANCE**
15. (a) <u>rigorous</u>   (b) rigerus   (c) rigorus   (d) **RIGOROUS**
16. (a) terarium   (b) <u>terrarium</u>   (c) terrarrium   (d) **TERRARIUM**
17. (a) <u>ammunition</u>   (b) amunition   (c) ammunittion   (d) **AMMUNITION**
18. (a) remot   (b) <u>remote</u>   (c) remmote   (d) **REMOTE**
19. (a) experiment   (b) <u>experiment</u>   (c) expeariment   (d) **EXPERIMENT**
20. (a) <u>barometer</u>   (b) barrometer   (c) barometter   (d) **BAROMETER**
21. (a) <u>souvenir</u>   (b) souvinir   (c) souvener   (d) **SOUVENIR**
22. (a) <u>javelin</u>   (b) javilin   (c) javellin   (d) **JAVELIN**
23. (a) dimmension   (b) <u>dimension</u>   (c) demension   (d) **DIMENSION**
24. (a) lubracate   (b) lubrikate   (c) <u>lubricate</u>   (d) **LUBRICATE**
25. (a) <u>fiberglass</u>   (b) fiberglas   (c) fibberglass   (d) **FIBERGLASS**
26. (a) prosession   (b) procesion   (c) <u>procession</u>   (d) **PROCESSION**
27. (a) turbalence   (b) <u>turbulence</u>   (c) turbulance   (d) **TURBULENCE**
28. (a) uncontrolable   (b) <u>uncontrollable</u>   (c) uncontrollabul   (d) **UNCONTROLLABLE**
29. (a) <u>mosquito</u>   (b) mosketo   (c) mosqueto   (d) **MOSQUITO**
30. (a) doormitory   (b) dormitery   (c) <u>dormitory</u>   (d) **DORMITORY**
31. (a) <u>victim</u>   (b) viktim   (d) victom   (d) **VICTIM**
32. (a) diagnos   (b) <u>diagnose</u>   (c) diagknose   (d) **DIAGNOSE**
33. (a) entroduce   (b) <u>introduce</u>   (c) introduc   (d) **INTRODUCE**
34. (a) <u>modesty</u>   (b) modestey   (c) moddesty   (d) **MODESTY**
35. (a) complane   (b) complaine   (c) <u>complain</u>   (d) **COMPLAIN**

Using a Dictionary

ab sent (ab′sənt) *adj.* not present; missing: Who is absent? (ab sent′) *v.* to take or keep (oneself) away

broom (brüm) *n.* a brush for sweeping: Sweep the floor with a broom.

cause (kôz) *n.* **1** something which produces a result **2** an activity which people are interested in and support *v.* to make happen; bring about; He did cause the accident.

ea gle (ē′gəl) *n.* any of a number of large, strong birds of prey

grab (grab) *v.* to seize or snatch suddenly *n.* a sudden seizing or snatching

har vest (här′vist) *n.* the season when grain, fruit, etc., are gathered in *v.* to reap and gather in

hol i day (hol′ə dā) *n.* **1** a day of freedom from work: Easter is a holiday. **2** a vacation: We went to Ohio for the holidays.

knee (nē) *n.* the joint between the thigh and the lower part of a person's leg

lone some (lōn′səm) *adj.* lonely

nail (nāl) *n.* **1** a slender piece of metal with a sharp point **2** the thin growth at the end of a finger or toe *v.* **1** to attach with a nail **2** to make certain

of fi cer (ôf′ə sər) *n.* **1** a person in position of authority **2** a policeman

pack age (pak′ij) *n.* **1** a bundle of things; parcel like a package of books **2** the thing in which something is packed

Your dictionary is a book containing the words of a language. Look at the sample list of entry words on this page. What does the dictionary tell you about each entry word?

1. The entry word is divided into syllables.
2. An accent mark shows you the stressed syllable.
3. The respelling shows you how to pronounce the word.
4. Diacritical marks show the sounds of the vowels.
5. Sometimes a picture illustrates the entry word.
6. The definition tells you the meaning of the word. Some words may have more than one meaning.

 Answer each question by using the list of entry words on this page.

1. How is "harvest" divided into syllables? __*har vest*__

2. How is "officer" divided into syllables? __**OF FI CER**__

3. What is the sound of the first vowel in "eagle"? __Ē__

4. Which entry word begins with a silent letter? __**KNEE**__

5. Which syllable is stressed in "lonesome"? __**LONE′SOME**__

6. What is the respelling of "nail"? __**NĀL**__

7. How many definitions are listed under "grab"? __2__

8. Which word on this page is illustrated with a picture? __**EAGLE**__

9. What two pronunciations are given for "absent"? __**AB′SƏNT   AB SENT′**__

10. What is the sound of the "c" in "cause"? __K__

309

Unit 128 cont'd ➡

Using Dictionary Information

A Put each list of words into alphabetical order.

1. dream — *brain*
2. column — **COLUMN**
3. brain — **DOZEN**
4. dozen — **DREAM**
5. eagle — **EAGLE**

6. fish — **FACT**
7. freeze — **FISH**
8. flag — **FLAG**
9. funny — **FREEZE**
10. fact — **FUNNY**

11. ready — **READ**
12. read — **READY**
13. real — **REAL**
14. rest — **REALLY**
15. really — **REST**

B Answer each question.

qui et (kwī′ət) *adj.* 1 silent 2 without motion 3 peaceful 4 gentle— *n.* 1 silence 2 peacefulness —*v.* to make or become silent or still

voice (vois) *n.* 1 the sound made by a person speaking, singing, etc. 2 the ability to make sounds through the mouth 3 an expressed opinion —*v.* to express

1. What are the entry words? **QUIET** **VOICE**
2. How is each word divided into syllables? **QUI ET** **VOICE**
3. What is the respelling of each word? **KWĪ ′ə T** **VOIS**
4. What parts of speech are given for "quiet"? **ADJ. N. V.**
5. What is the first definition given for "voice"? **THE SOUND MADE BY A PERSON SPEAKING, SINGING, ETC.**

C Write the word for each respelling.

1. lōn′səm — *lonesome*
2. flou′ər — **FLOWER**
3. kou′boi — **COWBOY**
4. dā — **DAY**

5. chüz — **CHOOSE**
6. jü′əl — **JEWEL**
7. puz′əl — **PUZZLE**
8. wô′tər — **WATER**

9. sē′zən — **SEASON**
10. chēz — **CHEESE**
11. ī′lənd — **ISLAND**
12. tik′əl — **TICKLE**

D How many syllables are in each word?

3 1. together
3 2. piano
3 3. difficult
1 4. ghost
3 5. remember

2 6. mountain
2 7. easy
3 8. hospital
2 9. nervous
3 10. idea

3 11. protection
2 12. valley
1 13. strange
1 14. north
2 15. somewhere

2 16. promise
3 17. adventure
1 18. thought
3 19. enormous
2 20. crowded

E Divide each word into syllables. Mark the accented syllable.

1. signature — *sig′ na ture*
2. tomato — **TO MA′TO**
3. excuse — **EX CUSE ′**

4. vacation — **VA CA′TION**
5. alphabet — **AL′PHA BET**
6. practice — **PRAC′TICE**

7. surprise — **SUR PRISE ′**
8. hungry — **HUN′GRY**
9. opinion — **O PIN′ION**

310

Words That Are Similar — Synonyms

Synonyms are words with similar meanings.

EXAMPLES:
a. glad   happy
b. note   letter
c. took   stole
d. plump   fat
e. friend   pal
f. several   many

A Match each word with its synonym.

_f_	1. academy	a.	bug
T	2. secret	b.	purchase
I	3. title	c.	own
H	4. call	d.	tornado
C	5. possess	e.	leap
L	6. accept	f.	school
Y	7. stone	g.	halt
X	8. dictionary	h.	cry
P	9. fat	i.	name
K	10. servant	j.	sick
J	11. ill	k.	maid
N	12. elect	l.	take
E	13. jump	m.	empty
S	14. command	n.	choose
V	15. raise	o.	mistake
Q	16. book	p.	plump
O	17. error	q.	novel
W	18. cause	r.	mathematics
G	19. stop	s.	order
M	20. vacant	t.	mystery
U	21. city	u.	town
D	22. storm	v.	lift
R	23. arithmetic	w.	reason
B	24. buy	x.	lexicon
A	25. insect	y.	rock

B In the blanks write synonyms of the words in parentheses.

(said) 1. The woman ___yelled___ at us.
(smart) 2. Jim is an __INTELLIGENT__ boy.
(angry) 3. Your dad was __FURIOUS__.
(protected) 4. He **DEFENDED** his rights.
(disappeared) 5. The ghost has __VANISHED__.
(job) 6. Nursing is a good __CAREER__.
(wind) 7. The __BREEZE__ feels cool.
(quiet) 8. Everyone remained __SILENT__.
(cried) 9. Sally __WEPT__.
(easy) 10. The problem was __SIMPLE__.
(cool) 11. It's __CHILLY__ in here.
(stove) 12. The __RANGE__ is hot.
(hints) 13. Do you have any __CLUES__?
(shy) 14. The new girl is __BASHFUL__.
(present) 15. We need to buy a __GIFT__.
(hat) 16. His __CAP__ looks silly.
(walk) 17. The class is going on a __HIKE__.
(sure) 18. Darrel is very __CONFIDENT__.
(dream) 19. The __NIGHTMARE__ was terrible.
(store) 20. He bought the pie at the __BAKERY__.
(gem) 21. The __JEWEL__ sparkled.
(dad) 22. My __FATHER__ is a minister.
(smudged) 23. The paint was __SMEARED__.
(spoke) 24. The tired boy __MUMBLED__.
(touched) 25. He **PATTED** the dog on the head.

COMPOSITION EXERCISE

Write a sentence with each synonym.

1. cause, reason

_____

_____

2. near, close

_____

_____

3. kinfolk, relative

_____

_____

4. skinny, thin

_____

_____

Unit 129 cont'd

Synonyms

Synonyms are words with similar meanings.

EXAMPLES:
  a. shy   bashful   **d.** wet   moist
  b. hint   clue   **e.** halt   stop
  c. hit   swat   **f.** forward   ahead

A Matching

c	1. blanket	a.	lucky
N	2. cause	b.	always
I	3. discover	c.	quilt
D	4. twelve	d.	dozen
O	5. honest	e.	prohibit
U	6. rush	f.	unusual
B	7. forever	g.	shield
T	8. freedom	h.	simple
M	9. separate	i.	find
K	10. nonsense	j.	exact
G	11. protect	k.	silliness
F	12. strange	l.	ask
E	13. forbid	m.	split
Y	14. vanish	n.	reason
P	15. identify	o.	truthful
L	16. consult	p.	recognize
Z	17. advice	q.	victory
J	18. precise	r.	part
X	19. damage	s.	ship
C	20. balance	t.	liberty
Q	21. triumph	u.	hurry
W	22. silent	v.	polite
R	23. section	w.	quiet
A	24. cozy	x.	hurt
D	25. ought	y.	disappear
V	26. courteous	z.	suggestion
S	27. yacht	A.	comfortable
A	28. fortunate	B.	back
B	29. rear	C.	equal
H	30. easy	D.	should

B Complete each sentence with a synonym of the word in the parentheses.

(permit) 1. Will you ___allow___ me to explain?

(chance) 2. It is an excellent **OPPORTUNITY**

(huge) 3. The whale is **ENORMOUS**.

(trip) 4. The **JOURNEY** lasted four months.

(possess) 5. Does he **OWN** the store?

(stop) 6. **QUIT** chewing your fingernails!

(error) 7. It was my **MISTAKE**.

(comprehend) 8. I cannot **UNDERSTAND** why.

(pest) 9. That dog is becoming a **NUISANCE**.

(vacant) 10. The building was **EMPTY**.

(combine) 11. **MIX** yellow and blue.

(delayed) 12. The meeting will be **POSTPONED**.

(perfect) 13. The diamond was **FLAWLESS**.

(pretended) 14. Al **IMAGINED** he saw a ghost.

(sure) 15. We must be **CERTAIN** of it.

(rude) 16. There was no reason to be **IMPOLITE**.

(purchase) 17. What did you **BUY**?

(remedy) 18. I know the perfect **SOLUTION**.

(assist) 19. Why won't you let me **HELP** you?

(fake) 20. This money is **COUNTERFEIT**

(lawyer) 21. Mr. Andrews is my dad's **ATTORNEY**

(tan) 22. My new coat is **BEIGE** and black.

(evidence) 23. We have no **PROOF**.

(jail) 24. The man was sent to **PRISON**.

(frighten) 25. You are trying to **SCARE** me.

(sketch) 26. I'll **DRAW** you a map.

(scheme) 27. Listen to my **PLAN**.

(frequently) 28. Do you come here **OFTEN**?

(sad) 29. The small child looked **UNHAPPY**

(hungry) 30. Some people in the world are **STARVING**.

Using Synonyms

Words that have similar meanings are
called synonyms.

EXAMPLES: a. space — area   c. voyage — trip   e. fix — repair
           b. look — watch   d. halt — stop   f. right — correct

A Matching

_d_	1. enormous	a. chilly
J	2. cry	b. freedom
Y	3. echo	c. incorrect
P	4. simple	d. huge
N	5. lullaby	e. elect
C	6. wrong	f. name
A	7. cool	g. silent
W	8. start	h. also
S	9. plenty	i. scare
H	10. and	j. weep
M	11. hurt	k. bad
R	12. fast	l. came
U	13. yard	m. injure
L	14. arrived	n. song
B	15. liberty	o. beautiful
T	16. small	p. easy
I	17. frighten	q. mistake
V	18. great	r. speedy
G	19. quiet	s. enough
K	20. evil	t. little
Q	21. error	u. lawn
E	22. choose	v. marvelous
O	23. pretty	w. begin
F	24. title	x. allow
X	25. permit	y. repeat

B In each blank write a synonym of the underlined word.

1. a. The house is huge.
   b. The house is **enormous**.
2. a. We will start now.
   b. We will **BEGIN** now.
3. a. They came last night.
   b. They **ARRIVED** last night.
4. a. The song was beautiful.
   b. The **LULLABY** was beautiful.
5. a. The answer is wrong.
   b. The answer is **INCORRECT**.
6. a. What is his name?
   b. What is his **TITLE**?
7. a. We will choose a president.
   b. We will **ELECT** a president.
8. a. The job was simple.
   b. The job was **EASY**.
9. a. The air feels cool.
   b. The air feels **CHILLY**.
10. a. We have enough.
    b. We have **PLENTY**.
11. a. He is a fast worker.
    b. He is a **SPEEDY** worker.
12. a. The children were quiet.
    b. The children were **SILENT**.

COMPOSITION EXERCISE

List 18 sets of synonyms.

1. _____   7. _____   13. _____
2. _____   8. _____   14. _____
3. _____   9. _____   15. _____
4. _____   10. _____ 16. _____
5. _____   11. _____ 17. _____
6. _____   12. _____ 18. _____

Unit 130 cont'd

Identifying Synonyms

Synonyms are words with similar meanings.

EXAMPLES:
- a. seldom   sometimes
- b. buy   purchase
- c. final   end
- d. lose   misplace
- e. count   number
- f. plan   organize

Match the synonyms in each part.

Part A

o	1. present	a.	moist
l, t	2. timid	b.	silent
l	3. shy	c.	wealthy
a	4. damp	d.	sack
w	5. below	e.	coat
q	6. dashed	f.	yell
b	7. quiet	g.	closed
v	8. remain	h.	end
x	9. near	i.	stone
c	10. rich	j.	high
m	11. large	k.	odd
g	12. shut	l.	bashful
d	13. bag	m.	big
i	14. rock	n.	fast
e	15. jacket	o.	gift
u	16. sad	p.	glad
p	17. happy	q.	raced
f	18. shout	r.	jump
k	19. queer	s.	forest
h	20. finish	t.	shy
r	21. leap	u.	unhappy
n	22. quick	v.	stay
j	23. tall	w.	under
s	24. woods	x.	close

Part B

h	1. also	a.	sleep
v	2. noise	b.	mannerly
s	3. cross	c.	questioned
u	4. shouted	d.	start
p	5. woman	e.	limb
r	6. merry	f.	visitor
n	7. circle	g.	several
x	8. build	h.	too
a	9. nap	i.	lake
d	10. begin	j.	speak
f	11. guest	k.	silly
w	12. invite	l.	excellent
e	13. branch	m.	scared
q	14. place	n.	ring
m	15. afraid	o.	insect
k	16. foolish	p.	lady
c	17. asked	q.	spot
g	18. some	r.	gay
j	19. talk	s.	angry
t	20. idea	t.	plan
i	21. pond	u.	called
b	22. polite	v.	sound
l	23. fine	w.	ask
o	24. bug	x.	make

Comprehension Check
Test 26

Ⓐ Write either "f" or "ph" in each blank.

1. _f_ ront	13. _ph_ obia
2. _ph_ rase	14. _ph_ easant
3. _ph_ ysical	15. _f_ ilter
4. _f_ og	16. _ph_ antom
5. _f_ rog	17. _f_ ancy
6. _f_ izzle	18. _f_ lock
7. _f_ orm	19. _f_ ifth
8. _ph_ armacy	20. _f_ ever
9. _ph_ ony	21. _ph_ onics
10. _ph_ ase	22. _ph_ one
11. _f_ ence	23. _f_ ilm
12. _f_ uture	24. _f_ inance

Ⓑ Write either "ch," "c," or "k" in each blank.

1. _k_ ing	13. _k_ id
2. _ch_ orus	14. _ch_ aracter
3. _c_ olor	15. _k_ it
4. _k_ ey	16. _c_ ontrast
5. _c_ ave	17. _c_ ool
6. _c_ anvas	18. _k_ ennel
7. _k_ ick	19. _k_ ind
8. _c_ aution	20. _ch_ oir
9. _c_ ontact	21. _k_ itchen
10. _c_ ount	22. _ch_ emical
11. _ch_ rome	23. _k_ eep
12. _k_ ingdom	24. _c_ ontrol

Ⓒ Write either "sh," "ch," "ti," or "s" in each blank.

1. _sh_ ould	13. contrac _ti_ on
2. _sh_ out	14. vaca _ti_ on
3. sun _sh_ ine	15. cu _sh_ ion
4. _s_ ugar	16. sta _ti_ on
5. fi _sh_	17. pu _sh_
6. bu _sh_ el	18. ac _ti_ on
7. in _s_ ure	19. sea _sh_ ell
8. greeni _sh_	20. mo _ti_ on
9. fa _sh_ ion	21. _sh_ ower
10. _sh_ ortage	22. inven _ti_ on
11. subtrac _ti_ on	23. _sh_ adow
12. _ch_ ute	24. _sh_ ine

Ⓓ Write either "ch," "tch," or "t" in each blank.

1. sa _tch_ el	13. na _t_ ure
2. mix _t_ ure	14. fix _t_ ure
3. wren _ch_	15. ea _ch_
4. _ch_ eckers	16. ma _t_ ure
5. bu _tch_ er	17. pea _ch_ es
6. na _t_ ural	18. ex _ch_ ange
7. _ch_ ance	19. for _t_ une
8. pic _t_ ure	20. tea _ch_ er
9. pi _tch_ er	21. por _ch_
10. _ch_ erish	22. ran _ch_
11. mu _ch_	23. tou _ch_
12. wi _tch_	24. di _tch_

Ⓔ Write either "c" or "s" in each blank.

1. _c_ ents	13. _c_ ell
2. _s_ imple	14. _c_ ement
3. _c_ elery	15. _s_ een
4. _c_ edar	16. _c_ ycle
5. _s_ alary	17. _c_ enter
6. _s_ cene	18. sin _c_ e
7. sen _s_ e	19. _s_ eed
8. _s_ ash	20. _c_ entral
9. _s_ ecret	21. _s_ ail
10. _c_ ypress	22. _s_ eize
11. _c_ ellar	23. _c_ ertain
12. _s_ ew	24. _s_ et

Ⓕ Write either "j" or "g" in each blank.

1. _g_ enius	13. _g_ el
2. _j_ elly	14. _g_ em
3. _j_ udge	15. _g_ enes
4. _g_ entle	16. _j_ oke
5. gara _g_ e	17. _j_ eans
6. _j_ ail	18. _g_ ym
7. _g_ iant	19. gau _g_ e
8. _g_ eneral	20. _j_ ewel
9. _g_ ender	21. _j_ olly
10. _j_ unk	22. _g_ erm
11. _g_ ypsy	23. _g_ entleman
12. _j_ acket	24. _j_ uice

315

Test 26 cont'd

Comprehension Check (continued)

G In each row, underline the word that is spelled correctly. Then write it in the sentence.

1. (a) <u>lonely</u>   (b) lonly   (c) lonelie   The dog is _____lonely_____ .
2. (a) <u>company</u>   (b) commpany   (c) companny   That ___company___ went out of business.
3. (a) famus   (b) phamus   (c) <u>famous</u>   Rock singers are sometimes ___famous___ .
4. (a) <u>career</u>   (b) carrer   (c) carear   Sarah wants a ___career___ in medicine.
5. (a) holliday   (b) holaday   (c) <u>holiday</u>   What is your favorite ___holiday___ ?
6. (a) usully   (b) <u>usually</u>   (c) usualy   We are ___usually___ early for school.
7. (a) ackros   (b) <u>across</u>   (c) accros   Richard jumped ___across___ the stream.
8. (a) <u>enemy</u>   (b) enimy   (c) enamy   A hawk is the ___enemy___ of a mouse.
9. (a) titil   (b) titel   (c) <u>title</u>   Put a ___title___ on your report.
10. (a) <u>interest</u>   (b) intrest   (c) intarest   Banks pay ___interest___ on savings accounts.
11. (a) languge   (b) <u>language</u>   (c) langage   Spanish is his first ___language___ .
12. (a) bannana   (b) bananna   (c) <u>banana</u>   A ___banana___ contains many vitamins.

H Read the dictionary entry. Answer each question about the entry.

har vest (här ′vist) *n.* the season when grain, fruit, etc., are gathered in *v.* to reap and gather in

1. How many syllables are in the entry word? ___two___
2. Which syllable receives the accent? ___first___
3. Name the parts of speech listed for the word. ___noun, verb___
4. Would the word appear before or after "grain" in the dictionary? ___after___
5. Write a sentence using "harvest" as a noun. ___The apple harvest is plentiful.___
6. Write a sentence using "harvest" as a verb. ___We'll harvest the wheat next month.___
7. Write the respelling. ___(här ′ vist)___
8. Write a word which rhymes with the first syllable of the entry word. ___car___
9. Write a synonym for "harvest." ___crop___
10. Write another two-syllable word. ___fortune___
11. Divide the two-syllable word into syllables. ___for ′ tune___
12. Place an accent mark in the word above.

Write a paragraph about your favorite television show. Use at least two sets of synonyms. Underline each synonym.

_____

_____

_____

_____

_____

_____

Words That Are Opposites — Antonyms

Antonyms are words with opposite meanings.

EXAMPLES:
a. hot	cold	d. dirty	clean
b. take	give	e. soft	hard
c. up	down	f. wide	narrow

A Match each word with its antonym.

_d_	1. clear	a.	danger
_H_	2. find	b.	tender
_O_	3. front	c.	awake
_U_	4. enormous	d.	cloudy
_G_	5. life	e.	necessity
_A_	6. safety	f.	after
_K_	7. narrow	g.	death
_J_	8. damage	h.	lose
_Q_	9. many	i.	cry
_E_	10. luxury	j.	repair
_S_	11. selfish	k.	wide
_X_	12. remember	l.	escape
_M_	13. wisdom	m.	ignorance
_R_	14. succeed	n.	ugly
_V_	15. valuable	o.	rear
_P_	16. brave	p.	cowardly
_C_	17. sleep	q.	few
_L_	18. capture	r.	fail
_I_	19. laugh	s.	generous
_W_	20. same	t.	rude
_F_	21. before	u.	tiny
_B_	22. tough	v.	worthless
_Y_	23. lie	w.	different
_N_	24. beautiful	x.	forget
_T_	25. courteous	y.	truth

B In each blank write an antonym for the word in parentheses.

(true) 1. That is a ___false___ statement.
(hit) 2. The bullet ___MISSED___.
(remember) 3. I ___FORGOT___ to tell him.
(friend) 4. He is my ___ENEMY___.
(odd) 5. Four is an ___EVEN___ number.
(began) 6. We ___FINISHED___ early.
(poor) 7. Mr. Adams is a ___RICH___ man.
(past) 8. I wonder what the ___FUTURE___ holds.
(cheap) 9. Diamonds are ___EXPENSIVE___.
(innocent) 10. The judge found him ___GUILTY___.
(question) 11. The ___ANSWER___ was wrong.
(attacked) 12. The army ___SURRENDERED___.
(inside) 13. Take him ___OUTSIDE___.
(fancy) 14. The dress is ___PLAIN___.
(early) 15. He will be ___LATE___ for dinner.
(held) 16. Heath ___DROPPED___ the lamp.
(strong) 17. The tired man was ___WEAK___.
(exit) 18. The ___ENTRANCE___ was locked.
(interesting) 19. Her story is ___BORING___.
(honest) 20. A crook is ___DISHONEST___.
(gave) 21. I ___RECEIVED___ two letters.
(wet) 22. Put on ___DRY___ clothes.
(easy) 23. The test was ___DIFFICULT___.
(silent) 24. The people were ___NOISY___.
(good-bye) 25. The woman said ___HELLO___.

COMPOSITION EXERCISE

Write a sentence with each antonym.

1. yes, no

_____
_____

2. none, all

_____
_____

3. energetic, tired

_____
_____

4. silent, noisy

_____
_____

Unit 131 cont'd

Using Antonyms

Words that have opposite meanings are called antonyms.

EXAMPLES: a. cold — hot   c. forward — backward   e. soon — later
          b. destroy — build   d. soft — hard   f. do — don't

A Matching

_g_	1. noisy	a.	sweet
Q	2. beginning	b.	dry
L	3. honest	c.	worse
A	4. bitter	d.	awake
Y	5. frown	e.	warm
K	6. inside	f.	bring
U	7. approve	g.	silent
D	8. asleep	h.	sad
R	9. lose	i.	uncertain
X	10. part	j.	full
H	11. happy	k.	outside
P	12. whisper	l.	dishonest
I	13. certain	m.	after
E	14. cool	n.	subtract
W	15. impolite	o.	ceiling
M	16. before	p.	scream
C	17. better	q.	end
T	18. dirty	r.	find
O	19. floor	s.	can
V	20. laugh	t.	clean
B	21. wet	u.	disapprove
N	22. add	v.	cry
S	23. can't	w.	polite
F	24. take	x.	all
J	25. empty	y.	smile

B Write the better word in each blank.

1. a. The lemon is __bitter__.   (bitter, sweet)
 b. The candy is __sweet__.
2. a. __DRY__ the dishes.   (wet, dry)
 b. Don't get your feet __WET__.
3. a. The __SAD__ girl cried.   (sad, happy)
 b. The __HAPPY__ girl smiled.
4. a. The ice is __COLD__.   (cold, hot)
 b. The iron is __HOT__.
5. a. I __CAN__ drive.   (can, can't)
 b. My dog __CAN'T__ fly.
6. a. __SUBTRACT__ what he lost.   (add, subtract)
 b. __ADD__ it to the end.
7. a. You are __HONEST__. (honest, dishonest)
 b. A thief is __DISHONEST__.
8. a. I hear a __SCREAM__.   (whisper, scream)
 b. __WHISPER__ the secret.
9. a. It's raining __OUTSIDE__.   (outside, inside)
 b. I came __INSIDE__.
10. a. __CLEAN__ your room.   (dirty, clean)
 b. Wipe your __DIRTY__ shoes.
11. a. Start at the __BEGINNING__. (beginning, end)
 b. The tail is at the __END__.
12. a. A light is on the __CEILING__. (floor, ceiling)
 b. Sit on the __FLOOR__.

COMPOSITION EXERCISE

List 18 sets of antonyms.

1. _____
2. _____
3. _____
4. _____
5. _____
6. _____

7. _____
8. _____
9. _____
10. _____
11. _____
12. _____

13. _____
14. _____
15. _____
16. _____
17. _____
18. _____

Antonyms

Antonyms are words with opposite meanings.

EXAMPLES:
a.	crooked	straight
b.	peace	war
c.	most	least

d.	freeze	melt
e.	true	false
f.	after	before

A Matching

_g_	1. greedy	a.	forbid
_o_	2. absent	b.	proud
_A_	3. allow	c.	unusual
_D_	4. host	d.	guest
_K_	5. prefix	e.	simple
_B_	6. ashamed	f.	shout
_P_	7. forward	g.	generous
_C_	8. include	h.	strong
_A_	9. impossible	i.	normal
_S_	10. borrow	j.	often
_R_	11. punish	k.	suffix
_J_	12. seldom	l.	weakness
_Y_	13. occupied	m.	applaud
_D_	14. patient	n.	light
_M_	15. boo	o.	present
_V_	16. smooth	p.	backward
_Q_	17. subtract	q.	add
_F_	18. whisper	r.	reward
_T_	19. succeed	s.	loan
_N_	20. heavy	t.	fail
_C_	21. ordinary	u.	slave
_X_	22. awkward	v.	rough
_W_	23. remember	w.	forget
_I_	24. abnormal	x.	graceful
_E_	25. difficult	y.	vacant
_H_	26. fragile	z.	disorganize
_Z_	27. organize	A.	possible
_U_	28. master	B.	happiness
_B_	29. sorrow	C.	omit
_L_	30. strength	D.	impatient

B Complete each sentence with an antonym of the word in the parentheses.

(toward) 1. The dog ran __away__ from us.

(safe) 2. It is a **DANGEROUS** mission.

(adult) 3. The painting was done by a **CHILD**.

(careless) 4. Please be **CAREFUL**.

(enormous) 5. The flea is a **TINY** animal.

(cause) 6. What was the **RESULT**?

(escaped) 7. The prisoner was **CAPTURED**.

(specific) 8. Your outline is too **GENERAL**.

(laugh) 9. The movie made me **CRY**.

(modern) 10. My mother is very **OLD-FASHIONED**.

(valuable) 11. This stone is **WORTHLESS**.

(aged) 12. Mr. Sanders is a **YOUNG** man.

(appear) 13. The ghost will **VANISH** if you talk.

(conquered) 14. The islanders **SURRENDERED**.

(rude) 15. Joanne is always **POLITE**.

(flawed) 16. The diamond is **PERFECT**.

(frown) 17. **SMILE** for the camera.

(plural) 18. ''**SINGULAR**'' means ''one.''

(interesting) 19. His speech was **BORING**.

(cheap) 20. She owns an **EXPENSIVE** car.

(friend) 21. This man is our **ENEMY**.

(doubt) 22. I **TRUST** his judgment.

(different) 23. These two are **ALIKE**.

(cruel) 24. Be **KIND** to the animals.

(beginning) 25. The **ENDING** was surprising.

(won) 26. We **LOST** the tournament.

(summer) 27. **WINTER** is the coldest season.

(stale) 28. Have a **FRESH** donut.

(worse) 29. I've never had a **BETTER** time.

(open) 30. The store is **CLOSED**.

Unit 132 cont'd

Words That Sound Alike — Homonyms

Homonyms are words that sound alike, but the spellings and meanings are different.

EXAMPLES:
a. see	sea	d. our	hour	
b. role	roll	e. knew	gnu	
c. write	right	f. air	heir	

A Match the homonyms.

_m_	1. aloud	a.	toad
E	2. buoy	b.	sail
O	3. to	c.	fare
G	4. pale	d.	kiln
T	5. new	e.	boy
P	6. hoo	f.	steal
C	7. fair	g.	pail
I	8. ate	h.	route
X	9. win	i.	eight
K	10. sun	j.	pear
B	11. sale	k.	son
R	12. ail	l.	wear
V	13. bye	m.	allowed
N	14. fir	n.	fur
A	15. towed	o.	too
J	16. pair	p.	who
F	17. steel	q.	pain
S	18. air	r.	ale
D	19. kill	s.	heir
L	20. ware	t.	knew
U	21. hi	u.	high
Q	22. pane	v.	buy
Y	23. doe	w.	tea
W	24. tee	x.	wen
H	25. root	y.	dough

B Underline the word which makes each sentence correct.

1. We (one, <u>won</u>) the game.
2. Did you (sea, <u>see</u>) that?
3. (<u>Who</u>, Hoo) is he?
4. The wind (blue, <u>blew</u>).
5. He is (<u>heir</u>, air) to the throne.
6. He is a (buoy, <u>boy</u>).
7. It is (to, <u>too</u>, two) large.
8. The (<u>maid</u>, made) is here.
9. What did Alex (ware, <u>wear</u>)?
10. There were (<u>eight</u>, ate) children.
11. We will (meat, <u>meet</u>) at school.
12. Read it (allowed, <u>aloud</u>).
13. The rule is not (<u>fair</u>, fare).
14. Your face is (<u>pale</u>, pail).
15. Drink your (tee, <u>tea</u>).
16. The shelf is too (hi, <u>high</u>).
17. (Their, <u>There</u>) is the lake.
18. He is a (<u>new</u>, knew) driver.
19. The (son, <u>sun</u>) is shining.
20. We burned the (<u>wood</u>, would).
21. The old man is (week, <u>weak</u>).
22. The baby deer is a (<u>doe</u>, dough).
23. He broke the window (pain, <u>pane</u>).
24. Did you (bye, <u>buy</u>) it?
25. Mom wants a (<u>fur</u>, fir) coat.

COMPOSITION EXERCISE

Write a sentence with each of these homonyms.

1. pane, pain

_____

_____

2. fair, fare

_____

_____

3. way, weigh

_____

_____

4. rain, reign

_____

_____

Homonyms

The **prophet** told us what would happen in the future.

Dad made a big **profit** on the wheat he sold.

The words underlined in the sentences above are pronounced exactly alike, but their spellings and definitions are completely different. These words are called **homonyms**. If you aren't sure when to use which spelling, just look up the word in your dictionary.

A Below is a list of homonyms. Use your dictionary to help you choose the correct tone for each sentence.

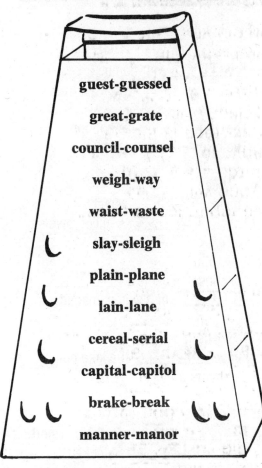

guest-guessed
great-grate
council-counsel
weigh-way
waist-waste
slay-sleigh
plain-plane
lain-lane
cereal-serial
capital-capitol
brake-break
manner-manor

1. She is a ___*guest*___ at this party.

2. Will you __**GRATE**__ some cheese for me?

3. Dad is a member of the city __**COUNCIL**__ .

4. Sue doesn't __**WEIGH**__ very much.

5. We must put the __**WASTE**__ into the basket.

6. Have you ever ridden in a __**SLEIGH**__ ?

7. Wheat grows on a __**PLAIN**__ in Kansas.

8. We strolled down the __**LANE**__ .

9. There is a new __**SERIAL**__ on television.

10. We saw the __**CAPITOL**__ in Washington last year.

11. Be careful, or you'll __**BREAK**__ your neck.

12. She was born in a __**MANOR**__ .

B Make a list here of the homonyms you use. Check in a dictionary to be sure you understand their meanings.

_____

_____

_____

_____

_____

_____

_____

Unit 133 cont'd

Using Homonyms

Homonyms are words that sound alike, but they have different spellings and different meanings.

EXAMPLES: *a. pore   poor   pour*   *d. sew   so   sow*
                   b. ants   aunts   *e. know   no*
                   c. to   too   two   *f. four   for*

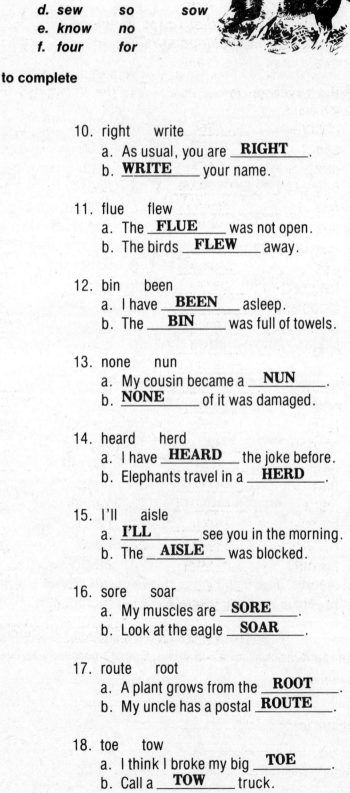

Write the correct homonym in the blank to complete each sentence.

1. eight   ate
   a. Benny __ate__ slowly.
   b. Joey is __eight__ years old.

2. wring   ring
   a. Did the bell __RING__?
   b. I could __WRING__ your neck!

3. waste   waist
   a. Tie this rope around your __WAIST__.
   b. Don't __WASTE__ your food.

4. bored   board
   a. Mr. Rivers looked __BORED__.
   b. This __BOARD__ will be our table.

5. hoarse   horse
   a. He was too __HOARSE__ to talk.
   b. The __HORSE__ jumped the fence.

6. way   weigh
   a. Which __WAY__ did they go?
   b. How much do you __WEIGH__?

7. knead   need
   a. We __NEED__ more time.
   b. I will __KNEAD__ the dough.

8. breaks   brakes
   a. China __BREAKS__ easily.
   b. The car's __BRAKES__ failed.

9. hear   here
   a. Come __HERE__.
   b. I didn't __HEAR__ anything.

10. right   write
    a. As usual, you are __RIGHT__.
    b. __WRITE__ your name.

11. flue   flew
    a. The __FLUE__ was not open.
    b. The birds __FLEW__ away.

12. bin   been
    a. I have __BEEN__ asleep.
    b. The __BIN__ was full of towels.

13. none   nun
    a. My cousin became a __NUN__.
    b. __NONE__ of it was damaged.

14. heard   herd
    a. I have __HEARD__ the joke before.
    b. Elephants travel in a __HERD__.

15. I'll   aisle
    a. __I'LL__ see you in the morning.
    b. The __AISLE__ was blocked.

16. sore   soar
    a. My muscles are __SORE__.
    b. Look at the eagle __SOAR__.

17. route   root
    a. A plant grows from the __ROOT__.
    b. My uncle has a postal __ROUTE__.

18. toe   tow
    a. I think I broke my big __TOE__.
    b. Call a __TOW__ truck.

Synonyms, Antonyms, and Homonyms

Synonyms are words with similar meanings.
EXAMPLE: get   receive

Antonyms are words with opposite meanings.
EXAMPLE: love   hate

Homonyms are words that sound the same, but the meanings and spellings are different.
EXAMPLE: sail   sale

A Write a synonym for each word.

1. change — *alter*
2. see — LOOK
3. need — LACK
4. buy — PURCHASE
5. hit — SMASH
6. mix — COMBINE
7. opinion — IDEA
8. use — EMPLOY
9. frequent — OFTEN
10. cloudless — SUNNY
11. check — GRADE
12. friend — CHUM
13. great — ENORMOUS
14. throw — PITCH
15. heal — CURE
16. lawn — YARD
17. pardon — FORGIVE
18. music — SONG
19. pan — KETTLE
20. learn — MEMORIZE
21. murder — KILL
22. hazard — DANGER
23. permit — ALLOW
24. sleep — NAP
25. liberty — FREEDOM

B Write an antonym for each word.

1. wet — *dry*
2. good — BAD
3. enter — EXIT
4. floor — CEILING
5. hearing — DEAF
6. sharp — DULL
7. night — DAY
8. hardness — SOFTNESS
9. weak — STRONG
10. talk — LISTEN
11. agree — DISAGREE
12. stand — SIT
13. remember — FORGET
14. happy — SAD
15. legal — ILLEGAL
16. remove — REPLACE
17. first — LAST
18. cooked — RAW
19. open — CLOSE
20. vanish — APPEAR
21. no — YES
22. never — ALWAYS
23. empty — FULL
24. answer — QUESTION
25. incomplete — COMPLETE

C Write a homonym for each word.

1. blue — *blew*
2. red — READ
3. sew — SO
4. two — TOO
5. weight — WAIT
6. steak — STAKE
7. wood — WOULD
8. sea — SEE
9. roll — ROLE
10. made — MAID
11. fore — FOUR
12. week — WEAK
13. meat — MEET
14. sail — SALE
15. cite — SIGHT
16. one — WON
17. tier — TEAR
18. stare — STAIR
19. write — RIGHT
20. peak — PEEK
21. sun — SON
22. our — HOUR
23. you're — YOUR
24. there — THEIR
25. inn — IN

COMPOSITION EXERCISE

Write the definition for each word. Supply an example not used in this lesson.

1. synonyms _____

_____

2. antonyms _____

_____

3. homonyms _____

_____

Unit 134 cont'd

Writing Numbers

A hyphen is used in compound names of numbers from twenty-one through ninety-nine.

EXAMPLES: 26   twenty-six   45   forty-five

38   thirty-eight   53   fifty-three

A Write the number name for each number.

1 - *one*	16 - SIXTEEN	31 - THIRTY-ONE	46 - FORTY-SIX
2 - TWO	17 - SEVENTEEN	32 - THIRTY-TWO	47 - FORTY-SEVEN
3 - THREE	18 - EIGHTEEN	33 - THIRTY-THREE	48 - FORTY-EIGHT
4 - FOUR	19 - NINETEEN	34 - THIRTY-FOUR	49 - FORTY-NINE
5 - FIVE	20 - TWENTY	35 - THIRTY-FIVE	50 - FIFTY
6 - SIX	21 - TWENTY-ONE	36 - THIRTY-SIX	51 - FIFTY-ONE
7 - SEVEN	22 - TWENTY-TWO	37 - THIRTY-SEVEN	52 - FIFTY-TWO
8 - EIGHT	23 - TWENTY-THREE	38 - THIRTY-EIGHT	53 - FIFTY-THREE
9 - NINE	24 - TWENTY-FOUR	39 - THIRTY-NINE	54 - FIFTY-FOUR
10 - TEN	25 - TWENTY-FIVE	40 - FORTY	55 - FIFTY-FIVE
11 - ELEVEN	26 - TWENTY-SIX	41 - FORTY-ONE	56 - FIFTY-SIX
12 - TWELVE	27 - TWENTY-SEVEN	42 - FORTY-TWO	57 - FIFTY-SEVEN
13 - THIRTEEN	28 - TWENTY-EIGHT	43 - FORTY-THREE	58 - FIFTY-EIGHT
14 - FOURTEEN	29 - TWENTY-NINE	44 - FORTY-FOUR	59 - FIFTY-NINE
15 - FIFTEEN	30 - THIRTY	45 - FORTY-FIVE	60 - SIXTY

Ordinal numbers are names like "first," "second," or "third." To write some ordinal numbers, simply add "th" to the regular number names.

EXAMPLES: 11   eleventh   16   sixteenth

Here are some exceptions:
1. five — fifth
2. nine — ninth
3. twelve — twelfth
4. eight — eighth
5. number names that end in "y" but change the "y" to "i" and add "eth" (twenty — twentieth)

B Write the ordinal number name for each number.

1 - *first*	11 - ELEVENTH	30 - THIRTIETH
2 - SECOND	12 - TWELFTH	31 - THIRTY-FIRST
3 - THIRD	13 - THIRTEENTH	40 - FORTIETH
4 - FOURTH	14 - FOURTEENTH	42 - FORTY-SECOND
5 - FIFTH	15 - FIFTEENTH	50 - FIFTIETH
6 - SIXTH	16 - SIXTEENTH	53 - FIFTY-THIRD
7 - SEVENTH	17 - SEVENTEENTH	60 - SIXTIETH
8 - EIGHTH	18 - EIGHTEENTH	64 - SIXTY-FOURTH
9 - NINTH	19 - NINETEENTH	70 - SEVENTIETH
10 - TENTH	20 - TWENTIETH	75 - SEVENTY-FIFTH

Writing Rhyme

Words rhyme when their sounds correspond.

EXAMPLES:

hold	gold	wait	late
dare	scare	table	label
ride	side	follow	hollow

 Complete each short verse with a word which rhymes with the last word in the first line.

1. The sly, old fox
   hid in a __box__.

2. The cat
   sat on my __BAT__.

3. The brown and white dog
   jumped over a __LOG__.

4. My mother
   spanked my __BROTHER__.

5. The happy little boy
   played with a __TOY__.

6. The big plane
   flew through the __RAIN__.

7. A fish
   doesn't live in a __DISH__.

8. The hungry mouse
   moved out of the __HOUSE__.

9. Young Paul
   likes to play __BALL__.

10. A red rose
    doesn't look like a __NOSE__.

11. A turtle
    can't wear a __GIRDLE__.

12. That silly fly
    got stuck in the __PIE__.

13. Honey
    reminds me of __MONEY__.

14. These bears
    like to eat __PEARS__.

15. The bread
    tasted like __LEAD__.

16. The queen
    didn't want to be __SEEN__.

17. The room
    was swept with a __BROOM__.

18. A rocket
    won't fit in a __POCKET__.

19. They never fail
    to deliver the __MAIL__.

20. Snow and ice
    are not very __NICE__.

21. The judge
    makes good __FUDGE__.

22. It was too hot to run
    in the heat of the __SUN__.

23. The egg
    broke on my __LEG__.

24. The fawn
    fell asleep on the __LAWN__.

25. My thumb
    looks like a __PLUM__.

26. The snake
    crawled into the __LAKE__.

27. In a car
    you can go __FAR__.

28. The letter
    made me feel __BETTER__.

29. Fishes are free
    when they swim in the __SEA__.

30. When I go to school,
    I follow the __RULE__.

31. The king
    wore a gold __RING__.

32. Sally's play
    lasted all __DAY__.

33. I turned on the light,
    but it was too __BRIGHT__.

Unit 135 cont'd

Words That Are Spelled Alike

In a two-syllable word one syllable is usually said harder than the other. We call this syllable the stressed syllable and mark it with an accent mark (').

It is often possible to change the pronunciation of a word by stressing a different syllable. In such cases, the spelling of the word does not change. The meaning, however, does. For example, look at the word "record." "Record" may be pronounced as "rek ' ərd" which means "a cylinder, disk, or roll prepared so as to reproduce sounds." "Record" may also be pronounced as "ri kord'" which means "to write down."

 Read each sentence. Then underline the pronunciation and meaning of the word which fits the use of the underlined word in the sentence.

1. Before us lay miles of endless desert.
   a. <u>dez'ərt   hot, dry region</u>
   b. di zûrt'   to abandon

2. The mayor will address the assembly.
   a. <u>ə dres'   to speak to</u>
   b. ad'res   residence of a person

3. The commercial lasted one minute.
   a. mi noot'   exceedingly small
   b. <u>min'it   the 60th part of an hour</u>

4. I am the king, and you are the subject.
   a. <u>sub'jikt   under power of another</u>
   b. səb jekt'   to offer for consideration

5. The essay contest was won by Nicholas.
   a. kən test'   to argue about
   b. <u>kon'test   competition</u>

6. He is a rebel without a cause.
   a. ri bel'   to resist authority
   b. <u>reb'əl   one who rises against</u>

7. Marcus was content to stay at home.
   a. kon'tent   all that a thing contains
   b. <u>kən tent'   satisfied</u>

8. You must be present to win the contest.
   a. pri zent'   to introduce
   b. <u>prez'ənt   being at hand</u>

9. The students protest the war.
   a. pro'test   the act of objecting
   b. <u>prə test'   to object to</u>

10. I refuse to answer that question.
    a. <u>ri fyooz'   to decline to do</u>
    b. ref'yoos   anything worthless

11. Mr. Green signed a five-year contract.
    a. <u>kon'trakt   formal agreement</u>
    b. kən trakt'   to draw together

12. The two classes will combine their efforts.
    a. kom'bīn   machine used for harvesting
    b. <u>kəm bin'   to put together</u>

13. Contrast a democracy and a dictatorship.
    a. <u>kən trast'   to show dissimilarities</u>
    b. kon'trast   the unlikeness between two things

14. The meeting will conflict with our plans.
    a. <u>kən flikt'   to be in mutual opposition</u>
    b. kon'flikt   a struggle

COMPOSITION EXERCISE

Each of these words has two pronunciations. Write a sentence with each version.

1. minute

_____

_____

2. desert

_____

_____

Comprehension Check

(A) Write a synonym for each word.

1. write	scribble	11. see	watch	
2. mow	cut	12. answer	reply	
3. gripe	complain	13. shop	store	
4. grin	smile	14. finish	end	
5. money	funds	15. brag	boast	
6. present	current	16. female	woman	
7. change	alter	17. chatter	talk	
8. easy	simple	18. tune	song	
9. quick	fast	19. pick	choose	
10. nuisance	pest	20. simple	plain	

(B) Write an antonym for each word.

1. first	last	11. good	bad	
2. out	in	12. short	tall	
3. rich	poor	13. cooked	raw	
4. sad	happy	14. full	empty	
5. over	under	15. winner	loser	
6. late	early	16. dirty	clean	
7. even	odd	17. polite	rude	
8. after	before	18. heavy	light	
9. cool	warm	19. part	all	
10. hard	soft	20. day	night	

(C) Write a homonym for each word.

1. week	weak	8. meet	meat	
2. feet	feat	9. peek	peak	
3. wear	ware	10. allowed	aloud	
4. herd	heard	11. hymn	him	
5. root	route	12. soar	sore	
6. bin	been	13. would	wood	
7. maid	made	14. aide	aid	

15. whole	hole		
16. flea	flee		
17. steel	steal		
18. bored	board		
19. groan	grown		
20. knew	new		
21. inn	in		

(D) Identify each set of words.

(1) synonyms   **(2) antonyms**   **(3) homonyms**

_1_	1. guide...show	
_2_	2. wide...narrow	
_3_	3. straight...strait	
_3_	4. hanger...hangar	
_1_	5. sound...noise	
_2_	6. difficult...easy	
_3_	7. mail...male	
_2_	8. remember...forget	
_3_	9. flower...flour	
_2_	10. higher...lower	
_1_	11. glance...look	
_3_	12. guerrilla...gorilla	
_3_	13. sale...sail	
_1_	14. save...keep	
_3_	15. peace...piece	

_1_	16. count...number
_2_	17. more...less
_1_	18. wise...smart
_3_	19. hour...our
_3_	20. desert...dessert
_2_	21. new...old
_1_	22. awkward...clumsy
_3_	23. principal...principle
_2_	24. freeze...melt
_3_	25. capitol...capital
_2_	26. thin...thick
_1_	27. yearly...annually
_3_	28. sweet...suite
_1_	29. hope...wish
_2_	30. expensive...cheap

Test 27 cont'd

Comprehension Check (continued)

E Write the number words.

1 -	*one*	6 -	*six*	11 -	*eleven*	30 -	*thirty*
2 -	*two*	7 -	*seven*	15 -	*fifteen*	50 -	*fifty*
3 -	*three*	8 -	*eight*	17 -	*seventeen*	75 -	*seventy-five*
4 -	*four*	9 -	*nine*	20 -	*twenty*	81 -	*eighty-one*
5 -	*five*	10 -	*ten*	21 -	*twenty-one*	100 -	*hundred*

F Write a rhyming word for each of these words.

1. rhyme	*time*	11. walkie	*talkie*	21. honey	*money*
2. song	*long*	12. ray	*stay*	22. gate	*late*
3. write	*light*	13. camp	*damp*	23. settle	*kettle*
4. look	*cook*	14. car	*far*	24. green	*seen*
5. mean	*scene*	15. hazy	*crazy*	25. blank	*bank*
6. catch	*patch*	16. river	*liver*	26. friend	*lend*
7. spell	*tell*	17. thirty	*dirty*	27. float	*goat*
8. number	*slumber*	18. flower	*power*	28. game	*tame*
9. wax	*tax*	19. rust	*dust*	29. double	*trouble*
10. fudge	*smudge*	20. hero	*zero*	30. freeze	*breeze*

Look at the picture on the right. Write a paragraph describing your reaction to the picture. Underline any sets of synonyms you use.

328

Words with More Than One Meaning

Sometimes a word may have more than one definition. The definition may determine how the word is to be used in a sentence.

 Match the definitions with the sentences which best illustrate them.

I. count
   a. to name numbers
   b. to number things
   c. to depend on
   d. to be of importance

1. I am counting on you to help me.
2. In an emergency every minute counts.
3. Count from one to fifty.
4. Bobby counted his pennies.

II. step
   e. putting one foot before another
   f. degree or rank
   g. a short distance
   h. measure or action
   i. place for foot on ladder

5. The process can be done in three steps.
6. Step forward.
7. He is one step below a captain.
8. We live one step from the store.
9. Each step on the ladder was broken.

III. weak
   j. lacking authority
   k. unable to bear strain
   l. lacks physical strength

10. The illness left him weak.
11. Charles was a weak president.
12. The chair was too weak to hold him.

IV. heart
   m. organ that pumps blood
   n. central part
   o. one's feelings

13. She lives in the heart of town.
14. The heart is a muscle.
15. The old woman had a kind heart.

V. keen
   p. sharp edge
   q. mentally alert
   r. sensitive

16. The eagle has keen eyesight.
17. The knife had a keen edge.
18. We need someone with keen intelligence.

VI. fail
   s. neglect
   t. lose strength
   u. not to succeed

19. I tried to win but failed.
20. The man's hearing was failing.
21. He failed to do his duties.

VII. ground
   v. surface of the earth
   w. foundation

22. On what grounds are these charges based?
23. The ground was frozen.

Unit 136 cont'd

Words That Look Similar

Many words in the English language look similar, but their meanings and usages are quite different. Learn to recognize such words and to use them correctly.

EXAMPLES: sit...to be seated
set...to place or put
a. Set the dishes on the table.
b. Would you like to sit by the window?

❋ Complete each sentence with the correct word.

1. later . . . refers to time
   latter . . . refers to last named of two
   a. The __**LATTER**__ suggestion is better.
   b. The bus is __**LATER**__ than usual.

2. leave . . . to depart from
   let . . . to permit
   a. We will __**LEAVE**__ in the morning.
   b. __**LET**__ me help you.

3. then . . . adverb of time
   than . . . shows comparison
   a. What happened __**THEN**__?
   b. I like blue better __**THAN**__ red.

4. already . . . before or by time specified
   all ready . . . completely prepared
   a. He had __**ALREADY**__ cooked supper.
   b. Supper was __**ALL READY**__.

5. advice . . . counsel (noun)
   advise . . . to give counsel (verb)
   a. I __**ADVISE**__ you to tell them.
   b. I need your __**ADVICE**__.

6. lose . . . to cease having
   loose . . . to be free, not fastened
   a. Your top button is __**LOOSE**__.
   b. Did you __**LOSE**__ anything?

7. dessert . . . sweets such as pie, cake, etc.
   desert . . . hot, barren land
   a. He could not survive the __**DESERT**__ heat.
   b. Would you care for any __**DESSERT**__?

8. except . . . to exclude
   accept . . . to receive, to take
   a. Everyone signed __**EXCEPT**__ you.
   b. Will he __**ACCEPT**__ the position?

9. affect . . . to influence (verb)
   effect . . . the result (noun)
   a. What __**EFFECT**__ did her words have?
   b. Will this __**AFFECT**__ our grades?

10. accident . . . a misfortune by chance
    incident . . . a happening in general
    a. Joe had an __**ACCIDENT**__ with his bike.
    b. The __**INCIDENT**__ occurred at noon.

11. emigrated . . . to have left
    immigrated . . . to have come
    a. The family __**EMIGRATED**__ from Russia.
    b. The family __**IMMIGRATED**__ to Germany.

12. rise . . . to move upward
    raise . . . to cause to move upward
    a. The sun will __**RISE**__ at 5 a.m.
    b. Why didn't you __**RAISE**__ your hand?

COMPOSITION EXERCISE

Write a sentence with each of these words.

1. already, all ready

_____

_____

2. dessert, desert

_____

_____

330

Words That Are Often Confused

Often two words are confused because their meanings are similar. Learn to recognize these troublesome words and to use them correctly.

EXAMPLES: can...to be able
            may...to give permission
            a. May Sally go to the party?
            b. I can stand on my head.

❋   **Complete each sentence with the correct word.**

1. hanged . . . refers to people
   hung . . . refers to things
   a. The picture was ___*hung*___ in the hall.
   b. The outlaw was ___*hanged*___.

2. among . . . mingled with
   between . . . in the middle
   a. Sit **BETWEEN** Ralph and me.
   b. He was one **AMONG** millions.

3. teach . . . to impart knowledge
   learn . . . to receive knowledge
   a. I will **TEACH** you to swim.
   b. You must **LEARN** to divide fractions.

4. wonder . . . to be curious about
   wander . . . to move or travel about
   a. They **WANDER** about in search of food.
   b. I **WONDER** if he will come today.

5. beside . . . at the side of
   besides . . . in addition to
   a. The path **BESIDE** the river was muddy.
   b. **BESIDES** being rich, he is very smart.

6. job . . . present occupation
   career . . . type of work extending through life
   a. Rod has a **JOB** delivering groceries.
   b. Rod plans to pursue a **CAREER** in law.

7. amount . . . sum total
   number...a collection of units
   a. The bills **AMOUNT** to ten dollars.
   b. A great **NUMBER** of people will suffer.

8. either . . . one or the other of two
   neither . . . not one nor the other of two
   a. Choose **EITHER** green or orange.
   b. **NEITHER** Tim nor I knew him.

9. who . . . refers to people
   which . . . refers to things
   a. Take the letter **WHICH** is the largest.
   b. The man **WHO** spoke to you is Kelsey.

10. fewer . . . limited in number
    less . . . not as much as before
    a. **FEWER** people are attending.
    b. We have **LESS** today than ever before.

11. reason . . . the ground for any action
    excuse . . . an apology for an action
    a. There is no **EXCUSE** for being late.
    b. My **REASON** for the change is clear.

12. good . . . excellent (adjective)
    well . . . satisfactory, in good health
    a. Hilda doesn't feel **WELL** today.
    b. Marvin is a **GOOD** worker.

Unit 137 cont'd ➡

"Good" — "Well"

"Good" means "excellent." It is an adjective.
"Well" means "satisfactory" or "in good health." It may be an adjective or an adverb.

EXAMPLES: a. *Sherry looks well.*
b. *I need a good worker.*

 Underline each sentence that uses "good" or "well" correctly.

1. <u>We had a good time.</u>
   We had a well time.
2. I feel good again.
   <u>I feel well again.</u>
3. <u>Give me some good advice.</u>
   Give me some well advice.
4. <u>The idea worked well.</u>
   The idea worked good.
5. <u>She doesn't look well.</u>
   <u>She doesn't look good.</u>
6. <u>It was a good story.</u>
   It was a well story.
7. The job was done good.
   <u>The job was well done.</u>
8. <u>My dog is well now.</u>
   My dog is good now.
9. Josh makes well grades.
   <u>Josh makes good grades.</u>
10. Was that a well show?
    <u>Was that a good show?</u>
11. <u>Everyone is well and happy.</u>
    Everyone is good and happy.
12. We had a well time.
    <u>We had a good time.</u>

13. <u>Sara feels well.</u>
    <u>Sara feels good.</u>
14. Lynne is a well friend.
    <u>Lynne is a good friend.</u>
15. <u>Are you well enough to go?</u>
    Are you good enough to go?
16. Kay is a well swimmer.
    <u>Kay is a good swimmer.</u>
17. This is a well book.
    <u>This is a good book.</u>
18. The medicine will make you good.
    <u>The medicine will make you well.</u>
19. <u>Don't you feel well?</u>
    Don't you feel good?
20. <u>A good player is needed.</u>
    A well player is needed.
21. She works good.
    <u>She works well.</u>
22. <u>My aunt is not well.</u>
    My aunt is not good.
23. <u>Have a good trip.</u>
    Have a well trip.
24. <u>She is a good student.</u>
    She is a well student.

COMPOSITION EXERCISE

Write 5 sentences using "good" and 5 using "well."

good

1. _____
2. _____
3. _____
4. _____
5. _____

well

1. _____
2. _____
3. _____
4. _____
5. _____

"Hear" — "Here"

"Hear" is a verb. It means "to listen to."
"Here" is an adverb. It refers to a place.

EXAMPLES: a. Sit here.   c. Sue can't hear us.
           b. I hear the whistle.   d. Let's stop here.

Write either "hear" or "here" in each blank.

1. Come __here__.
2. Mom will __HEAR__ us.
3. The bus is __HERE__.
4. Bring the book __HERE__.
5. __HERE__ is the money.
6. I can't __HEAR__ you.
7. Susan is __HERE__.
8. I __HEAR__ noises.
9. Can you __HEAR__ it?
10. __HERE__ come the police.
11. The plumber is __HERE__.
12. Did you __HEAR__ the bell?
13. I couldn't __HEAR__ anything.
14. __HERE__ is the answer.
15. I have been waiting __HERE__.
16. I can __HEAR__ the baby.
17. She will __HEAR__ you whisper.
18. I __HEAR__ the train.
19. The pain is __HERE__.
20. The dog will __HEAR__ them.
21. We moved __HERE__ in July.
22. Do you live __HERE__?
23. Let's sit __HERE__.
24. She will __HEAR__ me.
25. Wait __HERE__ for me.

26. I __HEAR__ the music.
27. John lives __HERE__.
28. They can __HEAR__ the radio.
29. __HERE__ is my idea.
30. Did Mary come __HERE__?
31. All of us are __HERE__.
32. When will you be __HERE__?
33. I __HEAR__ you singing.
34. You can stay __HERE__.
35. Why are you __HERE__?
36. Put the chair __HERE__.
37. Let's __HEAR__ your plan.
38. I can't __HEAR__ the questions.
39. Did you __HEAR__ the answer?
40. Why did you come __HERE__?
41. Tell him I am __HERE__.
42. I want to __HEAR__ it.
43. Do you __HEAR__ a piano?
44. I work __HERE__.
45. Let me __HEAR__ the speech.
46. I know you __HEAR__ me.
47. Set the box __HERE__.
48. Sign __HERE__ please.
49. I __HEAR__ footsteps.
50. Didn't you __HEAR__ me?

COMPOSITION EXERCISE

Write 5 sentences using "hear" and 5 using "here."

hear
1. _____
2. _____
3. _____
4. _____
5. _____

here
1. _____
2. _____
3. _____
4. _____
5. _____

Unit 138 cont'd

"It's" — "Its"

"It's" means "it is." "Its" shows ownership.

EXAMPLES: a. It's too early to go. c. Its branches are broken.
  b. Its eyes are red. d. It's starting to rain.

 Write "it's" or "its" in each blank.

1. __It's__ raining.
2. __ITS__ pages are torn.
3. __IT'S__ time to go.
4. __IT'S__ not an easy test.
5. What is __ITS__ name?
6. __IT'S__ too short.
7. Where is __ITS__ home?
8. __IT'S__ called an elephant.
9. __IT'S__ finally finished.
10. __ITS__ ending was sad.
11. This is __ITS__ engine.
12. __ITS__ wing is broken.
13. __IT'S__ after me again.
14. __ITS__ eyes are open.
15. __IT'S__ a beautiful gift.
16. __IT'S__ my party.
17. __IT'S__ three o'clock.
18. The kitten broke __ITS__ foot.
19. This is __ITS__ house.
20. __IT'S__ burning my hand.
21. __IT'S__ a pretty color.
22. Don't pull __ITS__ tail.
23. __IT'S__ too wet outside.
24. __IT'S__ working.
25. __IT'S__ never too late.

26. __ITS__ home is in Arizona.
27. __IT'S__ past your bedtime.
28. Did you see __ITS__ teeth?
29. The tree lost __ITS__ leaves.
30. __IT'S__ mine.
31. The bird hurt __ITS__ wing.
32. __IT'S__ cold outside.
33. I broke __ITS__ lid.
34. __IT'S__ for your birthday.
35. __IT'S__ my pencil.
36. Don't touch __ITS__ nose.
37. __IT'S__ my turn to wash.
38. I think __IT'S__ great.
39. __IT'S__ a footprint.
40. You hold __ITS__ head.
41. __IT'S__ for my sister.
42. I like __ITS__ ending.
43. __IT'S__ not long enough.
44. __IT'S__ the wrong color.
45. The train blew __ITS__ whistle.
46. I hope __IT'S__ ready.
47. __ITS__ nose is cold.
48. __ITS__ leaves are yellow.
49. __IT'S__ not yours.
50. __ITS__ cage was open.

COMPOSITION EXERCISE

Write 5 sentences using "it's" and 5 using "its."

it's

1. _____
2. _____
3. _____
4. _____
5. _____

its

1. _____
2. _____
3. _____
4. _____
5. _____

"Leave" — "Let"

"Leave" means "to go away." "Let" means "to allow."

EXAMPLES: a. I will leave Thursday. c. I will let you look.
b. Let me find you one. d. Leave the book on the table.

 Write "leave" or "let" in each blank.

1. Did you __leave__ this?
2. I __LET__ him go.
3. You must __LEAVE__ now.
4. I will __LEAVE__ tomorrow.
5. She __LET__ him have it.
6. Are you ready to __LEAVE__?
7. __LET__ us go.
8. __LEAVE__ me alone.
9. Did he __LEAVE__ yet?
10. We are going to __LEAVE__.
11. __LET__ us eat.
12. Don't __LEAVE__ me here.
13. Don't __LET__ it happen.
14. The bus will __LEAVE__ soon.
15. Who __LET__ him go?
16. __LET__ them speak.
17. May I __LEAVE__?
18. __LET__ it go.
19. When will he __LEAVE__?
20. No one may __LEAVE__ yet.
21. She wants to __LEAVE__.
22. Don't __LET__ him know.
23. I won't __LEAVE__ you.
24. __LET__ him eat.
25. Did you __LEAVE__ this book?

26. I will __LET__ you see it.
27. __LEAVE__ him at home.
28. The plane is going to __LEAVE__.
29. __LET__ her take it home.
30. We must __LEAVE__ for school.
31. I can't __LET__ you have it.
32. __LEAVE__ me the money.
33. __LET__ her in.
34. When will you __LEAVE__?
35. Did you __LEAVE__ anything?
36. She __LET__ me hold the dog.
37. Don't __LET__ her touch it.
38. __LET__ me feed the baby.
39. They will __LEAVE__ tonight.
40. Who __LET__ you in?
41. I know you __LEAVE__ early.
42. Don't __LET__ him stay here.
43. __LEAVE__ the room.
44. __LET__ me help you.
45. I will __LET__ you know.
46. Are you going to __LEAVE__ me?
47. __LET__ me taste the cake.
48. __LET__ him sleep.
49. You will __LEAVE__ now.
50. __LET__ the dog go outside.

COMPOSITION EXERCISE

Write 5 sentences using "leave" and 5 using "let."

leave	let
1. _____	1. _____
2. _____	2. _____
3. _____	3. _____
4. _____	4. _____
5. _____	5. _____

Unit 139 cont'd

"Lose" — "Loose"

"Lose" means "to not have any longer."
"Loose" means "not fastened."

EXAMPLES: a. I will lose the fight.   c. The doorknob seems loose.
               b. The chain is loose.   d. They always lose.

Write "lose" or "loose" in each blank.

1. The ribbon is __loose__.
2. Did you __LOSE__ this?
3. My belt is too __LOOSE__.
4. Where did you __LOSE__ it?
5. We will __LOSE__ the bet.
6. Don't pull __LOOSE__ threads.
7. A __LOOSE__ wheel is dangerous.
8. We can't __LOSE__ now.
9. Our team isn't going to __LOSE__.
10. The knob is __LOOSE__.
11. Did you __LOSE__ the race?
12. Your button is __LOOSE__.
13. Nothing is __LOOSE__.
14. How did it get __LOOSE__?
15. You will __LOSE__.
16. How much did you __LOSE__?
17. The dog is __LOOSE__.
18. Did you __LOSE__ a button?
19. The caboose came __LOOSE__.
20. Paul will __LOSE__ the race.
21. I never __LOSE__.
22. It feels __LOOSE__.
23. How could it be __LOOSE__?
24. You tried to __LOSE__.
25. Your tie is __LOOSE__.

26. They will __LOSE__ the game.
27. All of the animals are __LOOSE__.
28. The cap is not __LOOSE__.
29. What did you __LOSE__?
30. You can't __LOSE__ it.
31. Does it look __LOOSE__?
32. Is that all you __LOSE__?
33. This tooth is __LOOSE__.
34. The handle is __LOOSE__.
35. When did you __LOSE__ them?
36. Don't __LOSE__ your hat.
37. I won't __LOSE__ you.
38. The horse broke __LOOSE__.
39. Did we __LOSE__?
40. How could you __LOSE__ them?
41. This is too much to __LOSE__.
42. Everyone will __LOSE__.
43. The birds are __LOOSE__.
44. Did anyone __LOSE__ a pencil?
45. Your seatbelt is too __LOOSE__.
46. The prisoner is __LOOSE__.
47. What will we __LOSE__?
48. The screw was __LOOSE__.
49. I have nothing to __LOSE__.
50. When did you __LOSE__ your ball?

COMPOSITION EXERCISE

Write 5 sentences using "lose" and 5 using "loose."

lose
1. _____
2. _____
3. _____
4. _____
5. _____

loose
1. _____
2. _____
3. _____
4. _____
5. _____

"May" — "Can"

"May" is used to ask permission. It means "to be permitted or allowed." "Can" means "to be able."

EXAMPLES: **a. May I have a cookie?**   **c. I can do it.**

               b. Can you drive?   **d. You may play outside.**

 Write "may" or "can" in each blank.

1. __May__ I go?
2. I __CAN__ play ball.
3. When __MAY__ I have it?
4. __CAN__ you hear the noise?
5. What __CAN__ you do?
6. It __CAN__ be done.
7. You __MAY__ not talk.
8. I __CAN__ work the problem.
9. __MAY__ I have one now?
10. Sue __CAN__ play the piano.
11. You __MAY__ have your dessert.
12. I __CAN__ hear you.
13. When __MAY__ I see it?
14. __MAY__ I go to the show?
15. I __CAN__ not carry you.
16. I __CAN__ not find any.
17. You __MAY__ use mine.
18. I __CAN__ sew.
19. __MAY__ I come in?
20. You __MAY__ sit here.
21. I __CAN__ not see you.
22. We __CAN__ not close the box.
23. __MAY__ I talk to Sally?
24. __CAN__ you help me?
25. You __MAY__ watch the show.
26. __CAN__ you see it?
27. __MAY__ I help you?
28. You __MAY__ begin.
29. I __CAN__ fix it.
30. You __MAY__ go now.
31. I __CAN__ work the puzzle.
32. __MAY__ we have some candy?
33. I __CAN__ not walk.
34. You __CAN__ try.
35. She __CAN__ swim.
36. __MAY__ I buy this one?
37. __MAY__ Dan stay for lunch?
38. My mom __CAN__ drive a bus.
39. I __CAN__ change the tire.
40. __MAY__ I go home with you?
41. How many __CAN__ you eat?
42. I __CAN__ write my name.
43. You __MAY__ use my desk.
44. They __CAN__ see everything.
45. Jake __CAN__ run faster.
46. You __MAY__ answer the question.
47. I __CAN__ hear an echo.
48. We __CAN__ not finish on time.
49. You __MAY__ not go.
50. __MAY__ we go to the park?

COMPOSITION EXERCISE

Write 5 sentences using "may" and 5 using "can."

            may   **can**

1. _____   1. _____
2. _____   2. _____
3. _____   3. _____
4. _____   4. _____
5. _____   5. _____

Unit 140 cont'd

"Sit" — "Set"

"Sit" means "to rest." It does not require an object. "Set" means "to put." It requires an object.

EXAMPLES: a. *Karen will sit here.*   c. *Set the plate in the sink.*
               b. *I set the table.*   d. *Sit on the couch.*

✱ Write "sit" or "set" in each blank.

1. Did you __sit__ on my hat?
2. I __SET__ the glass on the table.
3. You may __SIT__ here.
4. __SET__ the box in the corner.
5. We will __SIT__ on the sofa.
6. __SIT__ next to the window.
7. Won't you __SIT__ down?
8. She __SET__ the package on the floor.
9. __SET__ the table.
10. We __SET__ the time.
11. Don't __SIT__ on the table.
12. Can't you __SIT__ still?
13. __SET__ this chair in the hallway.
14. I will __SET__ the alarm.
15. May I __SIT__ with you?
16. Please __SIT__ down and rest.
17. __SET__ those on the table.
18. I am going to __SIT__ here.
19. __SIT__ in the corner.
20. __SET__ the bottle down.
21. __SIT__ on my lap.
22. Let's __SET__ up camp.
23. Don't __SIT__ there.
24. __SET__ the dial on the TV.
25. Don't __SIT__ on the grass.

26. __SET__ the timer.
27. Did you __SIT__ in the mud?
28. Let's __SIT__ outside.
29. I __SET__ my watch.
30. __SIT__ down.
31. __SET__ the candle on the shelf.
32. Why did you __SIT__ alone?
33. __SIT__ at your own desk.
34. Tom __SET__ the books on my desk.
35. You can't __SIT__ there.
36. Where did you __SET__ them?
37. Would you __SET__ the clock here?
38. May I __SIT__ and rest?
39. We __SET__ the dishes in the cabinet.
40. The comedian will __SIT__ next to me.
41. Who __SET__ this here?
42. I want to __SIT__ on a horse.
43. Don't __SIT__ in the water.
44. The monkey will __SIT__ on your lap.
45. __SET__ the pan on the stove.
46. __SIT__ straight.
47. __SET__ your shoes in the closet.
48. Let's __SET__ the desk in the corner.
49. How could you __SIT__ on a fish?
50. I told you to __SIT__ .

COMPOSITION EXERCISE

Write 5 sentences using "sit" and 5 using "set."

sit	set
1. _____	1. _____
2. _____	2. _____
3. _____	3. _____
4. _____	4. _____
5. _____	5. _____

Comprehension Check

(A) Underline the correct answers.

1. Jim had an (accident, incident) on his skateboard.
2. The moon will (rise, raise) at 7:15 p.m.
3. I think your belt is too (lose, loose).
4. We'll discuss the (latter, later) topic.
5. We always eat (dessert, desert) after dinner.
6. How will this gas (affect, effect) the engine?
7. The (accident, incident) was a big argument.
8. (Then, Than) we bought a new tape.
9. Did you (loose, lose) Jan's address?
10. (Leave, Let) me alone!
11. You should take my (advice, advise).
12. The Pilgrims (immigrated, emigrated) from England.

13. We'll have (either, neither) hamburgers or hot dogs.
14. Large cactus plants are found in the (dessert, desert).
15. Put the paper (among, between) the two folders.
16. We (hanged, hung) the ornament on the tree.
17. The grass (beside, besides) the track is too high.
18. There are (fewer, less) students this year.
19. Jill (excepted, accepted) a car from her aunt.
20. (Either, Neither) Mom nor Dad is home.
21. We've (all ready, already) tried to call.
22. A large (amount, number) of people jogged today.
23. The animals (wandered, wondered) through the field.
24. Everyone attended (except, accept) three students.

(B) Write either "here" or "hear."

1. _Here_ comes my little brother.
2. Look _here_ .
3. I don't want to _hear_ another excuse.
4. Do you _hear_ well?
5. _Here_ is the new record.
6. Let's _hear_ your song.
7. You may stay _here_ with us.
8. She put the garbage _here_ .
9. Did you _hear_ the news?
10. Sarah could _hear_ Tim's voice.
11. Will you be _here_ Thursday?
12. Only the dog can _hear_ the whistle.

(C) Write either "its" or "it's."

1. The dog licked _its_ paw.
2. _It's_ my birthday!
3. _It's_ an interesting book.
4. I liked _its_ ending.
5. _It's_ a beautiful spring day.
6. Do you think _it's_ too late?
7. The bird flew from _its_ nest.
8. I dropped _its_ lid.
9. _Its_ color was too bright.
10. _It's_ a bright blue color.
11. The car lost _its_ wheel.
12. Do you know if _it's_ finished?

(D) Write either "lose" or "loose."

1. Did Brian _lose_ his keys?
2. Try not to _lose_ my notebook.
3. The screen is _loose_ .
4. Turn _loose_ of the handle.
5. Everyone will _lose_ .
6. The doorknob is _loose_ .
7. Do you think it's _loose_ ?
8. I don't intend to _lose_ the contest.
9. She knocked the fence _loose_ .
10. Give me your _loose_ change.
11. I can't get _loose_ from the rope.
12. I'll never _lose_ to you!

(E) Write either "good" or "well."

1. The medicine helped her get _well_ .
2. My sister doesn't feel _well_ .
3. Do you feel _well_ enough to go?
4. Her advice was _good_ .
5. The story was _good_ .
6. He told the story _well_ .
7. This is a _good_ movie.
8. She plays the guitar _well_ .
9. She's a _good_ musician.
10. Karen's plan worked _well_ .
11. Everyone is _good_ at the game.
12. Amy answered the question very _well_ .

Test 28 cont'd

Comprehension Check (continued)

(F) Write either "sit" or "set."

1. _____Set_____ the table, please.
2. We'll _____sit_____ on the sofa.
3. Did you _____set_____ the plant in the sun?
4. Please _____sit_____ down.
5. Let the puppy _____sit_____ on your lap.
6. Jenny _____set_____ her clock on the shelf.
7. Help me _____set_____ up the tent.
8. Don't _____sit_____ on my hat!
9. _____Set_____ the clock for six a.m.
10. Will you _____sit_____ beside me?
11. We'll _____sit_____ outside.
12. Ted, _____set_____ the package on the steps.

(G) Underline the sentences which best fit the definitions.

1. "Keen" means "mentally alert."   a. <u>Her idea showed keen intelligence.</u>   b. She was keen on the idea.
2. "Fan" means "cause air to move."   a. Please turn off the fan.   b. <u>Fan the smoke out of the kitchen.</u>
3. "Fail" means "neglect."   a. <u>Don't fail to do your homework.</u>   b. The engine will fail soon.
4. "Step" means "measure or action."   a. <u>Follow these steps.</u>   b. Take the steps off the ladder.
5. "Heart" means "central part."   a. Check your heart rate.   b. <u>This is the heart of the city.</u>
6. "Count" means "to name numbers."   a. You can count on his support.   b. <u>How many can you count?</u>
7. "Weak" means "lacking authority."   a. <u>The colonel is a weak leader.</u>   b. His legs felt weak.
8. "Ground" means "foundation."   a. <u>What are your grounds for refusal?</u>   b. Tina is grounded for a month.
9. "State" means "to speak."   a. <u>State your case.</u>   b. Which state is the largest?
10. "Light" means "make bright."   a. <u>Please light the fire.</u>   b. The light is dim.
11. "Shift" means "change."   a. Bob works on the late shift.   b. <u>Shift into third gear.</u>
12. "Type" means "kind."   a. <u>She bought this type of makeup.</u>   b. Type a letter for me.
13. "Float" means "remain suspended."   a. This parade float is pretty.   b. <u>Can you float in the water?</u>
14. "Drive" means "to operate."   a. We went for a drive.   b. <u>Marge learned to drive.</u>
15. "Answer" means "to respond."   a. <u>Can you answer the question?</u>   b. Your answer is silly.
16. "Time" means "to measure."   a. <u>Time our speeches for us.</u>   b. What time is it?

Write a paragraph about your favorite vacation. Choose one word to use two different ways. Underline it each time you use it.

_____
_____
_____
_____
_____
_____

"Teach" — "Learn"

"Teach" means "to help to learn." "Learn"
means "to find out about." Both are verbs.

EXAMPLES: a. *Dad teaches history to college students.*
b. *I would like to learn to play the organ.*

 Underline the correct sentences.

1. <u>The teacher teaches us.</u>
   The teacher learns us.
2. <u>The students learn to read</u>.
   The students teach to read.
3. I will learn you to write.
   <u>I will teach you to write</u>.
4. He learned me to swim.
   <u>He taught me to swim.</u>
5. <u>I learned to play football</u>.
   I taught to play football.
6. <u>She teaches math to fifth graders</u>.
   She learns math to fifth graders.
7. <u>I taught them about China</u>.
   I learned them about China.
8. <u>Coach Jones taught us the rules</u>.
   Coach Jones learned us the rules.
9. We are teaching to sew.
   <u>We are learning to sew</u>.
10. Will you learn me to ride?
    <u>Will you teach me to ride</u>?
11. <u>You will teach her how to divide</u>.
    You will learn her how to divide.
12. <u>Mrs. Sims taught us reading</u>.
    Mrs. Sims learned us reading.

13. I am teaching to cook.
    <u>I am learning to cook</u>.
14. <u>My dad teaches English to Chinese</u>.
    My dad learns English to Chinese.
15. <u>Where did you learn to spell</u>?
    Where did you teach to spell?
16. I learned Eric.
    <u>I taught Eric</u>.
17. My sister learned me to play.
    <u>My sister taught me to play</u>.
18. <u>I taught him their names</u>.
    I learned him their names.
19. Where did you learn her the song?
    <u>Where did you teach her the song</u>?
20. <u>I will teach the class</u>.
    I will learn the class.
21. <u>When did you learn the truth</u>?
    When did you taught the truth?
22. She learned me.
    <u>She teaches me</u>.
23. Learn me how to fly.
    <u>Teach me how to fly</u>.
24. I learn music to them.
    <u>I teach music to them</u>.

COMPOSITION EXERCISE

Write 5 sentences using "teach" and 5 using "learn."

teach	learn
1. _____	1. _____
2. _____	2. _____
3. _____	3. _____
4. _____	4. _____
5. _____	5. _____

Unit 141 cont'd →

"Their" — "They're" — "There"

"Their" shows ownership. "They're" means "they are." "There" shows direction; it may also begin a sentence.

EXAMPLES: a. This is their book.   c. There are twenty questions.
　　　　　 b. They're coming.   d. Tim lives there.

✱　Write "their," "they're", or "there" in each blank.

1. __They're__ my friends.
2. __THEIR__ house is brick.
3. __THERE__ is the thief.
4. Give them __THEIR__ money.
5. She is __THEIR__ mother.
6. __THEY'RE__ leaving today.
7. I lived __THERE__.
8. Dad works __THERE__.
9. __THEY'RE__ nice people.
10. __THEY'RE__ good students.
11. We will go __THERE__.
12. This is __THEIR__ home.
13. __THEY'RE__ always friendly.
14. __THERE__ it is.
15. Be __THERE__ at 10 o'clock.
16. You told __THEIR__ father.
17. __THEY'RE__ here to see you.
18. __THEY'RE__ ready to begin.
19. Janet lives __THERE__.
20. Show me __THEIR__ papers.
21. __THEY'RE__ going to New York.
22. __THEY'RE__ not listening.
23. Look over __THERE__.
24. I am __THEIR__ friend.
25. __THEY'RE__ always busy.

26. I am __THEIR__ father.
27. __THEIR__ teacher is Ms. Owens.
28. __THEY'RE__ from New York.
29. Have you seen __THEIR__ bus?
30. __THERE__ is my house.
31. What is __THEIR__ story?
32. Where is __THEIR__ home?
33. Jenny was __THERE__ too.
34. __THEIR__ house was robbed.
35. They did __THEIR__ best.
36. Have you been __THERE__?
37. __THEY'RE__ not coming today.
38. No one was __THERE__.
39. I went __THERE__ yesterday.
40. __THEY'RE__ not ready to go.
41. __THEY'RE__ working too hard.
42. I like __THEIR__ house.
43. Don't go __THERE__ again.
44. __THERE__ is my car.
45. __THEY'RE__ rude to everyone.
46. Do you know __THEIR__ names?
47. __THEY'RE__ going to help you.
48. What is __THEIR__ secret?
49. __THEY'RE__ talking about us.
50. I will meet you __THERE__.

COMPOSITION EXERCISE

Write three sentences for each of these words.

1. their

_____

_____

_____

2. they're

_____

3. there

_____

_____

_____

"This" — "These"

"This" and "these" are adjectives that refer to things which are near you.
"This" is singular.
"These" is plural.

EXAMPLES: a. This story is true.
            b. I picked these flowers.

c. These sentences are questions.
d. Did you write this note?

 Write "this" or "these" in each blank.

1. __This__ book is interesting.
2. __THESE__ stories are false.
3. __THESE__ cars were stolen.
4. __THIS__ show is good.
5. __THIS__ man is a doctor.
6. __THESE__ cookies are burned.
7. __THESE__ apples are rotten.
8. __THESE__ clues are helpful.
9. __THIS__ light is too bright.
10. I want __THIS__ desk.
11. __THESE__ people are my friends.
12. __THIS__ money is mine.
13. __THESE__ gifts are for you.
14. __THIS__ room is yours.
15. I made __THIS__ hat.
16. __THESE__ pencils are broken.
17. I know __THIS__ man.
18. Mail __THESE__ letters.
19. __THIS__ package came today.
20. I like __THIS__ color.
21. __THIS__ page is wet.
22. __THIS__ train is leaving now.
23. __THESE__ shirts are too small.
24. Can you work __THESE__ problems?
25. Have you read __THESE__ poems?

26. Have you seen __THESE__ pictures?
27. __THESE__ men know you.
28. __THIS__ house needs paint.
29. I found __THESE__ papers.
30. __THESE__ shoes are muddy.
31. __THIS__ bike is green.
32. __THIS__ dog is a poodle.
33. I will choose __THIS__ one.
34. Do you like __THESE__ games?
35. __THIS__ wagon is mine.
36. __THIS__ weather is terrible.
37. __THESE__ skates are bent.
38. Did you break __THESE__ dishes?
39. Do you like __THIS__ dress?
40. Take __THESE__ towels upstairs.
41. __THIS__ man is a thief.
42. I hate __THESE__ vegetables.
43. __THIS__ food is delicious.
44. __THESE__ men were working.
45. I've seen __THIS__ show.
46. I bought __THIS__ present for you.
47. __THIS__ candy is too soft.
48. __THESE__ flowers are beautiful.
49. __THIS__ class is over.
50. The meeting is __THIS__ morning.

COMPOSITION EXERCISE

Write 5 sentences using "this" and 5 using "these."

this

1. _____
2. _____
3. _____
4. _____
5. _____

these

1. _____
2. _____
3. _____
4. _____
5. _____

Unit 142 cont'd

"That" — "Those"

"That" and "those" are adjectives that refer to things which are away from you. "That" is singular. "Those" is plural.

EXAMPLES: a. I chose that poem.
  b. Those people are angry.
  c. Where are those books?
  d. That story is my favorite.

✱ Write "that" or "those" in each blank.

1. __That__ coat is mine.
2. __THOSE__ books were stolen.
3. Did you see __THAT__ car?
4. Who ate __THOSE__ cookies?
5. I like __THAT__ one.
6. __THAT__ man hit me.
7. __THOSE__ answers are incorrect.
8. __THAT__ paper is yours.
9. Is __THAT__ lady your mother?
10. __THOSE__ flowers are beautiful.
11. Who are __THOSE__ people?
12. Who closed __THOSE__ doors?
13. __THOSE__ dishes are dirty.
14. __THAT__ room is empty.
15. __THOSE__ tomatoes aren't ripe.
16. Who drew __THAT__ picture?
17. __THAT__ cartoon was funny.
18. __THAT__ nurse is pretty.
19. __THOSE__ questions were easy.
20. Can you spell __THOSE__ words?
21. __THAT__ bird is hurt.
22. Who fed __THOSE__ animals?
23. Why did you pick __THOSE__ apples?
24. __THAT__ radio doesn't work.
25. __THOSE__ girls look alike.

26. __THAT__ man is my father.
27. What happened to __THOSE__ books?
28. Who closed __THAT__ window?
29. Where are __THOSE__ pencils?
30. __THAT__ music is too loud.
31. __THOSE__ grapes are too sour.
32. Who brought __THOSE__ cookies?
33. __THAT__ woman is famous.
34. __THAT__ breeze feels cool.
35. __THOSE__ stars are far away.
36. __THAT__ dream was scary.
37. __THAT__ money was stolen.
38. Have you seen __THAT__ man before?
39. __THAT__ story was interesting.
40. I took __THOSE__ pictures.
41. Don't pull __THOSE__ strings.
42. __THOSE__ socks look terrible.
43. Can't you fix __THOSE__ skates?
44. __THAT__ boy was polite.
45. __THAT__ cake is too sweet.
46. __THOSE__ girls are my sisters.
47. __THOSE__ shoes need cleaning.
48. __THOSE__ roses are for you.
49. I caught __THAT__ fish.
50. Did you mail __THOSE__ letters?

COMPOSITION EXERCISE

Write 5 sentences using "that" and 5 using "those."

that
1. _____
2. _____
3. _____
4. _____
5. _____

those
1. _____
2. _____
3. _____
4. _____
5. _____

"To" — "Too" — "Two"

"To" is a preposition.
"Too" means "also" or "more than enough."
"Two" is a number.

EXAMPLES: a. *I went to the store.*   c. *This is too much homework.*
         b. *Here are two books.*   d. *I am going too.*

✳ In each blank write either "to," "too," or "two" to make each sentence correct.

1. Please go __to__ the pitcher's mound.
2. This is __TOO__ small.
3. __TWO__ men left work early.
4. We are going __TO__ town.
5. I ate __TWO__ apples.
6. Is this __TOO__ long?
7. The cake is __TOO__ sweet.
8. Go __TO__ bed now.
9. I bought __TWO__ hats.
10. The __TWO__ dogs were fighting.
11. Throw the ball __TO__ John.
12. The __TWO__ boys were playing.
13. The road was __TOO__ bumpy.
14. Don't go __TOO__ far.
15. I will come __TO__ the party.
16. You may have __TWO__ wishes.
17. I went __TO__ the beach with Sandra.
18. My hair is __TOO__ short.
19. Are you going __TO__ the library?
20. I have __TWO__ dimes.
21. Every Sunday we drive __TO__ the city.
22. The boys went __TO__ the creek.
23. You talk __TOO__ much.
24. We will be gone __TWO__ days.
25. I am going __TO__ school.

26. Am I __TOO__ late?
27. Go __TO__ your room.
28. Dean went __TO__ the store.
29. She needs __TWO__ tickets.
30. The show lasted __TWO__ hours.
31. They went __TO__ the zoo in Memphis.
32. I have __TWO__ pets.
33. I was absent __TWO__ days.
34. Don't go __TO__ the movies today.
35. I ate __TOO__ much.
36. You can come __TOO__.
37. Let's go __TO__ the zoo.
38. Joe ran __TO__ the park.
39. We baked __TWO__ pies.
40. We are moving __TO__ Chicago.
41. The shelf is __TOO__ high.
42. I have __TWO__ teachers.
43. The music is __TOO__ loud.
44. The tree fell __TO__ the ground.
45. Sit next __TO__ the window.
46. I have __TWO__ brothers.
47. The test is __TOO__ easy.
48. Susan is going __TO__ Kansas.
49. Who wrote this note __TO__ me?
50. I received __TWO__ letters.

COMPOSITION EXERCISE

Write three sentences for each of these words.

1. to
_____
_____
_____

2. two
_____

3. too
_____
_____
_____

Unit 143 cont'd ➡

Figures of Speech

When we speak or write exactly what we mean, we call this **literal** speech. For example, I **walked** to the kitchen to answer the telephone. Sometimes we use a figure of speech to give a picture of what we are trying to say — I **flew** to answer the telephone. As you see, figurative language is imaginative, picturesque, and effective. Figures of speech are called **similes** or **metaphors**. We all use them; many common ones are used too often, such as **cold as ice** or **busy as a bee**.

A Use your imagination and dictionary to make new figures of speech for these words. The picture with each shows the overworked expression. You make a new one.

1. slow as _____

2. hot as _____

3. sings like _____

4. as fast as _____

5. cold as _____

6. sharp as _____

7. smart as _____

8. mad as _____

B Write a short story here, and try to make it interesting by using figures of speech. Caution: don't use worn-out figures of speech.

_____
_____
_____
_____
_____
_____
_____
_____
_____
_____
_____
_____
_____
_____
_____
_____
_____
_____
_____
_____
_____
_____
_____
_____
_____
_____
_____
_____
_____
_____

Using Idioms

A Draw a line from each idiom to its meaning.

1.	by and by	a.	find out about
2.	in a nutshell	b.	try to get the favor of
3.	get wind of	c.	sometimes
4.	well-to-do	d.	in a few words
5.	in the nick of time	e.	look after
6.	play up to	f.	after a little while
7.	how about	g.	just at the right time
8.	on the sly	h.	having enough money to live well
9.	now and then	i.	what do you say to
10.	and so on	j.	to avoid someone
11.	give someone the slip	k.	more of the same
12.	keep an eye on	l.	secretly

B Here are some sentences that contain idiomatic phrases using the word "mind." Read each sentence; then find the definition that explains its meaning as it is used in the sentence. Write the letter of the definition in the blank by the sentence.

___e___ 1. The boy changed his mind about going to the game.

___c___ 2. I had my mind set on getting a dog.

___f___ 3. Reading took her mind off the sad event.

___a___ 4. Bear in mind the amount of homework you must do.

___h___ 5. I have a mind to tell her just what I think of her.

___b___ 6. Mother had to make up her mind what to fix for dinner.

___g___ 7. We were both of one mind.

___d___ 8. The job Mother told me to do passed right out of my mind.

a.	remember	d.	was forgotten	g.	have the same opinion
b.	decide	e.	to change one's intentions	h.	think of doing
c.	want very much	f.	to stop thinking about		

COMPOSITION EXERCISE

Use each idiom from part A in a sentence.

1. _____   7. _____

2. _____   8. _____

3. _____   9. _____

4. _____   10. _____

5. _____   11. _____

6. _____   12. _____

347

Unit 144 cont'd

Fun with Words

Sometimes we do not always say exactly what we mean. We may use short phrases which imply meanings. These phrases would not make sense if they were to be taken literally. For example, the phrase "cat's got your tongue" does not mean that you have lost your tongue to a cat. It is used to suggest that you cannot speak.

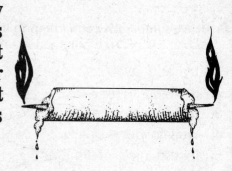

 Underline the best meaning of each phrase.

1. burning the candle at both ends
   a. setting fire to both sides of a candle
   b. <u>working very late in the evening</u>
   c. wasting electricity

2. in the doghouse
   a. <u>in trouble</u>
   b. living in a small house
   c. keeping a dog in the house

3. getting cold feet
   a. forgetting your shoes
   b. not wearing socks
   c. <u>having reservations about something</u>

4. nose buried in a book
   a. closing a book on your nose
   b. <u>reading</u>
   c. getting hit by a book

5. all thumbs
   a. <u>clumsy</u>
   b. having very short fingers
   c. using both thumbs

6. talking through your hat
   a. holding your hat before your mouth
   b. <u>not knowing what you're talking about</u>
   c. not talking loud enough

7. all ears
   a. <u>listening</u>
   b. having big ears
   c. pulling your hair behind your ears

8. pulling my leg
   a. getting my leg caught
   b. <u>telling me a ridiculous story</u>
   c. holding on to my leg

9. taking a catnap
   a. <u>taking a short sleep</u>
   b. taking a nap with a cat
   c. taking a long nap during the day

10. flying off the handle
    a. losing the handle from a pot
    b. <u>losing control of your temper</u>
    c. flying in a small plane

11. counting chickens before they hatch
    a. counting eggs
    b. counting chickens
    c. <u>getting ahead of yourself</u>

12. quiet as a mouse
    a. <u>very quiet</u>
    b. very noisy
    c. making squeaking noises

13. step on some toes
    a. <u>saying things people won't like</u>
    b. standing on someone's foot
    c. standing on your tiptoes

14. a fish out of water
    a. able to breathe out of water
    b. dead
    c. <u>out of place</u>

Just for Fun

A Every animal makes its own distinct sound. For example, you would not say that a cow talks. A cow moos. Fill in the blanks using the words from the box.

barks	hisses	gobbles	sings
neighs	squeaks	roars	meows
clucks	buzzes	caws	quacks
crows	oinks	chirps	honks
brays	croaks	laughs	hoots

1. A cricket ___*chirps*___.
2. A rooster ___CROWS___.
3. A dog ___BARKS___.
4. A donkey ___BRAYS___.
5. A pig ___OINKS___.
6. A goose ___HONKS___.
7. A mouse ___SQUEAKS___.
8. A canary ___SINGS___.
9. A frog ___CROAKS___.
10. A chicken ___CLUCKS___.

11. An owl ___HOOTS___.
12. A duck ___QUACKS___.
13. A bee ___BUZZES___.
14. A cat ___MEOWS___.
15. A turkey ___GOBBLES___.
16. A lion ___ROARS___.
17. A crow ___CAWS___.
18. A hyena ___LAUGHS___.
19. A snake ___HISSES___.
20. A horse ___NEIGHS___.

B Different words also tell us how something is said. For example, if you were to talk constantly about anything and everything, people would probably say you chatter. Fill in the blanks with the best words from the box.

shriek
repeat
ask
beg
lecture
recite
whisper
cry
laugh
scream
order
giggle
demand
sigh

1. If you spoke quietly, you would ___*whisper*___.
2. If you would say the same thing again, you would ___REPEAT___.
3. If you would say something from memory, you would ___RECITE___.
4. If you were very sad, you would ___CRY___.
5. If you were telling someone to do something, you would ___ORDER___.
6. If you would reprimand someone, you would ___LECTURE___.
7. If you were very happy, you would ___LAUGH___.
8. If you were to laugh nervously, you would ___GIGGLE___.
9. If you were to plead with someone, you would ___BEG___.
10. If you were hurt, you might ___SCREAM___.
11. If you were frightened by something, you might ___SHRIEK___.
12. If you were to insist on something, you would ___DEMAND___.
13. If you were very tired, you might ___SIGH___.
14. If you were to question something, you would ___ASK___.

Unit 145 cont'd ⟶

Letters That Represent Words

To abbreviate the titles of organizations, ideas, or positions, usually the first letter of each word is used.

EXAMPLES: **UNICEF** United Nations Children's Fund
NAACP National Association for Advancement of Colored People

 Write the letters to abbreviate the following. Check your answers with a dictionary.

FBI	1.	Federal Bureau of Investigation
M.I.A.	2.	Missing in Action
NBC	3.	National Broadcasting Co.
CBS	4.	Columbia Broadcasting System
ABC	5.	American Broadcasting Company
BBC	6.	British Broadcasting Corp.
C.O.D.	7.	Cash on Delivery
USA	8.	United States of America
M.P.	9.	Military Police
VIP	10.	Very Important Person
YMCA	11.	Young Men's Christian Assoc.
YWCA	12.	Young Women's Christian Assoc.
ESP	13.	Extrasensory Perception
A.M.A.	14.	American Medical Association
AFL	15.	American Federation of Labor
CIA	16.	Central Intelligence Agency
D.A.	17.	District Attorney
AFB	18.	Air Force Base
MD	19.	Medical Doctor
AWOL	20.	Absent Without Leave
C.S.T.	21.	Central Standard Time
E.S.T.	22.	Eastern Standard Time
P.S.T.	23.	Pacific Standard Time
M.S.T.	24.	Mountain Standard Time
D.C.	25.	District of Columbia
D.S.T.	26.	Daylight-Saving Time
FDA	27.	Food and Drug Administration
FFA	28.	Future Farmers of America
G.S.A.	29.	Girl Scouts of America
B.S.A.	30.	Boy Scouts of America
GMC	31.	General Motors Corporation
J.P.	32.	Justice of the Peace
TWA	33.	Trans-World Airlines
USSR	34.	Union of Soviet Socialist Republics
SDP	35.	Social Democratic Party
L.C.	36.	Library of Congress
N.Y.C.	37.	New York City
NYA	38.	National Youth Administration
OAS	39.	Organization of American States
UN	40.	United Nations
PHS	41.	Public Health Service
POW	42.	Prisoner of War
R.D.	43.	Rural Delivery
S.A.	44.	Salvation Army
UFO	45.	Unidentified Flying Object
USAF	46.	United States Air Force
WHO	47.	World Health Organization
N.G.	48.	National Guard
USN	49.	United States Navy
P.T.A.	50.	Parent-Teacher Association

COMPOSITION EXERCISE

Choose 12 abbreviations from today's exercise. Write a sentence with each.

1. _____
2. _____
3. _____
4. _____
5. _____
6. _____
7. _____
8. _____
9. _____
10. _____
11. _____
12. _____

Comprehension Check

A Write "teach" or "learn," or forms of the words, in each blank.

1. Will you __teach__ me how to knit?
2. I __learn__ very quickly.
3. My older sister will __teach__ you a lesson.
4. Can you __learn__ this music by Friday?
5. Mrs. Sinton will __teach__ the class today.
6. She will __teach__ us how to paint.
7. __Teach__ me how to add faster.
8. I want to __learn__ how to frost cakes.
9. Have you __learned__ to spell this word?
10. She __learned__ to read when she was four.
11. When did Mary __teach__ her the game?
12. Did you __learn__ how to score the points?
13. The dog __learned__ to obey his master.
14. You must __teach__ Sheila the steps.
15. She can __learn__ how to follow the beat.
16. She'll __learn__ very quickly.
17. I __teach__ students at the new school.
18. We are __teaching__ them to follow directions.
19. Nora can __teach__ you how to read faster.
20. Please __teach__ Chris to write larger.

B Use "their," "there," or "they're" in each blank.

1. My parents sold __their__ car.
2. The puppies ran to __their__ mother.
3. __They're__ not planning to attend.
4. We saw the notes on __their__ desks.
5. Place the decimal __there__ .
6. __They're__ going ice skating tonight.
7. __There__ are the new students.
8. __They're__ standing beside the cafeteria.
9. Have they lost __their__ instructions?
10. The three kittens have lost __their__ mittens.
11. __Their__ idea is a good one.
12. __There__ are the suggestions.
13. Do you think __they're__ willing to help?
14. I saw that no one was __there__ .
15. Do you know if __they're__ selling the computer?
16. __Their__ dishwasher broke three plates.
17. Did she grant __their__ wishes?
18. __There__ are three pages missing.
19. __Their__ house caught on fire last week.
20. I can't tell if __they're__ happy or sad.
21. Put the dish __there__ on the table.
22. They read __their__ insurance policy carefully.
23. __They're__ welcome to use our car.
24. __There__ is the president of the class.
25. She put her clean clothes __there__ .
26. __They're__ building a new carport.
27. Be __there__ before it closes.
28. __They're__ my best friends.

C Use "this" or "these" in each blank.

1. I like __this__ flavor of pudding.
2. Sharon likes __these__ flavors best.
3. __These__ cars are for sale.
4. __This__ one is my favorite.
5. Put on __these__ shoes.
6. I've worn out __this__ pair already.
7. Do you like __this__ picture?
8. I bought __this__ hat at the sale.
9. Make a copy of __this__ page.
10. We've taken __these__ tickets with us.
11. Do you want __these__ people to leave?
12. __That__ person asked a good question.

D Use "that" or "those" in each blank.

1. I saw __those__ students leave early.
2. __That__ is not a good policy.
3. I chose __that__ breakfast today.
4. Did Sam buy __those__ running shoes?
5. Fred likes __those__ kinds of stories.
6. Maria saw __that__ play last month.
7. __That__ bird flew into the window pane.
8. Mr. Sawyer wants __that__ answer changed.
9. Rob asked for __those__ pedals on his bike.
10. We want __that__ color of paint.
11. __Those__ boards are broken.
12. Did you see __that__ game?

Test 29 cont'd

Comprehension Check (continued)

E Use "to," "two," or "too" in each blank.

1. You are _____ too _____ late for the meeting.
2. We have _____ two _____ speakers today.
3. We'll leave in _____ two _____ hours.
4. Did you give the answers _____ to _____ Jim?
5. Her music is not _____ too _____ loud.
6. Brian said the test was _____ too _____ easy.
7. We're going _____ to _____ New York for Christmas.
8. There are _____ two _____ days left in this month.
9. Don't read ahead _____ too _____ far in the book.
10. Shane went _____ to _____ the late show.
11. You may go _____ too _____ .
12. It's not _____ too _____ late to get tickets.
13. They talked _____ to _____ the principal.
14. Our taxes are _____ too _____ high!
15. I, _____ too _____ , have to give a report.
16. Jean plans _____ to _____ stay up late.
17. Hand me _____ two _____ safety pins.
18. You may watch _____ two _____ programs.
19. Missy is _____ too _____ quiet to be heard.
20. Lance speaks quietly _____ too _____ .
21. We ran _____ too _____ far today.
22. You need _____ to _____ slow down.
23. The soup has _____ too _____ much salt in it.
24. June wrote _____ to _____ a movie star.
25. Mel slept _____ too _____ late this morning.
26. _____ Too _____ many people crowded on the bus.
27. They ran _____ to _____ the back exit.
28. Allen has _____ two _____ girlfriends.
29. They finished the test _____ too _____ quickly.
30. _____ Two _____ singers left the band.
31. The reporter filed _____ two _____ reports.
32. Did you teach the dog _____ to _____ roll over?
33. Marty drove _____ to _____ the teacher's house.
34. He spoke _____ to _____ our science class.
35. Ben bought _____ two _____ new albums.
36. The trains are _____ too _____ close together.

F Write the abbreviation for each title.

_UN_ 1. United Nations
WHO 2. World Health Organization
AMA 3. American Medical Association
MST 4. Mountain Standard Time
NYC 5. New York City
FBI 6. Federal Bureau of Investigation
NBC 7. National Broadcasting Co.
_JP_ 8. Justice of the Peace
CIA 9. Central Intelligence Agency
_NG_ 10. National Guard

MIA 11. Missing in Action
_RD_ 12. Rural Delivery
BSA 13. Boy Scouts of America
POW 14. Prisoner of War
USN 15. United States Navy
_MD_ 16. Medical Doctor
COD 17. Cash on Delivery
CST 18. Central Standard Time
FDA 19. Food and Drug Administration
AFB 20. Air Force Base

Write a paragraph describing a friend. Use at least one simile and one idiom. Underline the simile and the idiom.

_____
_____
_____
_____
_____
_____

Abbreviations and Titles

An abbreviation is a part of the word that stands for the whole.

EXAMPLES:
a. Tues.   Tuesday   c. Dr.   doctor
b. qt.   quart   d. adv.   adverb

A Identify each abbreviation.

1. st. **STREET**
2. cm **CENTIMETER**
3. mi. **MILE**
4. Nov. **NOVEMBER**
5. Mon. **MONDAY**
6. l **LITER**
7. Amer. **AMERICAN**

8. a.m. **MORNING**
9. Aug. **AUGUST**
10. lb. **POUND**
11. sing. **SINGULAR**
12. Fri. **FRIDAY**
13. yd. **YARD**
14. hwy. **HIGHWAY**

15. mo. **MONTH**
16. p.m. **AFTERNOON**
17. Sept. **SEPTEMBER**
18. co. **COMPANY**
19. Mr. **MISTER**
20. Capt. **CAPTAIN**
21. U.S. **UNITED STATES**

B Write the abbreviation for each of the following.

1. English **ENG.**
2. hour **HR.**
3. avenue **AVE.**
4. February **FEB.**
5. Wednesday **WED.**
6. plural **PL.**
7. road **RD.**
8. inch **IN.**
9. March **MAR.**
10. kilometer **KM**

11. January **JAN**
12. second **SEC.**
13. history **HIST.**
14. young girl **MISS**
15. minute **MIN.**
16. April **APR.**
17. subject **SUBJ.**
18. ounce **OZ.**
19. mathematics **MATH.**
20. Saturday **SAT.**

21. year **YR.**
22. Sunday **SUN.**
23. week **WK.**
24. October **OCT.**
25. gallon **GAL.**
26. woman **MS.**
27. December **DEC.**
28. conjunction **CONJ.**
29. Thursday **THURS.**
30. married lady **MRS.**

C Complete each sentence with "Mr.," "Mrs.," "Miss," or "Ms."

1. My dad is **MR.** Davis.
2. My mom is **MRS.** Davis.
3. **MISS** Andrews is not married.
4. The woman is **MS.** Fisher.
5. That man is **MR.** Banks.
6. **MRS.** Reed is my grandmother.
7. Your father is **MR.** Kelsey.

8. The actress is **MS.** Justin.
9. His grandfather is **MR.** Hough.
10. My sister married **MR.** Reynolds.
11. Her new name is **MRS.** Reynolds.
12. **MS.** Lewis is a nice lady.
13. Jan's uncle is **MR.** Carter.
14. Meet **MR.** and **MRS.** Filmore.

COMPOSITION EXERCISE

Write a sentence with each of these abbreviations.

(a.m.)   1. _____

(Mr.)   2. _____

(Capt.)   3. _____

(Mrs.)   4. _____

(p.m.)   5. _____

Unit 146 cont'd

Abbreviations

An abbreviation is a part of a word that stands for the whole.

EXAMPLES: a. Nov.   November
               b. mo.   month
               c. hwy.   highway

 Write the abbreviation for each word.

#	word	abbr.	#	word	abbr.	#	word	abbr.
1.	Tuesday	*Tues.*	26.	singular	SING.	51.	October	OCT.
2.	before noon	A.M.	27.	Friday	FRI.	52.	numbers	NOS.
3.	after noon	P.M.	28.	paragraph	PAR.	53.	biography	BIOG.
4.	foot	FT.	29.	minute	MIN.	54.	street	ST.
5.	Saturday	SAT.	30.	cubic	CU.	55.	in care of	C/O
6.	weekly	WKLY.	31.	dictionary	DICT.	56.	milliliter	ML
7.	quart	QT.	32.	September	SEPT.	57.	subject	SUBJ.
8.	doctor	DR.	33.	captain	CAPT.	58.	pound	LB.
9.	avenue	AVE.	34.	January	JAN.	59.	anonymous	ANON.
10.	apartment	APT.	35.	adjective	ADJ.	60.	February	FEB.
11.	United States	U.S.	36.	William	WM.	61.	centimeter	CM
12.	conjunction	CONJ.	37.	Thursday	THURS.	62.	company	CO.
13.	corporation	CORP.	38.	millimeter	MM	63.	December	DEC.
14.	Wednesday	WED.	39.	hospital	HOSP.	64.	department	DEPT.
15.	dozen	DOZ.	40.	tablespoon	TBSP.	65.	America	AMER.
16.	mathematics	MATH.	41.	general	GEN.	66.	Friday	FRI.
17.	language	LANG.	42.	gallon	GAL.	67.	year	YR.
18.	standard	STD.	43.	adverb	ADV.	68.	English	ENG.
19.	mister	MR.	44.	August	AUG.	69.	examination	EXAM.
20.	abbreviation	ABBREV.	45.	saint	ST.	70.	kilometer	KM
21.	liter	L	46.	mile	MI.	71.	president	PRES.
22.	boulevard	BLVD.	47.	hour	HR.	72.	plural	PL.
23.	secretary	SEC.	48.	building	BLDG.	73.	route	RT.
24.	post office	P.O.	49.	principal	PRIN.	74.	example	EX.
25.	lieutenant	LT.	50.	television	TV	75.	highway	HWY.

Identifying Symbols

A symbol is a picture that stands for the written word or phrase.

EXAMPLES:

tragedy = = comedy

smile =

birthday cake =

stop sign = STOP

 Match the symbol with the word or phrase for which it stands.

c	1. >	G	2. <	P	3. =			
T	4. +	D	5. ✗	K	6. ÷			
N	7. %	V	8. $	R	9. ¢			
I	10. #	S	11. 43°	B	12. ?			
L	13. !	U	14. '	W	15. " "			
X	16. ♫	E	17. 𝄞	M	18. 𝄢			
A	19. BALLOT BOX	F	20.	Q	21.			
J	22.	H	23.	O	24. 			

a.	democracy
b.	question mark
c.	greater than
d.	multiply
e.	treble clef
f.	victory
g.	less than
h.	poison
i.	number sign
j.	medicine
k.	divide
l.	exclamation point
m.	bass clef
n.	per cent
o.	peace
p.	equal to
q.	communism
r.	cent sign
s.	degree
t.	add
u.	comma — pause
v.	dollar sign
w.	quotation marks
x.	musical note

COMPOSITION EXERCISE

List 12 symbols not used in today's exercise.

1. _____
2. _____
3. _____
4. _____
5. _____
6. _____

7. _____
8. _____
9. _____
10. _____
11. _____
12. _____

Unit 147 cont'd

Symbols

A symbol is a sign or picture that stands for a word or thought.

EXAMPLES:

U.S. Navy

symbol of the Old South

U.S. flag

 Match the symbol with the word for which it stands.

__z__ 1. friendship	__H__ 13. yield	__m__ 25. colon
__C__ 2. bookworm	__k__ 14. period	__b__ 26. minus
__v__ 3. diamond	__r__ 15. square	__y__ 27. star
__a__ 4. plus	__F__ 16. poison	__x__ 28. cent sign
__o__ 5. question mark	__u__ 17. triangle	__q__ 29. musical note
__A__ 6. sunshine	__f__ 18. does not equal	__G__ 30. stop sign
__h__ 7. less than	__p__ 19. exclamation point	__I__ 31. railroad
__w__ 8. dollar sign	__i__ 20. therefore	__e__ 32. equals
__s__ 9. rectangle	__d__ 21. multiply	__E__ 33. sad
__J__ 10. red light	__t__ 22. circle	__j__ 34. comma
__D__ 11. happy	__g__ 23. greater than	__n__ 35. quotation marks
__c__ 12. divide	__l__ 24. semicolon	__B__ 36. medical sign

a. $+$ i. $\therefore$ q.
b. $-$ j. $,$ r. $\square$
c. $\div$ k. $.$ s. $\square$ (rectangle)
d. $\times$ l. $;$ t. $\bigcirc$
e. $=$ m. $:$ u. $\triangle$
f. $\neq$ n. " "   v. $\diamond$
g. $>$ o. $?$ w. $\$$
h. $<$ p. $!$ x. $\cent$

y.   C.   G.

z.   D.   H.

A.   E.   I.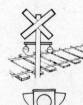

B.   F.   J.

COMPOSITION EXERCISE

When or where would you see these symbols used?

1. dollar sign
_____

2. equal sign
_____

3. stop sign
_____

4. comma
_____

5. musical note
_____

6. yield note
_____

7. poison skull
_____

8. American flag
_____

Organizing Information

Before a person writes a report, he must have a general idea about what he will say and how he will say it. Organization is the key. It is listing on paper the ideas which the writer thinks will be useful to him. Once his ideas are in front of him, the writer can look at them, think about them, and put them in order.

The writer must plan his report with care because he may not always be present to explain his intentions to the reader. He must see the link between his planning and his finished report. Careful organizing helps the writer to put his ideas in proper order. When the writer uses the right words and facts, this helps the reader to know what is meant. Remember that the quality of a report depends on the quality of the planning.

A Identify the sense illustrated by each of these pictures.

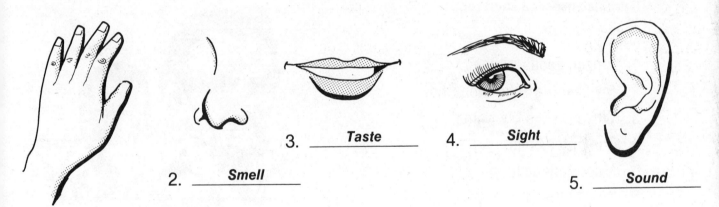

1. _____Touch_____

2. _____Smell_____

3. _____Taste_____

4. _____Sight_____

5. _____Sound_____

B Suppose you are to write a report on the five senses. Organize the words by putting the numbers of the senses beside the words that describe them.

1. touch   2. smell   3. taste   4. sight   5. sound

2, 3	a. coffee	4	j. fog	4	s. ugly
3	b. bitter	5	k. scream	1	t. slick
1	c. bumpy	4	l. picture	5	u. whisper
4	d. clear	2	m. perfume	4	v. dark
5	e. buzz	1	n. rough	1	w. icy
1	f. furry	3	o. salty	5	x. tinkle
2, 3	g. onion	2	p. rotten	2, 3	y. sweet
1, 2, 3, 4	h. burned	5	q. ringing	2, 3	z. spicy
5	i. clang	2, 3	r. sour	1, 3	aa. grainy

Unit 148 cont'd

Limiting Your Subject

The first step in writing a report is choosing a subject. Write about something that is interesting. Do not make the subject too broad. Be sure that information is available on the subject.

It would be hard to write a report on "People from Outer Space" because there is not enough material available on that subject. How could a writer make a good report on "Famous Indians"? He could pick three or four famous chiefs and tell about their achievements.

It is important for the writer to know how long his report is to be. This helps him limit his subject. He can develop it in a certain number of words. "The Importance of Milk" would be a good title for a paper of several thousand words. "Milk in a Child's Diet" would be a more limited subject and suitable for a paper of a few hundred words.

 Put an "l" beside each topic that a writer could use for a long report. Put an "s" beside each topic he could use for a short report.

L   1. Frozen Foods

S   2. My Favorite Television Show

S   3. Why I Dislike My Name

L   4. The Automobile

L   5. Modern Education

S   6. Why I Like Christmas

L   7. Presidents of the United States

S   8. My First Airplane Ride

L   9. Wild Animals

L   10. The Origin of Tennis

S   11. The First Money I Ever Earned

S   12. Going to the Circus

L   13. Sports in the United States

S   14. My Hobby and Why I Like It

S   15. My Neighborhood

L   16. Friends

S   17. My Favorite Time of Day

L   18. Bicycles

Grouping by Complexity

Material for a report should be arranged in an interesting and reasonable order. Three steps to follow are (1) read the material carefully, (2) decide on the main topics, and (3) choose facts and details that will develop or support the main topics. It is easy to understand a report when the ideas are arranged properly. The writer should make his report flow smoothly by developing and arranging each paragraph according to a plan of order. This order may be presented chronologically (according to time), logically, or in order of importance. Whichever method the writer chooses, he must remember to develop only one topic per paragraph.

 Matching

1. A person cannot write a good report

2. A good report must be

3. It is easier to prepare a written or oral report

4. If the ideas are well organized,

5. Always present the most important ideas first

6. The purpose of arranging material

7. The quality of a report

8. There are several ways

a. if your materials are arranged properly.

b. without arranging his ideas in a reasonable order.

c. depends on the quality of the planning.

d. for emphasis.

e. interesting to the reader.

f. to organize facts or ideas for a written or an oral report.

g. it is easier for the reader or the listener to understand the main topics.

h. is to put all the information in order before writing the report.

Unit 149 cont'd →

General to Specific

One way to begin a paragraph is by using a generalization, or broad statement. It is possible, however, that a statement is too general. Take, for example, this sentence: Apple pie is good. It would not make a good topic sentence for a report because it cannot be supported with details.

To test if a statement is too general, make a list of details to support its case. If you find that writing such a list is too difficult, you may wish to qualify the statement: Apple pie is my family's favorite dessert. Further qualify the statement: Homemade apple pie is my family's favorite dessert. The more you limit your topic, the easier it will be to list specific details to support your argument. The more support you have for your argument, the more credible your writing will be.

Mark each general statement with a "g."
Mark each specific statement with an "s."

__G__ a. Teen-agers should be allowed to drive.

__S__ b. Watching game shows is a waste of time.

__G__ c. Good athletes get college scholarships.

__G__ d. Small foreign cars use very little gasoline.

__S__ e. My father's car, a Mark V, gets poor gas mileage.

__G__ f. Some programs on television are educational.

__S__ g. <u>Sesame</u> <u>Street</u> is an educational television program.

__S__ h. <u>Star</u> <u>Wars</u> is a good movie.

__G__ i. Old people are wise.

__G__ j. Driving fast is dangerous.

__S__ k. Many good athletes earn college scholarships.

__G__ l. Television is getting better.

__G__ m. People become wiser as they grow older.

__S__ n. <u>Huckleberry</u> <u>Finn</u> is a good book.

__G__ o. The grocery store sells food.

__S__ p. Nighttime programs on television are improving.

__G__ q. Big sisters are helpful.

Narrowing the Scope

Narrowing the scope is simply the writer's way of stating his intentions. The writer of a report prepares the reader for what is coming by stating his purpose or main idea in a thesis sentence. This statement of purpose also helps the writer limit his subject. In the thesis sentence he states the main topics to be covered in the body of the report. The topics should be stated in the order in which they will be discussed. The thesis sentence serves as a miniature outline. It appears in the introductory paragraph.

The central idea runs like a "continuous thread" throughout a piece of writing. It gives the report unity by tying the supporting details together. The central idea is broken into its parts in the thesis sentence. A good writer knows how to relate every detail to the central idea. He is aided by his plan of procedure, which is his way of developing the thesis sentence.

 Matching

_b_	1. thesis sentence	a. where the thesis sentence appears in a piece of writing
_E_	2. narrowing the scope	b. the writer's statement of purpose
_A_	3. introduction	c. a "continuous thread" that runs throughout a piece of writing
_C_	4. central idea	d. provides support for a main topic
_G_	5. body	e. a way for the writer to state his intentions
_D_	6. detail	f. a purpose or plan
_H_	7. unity	g. where the main topics of a report are supported with details
_F_	8. intention	h. a state of oneness
_J_	9. plan of procedure	i. the central idea
_I_	10. theme of a report	j. the way or order used by a writer to develop his thesis sentence

Unit 150 cont'd

Taking Inventory

An inventory is a list of items with their estimated value. Most businesses take inventory of their stock at least once a year. Likewise, a writer must also take inventory of available material.

The next step after choosing the subject and narrowing the scope is organizing the material. Know what you already have and what you still need to work out. You may need to do more research, or you may need more specific examples to support your argument. Taking inventory helps you know in advance what your strong and weak points are. It warns you of what problems you may encounter when writing your paper.

Follow these steps when writing a paper:
(1) Choose a topic.
(2) Take inventory.
(3) Narrow the scope.
(4) Make notes.
(5) Organize the materials.
(6) Outline the material.
(7) Write the paper.
(8) Revise and rewrite.

✱ Place a check mark (✓) beside each sentence that applies to taking inventory.

✓ 1. Take some time to think ahead.
✓ 2. Look for materials that will help develop the subject.
___ 3. Emphasize the minor points.
✓ 4. Concentrate on a limited topic.
___ 5. Define every key word.
✓ 6. Try to see beforehand any problems that might arise.
___ 7. Support the main topics with general statements.
___ 8. Try to impress the reader with big words.
✓ 9. Select details that will give the report unity.
✓ 10. As material is found, make notes that will help in the writing of the report.
___ 11. Outline materials before organizing them.
✓ 12. Support a single point with related material.

Comprehension Check

A Beside each title, write its abbreviation. Beside each abbreviation, write the title for which it stands.

quart	1. qt.	*Aug.*	11. August	*Wm.*	21. William	*mm*	31. millimeter
etc.	2. etcetera	*conjunction*	12. conj.	*min.*	22. minute	*year*	32. yr.
hr.	3. hour	*oz.*	13. ounce	*gallon*	23. gal.	*wk.*	33. week
Dec.	4. December	*adj.*	14. adjective	*St.*	24. saint	*before noon*	34. a.m.
Capt.	5. Captain	*pound*	15. lb.	*doz.*	25. dozen	*singular*	35. sing.
doctor	6. Dr.	*street*	16. st.	*United States*	26. U.S.	*ex.*	36. example
Tuesday	7. Tues.	*pl.*	17. plural	*l*	27. liter	*Ms.*	37. woman
adverb	8. adv.	*rd.*	18. road	*p.o.*	28. post office	*second*	38. sec.
mon.	9. month	*subject*	19. sub.	*Lt.*	29. lieutenant	*cm*	39. centimeter
highway	10. hwy.	*department*	20. dept.	*mile*	30. mi.	*English*	40. Eng.

B Match each symbol with the word or phrase for which it stands.

1. =
2. +
3. $
4. >
5. <
6. ß
7. ÷
8. (star)
9. !
10. " "
11. (stop sign)
12. (musical note)
13. (skull and crossbones)
14. (dove)
15. (caduceus)
16. □
17. **43°**
18. (comedy face)
19. ○
20. (traffic signal)
21. △
22. (inverted triangle)
23. (clock)
24. (handicapped)

19	a.	circle
21	b.	triangle
23	c.	time
2	d.	plus
4	e.	greater than
14	f.	peace
8	g.	star
6	h.	cent
15	i.	medicine
18	j.	comedy
17	k.	degrees
10	l.	quotes

9	m.	exclamation point
20	n.	traffic signal
22	o.	yield
5	p.	less than
1	q.	equals
24	r.	for use of handicapped
16	s.	square
13	t.	poison
7	u.	divide
12	v.	musical note
3	w.	dollar sign
11	x.	stop sign

C Put a check (✓) beside each item which could be included in a report on each subject given.

	sports		school		flowers		money
✓	1. football	✓	1. bells	✓	1. stem	✓	1. dime
	2. gum		2. sun		2. rocks		2. ink
✓	3. gym	✓	3. teachers		3. question		3. ocean
	4. pencil		4. mall	✓	4. petal	✓	4. penny
	5. flowers	✓	5. students	✓	5. daisy	✓	5. nickel
✓	6. hockey		6. gift	✓	6. daffodil		6. napkin
✓	7. bats	✓	7. books		7. branch	✓	7. account
✓	8. tennis		8. lockers		8. wheel		8. ladder
✓	9. stadium	✓	9. pens	✓	9. leaves	✓	9. change
✓	10. score		10. fish		10. cloud		10. coffee
	11. lamp	✓	11. buses		11. gas	✓	11. bill
	12. comb	✓	12. paper		12. stones	✓	12. bank

Test 30 cont'd

Comprehension Check (continued)

(D) Write "t" beside each true statement.

__t__   1. A person should organize her ideas for the report.

_____   2. A good report need not interest the reader.

_____   3. "The Stars" could be a title for a short report.

_____   4. There is only one way to organize facts or ideas for a report.

__t__   5. Looking for materials is part of taking inventory.

__t__   6. The first step in writing a report is choosing a subject.

_____   7. The most important ideas in a report should appear at the end of the report.

__t__   8. "Whales" could be a title for a long report.

__t__   9. Arranging materials properly will make it easier to prepare the report.

__t__   10. "My Favorite Holiday" could be a title for a short report.

__t__   11. "Some people drive too slowly" is an example of a general statement.

__t__   12. "Watching television is bad" is an example of a general statement.

__t__   13. "Stamp collecting is my hobby" could be the title of a short report.

_____   14. "Children should eat green vegetables" is an example of a general statement.

_____   15. "People like to travel" is an example of a specific statement.

(E) Match each term with its definition.

__j__	1. central idea	a.	where the thesis sentence appears in a piece of writing
__f__	2. unity	b.	the writer's statement of purpose
__e__	3. theme of a report	c.	a purpose or plan
__d__	4. detail	d.	provides support for a main topic
__h__	5. narrowing the scope	e.	the central idea
__b__	6. thesis sentence	f.	a state of oneness
__a__	7. introduction	g.	where the main topics of a report are supported with details
__g__	8. body	h.	a way for the writer to state his intentions
__i__	9. plan of procedure	i.	method used by a writer to develop a thesis sentence
__c__	10. intention	j.	a "continuous thread" that runs throughout a piece of writing

Write a paragraph about your favorite sport. Include one sentence which does <u>not</u> relate to the topic and underline it.

_____

_____

_____

_____

_____

_____

_____

_____

_____

Using the Senses

Okay! So writing's tough! Maybe you're making it too tough. Try to think of writing as simple conversation or feelings which you just happen to write down. You can worry about "polishing up" your writing a bit later. <u>First</u>: get your ideas down on paper. After all, you've got to start somewhere! - - - - So let's get started!

TALKING (WRITING) ABOUT THINGS YOU SENSE

 Describe the following things as though you were talking to someone who had never even heard of such "strange" objects. Write your descriptions on another piece of paper, using your "wildest imagination."

1. **SIGHT** Using several sentences, talk about what a motorcycle <u>looks</u> like. Maybe you'll want to make it a "chopper." But remember, the person you are "talking" to has never seen one.

2. **SOUND** Write down a few sentences to talk about what a rock band <u>sounds</u> like. Use any rock group you might have heard as an example. But keep in mind — you are talking to someone who doesn't have <u>any</u> idea what a rock group sounds like!

3. **SMELL** Write about the <u>great</u> aromas of your favorite meal. Be sure and include several different types of foods that make up the complete meal. You're still talking to that same "clod" who hasn't seen or heard anything.

4. **TASTE** Explain to someone (in writing) what a hot dog <u>tastes</u> like. Put all the mustard, ketchup, or relish on it you wish — or leave it off! But remember, you're talking <u>only</u> about how it tastes. A tough job — but you can do it!

5. **TOUCH** Ever peeled an orange? Sure — who hasn't? Okay! Now describe what an orange <u>feels</u> like: when you first touch it, when you begin to peel it, and when you "get inside" the orange to separate its sections.

Now! Ideas to GROW on

* To help you "get started" in writing, try keeping a small notebook handy in which you can write down ideas about different things you see or think about. Keep your statements or descriptions short.

* Later, go back to your writings and expand them. Don't worry too much yet about how "correct" they are; get the "feel for writing" first!

Unit 151 cont'd →

Describing

In your last lesson, you were asked to make some very dead sentences breathe — at least a little. But today's lesson asks that you start from the very beginning. In other words, you won't be given sentences to change; rather, you must c-r-e-a-t-e some lively ideas and words and then "get it all together" in sentences.

First, L-O-O-S-E-N up! Let the ideas flow as you try to describe what you imagine you see in the pictures below. Don't be afraid to use your wildest imagination, but be certain you put that imagination to work in sentences that give life to the pictures!

 Describe each picture in at least two different ways. A picture might remind you of one thing the first time you look at it, and it might cause you to think of something else the next time. Write as many sentences as you need.

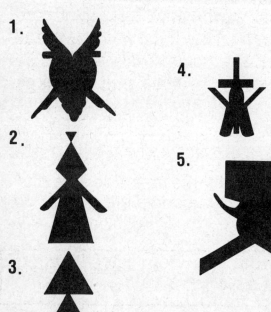

1.

2.

3.

4.

5.

IDEAS that help

1. What does the picture remind you of?
2. What does it make you feel?
3. What kinds of words go best with the picture?
4. What kinds of lines and curves are used?
5. Is there a short story you could write about the picture?

1. _____

2. _____

3. _____

4. _____

5. _____

Where to Get Help

Suppose you need material for a report on "dinosaurs." Where would you look first? The best place to get a general idea of your topic is the encyclopedia. Entries in an encyclopedia are arranged alphabetically. The guide words at the tops of the pages will help you find "dinosaurs" quickly.

The next place to look is in the card catalog. All the books your library has on the subject of "dinosaurs" will be listed on individual cards. Write down the call numbers of the books.

Then, locate each book. First, look at the book's table of contents which is located at the front of the book. It will list each chapter title. Then check the index which is located at the back of the book. The index is an alphabetical listing of every subject in the book and the page numbers where that subject is discussed.

Always have your pen and paper ready to take notes. Include the name of the book, the author, the page numbers, and all information you think might help you in writing your report.

 Fill in the blanks.

Guide words	index	Notes	table of contents
chapters	alphabetically	card catalog	encyclopedia

1. The ___*table of contents*___ appears at the front of a book.
2. The table of contents is arranged in the order in which the __**CHAPTERS**__ or stories appear.
3. The __**INDEX**__ appears in the back of a book.
4. The items in an index are arranged __**ALPHABETICALLY**__.
5. __**NOTES**__ are for the use of the person writing them.
6. An __**ENCYCLOPEDIA**__ gives a general idea about a particular topic.
7. The __**CARD CATALOG**__ contains cards in alphabetical order for every book in the library.
8. __**GUIDE WORDS**__ in an encyclopedia help you to find articles.

Unit 152 cont'd

The Library

Libraries are where books live. Each book in a library has its own place on its own shelf, where it can always be found when it is needed, just as you live in one particular house on one certain street. The library is not just rows and rows of books on shelves. It is a very carefully planned place. You will find fiction books in one section, globes and maps in another, records in another, and so on. Once you have become familiar with how a library is arranged, it becomes simple to find what you want.

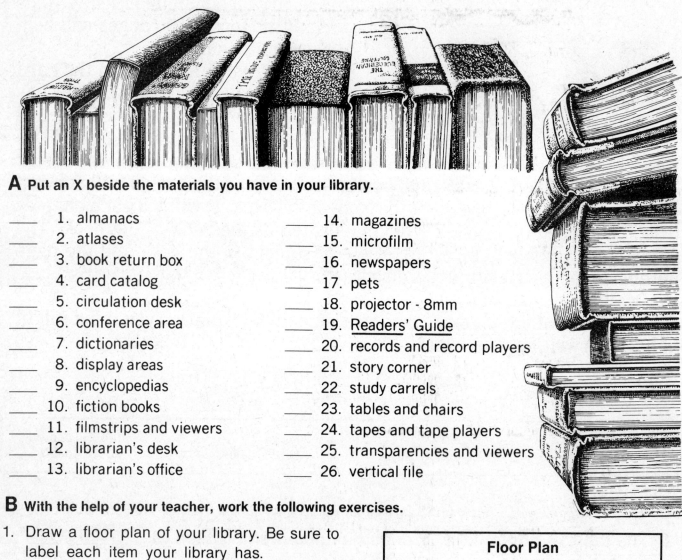

A Put an X beside the materials you have in your library.

____ 1. almanacs
____ 2. atlases
____ 3. book return box
____ 4. card catalog
____ 5. circulation desk
____ 6. conference area
____ 7. dictionaries
____ 8. display areas
____ 9. encyclopedias
____ 10. fiction books
____ 11. filmstrips and viewers
____ 12. librarian's desk
____ 13. librarian's office

____ 14. magazines
____ 15. microfilm
____ 16. newspapers
____ 17. pets
____ 18. projector - 8mm
____ 19. Readers' Guide
____ 20. records and record players
____ 21. story corner
____ 22. study carrels
____ 23. tables and chairs
____ 24. tapes and tape players
____ 25. transparencies and viewers
____ 26. vertical file

B With the help of your teacher, work the following exercises.

1. Draw a floor plan of your library. Be sure to label each item your library has.
2. Find out how many volumes your school library has. _____
3. Find out the name of the nearest library other than your school library. _____
   _____
4. How many volumes are in the nearest library outside of school? _____
5. Is there a university library near you? _____
6. Are you allowed to use its facilities? _____

Floor Plan

The Card Catalog

You will usually find a library's card catalog in a cabinet that has several drawers. Each drawer is arranged with tabbed dividers that are labeled with a key word or letter. The card catalog is arranged in alphabetical order. **A**, **an**, and **the** are not used in alphabetizing a title in the card catalog. **For example**, the book entitled **The Yellow Room** would be alphabetized under **Y** for **Yellow**.

A In the blank beside each book title, write the letter of the alphabet that each title would be listed under in the card catalog.

_B_	1. Baldy of Nome	_O_	11. The Odds Against Me	_T_	21. Two Years Before the Mast
_M_	2. Melanie	_L_	12. Little Women	_D_	22. The Diary of Anne Frank
_P_	3. Pickwick Papers	_D_	13. Doctor Doolittle	_T_	23. A Tale of Two Cities
_M_	4. Mt. Rainier	_A_	14. Away All Boats	_O_	24. The Old Man and the Sea
_R_	5. Roots	_S_	15. The Silver Chalice	_H_	25. House of Seven Gables
_W_	6. Winds of War	_A_	16. An Admiral's Fancy	_W_	26. Winter of Our Discontent
_B_	7. The Brain	_T_	17. The Thornbirds	_L_	27. Land over Norway
_O_	8. Old Yeller	_M_	18. Mary Poppins	_B_	28. Bury My Heart at Wounded Knee
_O_	9. On the Beach	_C_	19. A Cup of Stars	_W_	29. A White House Diary
_R_	10. Red Dawn	_R_	20. Robinson Crusoe	_T_	30. 20,000 Leagues Under the Sea

In the card catalog you can also find authors' names. They are listed with the **last** name **first**. Here are pictures of tabs that might be used as dividers in a card catalog:

BARN	CALDWELL	HEYER	KEYES	NORRIS
1.	2.	3.	4.	5.

B Below are authors' names, book subjects, and titles that could appear in a card catalog. In the blank space beside each one, write the number of the catalog divider above that you would look behind.

_2_	1. Dickens, Charles	_5_	7. Rhinehart, Mary Roberts
_5_	2. Treachery Trail	_2_	8. Clues in the Woods
_3_	3. Ice Age	_5_	9. Ocean
_1_	4. The Black Arrow	_2_	10. Costain, Thomas B.
_2_	5. Eakins, Phil	_2_	11. Chitty-Chitty Bang Bang
_1_	6. Breeding Livebearers	_4_	12. Kipling, Rudyard

Unit 153 cont'd →

Using the Card Catalog

Author, title, and subject cards for every book are filed alphabetically in the card catalog. A reader can find any book in a library's collection by looking up any of these cards. Each card has the book's location numbers in the upper left-hand corner. Often a fiction book just has a title card and an author card.

AUTHOR CARD	TITLE CARD	SUBJECT CARD
Pei, Mario 400 P6 　　All about language; decorations by Donat Ivanousky 　　Lippincott 1954 　　186 p illus maps	**ALL ABOUT LANGUAGE** 400 P6　Pei, Mario 　　All about language; decorations by Donat Ivanousky 　　Lippincott 1954 　　186 p illus maps	**LANGUAGE AND LANGUAGES** 400 P6　Pei, Mario 　　All about language; decorations by Donat Ivanousky 　　Lippincott 1954 　　186 p illus maps

A In the blank write the name of the kind of card you would check first to find each of the following:

1. a book on goldfish _____ *subject*

2. the author of **The Yearling** _____ *TITLE*

3. the newest book written by Dr. Seuss _____ *AUTHOR*

4. whether Louisa May Alcott, authoress of **Little Women**, also wrote **Little Men** _____ *TITLE*

5. a book of riddles _____ *SUBJECT*

6. a book of etiquette written by Emily Post_____ *AUTHOR*

7. number of pages contained in **Wind, Sand and Stars** _____ *TITLE*

8. the title of a book on gardening _____ *SUBJECT*

B In these three rectangles write the information needed for a title card, a subject card, and an author card for the following book: In the Court of King Arthur by Samuel E. Lowe, illustrated by Bob Nelson. It was published by Whitman Publishing Co. in 1918. It has 223 pages, and its call number is 398.2, L95.

AUTHOR CARD	TITLE CARD	SUBJECT CARD
LOWE, SAMUEL E. *398.2* *L95* *IN THE COURT OF KING ARTHUR;* *ILLUSTRATED BY BOB NELSON* *WHITMAN PUBLISHING CO. 1918* *223 P*	*IN THE COURT OF KING ARTHUR* *398.2* *L95　LOWE, SAMUEL E.* *IN THE COURT OF KING ARTHUR;* *ILLUSTRATED BY BOB NELSON* *WHITMAN PUBLISHING CO. 1918* *223 P*	*KING ARTHUR* *398.2* *L95　LOWE, SAMUEL E.* *IN THE COURT OF KING ARTHUR;* *ILLUSTRATED BY BOB NELSON* *WHITMAN PUBLISHING CO. 1918* *223 P*

The Dewey Decimal System Unit 154

I'm sure you have noticed numbers such as 919.8 on the backs of books in your library. These numbers are part of a book-classifying system called the **Dewey Decimal System.** Books are sorted into subject groups and subgroups by the use of whole numbers and decimals. Here are the ten categories of the **Dewey Decimal System:**

000-099 GENERAL WORKS — encyclopedias, bibliographies, etc.

100-199 PHILOSOPHY AND PSYCHOLOGY

200-299 RELIGION AND MYTHOLOGY

300-399 SOCIAL SCIENCES — civics, law, education

400-499 PHILOLOGY — language, dictionaries, grammar

500-599 SCIENCE — mathematics, astronomy, physics, chemistry, biology, etc.

600-699 USEFUL ARTS — medicine and other sciences that serve man's needs

700-799 FINE ARTS — music, painting, photography, architecture

800-899 LITERATURE — novels, poetry, plays, criticism

900-999 HISTORY, GEOGRAPHY, TRAVEL, BIOGRAPHY

✳ Using the Dewey Decimal System, write the number category in which each item or topic would be grouped. The first one is done for you.

1. folk music — 700-799
2. story of a goddess — 200-299
3. handicraft — 700-799
4. fire prevention — 600-699
5. Spanish music — 700-799
6. poems by Poe — 800-899
7. an encyclopedia — 000-099
8. how to make friends — 100-199
9. farm stories — 800-899
10. Eskimo stories — 900-999

11. etiquette — 300-399
12. fossil plants and animals — 500-599
13. a French dictionary — 400-499
14. a book of plays — 800-899
15. Bible stories — 200-299
16. cowboy stories — 900-999
17. Bartlett's Familiar Quotations — 000-099
18. picture history of hats — 900-999
19. how volcanoes form — 500-599
20. Greek architecture — 700-799

Unit 154 cont'd ➡

Special Books

What should you do after you read what encyclopedias say about your subject? You should consult dictionaries, maps, the <u>Readers' Guide</u>, the vertical file, and pamphlets. Then what should you do if you want some special information you haven't found? You should look for special books!

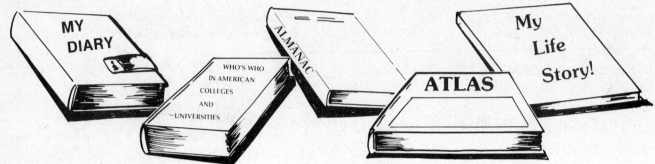

✳ *Answer these questions.*

1. Might a diary kept by a colonial farmer help you if you wanted to do a report about how our weather is changing? _____ *YES*

2. Which of the special books above might help you if you were trying to discover exactly where Benjamin Franklin's home was located? _____ *DIARY, BIOGRAPHY, ATLAS*

3. Which book would you consult to find out the latest information about Robert Hutchins? _____ *WHO'S WHO IN AMERICAN COLLEGES AND UNIVERSITIES*

4. Which book would give you some information about holidays? _____ *ALMANAC*

5. In which books would you be most apt to find a description of the kind of clothes worn by colonial ladies? _____ *DIARY, BIOGRAPHY*

6. Which book could help you find how to get to Lincoln's boyhood home? _____ *ATLAS*

7. Which book might help you learn who the president of France was in 1969? _____ *ALMANAC*

8. Which book could help you learn what zodiac sign George Washington was born under? _____ *ALMANAC*

9. Which book would tell you who Henry Commager is? _____ *WHO'S WHO IN AMERICAN COLLEGES AND UNIVERSITIES*

10. Which book would tell you about farm crops? _____ *ALMANAC*

> **Never neglect the special books in your library when you need special help!**

The Librarian

You may think librarians' duties are simply checking out and putting up books and maintaining quiet in the library. If this is your idea, you have been missing some valuable help. One of the librarians' main functions is helping library users. However, since librarians are busy people, you should always search for information before asking them for help. In other words, don't ask them to find a book that you could find by using the card catalog.

What kind of help can you get from a librarian? Take this paper with you to the library, and find the answers to these questions.

1. You want a book your library doesn't have. Can your librarian get it for you from another library? _____

2. Can your librarian make copies of certain pages in books for you? _____

3. Does your librarian give book reviews? _____

4. Can your librarian help you prepare bibliographies? _____

5. You want to write to a particular company but don't know the address. Can your librarian get it for you? _____

6. Can your librarian help you find information about a career you are interested in? _____

7. If your library does not have books in braille, can your librarian borrow them for you? _____

8. Can your librarian get microfilmed copies of newspapers for you? _____

9. Ask your librarian to help you trace your family history. _____

10. Can your librarian get copies of pictures for you?_____

11. Ask your librarian to help you find the population of Chicago, Illinois. _____

12. You want some information about the Red Cross. After using the card catalog and encyclopedias, you ask the librarian for help. Can she suggest areas for searching besides the two sources you have already used? _____

Unit 155 cont'd ➡

Using the Library

Answer these questions.

1. How are the books in your library classified? _Dewey Decimal System_

2. What would be the number category for a book about folk music? _____ _700-799_

3. Where would you look to see if your library has a book by Charles Dickens? _____ _CARD CATALOG_

4. Where would you look for encyclopedias and dictionaries? _____ _REFERENCE SECTION_

5. Do libraries ever have helpful materials other than books? _____ _YES_

6. How many **kinds** of dictionaries does your library have? _____ _ANSWERS VARY_

7. Which set of encyclopedias in your library is best for **you**? _____ _ANSWERS VARY_
   Why? _____

8. What three words can best describe good library behavior? _CONSIDERATION FOR OTHERS_

9. Where would you look for maps in your library? _IN ATLASES IN THE REFERENCE SECTION_

10. In what section of the library will you find tapes and recorders? _AUDIO-VISUAL_

11. Can you learn something from a film that you can't learn from a book? _YES_

12. What is one of the most common things a library has on microfilm? _NEWSPAPERS_

13. List three things that are stored in a vertical file. _PAMPHLETS, PICTURES, NEWSPAPER_ _CLIPPINGS_

14. Does a librarian have any special education? _____ _YES_

15. Briefly describe how to open a new book. _____ _ANSWERS VARY_

16. List at least five kinds of books you can find in a library. _____ _ANSWERS VARY_

17. Where would you look if you wanted to find a magazine article on birds? _READERS' GUIDE_

18. Where would you look to see if your library has a book of jokes? _____ _SUBJECT CARD_

19. List some things you can learn from a card in the card catalog. _AUTHOR, TITLE, PUBLISHER,_ _ILLUSTRATIONS, NUMBER OF PAGES, CALL NUMBER, DATE OF PUBLICATION_

20. Where in a library might you hear Martin Luther King, Jr's. voice? _AUDIO-VISUAL SECTION_

21. What are periodicals? _____ _MAGAZINES AND NEWSPAPERS_

22. How many places in your library can you use for research? _____ _ANSWERS VARY_
    Name them. _____

Comprehension Check

Ⓐ Match the description with the source.

j	1. appears at the front of a book	a.	circulation desk
l	2. for the use of the person writing them	b.	*Who's Who in American Colleges*
h	3. gives a general idea about a particular topic		*and Universities*
c	4. contains cards for every book in the library	c.	card catalog
g	5. help you to find articles in an encyclopedia	d.	alphabetical
d	6. arrangement of items in an index	e.	by chapters or stories
n	7. appears in the back of a book	f.	almanac
e	8. order in which the table of contents is arranged	g.	guide words
a	9. area at which library materials are checked out	h.	encyclopedia
i	10. index to magazine articles	i.	*Reader's Guide*
o	11. collection of newspaper articles and of pictures	j.	table of contents
k	12. a book of maps	k.	atlas
b	13. information about outstanding college students	l.	notes
f	14. information about such topics as	m.	biography
	farm production	n.	index
m	15. the story of a person's life	o.	vertical file

Ⓑ After each title or description, write the name of the kind of card you would use to find it. Then write the letter of the alphabet under which each item would be found.

1. information about furniture repair	subject	F
2. *Tales of a Fourth Grade Nothing*	title	T
3. information about tornadoes	subject	T
4. a book of poetry written by John Keats	author	K
5. the latest book written by Stephen King	author	K
6. the events leading up to the Civil War	subject	C
7. the name of the main character in *Life on the Mississippi*	title	L
8. the publication date of *A Cry in the Woods*	title	C
9. a list of all books written by Mark Twain	author	T
10. the author of *The Illustrated Man*	title	I
11. a book about the life of Edgar Allan Poe	author	P
12. a copy of the play, *Annie*.	title	A

Ⓒ Beside each description, write the sense which is used to perceive it.

taste	1. The hamburger is spicy.
sight	2. Ducks are flying high in the sky.
smell	3. Someone across town is burning leaves.
sound	4. Wedding bells are ringing.
touch	5. Snow is falling on your bare arms.
sight	6. A little girl smiles happily when she finds her doll.
touch	7. The thick carpet feels like velvet.
taste	8. The cake icing is too sweet.

Test 31 cont'd

Comprehension Check (continued)

(D) Study the Dewey Decimal System and then fill in the blanks below.

1. 000 - 099   General Works
2. 100 - 199   Philosophy and Psychology
3. 200 - 299   Religion and Mythology
4. 300 - 399   Social Sciences
5. 400 - 499   Philology

6. 500 - 599   Science
7. 600 - 699   Useful Arts
8. 700 - 799   Fine Arts
9. 800 - 899   Literature
10. 900 - 999   History, Geography, Travel, Biography

1. _**200 - 299**_ Religion and Mythology
2. 500 - 599 _**Science**_
3. _**100 - 199**_ Philosophy and Psychology
4. 800 - 899 _**Literature**_
5. 700 - 799 _**Fine Arts**_

6. _**900 - 999**_ History, Geography, Travel, Biography
7. 400 - 499 _**Philology**_
8. 600 - 699 _**Useful Arts**_
9. _**300 - 399**_ Social Studies
10. 000 - 999 _**General Works**_

(E) Use the numbers from the top of Part D to identify the location of each piece of information described below.

_8_ 1. a book about paintings by El Greco
_7_ 2. information about cancer research
_10_ 3. early history of Rome
_4_ 4. information about our court system
_3_ 5. description of early religious beliefs
_5_ 6. changes in the English language
_4_ 7. methods used in education
_1_ 8. general information about a topic
_6_ 9. theories in algebra
_8_ 10. Greek buildings
_3_ 11. information about the Greek god Apollo
_10_ 12. the life story of a famous person

_9_ 13. poetry about Robert Browning
_8_ 14. the story of jazz music
_6_ 15. movement of the stars
_8_ 16. photographs by Ansel Adams
_9_ 17. opinions about novels by Dickens
_2_ 18. study of behavior
_9_ 19. the early novel
_10_ 20. the Revolutionary War
_1_ 21. lists of books about various subjects
_7_ 22. important medical discoveries
_6_ 23. method for dissecting a frog
_5_ 24. a dictionary

Write a paragraph describing food which could be found in the kitchen. Include descriptions which would appeal to the senses of sight, smell, touch, taste, and sound.

_____
_____
_____
_____
_____
_____
_____
_____
_____

Fact or Opinion

A fact is something that can be proved. An opinion is a belief or judgment based on what seems to be true. A piece of writing is worthless unless it can be supported with reason. If the writer wants to express his personal feelings, he does so through an opinion; but he should base his opinion on fact if he wants it to have meaning. Facts play a major role in any writing assignment. They provide the details that are needed to support the main topics.

EXAMPLES:

facts:
a. *Los Angeles is a city in California.*
b. *Europe is a continent.*

opinions:
a. *Los Angeles is a beautiful city.*
b. *Europeans are good cooks.*

Write "f" before each fact. Write "o" before each opinion.

__O__ 1. Soap operas are enjoyed by people who cannot understand classical literature.

__O__ 2. People will eventually live on other planets.

__F__ 3. John F. Kennedy was the first Catholic to become President of the United States.

__O__ 4. People who do not like rock 'n' roll music do not know how to appreciate good music.

__F__ 5. The headquarters of the United Nations is in New York City.

__O__ 6. Teen-agers should not be allowed to vote.

__F__ 7. A fire needs fuel and oxygen to burn.

__F__ 8. Pineapples and sugar cane are the most common crops in Hawaii.

__O__ 9. Most people from foreign countries are strange.

__O__ 10. There are not very many worthwhile programs on television.

__F__ 11. Green plants provide food for many animals.

__O__ 12. Moby Dick is a fascinating book.

__F__ 13. The ocean bottom is part of the earth's crust.

__O__ 14. Mother is a good cook.

__F__ 15. Christopher Columbus discovered America.

__O__ 16. Careless people always have accidents.

__F__ 17. The Lewis and Clark Expedition ended at the Pacific Ocean.

__F__ 18. Boston is the capital of Massachusetts.

__O__ 19. My grandfather is polite.

__O__ 20. That blue car is ugly.

__F__ 21. Chinese is the most widely spoken language.

__F__ 22. Veterans Day is November 11th.

Unit 156 cont'd ➡

Chronological Order

In chronological order, events are arranged in the order in which they happened. Time is a natural organizer. A writer can use chronological order to develop his topic by taking the reader through time from the beginning to the end. Chronological order is especially useful in telling a story or outlining a process.

Many linking devices help a writer to move through chronological order more smoothly. Words like "now," "then," "when," "while," "before," "after," and "next" tie sentences to the preceding ones.

A Look at the pictures. They are in the wrong order. Number them correctly so that they will tell a story.

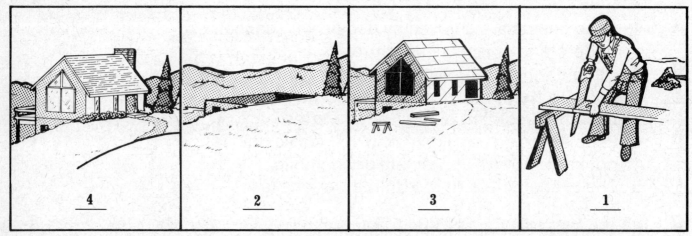

4   2   3   1

B Write a paragraph using the sentences. Fit them together so that they will make sense. Change the wording if necessary.

1. The city is full of life at night.
2. You can see its colorful, flashing lights for miles.
3. You can hear the night sounds of the city until the wee hours of the morning.
4. When evening falls, the city bursts with excitement.
5. During the early morning it is quiet.

When evening falls, the city bursts with excitement. It is full of life. You can see its colorful, flashing lights for miles. You can hear the city's night sounds until the wee hours of the morning. During the early morning hours, the city is quiet.

Logical Order

When a person writes to give information or to convince the reader, he must give special attention to the order of his sentences. They must be arranged clearly in a natural or logical order. This arrangement allows the writer to fit his sentences together for unity. It also makes the writing easier for the reader to understand.

Sometimes the logical order is the order of importance. This order begins with the least important fact and goes on to the most important. The order of importance is useful when the writer is supporting an opinion.

At other times, the logical order calls for a comparison between someone with something or somebody else. The writer shows how the two are alike. When he wants to show how the two are different, he writes a paragraph of contrast.

> Use the topic sentence "Meriwether Lewis and William Clark were alike in some ways." Compare the two men in a paragraph that tells how they were alike. Use the following details, but remember to arrange them in a logical order.

1. Both were born in Virginia.
2. Both were army officers.
3. Both were outstanding leaders.
4. Both took part in Indian wars.
5. Both liked the frontier life of the West.

Meriwether Lewis and William Clark were alike in some ways. Both of these explorers were born in Virginia. They were outstanding leaders as they both served as army officers. Lewis and Clark also took part in Indian wars. They liked the frontier life of the West.

A paragraph makes sense when its details are in logical order and related to one another.

Unit 157 cont'd

Constructing a Paragraph

A paragraph should have only one subject. This gives it unity. The writer must first decide what the subject of the paragraph is to be. The other sentences in the paragraph should relate to this subject. The topic sentence tells what the paragraph is about. One way the writer can develop a topic sentence into a paragraph is by giving reasons for the statement he has made. Another way is to give details to support his topic sentence.

Each sentence in a paragraph should naturally lead to the next. The writer must arrange his sentences so that they make sense. When he wants to tell a story, he should start at the chronological beginning. Then he should fit the details together in the order in which they happened. Connecting words such as "first," "then," "next," and "afterward" help the writer fit sentences together.

 Pretend you are writing a paragraph with the title "My Favorite Kind of Food." Put a check mark (✓) beside each sentence you could use.

✔ 1. My favorite kind of food is meat.

      2. I do not like vegetables very much.

✔ 3. I like steak cooked on the grill best of all.

✔ 4. I also like hamburgers.

      5. Sometimes I help my dad light the fire in the grill.

      6. He also lets me turn the meat while it's cooking.

✔ 7. It makes me hungry to hear steak sizzling on the grill.

      8. My mom makes me eat green beans sometimes.

      9. It rained the last time we cooked outside.

      10. When we have steak or hamburgers, I also like to have fried potatoes.

      11. Steak is good, but it also costs a great deal.

      12. Hamburgers are less expensive to serve than steak.

✔ 13. Roast beef is another meat that I like.

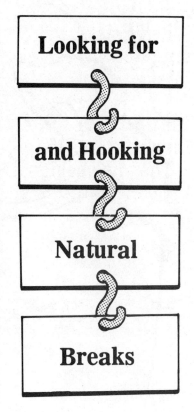

Looking for

and Hooking

Natural

Breaks

The main topic of a paragraph may be developed with facts, reasons, arguments, and so forth. Paragraphing causes problems for some young writers because they do not know when and where to begin a new paragraph. Follow these guidelines for paragraphing. A new paragraph should begin as follows:

1. when the writer changes to a different subject or to a different area of the subject
2. to show a lapse of time or a change in places or persons
3. to show a change in the writer's point of view
4. to show a shift in conversation from one person to another
5. with each change of topic (when one main topic has been developed and the writer is ready to develop another point)

Just as the writer works toward unity within a paragraph, he must also have unity between each paragraph. He does this through a clear line of thought that pulls the main topics together.

 Complete each sentence with a transitional term from the box.

1. ___Finally___, we arrived home after walking several miles out of the way.

2. ___AT THIS TIME___, I cannot accept the job offer.

3. There are several reasons for the delay. __FOR EXAMPLE__, the main highway is closed for repair work.

4. __ON THE OTHER HAND__, the delay can be blamed on inefficiency.

5. We won the game. ___IN FACT___, it was not even close.

6. __AS A RESULT__, they closed the pool for the rest of the summer.

for example
at this time
as a result
in fact
finally
on the other hand

Unit 158 cont'd

Pruning Your Material

Your report, like a tree, will have a better, more interesting shape if carefully pruned. Never leave out important information, but ruthlessly cut out all useless details.

 Here are some facts that might have been included in a report about your library. On the line before each, tell if the fact is important or unimportant.

important
1. The library opens at 8:00 a.m.

IMPORTANT
2. The library closes at six o'clock Monday through Friday.

UNIMPORTANT
3. The floors are parquet.

IMPORTANT
4. Microfilm viewers are available for use.

UNIMPORTANT
5. Our library has 432 books with green covers.

UNIMPORTANT
6. The librarian has grey hair.

IMPORTANT
7. On Saturday and Sunday the library is open until 10:00 p.m.

IMPORTANT
8. The library is on Madison Avenue.

IMPORTANT
9. The librarian has a story hour for children on Saturday.

UNIMPORTANT
10. The walls are painted blue.

UNIMPORTANT
11. Some of the books are dusty.

UNIMPORTANT
12. There is a plaque over the door.

IMPORTANT
13. The library has microfilmed copies of the local newspaper for the last 83 years.

IMPORTANT
14. There are study carrels for people to use.

IMPORTANT
15. The card catalog is easily accessible and kept up-to-date.

IMPORTANT
16. The library has a truly great selection of records that can be checked out.

UNIMPORTANT
17. The library has three waste paper baskets.

IMPORTANT
18. The librarian knows how to borrow material from other libraries for you.

IMPORTANT
19. The library keeps many genealogical books.

UNIMPORTANT
20. There is a spider's web in one window.

IMPORTANT
21. All the latest best sellers are available at the library.

UNIMPORTANT
22. The librarian wears a wig.

IMPORTANT
23. The library has books in braille.

UNIMPORTANT
24. The library has some windows.

Topic Outline

The purpose of an outline is to help the writer put all of the material he has gathered for a report in order before he writes his paper. The order he chooses must fit his subject. He must study his material before he decides how to arrange it.

In a topic outline, each item to be discussed in the report is simply a topic; it is not a sentence. Main headings are the most important ideas. They are marked by Roman numerals. Subtopics are divisions of the main headings. They are marked by capital letters. Both Roman numerals and capital letters are followed by periods.

Study the sample topic outline on George Washington. Notice that all Roman numerals are aligned at the left. All capital letters are aligned under the first letter of the main heading. The beginning of each topic begins with a capital letter. Each entry is parallel in structure. No punctuation follows the entry. At least two subtopics must appear under each main heading or none at all.

George Washington

I. His background
   A. Birthplace
   B. Education
II. His leadership ability
   A. In the military
   B. In the White House
III. Reasons for his fame
   A. "Father of His Country"
   B. First U.S. President

True or False

_F_ 1. Each topic in the outline must be in sentence form.

_T_ 2. Mark each main heading with a Roman numeral.

_F_ 3. It is not important to make notes before writing a report.

_T_ 4. Subtopics are the smaller topics under the main topics.

_T_ 5. An outline helps the writer organize his material.

_F_ 6. Periods are never used in a topic outline.

_F_ 7. Numerals, capital letters, topics, and subtopics need not appear in any specific arrangement.

_F_ 8. Subtopics of main headings are marked with small letters.

_T_ 9. The main headings represent the main ideas to be discussed in the report.

_F_ 10. A topic outline does not need a title.

Unit 159 cont'd

Sentence Outline

The sentence outline has the same parts as the topic outline. In the sentence outline, each main idea and each subtopic is expressed in a complete sentence. (Do not confuse phrases with sentences.) A Roman numeral is used to mark each main heading. Each subtopic is marked with a capital letter.

Each main heading in the sentence outline can be used as the topic sentence for each paragraph in the report. The subtopic supports the main heading.

Remember that writing a good report hinges on the writing of a good outline. Follow these steps when making a sentence outline:

(1) Review all of the material that has been collected.
(2) Choose the main ideas to be discussed in the report. (main headings)
(3) Select two to four details to use as subtopics.

A Arrange the following numbers and letters so that they will be in proper form for an outline: I, A, B, II, A, B, C, III, A, B, C, D, IV, A, B.

I.

   A.

   B.

II.

   A.

   B.

   C.

III.

   A.

   B.

   C.

   D.

IV.

   A.

   B.

B Fill in the blanks.

> period
> main headings
> subtopics
> Roman numeral
> sentence

1. Each main heading and subtopic in a sentence outline must end with a __PERIOD__.
2. Topics cannot be used in a __SENTENCE__ outline.
3. Capital letters followed by a period are used to mark __SUBTOPICS__.
4. The major ideas for a report are the __MAIN HEADINGS__ of an outline.
5. Mark each main heading with a __ROMAN NUMERAL__.

Main Topics

The writer must organize his materials by selecting main topics. The main topics can be developed in books, reports, or paragraphs. Facts, arguments, examples, causes, or results are used to support main topics. Good writing deals with only one point at a time. If too many points are covered, the reader will not remember what they were. When the writer chooses the most important point to develop, the reader will remember it.

The outline serves to keep the writer from covering too much material in too little space. First, decide how long the composition will be, limit the subject accordingly, and choose specific points you wish to cover. Avoid general statements. An example of a general statement is "Everyone likes to read." (Not only is the statement too broad, but it is also false.) A more specific statement is "Everyone in my English class likes to read." Specific statements make up the main topics of your paragraphs. They in turn reinforce the main topic of the composition.

✳ Put a check mark (✔) beside each topic that could be used for a class report. Put an X beside each topic that is too broad.

_X_	1.	Famous Athletes
X	2.	Birds of North America
✔	3.	Historical Places in My State
✔	4.	Washington: the First President
X	5.	The History of Canada
X	6.	Government in the United States
✔	7.	Why I Value My Freedom
✔	8.	How I Can Help Conserve Energy
✔	9.	Foods I Like but Never Have
✔	10.	An Unusual Trait of Abraham Lincoln
X	11.	Indians
✔	12.	Being an Only Child
X	13.	Musical Instruments
X	14.	Business in America
✔	15.	My Best Friend
X	16.	Citizenship

COMPOSITION EXERCISE

Write a specific subject for each of the answers you marked X in today's exercise.

1. _____
2. _____
3. _____
4. _____
5. _____
6. _____
7. _____
8. _____

Unit 160 cont'd ➔

Subtopics

The main topics of an outline are divided into smaller topics known as subtopics. Subtopics are details. Each subtopic in an outline is numbered with a capital letter followed by a period. Subtopics should be indented so that they will be in a straight line under one another. Each subtopic should begin with a capital letter. In a topic outline do not use a period at the end of the subtopic. A period must follow each subtopic in a sentence outline. Never have a single subtopic. There must be at least two subtopics under a main topic or none at all.

 Match each subtopic with the main heading which it supports.

_I_	1. buses	I. land transportation
III	2. sailboats	II. air transportation
I	3. automobiles	III. water transportation
II	4. helicopters	
I	5. trains	
III	6. steamships	
II	7. airplanes	
I	8. motorcycles	
III	9. barges	
I	10. subways	
III	11. canoes	
II	12. spaceships	
I	13. trucks	
I	14. bicycles	

COMPOSITION EXERCISE

Use this information to write an outline for a report on "How Seeds Scatter": by wind, by water, by animals, parachutes, lightness, furry coats, digestive wastes. Use capital letters and indentions correctly.

_____
_____
_____
_____
_____
_____
_____
_____

Comprehension Check

(A) **Write "f" beside each fact; write "o" beside each opinion.**

__o__ 1. Watching television is bad for you.
__f__ 2. My sister lives in Washington.
__f__ 3. Sharon has dark brown hair.
__o__ 4. Tennis is a great sport.
__f__ 5. Aunt Carla bakes chocolate cakes.
__o__ 6. Her cakes are the best!
__o__ 7. You shouldn't complain so much.
__o__ 8. Tuesday night's programs are the best.
__f__ 9. The large fan is set on the high speed.
__f__ 10. This coat belongs to Rick.

__f__ 11. Alaska is the largest state.
__o__ 12. Colorado is my favorite place to live.
__o__ 13. That car is beautiful.
__f__ 14. Marla needs to borrow a pen.
__f__ 15. Austin is the capital of Texas.
__o__ 16. The sun is too bright.
__o__ 17. Halloween is my favorite day.
__o__ 18. Roses smell wonderful.
__f__ 19. Jean is late for her first class.
__f__ 20. The truck is a four-wheel drive.

(B) **Here are some facts that might be included in a report about bicycle safety. Put a check (✓) beside each statement that gives safety information.**

__✓__ 1. Signal your turns and stops with your left arm.
____ 2. Some bikes have balloon-tire wheels.
____ 3. Bicycles come in many sizes.
__✓__ 4. Never carry anyone else on your bicycle.
____ 5. A bicycle is a cheap form of transportation.
__✓__ 6. The brake control is on the right handlebar.
____ 7. Have you ridden on a bicycle built for two?
____ 8. A bicycle is fun to own.
____ 9. Tom has a new red bike.
__✓__ 10. Tires should be checked for defects.
__✓__ 11. A bicycle rider should travel on the right side of the road.

____ 12. Bicycles became very popular in the late 1800's.
____ 13. Some spokes are painted in bright colors.
__✓__ 14. Never swerve from side to side.
__✓__ 15. Weaving in and out of traffic is dangerous.
__✓__ 16. Two or more riders should travel in single file.
____ 17. Some people go on bicycle tours.
__✓__ 18. A red reflector should be on the back of your bike.
__✓__ 19. Bicycles should have horns or bells to warn other people.
__✓__ 20. Don't cut in front of cars.

(C) **Put "t" beside each true statement about outlines.**

__t__ 1. Mark each main heading with a Roman numeral.
__t__ 2. An outline helps the writer organize his material.
____ 3. Each topic in a topic outline ends with a period.
____ 4. Outlines do not need titles.
__t__ 5. Main headings represent main ideas.
__t__ 6. Topics are not used in a sentence outline.
__t__ 7. All headings in a sentence outline are written in sentences.
__t__ 8. Capital letters followed by a period are used to mark subtopics.
____ 9. Notes are actually not important.
__t__ 10. Subtopics are the smaller topics under the main topics.
__t__ 11. Outlines follow a specific arrangement of numerals.
____ 12. An outline has no real purpose.
__t__ 13. "B. He was the first U.S. President" belongs in a sentence outline.
__t__ 14. Writing a good report depends on writing a good outline.
__t__ 15. "B. In the White House" belongs in a topic outline.

Test 32 cont'd ➡

Comprehension Check (continued)

D **Number each set of sentences 1-5 in the order in which each event occurred.**

_5_ a. I didn't get to watch my show after all.
_2_ b. I turned on the television.
_4_ c. She was giving a report on the economy.
_1_ d. My favorite show came on last night.
_3_ e. I saw a newscaster on the screen.

_3_ a. Bill turned on all the lights.
_4_ b. Then we searched the house.
_1_ c. When we arrived home, our front door was open.
_2_ d. We carefully walked into the house.
_5_ e. We decided that someone had forgotten to close the door.

_2_ a. It cast its blue light over the yard.
_5_ b. They stayed in hiding until they felt safe.
_1_ c. When the sun went down, the moon rose.
_3_ d. In the soft light, you could see tiny creatures.
_4_ e. The creatures hid from our eyes.

_5_ a. We'll visit the Rocky Mountains this summer.
_2_ b. We looked at pictures of places to visit.
_4_ c. Finally, we flipped a coin.
_1_ d. Our family decided to take a vacation.
_3_ e. Each of us chose a different vacation spot.

E **Fill in the title, numerals, letters, and topics in outline form. Choose from the topics in the right column.**

_____ *Pioneers on the Frontier* _____

_I._ **Homes**
    A. **Sod shanties**
    B. **Dugouts**

_II._ **Education**
    A. **Wandering teachers**
    B. **Basic subjects**

III. **Entertainment**
    A. **Harvest parties**
    B. **Dances**

A. Harvest parties
B. Basic subjects
I. Homes
B. Dugouts
B. Dances
    Pioneers on the Frontier
A. Sod shanties
A. Wandering teachers
III. Entertainment
II. Education

Write a paragraph expressing your opinion of the U.S. President. Use at least two transitional terms. Underline the transitional terms. (Examples: finally, for example, at this time, as a result, in fact, on the other hand)

_____
_____
_____
_____
_____
_____
_____
_____

Detail Headings

A good description helps the reader see clearly what the writer is trying to picture. Writing good description makes use of details that appeal to the senses. These five senses are sight, sound, smell, taste, and touch. Imagine how dull life would be without the ability to see, hear, smell, taste, and touch. The writer of good description has an eye for detail. He knows how to choose the right words to describe each detail. Most importantly, he can arrange the details so that the reader will see what he is describing. Good description calls for the use of exact adjectives to paint a clear picture. Adjectives help the writer say what he means.

A Underline the more exact adjective in each pair. Write a sentence with it.

1. good, <u>tasty</u>
   These cookies are tasty.

2. <u>brisk</u>, cold
   We went for a brisk walk.

3. <u>sturdy</u>, strong
   The shelves are sturdy.

4. happy, <u>pleasing</u>
   She has a pleasing attitude.

5. clean, <u>tidy</u>
   His room is always tidy.

6. <u>sultry</u>, hot
   Hot weather is sultry.

7. friendly, <u>nice</u>
   Her parents are nice.

8. tall, <u>lanky</u>
   The lanky boy plays basketball.

9. <u>clever</u>, smart
   A clever person could solve it.

10. little, <u>wee</u>
    I want a wee piece of pie.

11. quiet, <u>calm</u>
    The winds are calm now.

12. <u>circular</u>, round
    He swung it in a circular motion.

13. <u>drizzly</u>, rainy
    The rain is drizzly.

14. large, <u>great</u>
    You have made great progress.

B Which sense is used in each of the following descriptive sentences?

_____*taste*_____ 1. Chilled grape juice sliding down your throat is refreshing.

_____*smell*_____ 2. The aroma of frying bacon makes me hungry.

_____*sound*_____ 3. The distant bell clanged loudly as the storm approached.

_____*sight*_____ 4. Nothing is prettier than a glowing fire on a fall evening.

_____*touch*_____ 5. My mother's coat is soft and furry.

Unit 161 cont'd ⟶

Parallel Structure

The first item in a series sets the pattern for parallel structure. All of the other items in the series must be like the first one. If the first word in a list is a noun, the others should be nouns. If the first word is an adjective, the others should be adjectives.

A Draw a line under each term that is not parallel with the others.

1. books, pamphlets, magazines, <u>reading</u>
2. laughing, crying, <u>sing</u>, smiling
3. beans, peas, <u>whipped potatoes</u>, okra, squash
4. thirsty, <u>rest</u>, hungry, lazy, sleepy
5. watching TV, <u>listened to the radio</u>, writing letters
6. mixing paints, blending colors, <u>draws pictures</u>
7. to sing, to dance, <u>perform</u>, to entertain
8. baffled, excited, <u>fascinating</u>
9. by canoe, by rowboat, by walking, <u>flying</u>
10. a rough voice, <u>stocky build</u>, a ruddy face

In an outline, parallel structure means that all of the subtopics (A, B, C) under main topics (I, II, III) will be alike in structure. However, the subtopics under main topic I do not have to be parallel with the subtopics under main topic II, etc. As a rule, main topics should be parallel with one another.

B Rewrite the topic outline. Correct all errors in punctuation and in parallel structure. Use capital letters properly.

Baseball Fans

I. The men
   a. Typical appearance
   B. Actions that are typical
II. The women
   A. Those who came to see game
   b. Some want to watch the crowd.
3. More boys than anyone else
   a. They are restless.
   b. Noisy
   c. Always hungry

Baseball Fans

I. The men
   A. Typical appearance
   B. Typical actions
II. The women
   A. Those who came to see game
   B. Those who came to watch crowd
III. The boys
   A. Restless
   B. Noisy
   C. Hungry

The writer uses a paragraph of introduction to acquaint the reader with the subject. A good introduction does several things. The two most important ones are (1) it catches the reader's attention and makes him want to read the entire paper and (2) it gives the reader an idea of what the paper is about so that he can better understand what the writer is trying to say. The introduction should be short and interesting. It must be well organized and to the point. The introductory paragraph introduces the subject and presents the purpose of the paper.

A True or False

TRUE 1. Most subjects can be introduced in a single opening paragraph.

TRUE 2. The introductory paragraph should introduce the subject and come to a point.

FALSE 3. The introduction should be long and full of details.

FALSE 4. Definitions for hard words used in the paper should be given in the introduction.

TRUE 5. The introduction should interest the reader and catch his attention.

A good introduction begins with a general statement and then narrows quickly to the scope of the paper. It mentions the main topics in the order that they will be developed. It also states the writer's plan of development.

B Number the following sentences so that they will be in proper order for an introductory paragraph.

___3___ We have all heard about the importance of higher education, and I came to college to get an education.

___4___ Pressure from my parents, a desire to be with my friends, and a need to be trained for a good job brought me to college.

___1___ In the fall many high school graduates enter college.

___2___ As one of those graduates, I am wondering why I am here.

Unit 162 cont'd ⟶

Body

A written report has three parts: the introduction, the body, and the conclusion. The body is the most important part. It is the middle paragraphs. The main topics are developed in the body of a report. Each body paragraph must relate to the one before it. The writer does this through the use of terms of transition. He may link his paragraphs with terms like "but," "nevertheless," "therefore," "for example," "indeed," "of course," or any of the many other transitional terms; or he may repeat a term from the sentence that ended the paragraph just above it.

A report of five paragraphs consists of one paragraph each for introduction and conclusion and three paragraphs in the body for the development of the main topics. This arrangement is called three-point enumeration because three main points are covered in the body.

A Matching

1. The main purpose of paragraphing is
2. The first sentence in a body paragraph tells
3. The topic sentence is
4. The main topics are

a. usually the first sentence in a body paragraph.
b. to separate ideas.
c. developed in the body.
d. the reader what the paragraph is about.

"He," "they," "this," "that," "those," "them," and "it" are pronouns that provide transition by referring to persons or ideas in the preceding paragraph.

B Underline the transitional terms.

1. This is all very confusing.
2. It was because of these.
3. They are typical tourists, not just sightseers.
4. Unfortunately, this is not a good excuse.
5. That was not very funny.
6. Those are not acceptable.
7. Nevertheless, he lost the race.
8. It is a good example.

C Write a sentence using each transition word from the above paragraph.

1. _____
2. _____
3. _____
4. _____
5. _____
6. _____
7. _____

Conclusion Unit 163

A good conclusion gives the writer one last chance to persuade or convince the reader. It is the final paragraph in a report. The conclusion should be short and clear. It reminds the reader what the writer has said in the report. The conclusion restates the thesis sentence of the report and then broadens it into a generalization at the end. As the conclusion broadens out to the last sentence, the writer should borrow key words and phrases from both the introduction and the body. He should not announce his intentions by using such phrases as "in conclusion" or "to sum up." Instead, the writer should try to keep the reader's interest to the very last word. He should not repeat himself or start a new "train of thought." A good conclusion does two things: First, it makes a report seem complete. Second, it allows the writer to re-emphasize his main idea. A conclusion is not a summary; it is a restatement.

generalization	writer	purpose	topic sentence
reminder	reports	interest	conclusion

✳ Fill in the blanks.

1. Most _____reports_____ require a conclusion.

2. The __CONCLUSION__ is the final paragraph in a report.

3. The last sentence in the conclusion tends to be a __GENERALIZATION__.

4. The __TOPIC SENTENCE__ of a conclusion is a re-statement of the thesis sentence.

5. One __PURPOSE__ of the conclusion is to make the report seem complete.

6. A conclusion should keep the reader's __INTEREST__ until the last word.

7. The conclusion gives the __WRITER__ one last chance to persuade or convince the reader.

8. The conclusion is a __REMINDER__ to the reader.

COMPOSITION EXERCISE

Define these terms.

1. conclusion _____

2. topic sentence _____

3. key words _____

4. restatement _____

5. generalization _____

Unit 163 cont'd ⟶

Putting Parts Together

The structure of a report may be compared to the structure of a ham sandwich — a thick slice of ham (the body) between two thin slices of bread (the introduction and conclusion). To make the three parts of the sandwich stick together without falling apart — and to give it flavor, perhaps — you should spread mustard on one side of the top piece of bread and mayonnaise on one side of the botton piece. Therefore, when you eat the sandwich, it won't fall apart.

The introduction of a report introduces the subject with a generalization and then narrows to a thesis sentence. The body of the report develops the main topics. Each body paragraph has a topic sentence and is tied to the other paragraphs with words of transition. The conclusion is a restatement of the thesis sentence. It begins with a reworded thesis and broadens to a generalization. It makes the report seem complete.

 Matching

_7_ a. outline

_4_ b. topic sentence

_1_ c. introduction

_6_ d. body

_8_ e. conclusion

_2_ f. main ideas

_5_ g. transitional devices

_3_ h. Roman numerals

1. the first paragraph in a report

2. what each body paragraph develops

3. used to number main topics in an outline

4. begins a body paragraph

5. words or expressions used to link sentences or paragraphs

6. the middle section of a report

7. what the writer should develop before he begins writing a report

8. the final paragraph in a report

COMPOSITION EXERCISE

List the parts of a composition and define each part.

_____

_____

_____

_____

Maintaining Unity

"Unity" means "oneness." A sentence should contain one thought. A writer must be sure that his thought has unity. He does so by combining related ideas with each other. Many writers make the mistake of using "and" to form a compound sentence in hopes of creating unity. If the main ideas are not closely related, they should be separated into two separate sentences. The writer usually knows when he has written a poor sentence. If the sentence still does not sound right after two or three revisions, the writer should begin again, using an entirely different sentence pattern.

A writer must also have unity in each paragraph. Each paragraph should deal with only one topic. The writer should express the central thought of a paragraph in a topic sentence. Usually the sentence should be at or near the beginning of a paragraph. The other sentences should be related to the topic sentence. Unity in a paragraph comes when each sentence helps develop the topic sentence.

 The following paragraph is made up of short statements. Revise it by combining the first two sentences and the last two sentences.

Write a new paragraph.

Christopher Columbus was born in Italy. His birth date was more than five hundred years ago. Genoa, Italy, was his hometown and a major seaport. As a young boy, he often visited the harbor. He visited with the sailors. They told him about their voyages. They also told him about the towns they had seen.

_____

_____

_____

More than five hundred years ago, Christopher Columbus was born in Italy. As a young boy, Columbus liked to visit the harbor in his hometown of Genoa, a major seaport. There he visited with the sailors. They told him about their voyages and the towns they had seen.

_____

_____

_____

_____

_____

Unit 164 cont'd →

Revisions

Rewriting, or revision, is an important part of the writing process. When his outline is finished, the writer should complete the first draft of his report. Then he should read what he has written. He should look for ways to improve his piece of writing. He may want to add or leave out certain ideas. He may simply change the order of his ideas. He may rewrite a sentence or two for clearer meaning. Certainly, he should check his spelling and punctuation. The writer should ask himself these questions:

(1) Is my purpose clear from the beginning?
(2) Are the paragraphs clear and to the point; do they relate to each other?
(3) Have I been too wordy?

When the writer has finished revising his first draft, he is ready to begin his final draft. He should be certain that he has the right word, the right sentence, and the right paragraph for each idea he is trying to express. The writer must learn to revise his work with a critical eye. It may take several readings and several revisions before he can start on his finished product.

 Put a plus sign (+) beside each statement that deals with revision.

__+__ 1. Be sure to check all punctuation.

_____ 2. Develop a title for the report.

__+__ 3. Be certain the main topics are clearly developed.

_____ 4. Make an outline of the first draft.

_____ 5. Look for big words that will impress the reader.

__+__ 6. Check for short, choppy sentences.

__+__ 7. Make sure generalizations are supported by facts.

__+__ 8. Be sure each paragraph relates to another.

__+__ 9. Make certain each paragraph begins with a topic sentence.

_____ 10. Select a subject for the report.

__+__ 11. Mark out any unnecessary words or sentences.

_____ 12. Go to the library to find materials to use.

Let's Pretend

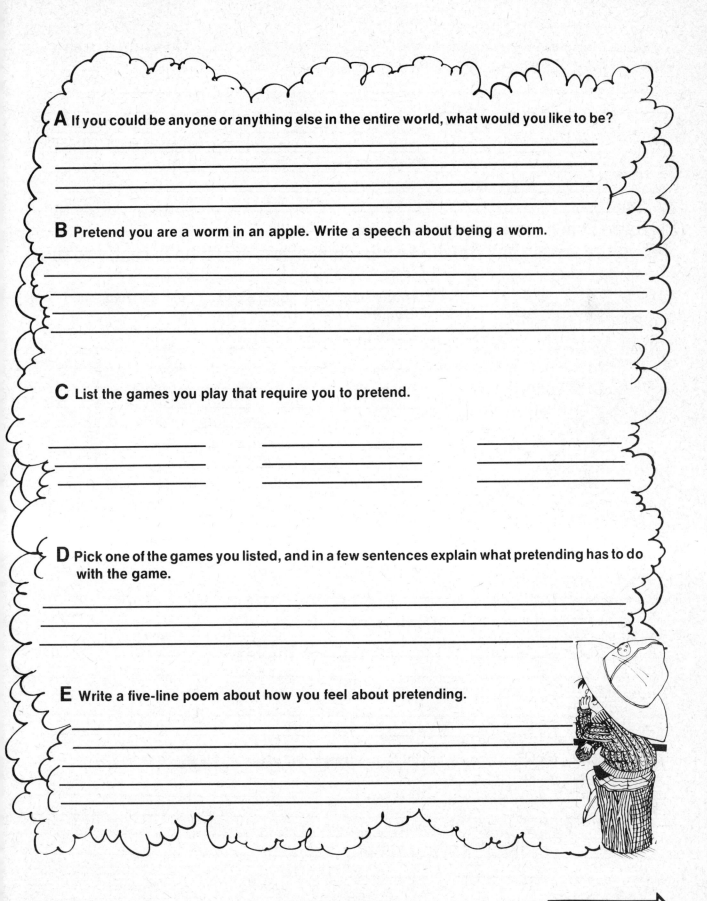

A If you could be anyone or anything else in the entire world, what would you like to be?

_____
_____
_____
_____

B Pretend you are a worm in an apple. Write a speech about being a worm.

_____
_____
_____
_____
_____

C List the games you play that require you to pretend.

_____   _____   _____
_____   _____   _____

D Pick one of the games you listed, and in a few sentences explain what pretending has to do with the game.

_____
_____
_____

E Write a five-line poem about how you feel about pretending.

_____
_____
_____
_____

Unit 165 cont'd →

Writing About Surprises

A There are many different types of surprises. Some surprises are good, and some are not so good. Write a paragraph about a good surprise that has happened to you.

_____
_____
_____
_____
_____
_____

_____

B Write a paragraph about a bad surprise that happened to you.

_____
_____
_____
_____
_____
_____

C Pretend you are at a circus. Write a poem about some of the things that are surprising to you.

_____
_____
_____
_____
_____
_____
_____

D Think of all the creative writing forms you have studied. List below all the possible ways you could write about surprises.

_____
_____
_____
_____

Comprehension Check

A) Draw a line under each term that is not parallel with the others.

1. talked, laughed, jumping, sang
2. happy, sad, grinning, thoughtful
3. by car, by plane, walking, by boat
4. chairs, sofas, tables, lamp
5. watching a movie, listening to music, singing
6. asking, listening, thinking, thoughts
7. jumped, ran, climbed, playing
8. sleepy, tired, weary, rested
9. reading, writing, some arithmetic
10. height, tall, short, medium

11. adding water, stirring the mix, blend
12. draws trees, sketches animals, sunsets
13. to stop, to look, to listen, careful
14. a loud voice, a pale complexion, red hair
15. ice cream, candy, popcorn, delicious hot dogs
16. shopping, reading, cooking a meal, riding
17. smiling, nodding, a happy face, singing
18. hot dogs, ketchup, mustard, a bag of chips
19. guitar, flute, beautiful harp, piano
20. pens, pencils, books, studying

B) Rewrite the topic outline. Correct all errors in numerals, letters, and parallel structure.

Mexico

I. The people
   A. The Indians
   B. There are fifty tribes.
2. The language
   A. Spanish
   b. There are many speech patterns.
III. The climate is varied.
   a. Temperature zones
   B. There are two seasons.

Mexico		
I. The people		
	A. The Indians	
	B. The tribes	
II. The language		
	A. Spanish	
	B. Speech patterns	
III. The climate		
	A. Temperature zones	
	B. Seasons	

C) Read each set of topic sentences and supporting sentences. Underline the sentence which would best support the topic sentence.

1. Beagles make nice pets.
   a. They are cheerful and easygoing.
   b. They are usually black, tan, and white.

2. A good breakfast will help your body.
   a. Cereal is a good breakfast food.
   b. Your body will have food for energy.

3. Horses need a great deal of care.
   a. They must be brushed regularly.
   b. They can win races sometimes.

4. Thomas Jefferson was a talented man.
   a. Benjamin Franklin was also talented.
   b. He was the author of the Declaration of Independence.

5. The discovery of gold was important in U.S. history.
   a. Gold is a valuable metal.
   b. The West was rapidly settled.

6. Franklin Roosevelt was a memorable President.
   a. One of his cousins was also a U.S. President.
   b. He was elected President four times.

7. Jazz is native American music.
   a. Most jazz is played by Americans.
   b. Jazz has also been called "swing music."

8. Every U.S. state has a motto.
   a. "The First State" is Delaware's motto.
   b. Most states have a state song, too.

Test 33 cont'd →

Comprehension Check (continued)

D The answers are in the right column. Put the letter of the answer beside the sentence in which it belongs.

_j_   1. A conclusion should keep the reader's _____ until the last word.

_i_   2. The last sentence in the conclusion tends to be a _____ .

_b_   3. The first paragraph in a report is the _____ .

_g_   4. The _____ is the middle section of a report.

_a_   5. The writer should develop an _____ before beginning to write a report.

_h_   6. A _____ begins a body paragraph.

_d_   7. _____ are words used to link sentences or paragraphs.

_c_   8. The final paragraph of a report is the _____ .

_f_   9. Each body paragraph develops the _____ .

_e_   10. _____ are used to number main topics in an outline.

a. outline
b. introduction
c. conclusion
d. transitional devices
e. Roman numerals
f. main ideas
g. body
h. topic sentence
i. generalization
j. interest

E Beside each sentence, write "i" for introductory paragraph, "b" for body paragraph, and "c" for concluding paragraph.

_i_   1. There are three improvements to be made.

_c_   2. Those are the methods you should use.

_i_   3. I'll discuss three methods.

_b_   4. Her second question concerned the economy.

_i_   5. You can learn to play these instruments.

_b_   6. Your final duty is to lock the door.

_i_   7. Follow these steps to paint the boat.

_b_   8. The first job is easy to complete.

_i_   9. I'll tell you about my friends.

_c_   10. Those are our plans for the changes.

_c_   11. Now·you know how vitamins help your body.

_c_   12. For those reasons, you should attend school.

_b_   13. The second instrument is the trumpet.

_b_   14. You should first check for jagged edges.

_b_   15. Another factor is the economy.

_i_   16. Christopher Columbus had three ships.

F Put a check (✓) beside each statement that deals with revision.

✓   1. Correct short, choppy sentences.

✓   2. Check to see that all paragraphs begin with a topic sentence.

✓   3. Be sure all paragraphs are related.

✓   4. Check all punctuation.

  5. Select a subject for your report.

  6. Develop an outline.

✓   7. Be sure the main topics are clearly developed.

✓   8. Mark out unnecessary words or sentences.

  9. Collect all materials and make notes.

  10. Replace common words with impressive words.

Write a paragraph describing your favorite meal. Underline the descriptive words.

_____

_____

_____

_____

_____

_____

_____